MW00425231

Understanding Telecommunications 2

Ericsson: EN/LZT 101 1404 R1A
Telia: EN/LZT 101 1404 R1A

Art.nr 3783
ISBN 91-44-00214-9

Cover Illustration: IMS Bildbyrå
Design: Roos & Co

Printed in Sweden
Studentlitteratur, Lund
Webbadress: www.studentlitteratur.se

Printing/year 1 2 3 4 5 6 7 8 9 10 | 02 01 2000 1999 98

Preface

From a general point of view, "Understanding Telecommunications" is about one of our most important ambitions: to promote interpersonal communication as well as communication between people and information systems. More and more people require basic but comprehensive knowledge of telecommunications – of its systems and services, and not least of its special terminology. We also know that there is a great need for *state-of-the-art* literature in the technical training provided at Ericsson, Telia, and universities.

This is the second volume of a two-volume guide to telecommunications jointly produced by Ericsson and Telia. Our books provide an integrated view of what has traditionally been perceived as two distinct areas: telecommunications and data communication. We are convinced that this integrated view is very useful now that the Internet and multimedia are being used on a larger scale, increasing the need for cooperation between *telecom* and *datacom*. As the technical differences between public and business networks begin to blur, much of the content in our books is also applicable to business networks.

The rapid development in information technology and telecommunications will no doubt demand new releases of our books in order to keep them up to date. For this purpose we would greatly appreciate input from our readers (see e-mail address on the next page).

Ericsson Telecom AB
Internal Training Marievik

Telia AB
Telia Kompetens

Ericsson

Project owner:	Christina Truuberg
Project manager:	Micael Narup
Editor and main author:	Anders Olsson
Facts:	Ericsson tutors, course developers, and subject matter experts.
Chapter authors:	Marika Stålnacke, Håkan Karlsson, Jonas Nordström, Anders Lindberg, Thomas Muth, Jan Carlbom, Sören Johansson, Lars Bergquist, Elinor Aminoff, Fredrick Andersson, Johan Nyquist
Graphics:	Peter Nyström
Translation and editing:	Bertil Edin and Rebecca Foreman

Telia

Project owner:	Kjell Jonsson
Project manager:	Lars-Erik Andersson
Facts:	Telia Kompetens and Telia Academy tutors and course developers.

Address for feedback: understanding.telecom@etx.ericsson.se

Table of Contents

To the Reader

Introduction

The global telecommunications network is the largest and most complex technical system that humans have created. It also makes up a substantial part of a country's infrastructure and is vital to the development of that country.

Development in the field of telecommunications has been very rapid in recent years. By "telecommunications" we mean all processes that render it possible to transfer voice, data and video with the help of some form of electromagnetic system, including optical transfer methods.

This rapid development points to new demands on knowledge and competence for everyone who takes an active part in modern telecommunications. This field's growing complexity also calls for a structured approach, especially concerning the *principles* of telecommunications. For anyone willing to tackle writing books to broaden users' knowledge of this subject, a clear structure is particularly important, so that the books are easy to understand and easy to navigate.

The prime focus of our books is on principles and context rather than on profound technical descriptions. It is also important to point out that the contents are not associated with any particular technical system.

To the uninitiated, the telecommunications world may seem to be rather intangible: some familiar, commonplace phenomena and an abstract system that for the most part works without anyone needing to think about how. See *Figure 0.1*. One might know about some types of equipment connected to the telecommunications network but not very much more than that.

Figure 0.1 Telecommunications network

People who want to learn more realise fairly soon that telecommunications networks are mainly composed of "nodes" (exchanges) and "links", and that "terminals" are connected to the network. (See *Figure 0.2.*)

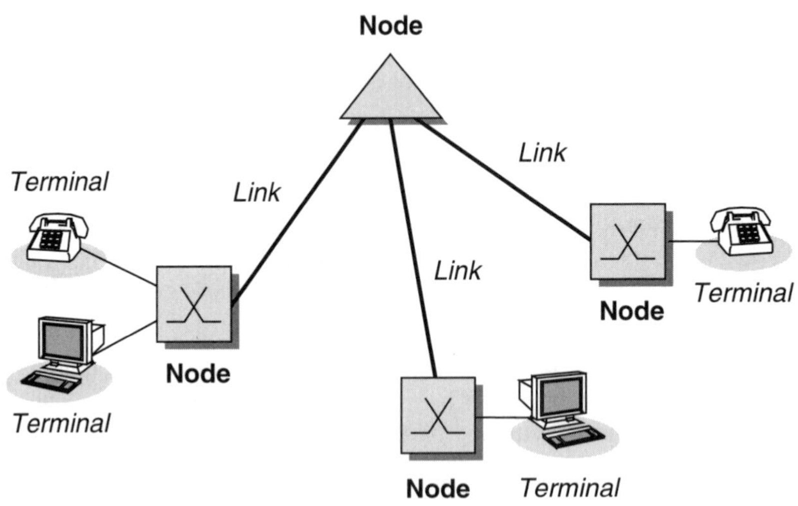

Figure 0.2 Main components of a telecommunications network

But still many things are unclear, not only in the networks themselves but also in the complicated interworking between different types of network.

Book structure

To be able to unravel the mystery surrounding this subject, we will start by describing our book structure and its purpose. A well-thought-out structure is a good aid to the reader who is looking for information on a certain part of a subject. Furthermore, it makes it easier to transfer information to databases and to search in them. As the books are designed to be used for different types of competence development in *parts* of the telecommunications field – signalling, broadband, access, and so forth – we have come to the conclusion that a strictly logical structure also has a certain pedagogical value.

Understanding Telecommunications consists of eight parts: Part A is in Volume 1, and Parts B – H are in Volume 2. All the parts are divided into 10 chapters, each of which deals with a specific topic (see *Figure 0.3*). In Volume 2, *To the Reader* is followed by an introductory section – *The telecommunications services market* – that describes current and forecast trends in the field of *teleservices.*

Conclusion, at the end of Volume 2, includes a two-page table showing the characteristics of the different networks described in *Part B – Part H.*

	Volume 1	**Volume 2**						
Chapter	*Part A* General review	*Part B* PSTN	*Part C* N-ISDN	*Part D* PLMN	*Part E* Signalling network	*Part F* X.25 / Frame relay	*Part G* ATM / B-ISDN	*Part H* The Internet
0	To the Reader	To the Reader – The telecommunications services market						
1	User services	User services, terminals						
2	Standards							
3	Switching and switch control							
4	Transmission techniques							
5	Trunk and access networks							
6	Network intelligence and value-added services							
7	Signalling							
8	Network management							
9	Interworking between networks							
10	Network planning							

Figure 0.3 Division into parts and chapters

Part A – General review

To understand the structuring of telecommunications networks, it is important to understand the demands that *basic services* place on the network. Voice, data and video transmission belong to this category of services. As far as voice is concerned, we may say that the telephone network is tailor-made to be able to provide the *telephony* service at a reasonable cost.

The remarkably rapid development in the field of telecommunications is characterised by many new bearer networks coming into being alongside the telephone network. This depends to a great extent on the growth of data communication services which are far more richly varied than telephony. A future field of growth is multimedia services, usually including video. Another reason for the proliferation of new bearer networks is that it has become so popular to make services mobile.

Operators also aim at *integrating* many services into the same network to reduce the number of networks in the long term. But the short-term effect will be a larger number of networks to handle, as long as the old ones still exist.

This technical development is reflected in our book structure: the different tailor-made – fixed, mobile and integrated – networks are described in separate parts of Volume 2.

Another question of structure applies to public networks as opposed to business networks. However, the field of business networks will not be explicitly dealt with in the first edition of our books.

Many features are common to two or more bearer networks: cables, buildings and other types of infrastructure. In the future we may even have a switching technique that can be developed to form part of the infrastructure (ATM technique). To avoid tiring repetition, we have collected common aspects like these in **Part A**, which is a general review and a sort of frame for the different parts that make up Volume 2.

To take into account the development of increasingly integrated telecommunications networks – a trend sometimes described as "bearer networks migrating together" – Part A must also deal with tomorrow's situation. In the descriptions of the specialised networks in Parts B – G, the main emphasis is instead on the current situation, before migration.

Parts B–H – Network-specific topics

Below follows a brief presentation of the network-specific topics dealt with in the different parts of Volume 2.

Telephony and data communication – A comparison

The demands that users put on telephony and data communication are different in many ways. Telephony can manage relatively poor transmission quality because of the redundancy built into natural language and speech and because people engaged in a telephone conversation can easily overcome temporary disturbances and interruptions by repeating what they have just said. On the other hand, we find it difficult to accept *delays* in a telephone connection. Delay must be kept below a certain value so as not to be experienced as irritating, and variations can be inconvenient even if the total delay is moderate.

Data traffic, in contrast, is relatively insensitive to delay (within reasonable limits), whereas poor transmission quality can cause bit errors and a garbled message. Information must arrive at the receiving end in exactly the same shape that it was when transmitted; otherwise, it is practically worthless. Sometimes large files or the entire contents of mass storage devices must be retransmitted when a fault has occurred. Because reliable transmission is so important, mechanisms have been introduced which will guarantee error-free transfer of information. But security has a price: complex routines and an extensive need of processor capacity.

Another difference is that telephony generates a continuous stream of information, while data traffic is more intermittent. During a telephone call, about 40% of the capacity is used for transfer of "useful" information, while a line for data traffic might not be made very good use of even when traffic is formally in progress.

Networks carrying telephony (with a few minor exceptions) are *circuit-switched* networks that set up a connection between subscribers who want to come into contact with each other. The connection remains established throughout the call, irrespective of whether subscribers speak with each other or not, and there is no chance of any other subscriber using that particular accessible capacity.

A special technique, called *packet switching*, has been developed to expand the degree of utilisation in data networks when traffic sources (computers) are only sending scattered information. Each data-traffic packet has an address that controls the switching process in the exchanges (nodes).

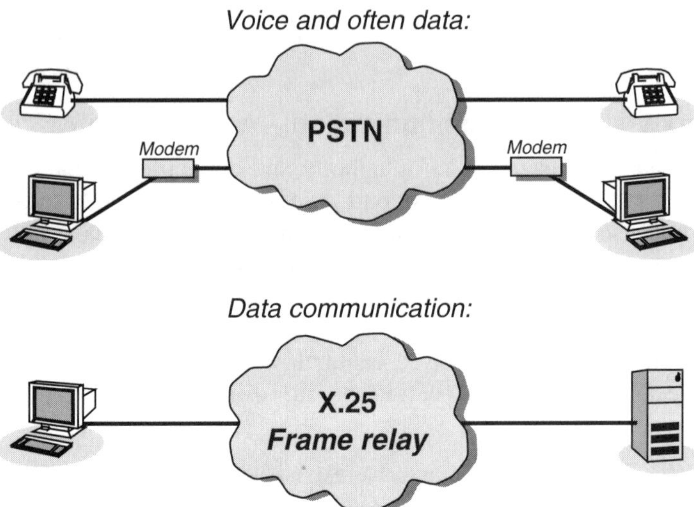

Figure 0.4 Networks for telephony and data communication

For the sake of completeness, we will add here that circuit-switched networks in certain cases are well suited for data traffic, especially for the transfer of large amounts of data on sections with good transmission quality.

The public switched telephone network (PSTN) is described in greater detail in **Part B**. Two types of dedicated data networks (X.25 and frame relay) are described in **Part F**.

Integration of services

Every network operator naturally wants to minimise the number of networks needed to provide, in an economically viable way, the services demanded by the public and by business subscribers. Besides, bearer networks ought to be reasonably homogeneous in technical respects. These have been realistic requirements in the case of bearer networks recently introduced but impossible for telephony networks that are more than 100 years old. There is a special boundary line between *analog* and *digital* techniques.

The desire to create service integration as well as a more homogeneous technique brought about the integrated services digital network (ISDN). After a slow start during the1980s, this network is now growing considerably, partly at the expense of a reduced expansion of telephone and data networks. ISDN was specified for bandwidth requirements in the range called *narrowband* but to a growing extent handles *wideband* as well (up to 2 Mbit/s).

ISDN – described in **Part C** – is principally a circuit-switched network but can also handle packet traffic. This traffic is directed to special packet handlers or to the packet networks we describe in Part F.

For *broadband* services above 2 Mbit/s, an elaborated packet technique called asynchronous transfer mode (ATM) has captured the interest of the telecommunications world. At the imminent turn of the century, telecommunications systems of this type ought to be common. For public ATM networks the term broadband ISDN (B-ISDN) is sometimes used. Hence, our present ISDN is referred to as narrowband ISDN (N-ISDN).

B-ISDN is a "truly integrated network" designed to handle all services in the same way. ATM and B-ISDN are described in **Part G**.

Figure 0.5 Networks for integrated services

Mobile networks

The continuing popularity of mobile telecommunications is obviously due to the fact that there are evident needs for this facility in society, not only in cars, on trains and on ships but also in the home and in the workplace. Mobile telephony is sometimes considered a "special access" to the telephone network, because the normal call is made between a fixed and a mobile telephone. But bearing in mind the rapidly growing significance of mobility, it will soon be provided as a standard rather than a special case.

Because public land mobile networks (PLMNs) often have their own network operators, these networks thoroughly deserve their own part in our books: **Part D**. (See *Figure 0.6.*)

Figure 0.6 Mobile telecommunications

Internetworking

The Internet, intended for internetworking between computers, has grown faster than any other network. **Part H** covers this subject.

Signalling network

More and more processor capacity is needed in telecommunications networks. The reasons for this are numerous.

- The number of connections is expanding.
- Setting up a connection requires increasing processor capacity. Mobile telecommunications is a typical example, ISDN another.
- Processor capacity is distributed in the networks (which requires increased communication and, hence, more processor capacity).
- The number of supplementary services in the networks is growing.

Naturally, the rapidly growing and increasingly distributed processor capacity requires expanded processor communication. In the digital circuit-switched networks, there is in most cases a special data network – conforming to a standard known as signalling system No. 7 (SS7) – for this extremely important communication.

This network, which only in exceptional cases carries traffic between subscribers, is very small in terms of capacity, compared to telephone and mobile networks, but dependability requirements are extremely high. It is usually called the signalling network and is dealt with in **Part E**.

Business networks/private networks

As we mentioned earlier, business networks are not explicitly dealt with in our books. The trend is towards business networks that employ the same techniques as public networks: ATM technique, multimedia traffic and mobile communication. A large part of the contents in our books is therefore applicable to business networks as well.

Figure 0.7 Business networks / private networks

Division into chapters

Principles

The division into chapters has been made with a view to identifying

- what the networks produce, that is, user services, often illustrated with a picture of a terminal;
- the different building blocks and functions of the networks;
- the network operators' main processes; and
- interworking between networks.

Each one of these topics has been given a chapter of its own in the seven parts of Volume 2.

Chapter contents

One could be led to believe that there is a fixed connection between different services and different bearer networks, especially in the context of what we mentioned about tailor-made bearer networks. However, that is not the case.

Many bearer networks have a standardised interface that permits many different services to be provided over the same bearer network. It is therefore natural in **Chapter 1** in Volume 1 to provide overall information on user services, and then in Chapter 1 of each *part* of Volume 2 to give an example of terminals designed for connection to specific bearer networks.

Terminals link networks and services together and, hence, are considered to consist of two main entities:

- one entity related to “the service” (transfer of voice, data and video with the respective “subservices”); and
- one entity related to a bearer network, in principle corresponding to one of the parts of Volume 2.

In **Chapter 2** we deal with *standardisation,* a field that is very important for us to be able to communicate internationally. To achieve standardisation, we must apply standardised reference models to the greatest extent possible. Here we have also covered techniques that are important to many of the main functions in the networks: analog/digital conversion (A/D conversion); and the three transfer modes *circuit mode*, *packet mode*, including frame relay, and *cell mode*.

Switching and switch control are described in **Chapter 3**. By “switching”, we refer here to the techniques and equipment used to control the network in order to establish contact with the person we wish to reach, which we normally do by dialling his telephone number. (In modern English usage, “dial” is an accepted term for “pressing keys to call a number”.) This requires that we associate the called party with a geographical point in the telecommunications network (normally his telephone jack), in the vicinity of which there is a terminal. Consequently, the number in the telephone directory corresponds to a telephone jack. Similar numbering schemes apply to other networks (telex numbers, data network numbers and the like). If a number of connection points (exchanges) must be passed before the caller is connected to the called party, this is known as *routing* the call.

For a telecommunications network to function and deliver the services we are willing to pay for, it must be able to span distances which in extreme cases can be up to 12,500 miles, that is, on the other side of the earth. The technique used to transfer services over long and short distances is called *transmission* and is dealt with in a chapter of its own (**Chapter 4**).

Using this kind of technique, we build transmission networks. For different reasons, they are divided into *access* and *trunk networks* – terms that are explained in detail in the important **Chapter 5**. Principal terms in this field have already been mentioned in Chapters 3 and 4.

In Chapter 3, we describe basic, "unintelligent" switching and routing. People might wonder whether "intelligent" routing would enable them to be independent of a geographical point and instead direct a call straight to a particular person. Or why not inform the network that you can be reached at another number and have the call rerouted, or that you want your call to be directed to your car?

As we all know, much of this is already possible, so the subject clearly deserves a chapter in our books. The key term would consequently be "intelligent routing", but many more intelligent network (IN) services can be included here. The intelligent functions and services are described in **Chapter 6**. Normally, the IN functions are centrally deployed in the network, but Chapter 6 also deals with distributed supplementary services and information services.

A fundamental, linking function in the traffic machine is *signalling*, which in effect is data communication between nodes and between terminals and nodes. In **Chapter 7** of Volume 1, we provide an overview of different signalling systems. The specific signalling for each bearer network is described in Chapter 7 in the respective parts of Volume 2.

Network management and *network planning* are part of the network operator's main processes. Unlike network planning, network management requires a large amount of equipment associated with the traffic functions. The management network and the corresponding processes for control, modification and maintenance are described in Volume 1 – in Chapter 8 in particular.

There is only one function in the network that we have not mentioned so far: *interworking between networks*. This is an important function, because the same service may be implemented in many networks. The introduction of integrated networks and the growing number of operators notably contribute to the need for intercommunication. Interworking between networks is described in **Chapter 9**.

Chapter 10 has two main purposes:

- to describe the network planning process (applies especially to Volume 1);
- to link the previous chapters (applies especially to Volume 1).

Here we describe areas associated with the network development plan, such as: network architecture, fundamental technical plans and network dimensioning.

Network model and theme of Volume 2

In Volume 2, each Part starts with a reference model of the bearer network described in that Part. The model shows network functions and characteristic properties of the bearer network presented.

The specific theme of Volume 2 – the expanding service market and the competing bearar networks – is illustrated in *Figure 0.8*.

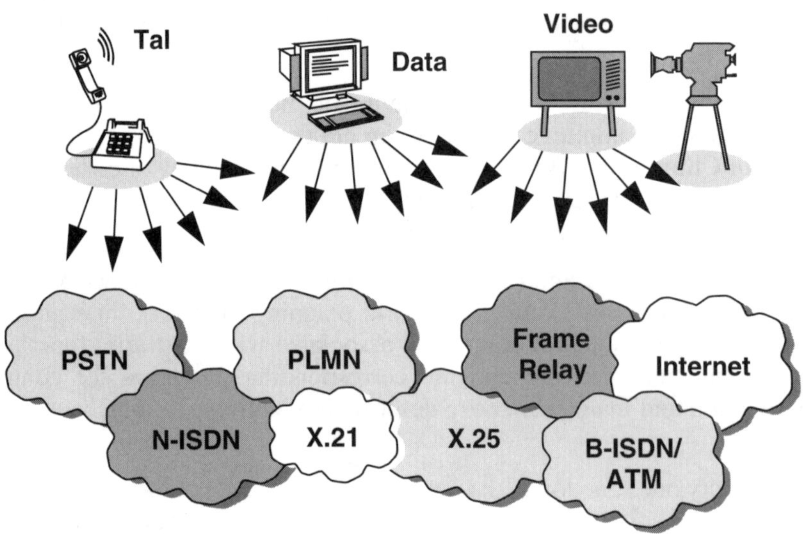

Figure 0.8 Theme of Volume 2

The telecommunications services market

1 Overview

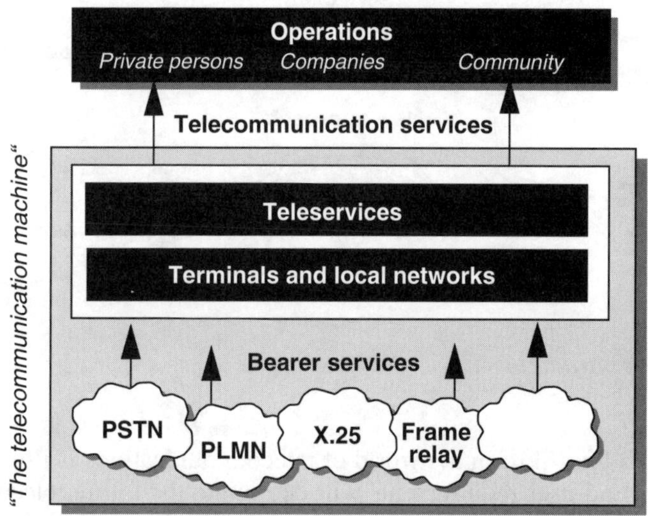

Figure 1.1 The layering of operations, telecommunications and networks

This introductory part provides a survey of development taking place in the rapidly changing telecommunications services sector. Our aim has been to present a review of the various services and their market potential and describe the demands they make on the bearer networks.

The relationship between a service and its bearer network is becoming less evident. Nowadays, data is transmitted over voice-oriented networks, and in the future it will be possible to transmit voice over networks that are now considered to be exclusively data networks, such as frame relay. The telefax service currently utilises the PSTN but will very likely migrate to bearer networks more closely associated with data transfer. Clearly, the overall trend is towards increased focus on interworking between networks.

Bearer networks are addressed in Parts B – H.

The development of new services is affected to a large degree by the ongoing integration of the telecommunications and data communication markets and, to an increasing extent, even by the media markets (film, TV, music and newspapers).

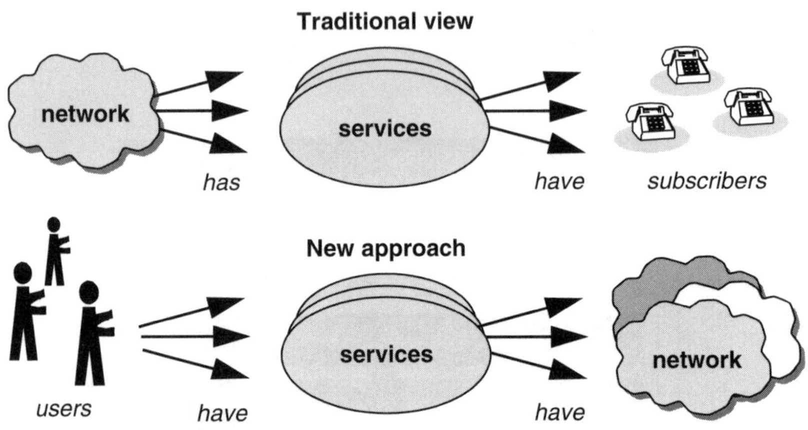

Figure 1.2 A paradigm shift

Another paradigm shift in the world of telecommunications is illustrated in *Figure 1.2*. End-user requirements will determine the future telecommunications services that will be in demand, and the resulting offering will form the foundation for the choice of technique and for network planning. Currently forecast services are naturally based on today's lifestyles and ways of thinking – which are in turn determined by present communication possibilities. Future technical advances will very likely affect our set of values and our assessment of what is necessary and worthwhile.

2 Roles and players

Players in the telecommunications market – companies and private users – can have more than one role, and many players can share the same role.

- *End-users* – "the consumers" – are those utilising the telecommunications services. Our presentation focuses on the end-user.

- *Information service providers* sell their information services to end-users.
- *Network operators* provide network services, such as PSTN, ISDN and PLMN services. They act as intermediaries in the supply of information services and other value-added services to the end-users and bill for what they provide. Some network operators may play more specialised roles: as access network operators or as transport network operators.
- *Content providers* are those who actually produce the content of the services offered to end-users by the aforementioned service providers: films, music or database information. This role is played, in many cases, by film companies and other media enterprises.

The increasing number of services and service providers creates a demand for brokers (or go-betweens) who are qualified to aid users in selecting the right combination of services and the vendor who offers the most favourable conditions.

- *Service brokers* combine services from a number of service providers and then offer complete service packages to end-users.
- *Content brokers* can support service providers in their selection of the contents to be included in their services, or they can support content providers in their attempts to market their products to service providers.
- *Capacity brokers* act as dealers in the distribution of capacity between the different network operators.
- Vendors of systems and equipment provide the systems – including the hardware and software – that are required for the implementation and control of the various services and networks.

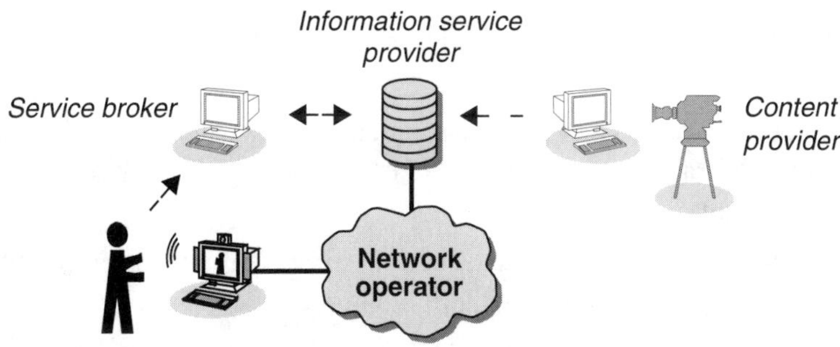

Figure 2.1 The various roles in the telecommunications market

3 End-user requirements

3.1 Private persons

Among the more important requirements are:

- contact with other people;
- services (bank, businesses, health care);
- good environment;
- comfort, means of time-saving communication;
- personal development;
- information, entertainment; and
- personal security and the protection of property.

Modern communities have endeavoured to provide for these requirements but have unfortunately failed in some respects. The urbanisation process has led to the depopulation of rural areas, resulting in reduced personal contact and deteriorated service, not to mention overpopulated cities that are overwhelmed by air-pollution and traffic problems. Places of employment are often concentrated in certain areas, which means that great hordes of people must be transported over long distances to and from their jobs. This situation is time-consuming for the individual and contributes to increased environmental pollution.

3.1.1 Telecommunications for private persons – Examples

Examples of telecommunications for private persons are:

- social contact made possible by the telephone, electronic mail and soon perhaps multimedia mail and video telephony;
- bank transactions, shopping and certain remote medical treatment and health-care services;
- indirect improvement of the environment through the reduction of air and automobile travel which is replaced by increased teleworking and videoconferencing;
- teleworking, which reduces travelling time and makes it possible to change one's employment without having to move;
- personal development through distance education and information retrieval services;

- information and entertainment via the TV, radio, video-on-demand, interactive games and lotteries; and
- security through remote surveillance services and various forms of alarm.

3.2 The company

All companies are, of course, interested in being competitive in their particular niches. They strive towards achieving maximum profit while adapting to changing market conditions and continuously developing their operations and their product and service offerings. They are able to achieve these objectives through

- marketing, that is, the distribution of information to existing and potential customers;
- effective interactive communication with their customers, suppliers and other business partners, to reduce lead times;
- competitive customer services;
- quick access to relevant information (both internal and external);
- distribution of information to employees who might be located away from the organisation's premises;
- support for teleworking and collaborative working in new company structures; and
- low administration costs.

3.2.1 Telecommunications in the company – Examples

- Telecommunications is used as a sales channel; for example, by telemarketing companies that market their products directly to households by means of IN services, especially the "freephone" service. The marketing of goods and services via the Internet is also developing rapidly.
- Customer service is increasing in importance as a competitive tool. Companies aspire to establish effective information channels that provide quick and correct service. At the same time, companies are interested in reducing their costs, often through increasing employee productivity so that fewer people can perform more duties.
- Telecommunications can enable a company to move a portion of its operations to areas with a better supply of labour. This might involve moving the company's telephone exchange, the customer service staff or individ-

ual employees who are to be separately located and perform their duties through teleworking.

- Manufacturing processes can be remotely controlled and supervised.

3.3 The community

Vital social undertakings are:

- education;
- administration of justice;
- environmental protection;
- health care and care of the elderly; and
- other social services.

3.3.1 Telecommunications in the community – Examples

Examples of telecommunications in the service of the community are:

- telemedicine;
- the monitoring of air, forests and water as part of pollution-protection measures;
- dissemination of civic information, currently via TV, tomorrow via the Internet?

3.4 Classifying end-user needs

In the table in *Figure 3.1* we have subdivided end-user needs into a number of categories. (This subdivision facilitates the "translation" that is performed later between needs and services.) The table indicates those services in the different categories that have been given the highest priority according to a Swedish survey.

According to a European survey, the following areas have been found to have the greatest growth potential:

- knowledge;
- entertainment;
- service (home shopping and home banking); and
- remote control and supervision.

Category	Most important *(Swedish survey)*
Communication	teleworking multimedia mail e-mail
Knowledge	distance education
Entertainment	TV games
Information	marketing "yellow pages" catalogues
Service	telemedicine home shopping home banking
Remote control / Remote supervision	

Figure 3.1 End-user needs

4 Operations, telecommunications and networks

Figure 1.1 illustrates in broad outline the support that telecommunications can provide to end-users.

4.1 End-user operations

In *Figure 1.1* we have placed operations of great telecommunications interest in the upper layer.

For private persons:

- interactive communication;
- home shopping and home banking;
- teleworking;

- distance education; and
- entertainment.

For companies:

- marketing and sales;
- customer services;
- project work; and
- procurement.

For the community:

- education and information; and
- health care.

4.2 Telecommunications services

Operations are supported by telecommunications services. Some of these services compete with other types of service: with newspapers (information dissemination) and the post office (message communication).

From an operator's perspective, available telecommunications services can be structured as follows:

- teleservices and bearer services; and
- basic services, supplementary services and value-added services.

These terms are described in Volume 1, Chapter 1.

4.3 Terminals and local networks

There are tailor-made terminals, such as the telephone and the fax machine, that are designed for special networks. There are also generic terminals, first and foremost computers, that can be adapted for connection to various networks. Both of these terminal types are addressed in Chapter 1 of each Part of this volume.

Local networks serve to interconnect the workstations of a company, an institution, a government agency or some other defined group.

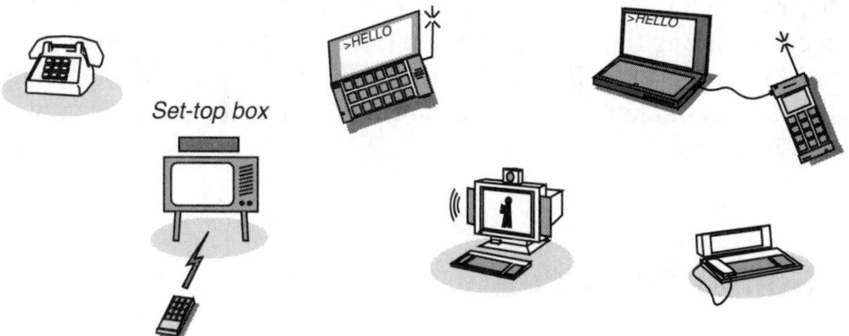

Figure 4.1 Examples of end-user terminals

End-user terminals that are connected to local networks are in principle the same as those intended for connection to public networks. Some functions can be different, however. We have chosen to refer to equipment that connects a local network to a wide area network as *network connection elements*.

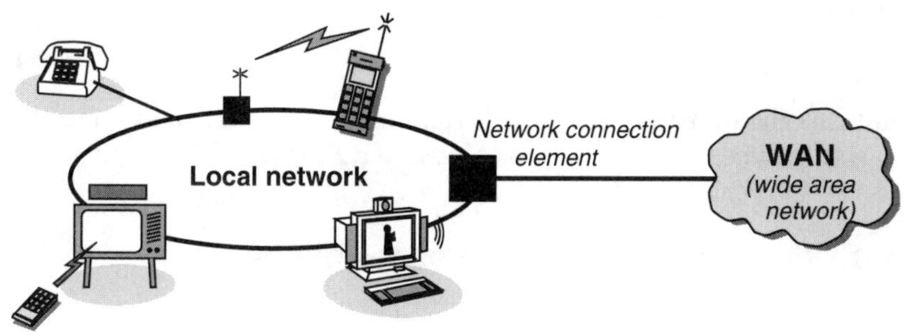

Figure 4.2 A local network connected to a WAN

4.4 Bearer services

Telecommunication bearer services reside in the lowest layer in *Figure 1.1*. As mentioned in the introductory overview, the choice of bearer service for a given offering of telecommunications services is not always self-evident.

5 Important teleservices

The following contains brief descriptions of some of the more important teleservices, including their most common fields of application. Bearer services are addressed in Parts B – H, where the basic services, supplementary services and value-added services that are relevant to a particular network are also dealt with.

5.1 Solitary services

5.1.1 Telephony

Telephony – the oldest and by far the most common teleservice in existence – deals with the transmission of voice between two (occasionally more than two) users who may, in principle, be located anywhere in the world. To increase accessibility, mobile telephony, wireless telephony and a number of supplementary and value-added services have been developed, such as the universal personal communication service (UPT).

Telephony will undoubtedly continue to be enhanced. See *Part B – PSTN*, *Part C – N-ISDN*, *Part D – PLM* and Volume 1, Chapter 1, for more information.

5.1.2 Telefax

Telefax is the transmission of stills (text matter is "read" and transmitted as images) between two telefax machines. See *Part B – PSTN* and Volume 1, Chapter 1.

5.1.3 Videoconferencing – Video telephony

A videoconference is a virtual meeting aided by voice and video communication. The service is not only a substitute for travel but can also enable meetings that would otherwise fail to take place. Videoconferencing is increasingly being supplemented with functions for the transmission of stills, prerecorded video, fax and text files and functionality that enables participants to work jointly in a common document or on a common "electronic whiteboard".

We differentiate between group conferencing and individual videoconferencing. The most common group systems have primarily been used in conjunction with larger, formal meetings and for training purposes. Three or more parties can participate. Special studios have been designed to achieve high quality, but portable videoconferencing equipment is also available.

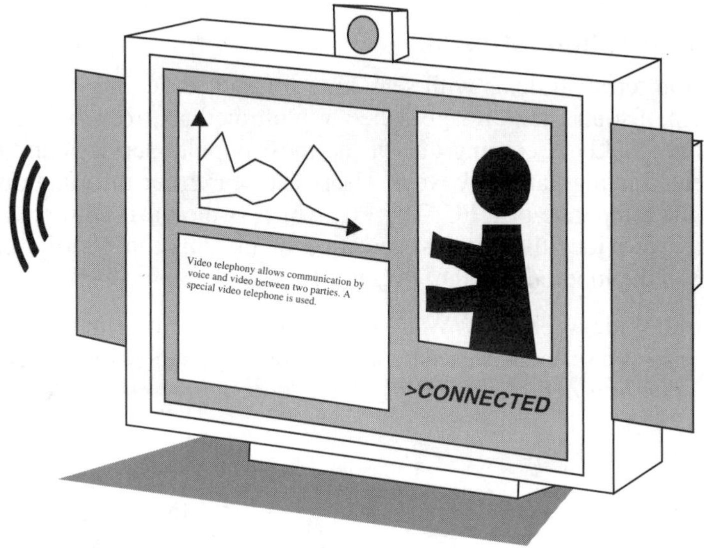

Figure 5.1 Desktop conference

Individual videoconferences, commonly referred to as desktop conferences, are ordinarily arranged as working and project meetings. The equipment is based on PCs or workstations. Desktop conferencing is a meeting form that is increasingly being used, thanks to better and less expensive equipment and more efficient video compression that reduces bandwidth requirements.

Video-telephony is voice and video communication between two parties. A specially designed videophone is used.

5.1.4 High-quality voice transmission – audio

Audio refers to voice, music and, generally, any other sound-type information. The term "audio" normally indicates higher quality sound than ordinary "voice". Examples of applications requiring high-quality transfer of sound are:

- music to and from a radio station;
- sound transmitted from sports arenas and musical events, or from radio and TV field reporters to their networks' viewers and listeners; transfer requirements are temporary – that is, requirements exist for the duration of the event or the report that is transmitted; and

- transmission of radio programmes or commercials from production companies to radio stations.

5.1.5 Information retrieval

Information retrieval deals with searching for and retrieving information – in the form of sound, text, image, video or multimedia – from different databases. It is quickly becoming one of the most popular services and can be implemented in a great many ways. Users can search for information using the TV, the telephone or a PC. The PC, which is the most commonly used tool today, provides the greatest selection of information and the greatest variation in the methods used to present it.

The World Wide Web (WWW) – the most popular information retrieval application – is a service offered by the Internet and is therefore described in *Part H – The Internet.*

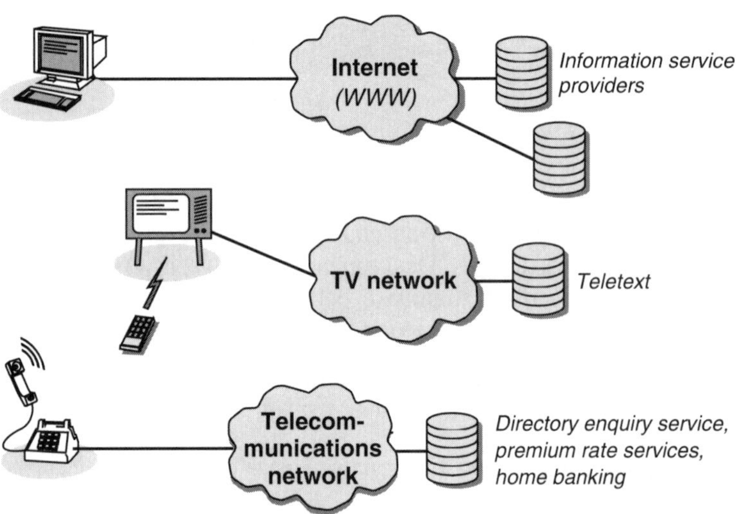

Figure 5.2 Information retrieval

5.1.6 File transfer

File transfer is a term used to describe the transmission of data files from one computer to another. The content of the files can vary from simple text, news articles, administrative information or simple images, to advanced graphics and complete newspapers – articles, illustrations, images and advertisements including logotypes.

File size, data transmission quality requirements and the frequency at which files are to be transferred are factors that determine transfer rate and network capacity requirements. Documents containing stills, graphics and multimedia generally result in large files.

A number of terms that are often used in connection with file transfer:

- host-to-host – transfer between mainframes, such as in connection with the update of databases;
- CAD/CAM files – computer-aided design (CAD) – computerised production of design drawings; computer-aided manufacturing (CAM) – computerised production of manufacturing information, often based on the contents of a CAD drawing; the manufacturing information can then be transferred (as file) to the production department or to a subcontractor;
- high-resolution graphics – stills of extremely high quality; hospitals and the graphic arts industry rely heavily on the transfer of files containing such graphical information.

5.1.7 LAN interconnect

The interconnection of local area networks (LANs) is referred to as LAN interconnect. The number of LANs is growing rapidly, due in part to companies' increased use of client-server solutions. Capacity requirements for LAN–LAN connections are a function of network size and the size of the files that are transferred.

The use of ATM techniques for LAN communication is increasing.

5.1.8 Remote connection to LAN

Individual workplaces can be connected to a corporate LAN. Examples include: an employee who is teleworking; a travelling sales representative who requires access to the company's mail system, servers and printers; and small offices and shops that share a common LAN.

5.1.9 Messaging services

Messaging services are a vital telecommunications growth area. Applications include voice mailboxes, short message service (SMS), telefax message service, electronic mail and electronic data interchange (EDI). These are all described in Volume 1, Chapter 6, and some are dealt with in more detail in the various Parts of this volume.

The electronic mail of the future will very likely develop into forms of video mail and multimedia mail.

The term *unified messaging* refers to all types of messages that are stored at one place and then picked up by a computer or telephone. Conversion between text and voice makes it possible to receive text messages over the telephone.

5.1.10 Telemetry and related applications

Telemetry refers to the remote reading of various types of measurement devices and instrumentation. Measured values are transferred via the telecommunications network – or a data network – to people or to a machine, usually a computer.

Using telemetry, a variety of applications can be created. Two examples are the remote monitoring of alarms and the remote-controlled distribution of electric power.

The following are a few examples of the design of services related to remote monitoring and alarms.

- Alarm signals are transferred to a guard centre. Alternatively, video cameras can be activated in the event of an alarm and their images transmitted to the centre. Watching directly what is happening, the security guards will respond and act as required by the circumstances.
- Continuous video surveillance as an alternative to guards on patrol.
- Access control. A guard is placed at a location other than the actual entrance and can monitor that entrance using remote video cameras. The guard can also have voice contact with persons wishing to gain access.

Many producers and distributors of electric power are interested in remote-controlled activities, such as reading electricity meters and connecting and disconnecting electricity subscribers. The service can be extended so that subscribers themselves can remotely control their consumption of electricity. Producers and distributors of electric power in the US and in Sweden have begun field tests in this area.

5.1.11 Access to the Internet

The Internet is not a service but a network (actually a network of networks) that is used to offer many different services. See *Part H – The Internet.* Users can gain access to the Internet in a number of ways, for example, via a dial-up connection or via a direct data link. Operators of other networks offer Internet access as a service to their subscribers.

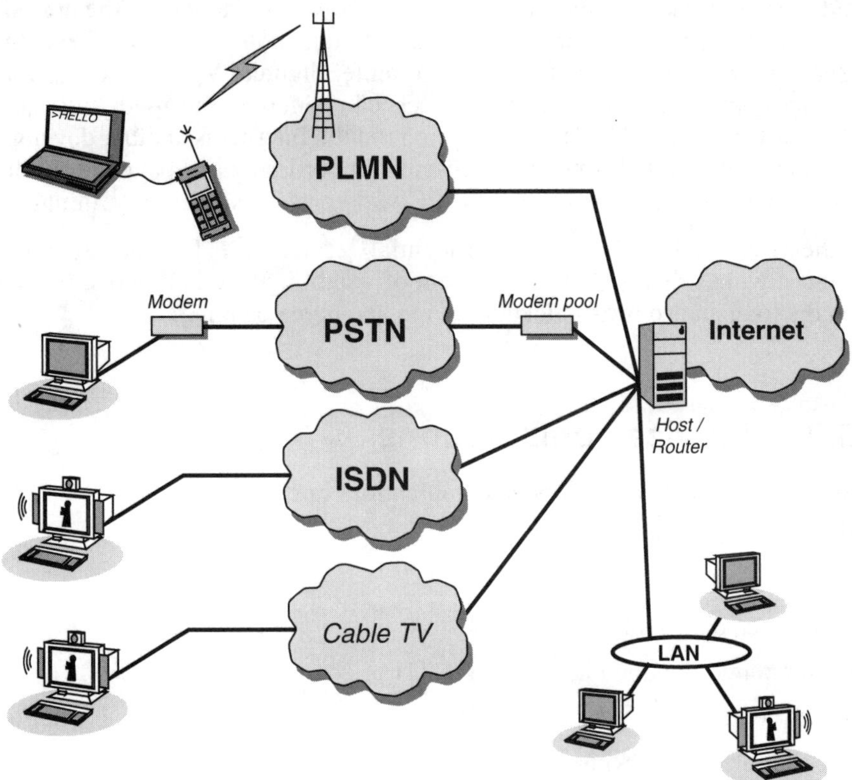

Figure 5.3 Access to the Internet

5.1.12 Paging

Wide area paging (WAP) allows subscribers to be paged over large geographical areas. This service is described in Volume 1, Chapter 6.

5.1.13 Interactive residential services

Service providers offer households a variety of interactive and entertainment services. These services are sometimes referred to a residential interactive broadband services (RIBS), but they do not all require broadband capacity.

Video-on-demand is perhaps the most popular service. A subscriber can order a film from a centrally located database and have it transmitted to his TV. This service is interactive in that subscribers themselves are able to pause, stop and rewind or fast-forward the film.

The term "home shopping" refers to making purchases from home with the aid of telecommunications. The TV is commonly used today for the presentation of the goods, and orders are placed by telephone or telefax. Developments within the TV industry (for example, digital TV) could make this service completely interactive: customers can both view the goods and place their orders via the TV. Home shopping via the Internet is another developing trend. Here a PC is used for presentation, ordering and payment. In the future, perhaps both the TV and the PC will be used as Internet terminals.

Other examples of interactive residential services are TV and computer games, games that include an element of gambling (football pools, betting on the tote, and so forth), ticket booking and home banking.

5.2 Service combinations

Some common types of service combinations are:

- teleworking / home office
- mobile office
- distance education
- computer telephony integration (CTI)
- call centre
- collaborative working
- graphic arts production
- telemedicine

5.2.1 Teleworking / home office

People who choose to work at home or at another place away from the company's premises require access to various services (depending on the type of job performed and the percentage of time spent working away from the company office):

- telephony;
- telefax;
- remote connection to the company's LAN, including servers, electronic mail and so forth;
- file transfer to and from on-site company computers: text files, CAD files, images – depending on the nature of the job;

- access to the company's electronic mail system and databases for those who are not connected to the company's LAN;
- desktop conferencing with in-house personnel and, on occasion, even with the personnel of other companies;
- large-scale videoconferencing (a current Swedish example of such users are cabinet ministers who work at home during certain days of the week);
- the possibility of searching external databases; and
- access to the Internet.

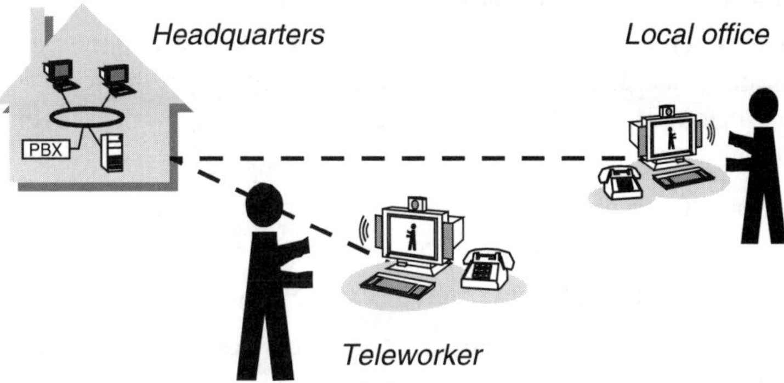

Figure 5.4 Teleworking

5.2.2 Mobile office

People who often work in their hotel rooms, in the car, at airports or at customers' offices require a mobile workplace. The services they need are in principle the same as for those who are teleworking, but they must also have mobile access. Message services are especially interesting for this category, as is UPT.

Up to now, mobile offices have been less demanding than traditional offices, in terms of service offerings and service quality, but their demands will become more pronounced as services, networks and terminals develop.

5.2.3 Distance education

Distance education supported by telecommunications is relatively widespread, especially in large or sparsely populated countries, such as Canada, Australia, the US, Sweden and Norway.

University-level education as well as other adult education can be offered to people who either cannot or will not move to larger cities where the universities are located. Universities and other institutes of higher education can now extend their catchment area, even to a global level. Companies can utilise distance training to reduce travel costs as well as costs related to their employees' absence from work during training. Telecommunications provides greater access to experts around the world, because they can instruct and participate in multiple seminars held at more than one geographical location at the same time. Travel is no longer necessary.

Course participants can be assembled at a number of course centres where the necessary equipment is available, or they can participate from home or from their ordinary workplaces using their own or borrowed equipment.

The following telecommunication services can be of use:

- Videoconferencing for lectures and lessons for participants in different locations. Access to shared information sources – in the form of a common "electronic whiteboard", for example – can result in even greater efficiency.
- Desktop conferencing for group work and communication with other students outside ordinary class sessions.
- Information retrieval from databases and electronic libraries.
- Electronic mail or multimedia that supports communication with tutors and with other students.
- Transfer of files with exercises.

A probable future scenario is that remote education and training activities in our own homes will become increasingly common.

5.2.4 Computer telephony integration

CTI can refer to many things – from connecting one's PC to a telephone, to the integration of a large company's computer network with all its private branch exchanges (PBXs) or centrex systems. CTI can be used for the creation of a range of different applications, including the following.

- Screen-based call handling. Services such as "call forwarding" and "conference call" can be activated with the aid of a mouse and a keyboard.
- Call-based data selection. The system retrieves information that is related to an incoming or outgoing call and displays it on the screen. Calls, together with the relevant information, can also be transferred within a company.
- Interception system. A company's employees can use their PCs or their keypad telephones to enter information on absence, time of return, call forwarding to another extension and so forth. When that extension is

called, the information entered automatically appears on a display to assist the company's telephonist.

- Message handling, such as voice mailboxes, electronic mail, fax messages, SMS and paging. Message systems are often combined with the use of an interception computer, thereby increasing reception and call-handling efficiency.
- Intelligent routing of both incoming and outgoing calls (see Subsection 5.2.5 below).

Early CTI solutions were tailor-made to suit individual users' computing and telephony environments. They were complex and expensive and thus only of interest to large, financially powerful companies.

At the present time, standards are undergoing intensive development. Computer-supported telecommunications applications (CSTA) is a European standard for the interface between telephones and computers; switch computer application interface (SCAI) is the US equivalent. Telecommunications applications for switches and computers (TASC) is an ITU-T standard related to centrex.

Development platforms from different computer companies have become de facto standards. General, standardised interfaces make the development of CTI applications easier and less expensive and contribute to increased competition.

Many feel that the CTI market is developing along the lines of the PC market. Customers can purchase a PBX from the manufacturer of their choice and then select among the numerous CTI solutions available from different vendors.

Call centres, perhaps the most common application of CTI, are still very important and a major driving force behind the continued development of CTI. Unified messaging is another field of application that is quickly gaining recognition.

5.2.5 Call centre

Call centre is the collective term for systems that support the effective management of a large number of telephone calls. In the following, we will primarily concern ourselves with call centre activities and functions related to incoming calls. Ordinarily, call-centre users can be found among telebanking companies, insurance companies and other companies that offer intensive customer service by telephone. As a rule, two main functions are offered: automatic queue management and the coordination of calls and customer data.

A call centre can operate as follows. Incoming calls are answered by prerecorded messages. Voice response systems can be used to categorise telephone calls. Automatic queue management and intelligent routing distribute incoming calls to available and suitable agents. The call arrives at an agent's telephone at the same time as a pop-up window displays customer data. The agent can enter new information and, if required, can transfer the call plus the information to another agent. Some calls are instead connected to a fax polling system, a voice mailbox or a voice response system that allows the customer to process his transaction himself.

The operation of a call centre is based on the utilisation of a range of CTI applications. Other common functions and subsystems are:

- Interactive voice response (IVR): an IVR system can be likened to an interactive telephone answering machine that provides information or instructions. The calling party uses a keypad telephone to communicate with the system.
- Automatic call distributor (ACD) is a system for managing queues and distributing calls to agents. It can be implemented in a number of ways, for example, in a PBX or by the introduction of network intelligence.
- Freephone, premium rate services and universal access numbers are described in Volume 1, Chapter 6.
- Statistics systems for follow-up.

Call-centre solutions – featuring functions such as screen-based dial-up and call-based data selection – also exist for outgoing calls. The vast majority of users are companies engaged in telemarketing.

Using centrex and virtual private networks (VPNs), call centres can be geographically distributed while customers still perceive them as being centralised operations.

5.2.6 Collaborative working

We define collaborative working as follows: The cooperation between several people engaged in a common task although working – with some form of telecommunications support – at geographically separate locations. Product development and design activities are of special interest in the application of collaborative working as a means of reducing lead times.

A relatively simple scenario is one in which one person works on a file and at the end of the day transmits this file to the next person, working in another time zone. Ideally, design or development can then continue around the clock. Communication and discussions are carried on via the telephone, electronic mail and fax.

The expression "computer-supported collaborative working" is often used in this context; that is, a number of people operate on one and the same document or object (a CAD file, for example) while maintaining simultaneous voice and video contact. Desktop conferencing is a service that suits this approach.

Future services in the area of collaborative working are very likely to be increasingly advanced. Shared 3-D models in combination with broadband videoconferencing are being tested in Sweden.

5.2.7 Graphic arts production

A typical telecommunications requirement in the area of graphic arts production is the fast transmission of high-quality images. Requirements can also exist for the transmission of advertisements including text and images, complete newspaper pages and final art for printing.

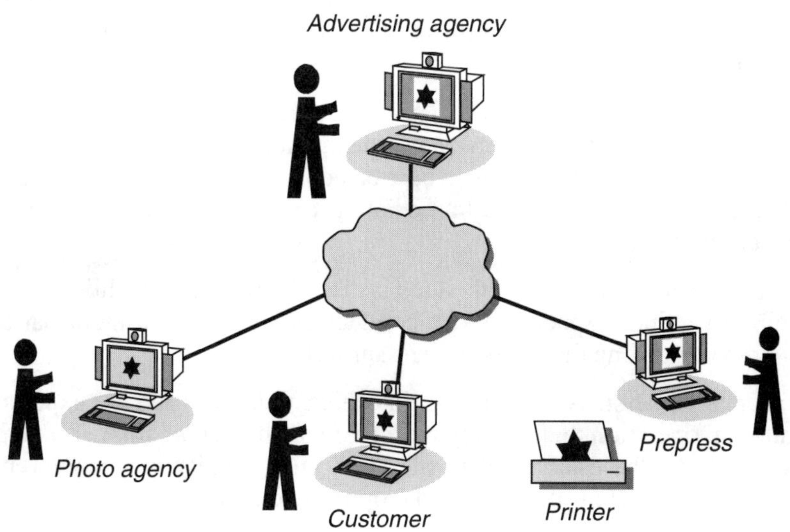

Figure 5.5 Speedier graphic arts production

A few examples:

- An advertising agency is to produce a brochure. A PC is used to study and evaluate photographic material from a photo agency, to order the pictures that are to be used in the brochure and to receive them directly over the network. Brochure proofs are then transmitted via the network to the customer, who is able to perform an on-screen evaluation of the material.

After making the necessary modifications (if any), the material can be transmitted directly to repro and then on to the printer.

- A daily newspaper printed in various regions for distribution is transmitted in its entirety to each of the different printing sites via the network. Deadlines become less critical, because more time is available to meet printing and distribution timing requirements.
- A small company is involved in the layout process for a number of periodicals. Photos arrive from prepress, and text from the various editorial departments. After layout is complete, all materials are sent to the printer.

5.2.8 Telemedicine

Telediagnostics is a type of service within the realm of telemedicine. Instead of physically sending patients from one hospital to another, the patient's journal, x-rays, ultrasonic pictures and pictures of slides for microscopic examination are transmitted. Groups of general practitioners and specialists can then discuss possible diagnoses and treatments while making their "virtual rounds".

Telediagnostics is of great value in on-call situations – in cases where medical personnel must quickly determine whether a patient requires transportation to another hospital or must be treated immediately. These types of application require secure and immediate access to the necessary telecommunication services.

Applications also exist in which video is directly transmitted while a patient is being examined. Specialists can conduct examinations without patients having to travel long distances to their surgeries.

Another application is telesurgery, in which video is used by experts to monitor an operation that is being performed at another location. The application requires the establishment of a very high quality videoconference. Voice contact is often sufficient in the opposite direction.

Telecommunications is also used in the training of medical personnel. Aided by videoconferencing, personnel participate in training sessions that are conducted at major hospitals. Telediagnostics as a form of on-the-job training thus contributes to the dissemination of knowledge.

The following teleservices are utilised to meet these needs:

- transmission of high-resolution photographic or video information;
- file transfer (of medical journals); and
- videoconferencing or desktop conferencing.

5.3 User groups' need of telecommunications

The table shown in *Figure 5.6* indicates the services considered relevant by the various user groups. The grouping of the services is based on the underlying needs that they contribute to fulfilling. (X = relevant; (X) = partly relevant)

Underlying need – teleservice	Company	Household
Interactive communication		
– telephony	X	X
– videoconferencing / desktop conferencing	X	(X)
– multimedia communication	X	
– information exchange between network computers	X	
– client–server applications	X	
Knowledge		
– education	(X)	X
– information retrieval		
– business information	X	
– general information, news	(X)	X
– voice – audio		X
– text, video, multimedia	X	X
Information dissemination		
– direct		
– distributive video, audio	X (P)	X (R)
– included in entertainment applications (infotainment)	X (P)	X (R)
– on demand	X (P)	X (R)
web pages, yellow pages, databases, on-line catalogues		
Service		
– telemedicine	X (public)	X (client)
– home banking	X (server)	X (client)
– home shopping	X (server)	
Remote control / supervision		
– surveillance	X	(X)
– alarms	X	(X)
– control (of manufacturing processes or the distribution of electric power)	X	(X)

Underlying need – teleservice	Company	Household
Message communication		
– voice messages	X	X
– text messages	X	X
– video and multimedia messages	X	X
– paging	X	X
Entertainment *(P = provider, R = recipient)*		
– TV programmes, films, and the like	X (P)	X (R)
– distributive (TV, radio)	X (P)	X (R)
– on demand	X (P)	X (R)
– interactive games		

Figure 5.6 Services and user groups

6 Local networks

Local networks are not addressed in detail in this set of volumes; if they were, they would certainly fill up the better part of a volume. Instead, our study will focus on the interface between local networks and WANs.

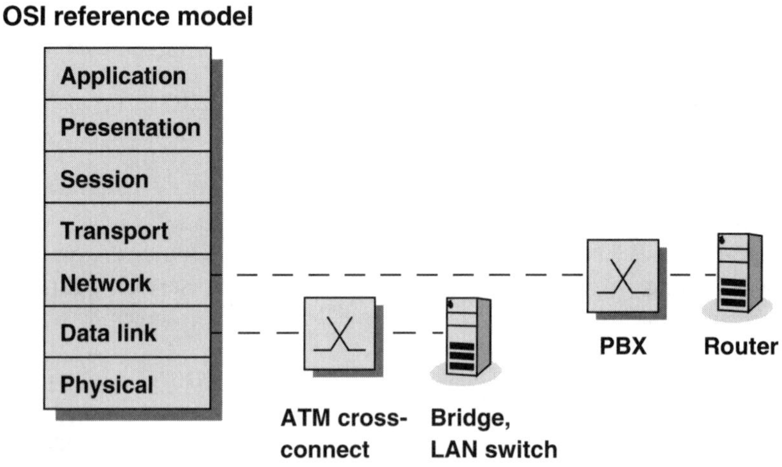

Figure 6.1 Network connection elements in a local network and their relation to the OSI model

Figure 6.1 shows several different network connection elements for local networks and their relation to the open systems interconnection (OSI) model.

6.1 PBX networks

The majority of companies have internal telephone networks using a PBX as the interface to the public network.

Larger companies may wish to interconnect a number of PBXs that are distributed throughout their organisation. This can be achieved through the use of leased lines or a virtual private network.

A PBX can provide a range of functions and services:

- telephony systems with facilities for direct dialling-in;
- key systems, in which some or all of the connections serve as telephonist positions and receive and transfer calls;
- automatic call distribution;
- handling of voice and text messages;
- paging;
- call centre;
- interactive voice response;
- cordless extensions;
- ISDN extensions able to transmit voice, data and images via the PBX; and
- UPT.

6.2 Local area networks

It was not until the 1980s that local data networks really made their breakthrough. The LAN configuration represented the decentralisation of a company's processor power.

Typical LAN characteristics are:

- geographic limit, normally to one company site;
- high transfer rates, from 4–10 Mbit/s and above;

- star or ring topology in which all terminals share the available bandwidth; and
- transmission in the form of broadcasts.

The average data-transfer rate and the level of burstiness rise as the total processor power in the local networks increases and as information becomes increasingly graphics-oriented. Also, data communication will be supplemented with multimedia communication to a growing extent.

This situation has created a need for LAN switches capable of distributing the available bandwidth efficiently and a need for ATM switching for high-speed LANs carrying multimedia traffic.

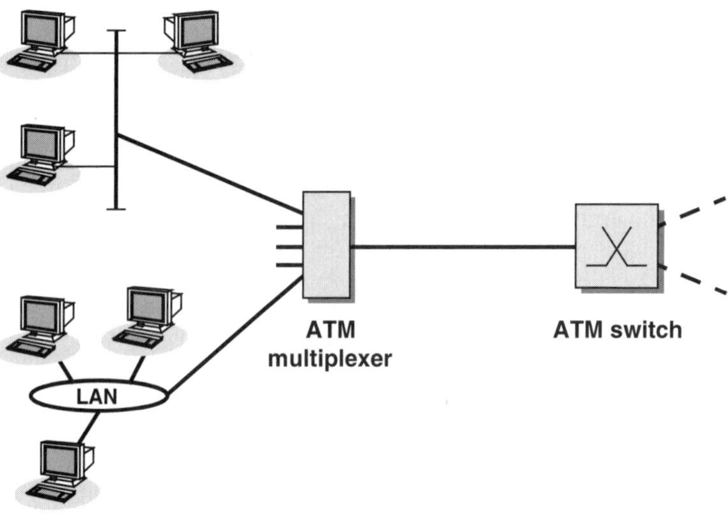

Figure 6.2 Example of a LAN switch with ATM

A LAN switch is a specialised bridge equipped with multiple ports. A given segment of the local network is connected to each port. Each port isolates its network segment from the rest of the network, so fewer workstations share the bandwidth of the segment or ring. The LAN switch routes messages between the ports.

The central ATM nodes of a company's network can form part of an ATM-LAN, constituting a LAN switch, and serve as a switching point for PBX traffic – if not at the present time then certainly in the future.

A router is another type of switching point between a public network (or WAN) and a LAN. A router is similar to a public switching node. It switches connections by using network layer addresses (IP addresses, for example) and routing tables. An intelligent router is also capable of filtering traffic: It can allow electronic mail to pass while blocking file transfers or it can function as a firewall. Routers can ordinarily handle several protocols.

7 Network requirements

Different services make different demands on the networks. These demands determine which networks are suitable for a specific service, and also affect network planning and dimensioning. Important parameters are:

- bandwidth;
- burstiness – variations in bandwidth requirements;
- bit errors and blocking; and
- delay.

Security is another pressing concern that has come into focus as a result of the ongoing debate on Internet security.

Seizure times and traffic interest are important factors to be considered in the dimensioning process.

7.1 Bandwidth

It is difficult to specify the bandwidth requirements for a specific type of service in general terms; such specifications must always be related to transmission quality, acceptable transmission time, and other factors. Videoconferencing is a typical example. Video can be transmitted at 32 kbit/s, if the participants keep fairly still. 2 •64 kbit/s results in better quality, but the use of a portable camera and zooming probably require 6 •64 kbit/s or more. In general, the choice of bandwidth – and thereby quality – is a question of cost.

On the other hand, less bandwidth will be required for a given level of picture quality as compression techniques advance. *Figure 7.1* illustrates the bandwidth requirements of different service types.

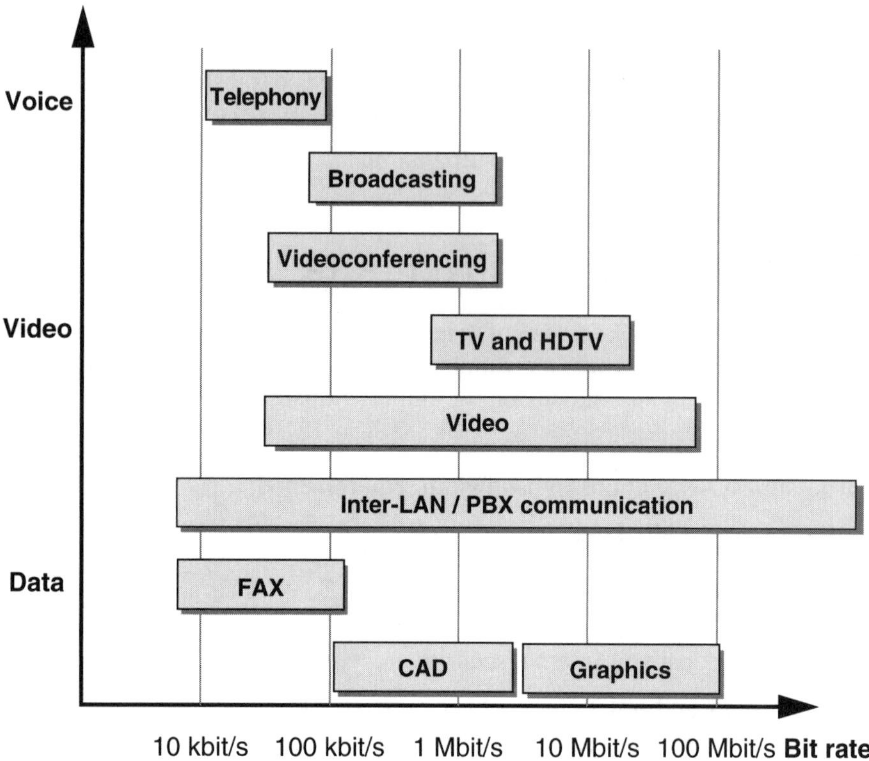

Figure 7.1 Bandwidth requirements for different services

7.2 Burstiness

Burstiness refers to the relation between the highest and the average traffic values. A high burstiness value implies great bit-rate variation. In Volume 1, Chapter 1, Section 1.4, teleservices are subdivided into voice, data (including stills), video and multimedia. Typically, the information flows of data traffic can display high levels of burstiness, but this applies to video and multimedia as well. Services also differ in their requirements for isochronism (even pace – in practice that the transmitter and receiver equipment operate at the same pace). See *Figure 7.2.*

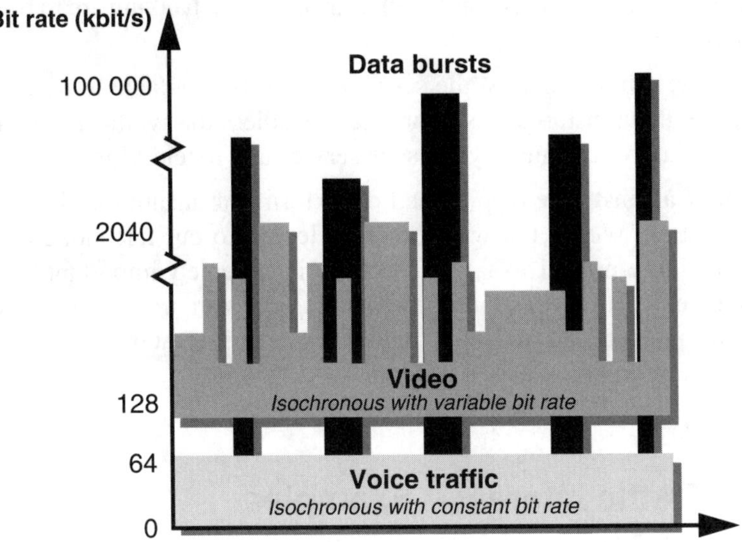

Figure 7.2 Variation in bit rates for different types of service

7.3 Symmetry

- Fixed and mobile telephony offer an entirely symmetrical, interactive telecommunications service that has the same bandwidth in both directions.
- TV is exclusively distributive and information is transmitted only in one direction (simplex).
- Internet services and video-on-demand are interactive and asymmetrical, with considerably higher bandwidth requirements in the receive direction and less upstream bandwidth.

7.4 Security and secrecy

Security is a subtle concept, open to great interpretation. The following describes three important security aspects.

- Secure payment mechanisms; that is, reliable and secure handling of monetary transfers between accounts and in the use of credit cards when making payment over a network. It is critical that both parties are identifiable if services such as home shopping and home banking are to become widely used.
- 100% availability; that is, the services are to be available to users at all times, without disturbances or outages. Needless to say, this requirement is essential to a community's rescue service and to telesurgery.
- Security against wire tapping and other forms of unauthorised access to information. We do not want others listening to our telephone calls or reading our e-mail. This type of security is extremely important for telemedicine, where medical journals and diagnoses are transmitted between health care units and specialists, and for companies that transmit sensitive business information over a network.

7.5 Traffic interest – Examples

Long-distance traffic dominates in the trunk network; for example, the large portion of Internet traffic in transatlantic cables.

Application	% interurban traffic (portion of long-distance traffic)
Video telephony	20
Videoconferencing	50
Video surveillance	0
Telemetry	0
Alarms	0
High-speed fax	20
LAN interconnect	20
Host-to-host communication	10
Data transfer, large volumes	20
CAD/CAM	20

Application	% interurban traffic (portion of long-distance traffic)
High-resolution graphics	20
Medical photographs	20
Multimedia desktop	50
Multimedia conferencing	50
Multimedia mail	20
Internet	High

Figure 7.3 Traffic interest

7.6 Geographical dispersion

Network planning is strongly influenced by the geographical dispersion of end-users and their varying requirements. Three categories of end-users were described in the introduction: private persons, companies and the community. Quite naturally, the first category is found in residential areas (cities and rural areas), and the second in commercial districts (ordinarily forming part of a city). There was a time when residential areas were made up exclusively of private subscribers; today these areas also contain an increasing number of business subscribers represented by small companies and teleworking employees. For the most part, medium-sized and large companies are still found in cities.

The dispersion of rural subscribers strongly affects the cost of sites and therefore the choice of suitable techniques. The different geographical areas can be described with the help of the following three parameters:

- *Density* – The number of subscribers per unit of area is an important parameter for fixed networks (wire); traffic per unit of area is the corresponding parameter for wireless networks. The number of potential subscribers is another important parameter since it can lead to an increase in density.
- *Cluster* – This term denotes the number of subscribers gathered into a cluster. The term “granularity” is also used.
- *Grouping* – This term describes the geographic grouping of buildings, depending on topography and other factors.

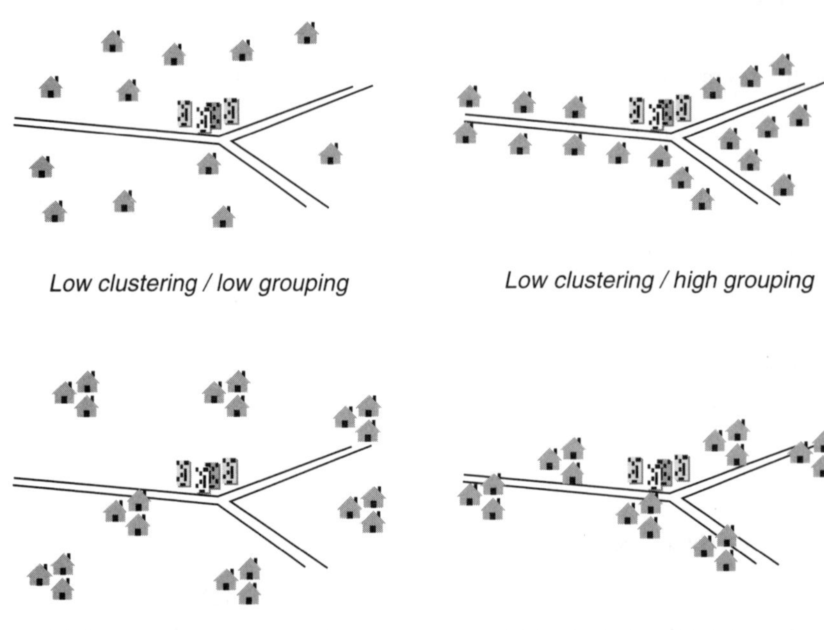

Figure 7.4 Clusters and grouping

8 Forecasts and trends

8.1 General

The integration of telecommunications, data communications and media will continue. There will be stiffer competition, between market players and between the various services and techniques.

Network development will be financed, to an ever-increasing degree, by revenues from services rather than through government infrastructure-related grants. Service offerings will increase considerably.

Many experts feel that one universal network for all types of services is not forthcoming. Instead, they feel that there will be an increase in interworking between networks and network interconnection. It is easier, and very likely more cost-effective, to base the introduction of new services on existing networks. Services can then be further developed as the network is improved.

8.2 Which services will be successful?

Forecasting is a difficult proposition. Mobile telephony – to name one example – continues to exceed expectations year after year. Few were able to anticipate, some years ago, the immense increase in the number of Internet users. On the other hand, videophones have been around for a long time and have not achieved any great success.

Three factors are of special importance from the end-user's point of view. A service must be:

- worth its price – users can even accept lower quality if the price is sufficiently low, such as telephony over the Internet;
- user-friendly – it should be easy to subscribe to the service and easy to use it; charging and invoicing must be explicit, understandable and flexible; "one-stop shopping" and "one-stop billing" are often mentioned in this context; and
- "globally compatible" – world-wide communication must be possible; in this respect, the Internet has been an exceptional success; in contrast, multimedia services over N-ISDN and ATM networks have had some difficulty in solving the problems related to global interoperability, which has contributed to slowing their breakthrough.

8.3 End-user groups

It is especially difficult to forecast the demands made on services by private persons, because their motives are often psychological or social in nature – a feeling that the service, in some way, will increase the quality of their lives. Generally, their private finances are a limiting factor, making cost an important element. Time is another limited resource. Many of the new telecommunications services compete with other activities, for both time and money, and time-saving services are therefore likely to be successful.

Company needs and requirements are generally based on a greater level of fiscal discipline. Although companies are cost-conscious, they are generally positively inclined towards paying more for a service since they are able to generate revenue through its use. They are strongly driven to increase efficiency and effectivity. A company is likely to use a new service if there is reason to believe that the service will improve the company's competitive strength with a reasonable level of risk.

8.4 A business case: Is the service profitable?

A software consulting company with offices in two cities is offered a desktop conferencing system with a connection to N-ISDN. The profitability of a possible investment should be based upon:

- *Investment costs*: Desktop-conference equipment for six people, N-ISDN access and personnel training.
- *Operating costs*: Higher telephone bills, equipment maintenance.
- *Revenue (or cost reductions)*: Savings on travel expenses for six people who ordinarily travel every other month. Travel time for these employees can now be used for productive work, thereby increasing company revenue.
- *Other positive effects*: The project can be started regardless of where the participants work. The utilisation of available resources is more efficient.
- *Risks*: The personnel do not learn to handle the equipment, which will either result in the service not being used or in an additional burden being placed on those responsible for IT support.
  The existence of a number of "mixed" project groups can mean that more personnel travel, perhaps leading to no reduction in travel expenses.

8.5 Forecast for a number of service types

We have already discussed the outlook for some specific telecommunications services. For development trends in general, the following points seem to summarise a broad consensus on the future course of events:

- Data communication over public networks will increase.
- The number of company-owned ATM exchanges will increase.
- Mobility will be of great importance to all services. Some experts go as far as predicting that mobility will become a basic requirement.
- Companies will have an increasing number of teleworking employees.
- Multimedia communication will increase; companies will be the first to start, followed by private individuals.
- The Internet will continue to grow. Many interactive services for private persons – home shopping, information retrieval, home banking, interactive entertainment – are being offered on the Internet. However, a number

of issues such as quality, network overload and security remain to be solved.

- More private individuals will have PC equipment.

In 1995, the European Telecommunications Standards Institute (ETSI) published the following table:

Type of service	**Typical telecommunications services**	**Current value**	**Future value**
Interactive voice communication	Telephony; Audio conferencing	High	High (but lower than today)
Real-time image transmission	Fax	High	Low
Messaging services	Text; Voice mailbox; Fax mailbox	Low	Medium
Information retrieval – multimedia	World Wide Web; Image databases	Low	High
Video-on-demand	Film; Music; News; Channels	Low	High
Interactive video services	Video telephony; Videoconferencing; Interactive games, including virtual reality; Home shopping; Telemedicine; Distance education	Low	High
Computer-aided "collaborative working"	Teleworking; Editing; Design – development	Low	High
Distributive TV/radio/data – production	Program production	Low	Medium
Distributive TV/radio/data – broadcasting	"Ordinary" TV; Pay-TV (pay-per-view); Pay-TV (pay-per-channel)	Medium	High

Type of service	Typical telecommunica-tions services	Current value	Future value
Distributed com-puter capacity	Distributed manufacturing; Real-time stock control; Control, management and supervision of networks and services	Low	High
Real-time infor-mation gathering	Video surveillance; News gathering; Televoting	Low	Medium

Figure 8.1 Forecast for different types of services

8.6 Terminals and local networks – A scenario

The telephone, PC and TV will still exist and develop in parallel – as usual, depending on market demands. The PC will develop into a general-purpose office terminal used for desktop conferences, data communication, electronic mail, information retrieval and the like. Mobile access will be required in many cases. Cordless or mobile telephony will complement the use of the PC.

TVs, telephones and, to an ever-increasing extent, PCs are available in many of today's homes. The home TV is the dominant source of entertainment, also making available a limited level of interactive information access (via teletext) and home shopping (here the services of the TV and telephone are combined). PCs are generally used for accessing Internet services. The telephone will continue to be an important device, but the replacement of fixed telephones will accelerate so that both cordless and mobile telephones will be used at home. PCs will be used by teleworking personnel in the same way as they are used in offices.

Home interactive services (such as entertainment, distance education, home shopping and home banking) can be offered either via the PC or the TV. At present, TV manufacturers and the PC industry are battling over the control of this sector. Will the winner be a TV with a set-top box that can provide Internet access via a modem or a PC that can receive TV broadcasts?

A forecast of terminals connected to public networks is shown in *Figure 8.2*.

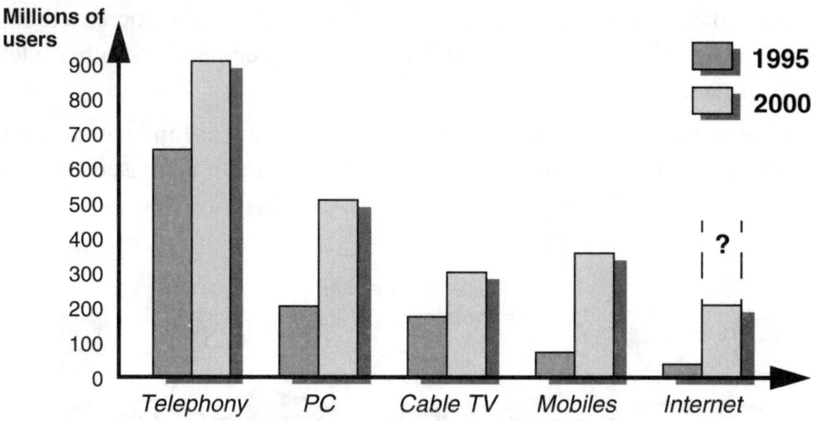

Figure 8.2 Terminals connected to public networks

8.7 Residential LANs

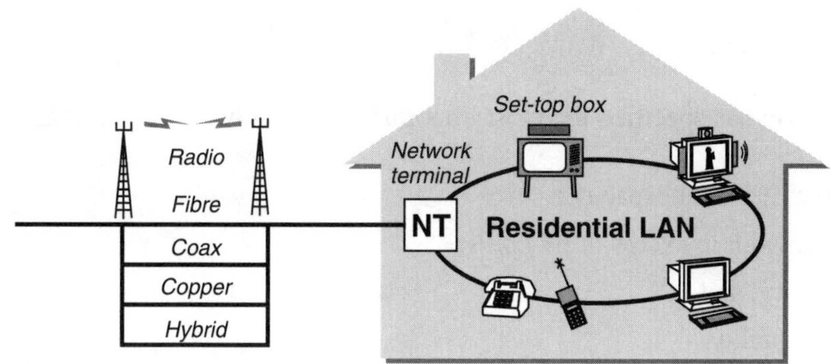

Figure 8.3 A residential LAN

Residential subscribers can also benefit from LAN techniques by being able to connect – via one and the same bus or ring – their PCs, telephones, printers, faxes, TVs, alarm monitoring circuits and other circuits for reading household metering devices, including electricity meters.

8.8 Requirements

- Greater bandwidth due to the use of multimedia services, increased data traffic due to the transfer of larger files, video-on demand and other interactive services.
- A greater amount of bursty traffic owing to an increase in switched data traffic as a percentage of total WAN traffic and to an increased need for virtual private networks.

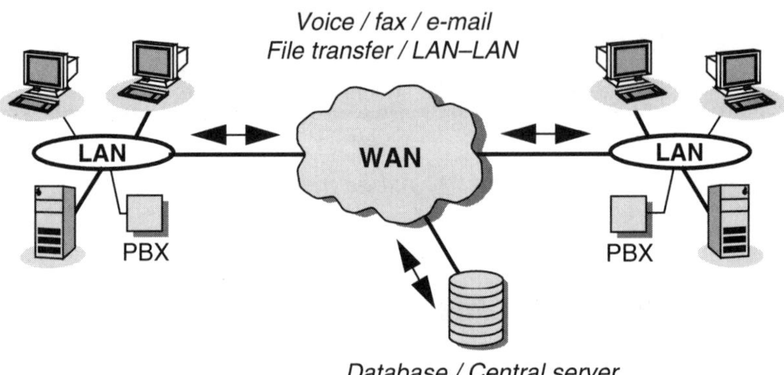

Figure 8.4 Traffic in a WAN

One study has specified the most important future network requirements to be:

- large real-time capacity;
- bandwidth in excess of 64 kbit/s;
- security; and
- high quality.

As mentioned earlier, requirements and costs go hand-in-hand. Requirements can be relaxed if costs are kept low.

8.9 Geographical trends

The number of urban residential subscribers will increase substantially. See *Figure 8.5* and *Figure 8.6*. The number of rural subscribers will decrease due to the urbanisation process.

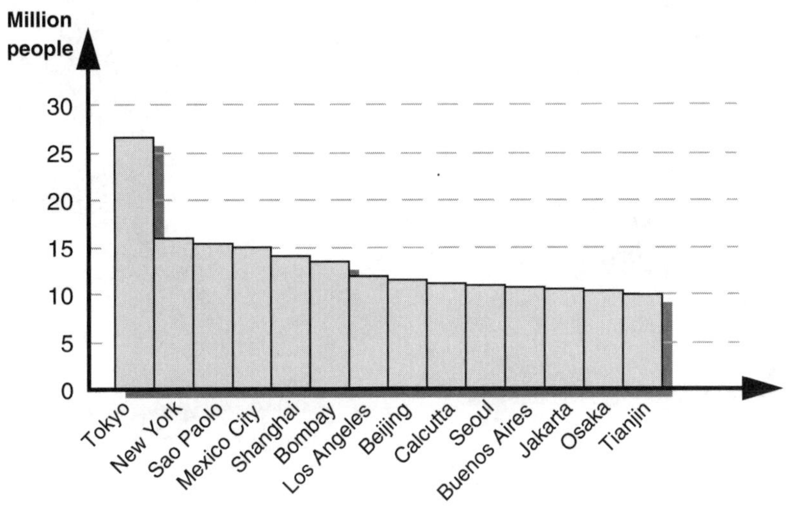

Figure 8.5 A world of cities – cities having a population exceeding 10 million inhabitants in 1994. Source: World Bank

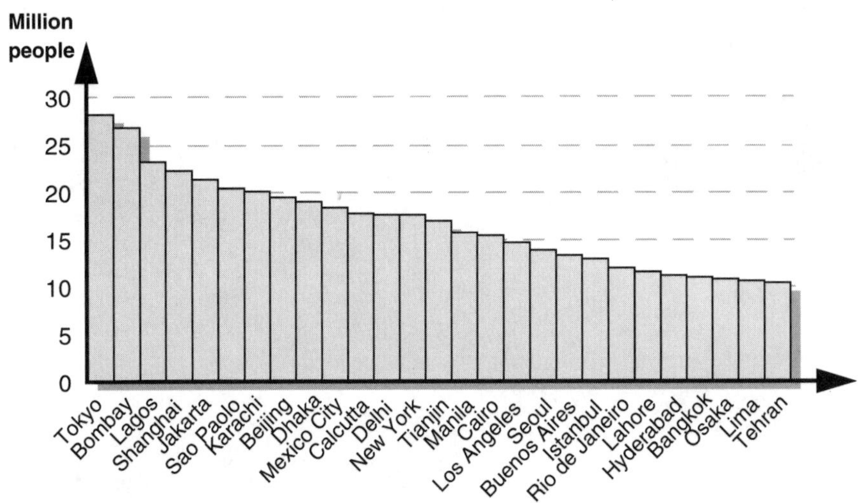

Figure 8.6 A world of cities – cities having a population exceeding 10 million inhabitants. Forecast for 2015. Source: World Bank

Part B – PSTN

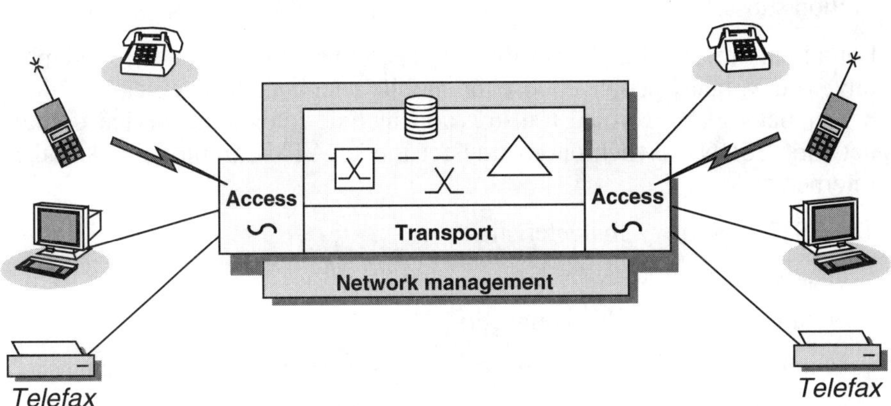

Figure B.0.1 Reference model

1 User services and terminals

1.1 Introduction

The oldest and hitherto largest telecommunications network in existence is the public switched telephone network (PSTN) which has in excess of 700 million subscribers.

For a long time, the PSTN was the only bearer network available for telephony. Today, many people choose the mobile telephone for their calls. Other bearer networks for voice transmission include integrated service digital network (ISDN), asynchronous transfer mode (ATM), frame relay and the Internet.

The PSTN's primary characteristics:

- analog access, 300–3,400 Hz;
- circuit-switched duplex connection;
- switched bandwidth, 64 kbit/s, or 300–3,400 Hz for analog exchanges;
- immobility or, at best, very limited mobility; and
- many functions in common with another bearer network: N-ISDN.

See the PSTN reference model in *Figure B.1.1.*

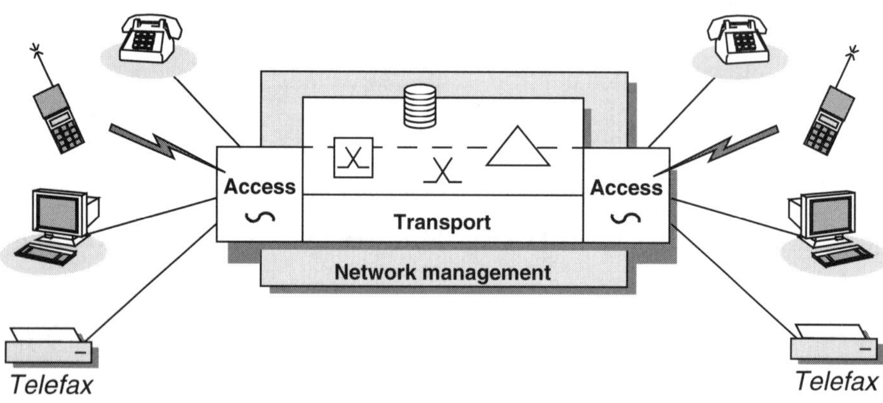

Figure B.1.1 PSTN reference model

In the course of its long history, which started in 1876, the PSTN has undergone a complete technical metamorphosis. Even factors such as network structure and network utilisation have changed radically. The truly revolutionary changes have come about from the 1960s onwards – innovations such as data communication, telefax, processor control technique, digital voice transmission, satellite communication, digital switching, optoelectronics, network intelligence structures and the Internet.

To facilitate your understanding of the PSTN and the "culture" that formed today's telecommunications, we will briefly digress and step back in time to the early 1960s.

1.2 The PSTN of the 1960s

As part of the reference model that is used throughout our books, a number of main elements are included: terminals, transport, access, switching, network intelligence and network management. These are concepts and terms that were seldom, if ever, used in the 1960s.

While today's digitised PSTN is a "logical" network, utilising the same resources as those used by other networks, the PSTN of the 1960s was certainly a physical network – one in which you could touch the selectors in an exchange and the conductors of a subscriber's line, a network in which nothing resembling today's software existed. Electronic tubes were still commonplace in the amplifiers of that day.

Figure B.1.2 The network of the 1960s

1.2.1 Terminals

Broadly speaking, dial telephones were the only form of terminal that existed. The number of pulses generated as the dial rotated back to its initial position indicated the digit that was dialled. The pulses were then detected by the local exchange.

Although many of today's telephone users feel that this form of dialling is too slow, a considerable number of these older units are still in operation in many countries around the world.

The first modems to be used for data transmission were connected to the PSTN during the 1960s. Bit rates were low, generally 300 or 600 bit/s. Telefax units started to appear on the market towards the end of the decade.

1.2.2 The access network

The access network was referred to as the local network, local loop or subscriber network. The technique was simple: a copper wire (or an open wire) connected the subscriber to the exchange. This part of the network of the 1960s has proved to be more competitive than other parts. Copper pairs are ideally suited to supplying power to the telephones; they also lend themselves to baseband transmission of voice – no modulation is required as in the case of fibre and radio applications. Moreover, copper can be utilised at higher frequencies than those originally intended. This means that the existing copper pair can also be used to access services of greater bandwidth in other networks.

In the entirely analog networks that existed before the introduction of pulse code modulation (PCM) systems, the attenuation of voice signals represented a problem for network planners. Attenuation occurred not only in the local network but also in the exchanges and in the two-wire sections of the trunk network (between exchanges). To solve the attenuation problem, operators had to install special lines (conductors of greater diameter) for remote subscribers, which increased the cost of the subscriber network.

Today's exchanges and trunk networks are normally digital and, hence, attenuation-free. Digital transmission is also being introduced into the access network. All of this serves to make the network's copper sections less expensive and more competitive (normally, 0.4-mm diameter wire is used).

1.2.3 Telephone exchanges

As mentioned in Chapter 3 of Volume 1, a well-developed hierarchy of automatic telephone exchanges existed in the 1960s alongside exchanges that were manually served. The hierarchical structure had been brought on by the high transmission costs of that period – possibly as much as 100 times higher per channel-kilometre than current costs.

There were two-wire (for the most part local exchanges) and four-wire, analog telephone exchanges. (See Volume 1, Chapter 4.) Remote subscriber stages did not exist at that time; all functionality resided in the exchanges.

The fact that there are still a great number of analog exchanges in operation motivates some study of the subject.

The lines of an analog switching network are galvanically connected together. The electromechanical selector is the network's most important component; the symbol for this component is commonly drawn as shown in *Figure B.1.3.* As illustrated, an incoming line can be connected to one of 10 outgoing lines.

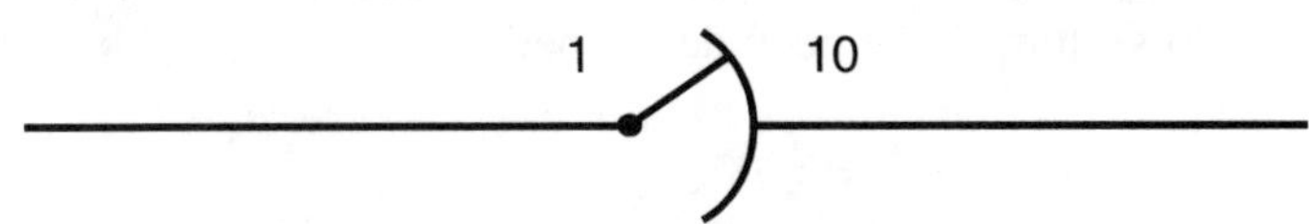

Figure B.1.3 Symbol for an electromechanical selector

A number of different switch-types existed, such as the Strowger switch, the 500-line selector, the crossbar switch and the matrix switch. It would take us too long to describe these switches in detail. Instead, we will study their use in a private branch exchange (PBX) of the type used by companies and hotels.

Analog PBXs make use of a number of different electromechanical selectors. The first one is the *call finder.* The subscribers' lines are connected to this selector; for example, 10 subscribers to each selector. The second one is the *line selector*, to which the 10 outgoing lines of the aforementioned example can be connected.

Figure B.1.4 illustrates a PBX for 100 extensions. It consists of 10 call finders, 10 line selectors and 10 *group selectors*. The function of the group selector is to select the line selector connected to the called B-number. This exchange allows 10 calls to be connected simultaneously.

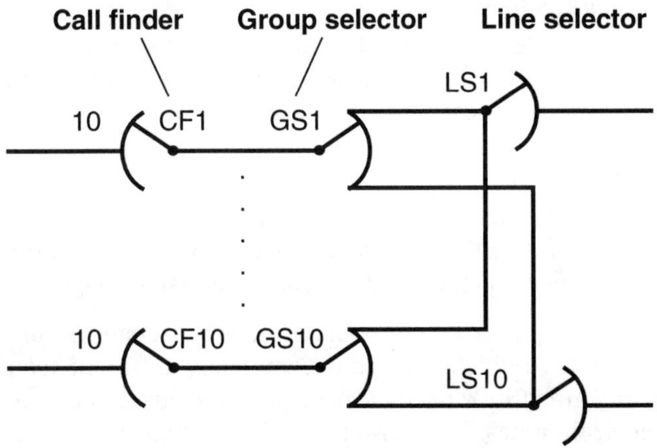

Figure B.1.4 PBX with a group selector for 100 extensions

Methods of controlling call switching in an analog exchange

The switching of calls in analog exchanges can be controlled in a number of ways. The most primitive of these is the "step-by-step" method in which the A-subscriber controls the call set-up with his dial. We will review this process in broad outline, because it represents the foundation on which today's most advanced systems have been developed.

Subscriber-controlled call set-up

One of the subscribers of a 100-subscriber exchange lifts his handset, causing the following to occur:

- A relay activates the call finder (CF), which immediately starts to search for the A-subscriber's line.
- The search is interrupted when the line has been identified. Other relays connect the tone generator, which sends a dial tone to the A-subscriber.
- The A-subscriber starts to dial the digits of the number to be called. In this case, two digits are sufficient to reach any of the subscribers. The first digit specifies the desired subscriber group. The group selector (GS) starts to move forward in step with the incoming pulses and stops at the line selector connected to the B-subscriber.
- The next digit of the subscriber number arrives. Now the line selector (LS) is affected by the incoming pulses, and the B-subscriber's line is selected.
- Connection is established. A ringing signal is sent to the B-subscriber, and a ringing tone is sent to the A-subscriber.

Register-controlled set-up

The next phase in the development of switching technique is the connection of a *register* that receives the B-number. This register then controls the remainder of the set-up process through the exchange.

Distributed control

This is yet another developmental stage: *markers* have been placed in the exchange. A marker keeps track of which selector stage connections are idle and which are occupied and thus controls path selection through the selector.

The interworking required between these slower exchanges and today's high-speed machines (which represent completely different technologies and levels of functionality) makes it necessary for our modern systems to "simulate" old techniques. The reason for this is simply the high cost of upgrading all the old equipment. (For more information about the digitisation process, see Chapter 10.)

1.2.4 The trunk network

Transmission remained analog until the end of the 1960s. The trunk network employed both frequency division multiplexing (FDM) and “baseband” over paired cable. In the latter case, coil loading was often utilised. This means that *loading coils* were inserted into the lines at fixed intervals (approximately every 1,500–2,000 metres). In combination with the lines’ intrinsic resistance (R) and the capacitance (C) always present between the conductors of the paired cable, the inserted coils form a filter. This filter reduces attenuation in the upper part of the voice band, thereby counteracting or entirely eliminating the line’s frequency-dependent attenuation in the frequency band 300–3,400 Hz. See *Figure B.1.5.*

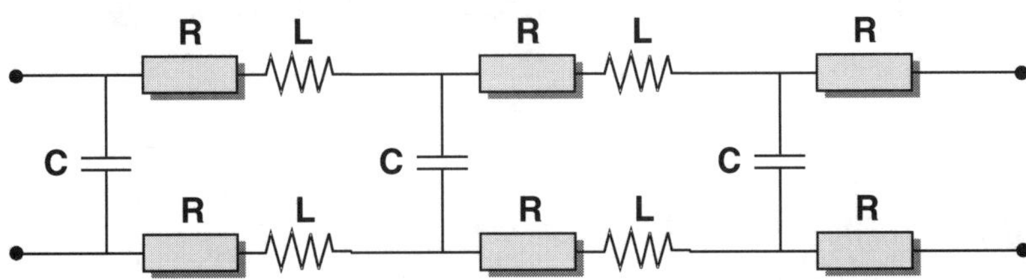

Figure B.1.5 Coil-loaded paired cable

FDM was the backbone of the trunk networks of the 1960s, and it took a good while before the new, digital time division multiplexing (TDM) systems had the same capacity. Although the installation of new FDM systems is hardly likely, frequency division multiplexers still exist in today’s PSTNs. Multiplexing according to the FDM principle is performed as follows:

- A carrier frequency (f_c) is modulated with the signal from a voice channel (frequency range f_1–f_2).
- The result is a number of frequency bands $f_c \pm n \cdot (f_2 - f_1)$, where n is 1, 3, 5, etc. Only one of the frequency bands is required ($n = 1$). The remaining bands are filtered out.
- Every frequency band consists of an upper and a lower sideband. Only one sideband is transmitted (as a rule, the lower one). If the carrier frequency is selected such that $f_c = 12{,}000$ Hz, then the FDM channel’s frequency range is 8,600–11,700 Hz, because $f_1 = 300$, $f_2 = 3{,}400$ Hz, $f_c - f_1 = 11{,}700$ and $f_c - f_2 = 8{,}600$ Hz.

The carrier frequency f_c need not be transmitted (carrier wave suppression). It can be added in the receiver provided that its frequency and phase are exactly correct.

Adding another two channels having carrier frequencies of 16 and 20 kHz results in a three-channel FDM system as shown in *Figure B.1.6.*

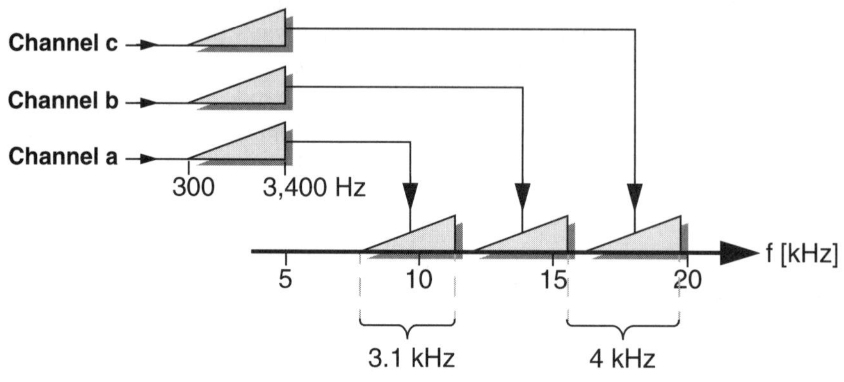

Figure B.1.6 Three-channel FDM system

ITU-T has published recommendations that specify capacity and frequencies for FDM systems with 12, 60, 300, 900, 960, 2,700 and 10,800 channels. Carrier frequencies are between 60 kHz and just under 60 MHz.

FDM systems can be used with a number of different transmission media: symmetrical paired cable, coaxial cable, radio link and satellite.

1.2.5 Network intelligence and value-added services

Network intelligence and value-added services were unknown concepts in the 1960s. Nevertheless, very intelligent switching nodes did exist: the combination of the manual telephone switchboards and the operators who attended them. (Here, and in the historical review in Chapter 3, we use the term "operator" in the traditional sense of the word: a person who operates a telephone switchboard. Elsewhere in our books, the modern synonym "telephonist" is used to avoid confusion with "network operator".) Rural operators were able to keep track of just about everything that concerned their subscribers, so they could complete relatively more calls than the automatic exchanges that existed in those days. These operators could also provide "value-added services"; in other words, share information.

1.2.6 Interexchange signalling

As a result of the low intelligence level of the automatic exchanges, a relatively small "vocabulary" was required for the communication between them. In signalling terms, they made use of very limited protocols. Signalling usually took considerable time – up to 15 seconds for the set-up of a call in a long-distance network. In addition, signalling utilised the same lines as voice traffic (channel-associated signalling). As a result, extra trunk lines were required, because up to 10% of the lines were busy carrying signalling traffic instead of voice.

1.2.7 Operation and maintenance

Maintenance was handled on a local basis, and the workforce required for a given network volume, expressed in subscriber lines, was significantly larger than that required by today's centralised functions and sophisticated transmission systems with cross-connect facilities.

1.3 The services of "PSTN 2000"

1.3.1 The PSTN bearer service

The PSTN has only one bearer service: "the PSTN bearer service". In terms of transfer, the network utilises circuit mode and is designed and optimised for voice transmission in the 300–3,400 Hz interval.

The best level of transparency is provided by duplex operation; in other words, voice (as well as other information) can be transmitted simultaneously in both directions.

The network of the 1960s that we have just described is significantly different from the PSTN frequently referred to in Volume 1 and exhaustively described in the following. The most significant difference lies in the fact that current networks are digitised, an ongoing process in the majority of today's countries. The change-over to new techniques has had the effect of making the PSTN bearer service heterogeneous. For a long time, the networks have involved numerous analog-to-digital conversions and many generations of signalling systems. The result is wide variation in call set-up time and uneven transmission quality.

1.3.2 Teleservices

Terminals

We will first take a look at what is connected to the PSTN.

Equipment (terminals or the equivalent)	**Generated information (analog/digital)**
Fixed telephone	analog (= voice)
Cordless telephone	analog with an A/D converter in the terminal
Telefax	digital (= data), with a built-in modem providing an analog signal
Computer	digital (= data), connected via a modem
Pay phone (PSTN type)	analog
PBX (PSTN type)	A/D conversion normally in the business network (digital interface to the local exchange)

Figure B.1.7 Terminals connected to the PSTN

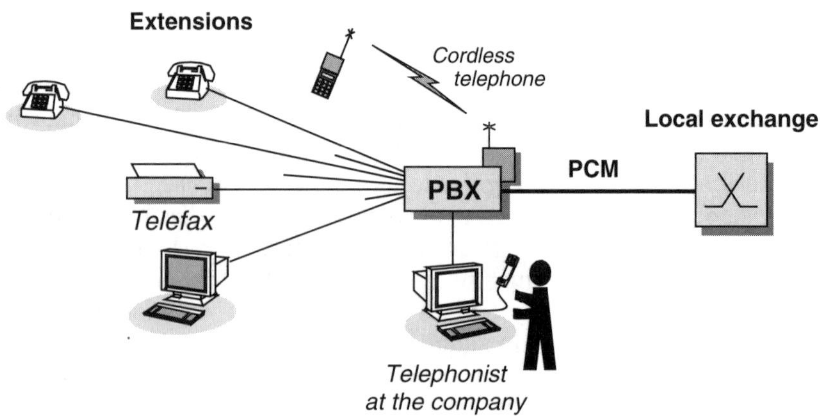

Figure B.1.8 PBX having extensions and lines to the local exchange (PSTN)

From a purely technical standpoint, a PBX is not a terminal. It has its own terminals (see *Figure B.1.8*) and is often connected to the group selector of the local exchange and not to its subscriber stage. If we disregard PBXs and count pay phones among the fixed telephones, we arrive at the terminal types shown in *Figure B.1.9*.

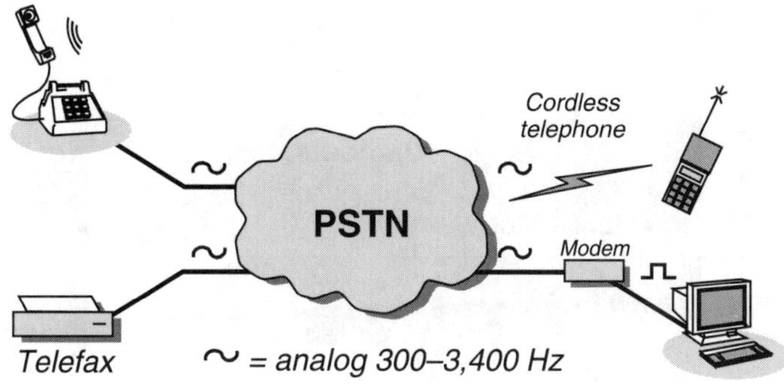

Figure B.1.9 Terminals that can be connected to the PSTN

The computer alternative is primarily used today when connecting to the Internet, where the PSTN serves as a transit network for all those who do not have a fixed Internet connection. See *Figure B.1.10*.

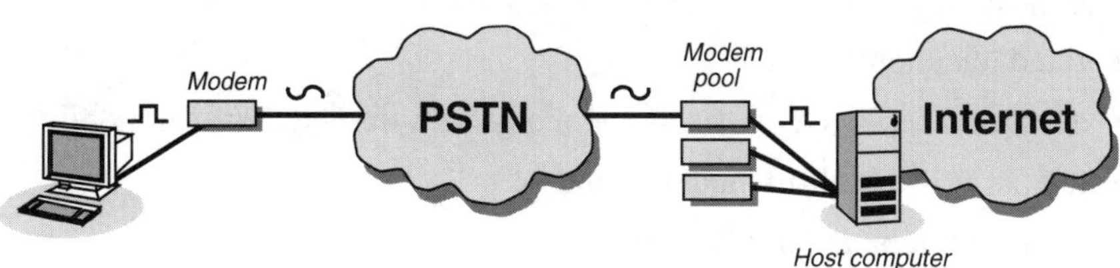

Figure B.1.10 Connecting a computer to the Internet over the PSTN

Since the PSTN interface is analog, telefax and data traffic must be converted to analog signals in the frequency band 300–3,400 Hz with the help of a built-in or stand-alone modem (*mo*dulator-*dem*odulator).

Typical modem construction is illustrated in *Figure B.1.11*. Stand-alone modems are connected via a connector, usually complying with ITU-T Recommendation V.24. The interface portion handles the digital adaptation between the modem and the terminal, and the line unit adapts the modem's analog side to the telecommunications network. The modem unit adapts the signal to the PSTN by converting information from digital form to analog form and vice versa. Modems are equipped with a diagnostic unit that helps check for faults in the information transmitted and localise any faults that may arise. In many instances, data compression functionality is also available.

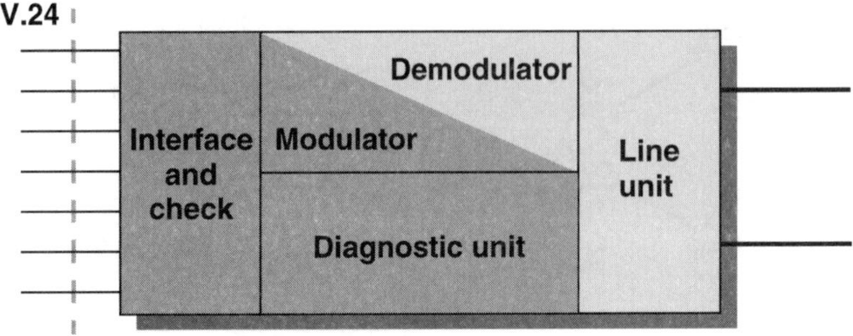

Figure B.1.11 Principles of modem construction

Dial-up modems are also available in the form of PC cards (referred to earlier as PCM-CIA) or as pocket models. With one of these cards, a user can connect portable equipment to the PSTN. (Modem standards are addressed in Chapter 2.)

The most important teleservices provided by a PSTN are thus

- fixed telephony;
- cordless telephony, or "fixed telephony with limited terminal mobility";
- telefax (via a built-in modem); and
- data communication (via modem).

The PSTN's telephony services will become integrated in phase 1 of the introduction of universal personal telecommunication (UPT).

UPT is addressed in detail in Chapter 6 of Volume 1. UPT will not require any special terminals (telephones).

1.3.3 Data communication over the PSTN

The volumes of PSTN data and telefax traffic have now become so great as to affect PSTN network design. For many years, the opposite was true: Data communication had to be on telephony's terms. Transmission quality in the

PSTN (see Subsection 1.3.1) varied greatly, yet the requirements for low bit error ratio (BER) are much more stringent in data communication than in telephony. So it is easy to understand why dedicated digital data networks developed. We are speaking here of networks such as X.25 and frame relay, or narrowband ISDN (N-ISDN) with no A/D conversion between terminals.

Simply stated, the PSTN presents some obstacles to data traffic:

- Long connection set-up time (using signalling system No. 7 solves the problem).
- PSTN echo suppression is advantageous for telephony but must be disconnected for data transmission.
- Not until recently has transmission quality enabled speeds of 14,400, 28,800 or 33,600 bit/s – while at the same time allowing requirements for low BER to be met. The widespread installation of optical fibre and modem developments in coding and fault correction techniques have greatly contributed to improvements in PSTN data transmission capabilities. The next step in the ongoing development process is to increase the bit rate to 56 kbit/s "downstream".

If we combine a line bit rate of 33.6 kbit/s with a modern compression algorithm, we can now achieve a transfer rate of 230 kbit/s.

1.3.4 Telefax communication over the PSTN

Telefax is a distributive service having only one recipient. It is a service that principally involves unidirectional communication, along with certain control signalling in the reverse direction. An interest in *broadcasting* has been expressed for applications dealing with the distribution of information – not least in the case of advertising – where one sender distributes a fax to a large number of recipients.

Telefax is neither an interactive nor an isochronous service, which means that the requirements for short delays are not stringent. On the other hand, quality is more sensitive to bit errors because the scanned image is coded before being transmitted. Because the PSTN is optimised for the transfer of voice (where short delays are more important than low BER), transmission has been slow from its inception. As a result of PSTN's digitisation, though, the speed of fax service has increased, in much the same manner as for data communication.

1.3.5 Asymmetrical services over the PSTN

Telefax, file transfer, broadcasting and Internet communication are examples of asymmetrical services, which are also – to a great extent – unidirectional. Since the PSTN utilises a relatively small portion of the network's available bandwidth, bidirectional (symmetrical) connections are nevertheless set up for these services.

1.3.6 Value-added services and telephonist services

The number of value-added PSTN services varies from country to country. Distributed value-added services are dealt with in Section 6.2, and centralised value-added services in Section 6.3. Telephonist services are discussed in Section 6.5.

1.3.7 Special PSTN business services

Small companies may find it costly to purchase and run their own PBXs. Today, local PSTN exchanges can offer logical interconnection of a number of subscribers, as if the subscribers had a PBX of their own. This functionality is referred to as centrex. See *Figure B.1.12*.

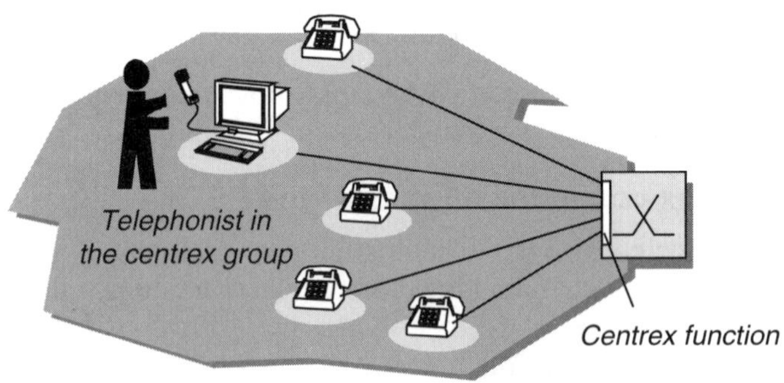

Figure B.1.12 A company using centrex ("virtual PBX")

The services of a centrex group resemble more closely the services of a PBX than those private subscribers have. A company with several local offices naturally wishes to be able to connect the different local PBXs (or centrex groups) with one another. This can be accomplished in the PSTN. Either the company contracts for the use of leased lines or utilises network intelligence to create a virtual private network (VPN). (See Subsection 6.6.)

1.3.8 Video, multimedia and teleworking over the PSTN

The limited bandwidth of the network represents a bottleneck to the introduction of video and multimedia services into the PSTN. Video-telephony is the only multimedia service that has been offered so far, but it has not enjoyed widespread acceptance. This is partly owing to the lack of a videophone standard (the different manufacturers' videophones do not always operate well together). But standardisation is under way, and the ongoing development of data compression and modem techniques seems to be arousing new interest in video telephony.

As for teleworking, the equipment most commonly used has been a telephone, a fax and a computer with a modem – all connected to the PSTN, because this network has the widest coverage. The PSTN telephone will very likely serve its purpose even at tomorrow's teleworkstation. Aside from providing ordinary telephony services, it can be used for ordering or controlling other services via its keypad or via the use of voice recognition. In addition, PSTN subscriber lines – the paired cable – can be utilised for high-speed modems that provide the necessary bandwidth for other services, such as data communication.

1.3.9 Mobility in the PSTN

Mobility-related functionality is very important to the PSTN in maintaining its competitive position vis-à-vis other network services. This area of the PSTN is referred to as cordless communication and is governed by standards such as digital enhanced cordless telecommunications (DECT).

Other forms of mobility available in the PSTN are cordless terminal mobility and the UPT service (see Volume 1, Chapter 6).

Development

Cordless telephony was originally introduced as a means of replacing the cord between the telephone set and the handset by a radio connection. The first generation of cordless telephones was called CT-0 (CT standing for cordless telephony). Capacity and interference problems resulted in the development of a European standard based on techniques applied in the field of analog cellular networks. That standard – from the beginning of the 1980s – is referred to as CT-1. Although CT-1 contributed to an increase in the use of cordless telephones, it did not provide sufficient mobility. Subscribers could not move around, taking their terminals between the different radio transmitters (base stations).

Two different standards, based on digital radio interfaces, were presented at the end of the 1980s. The first was CT-2; it was developed in Great Britain and allowed private subscribers to use their terminals from a number of telepoints. Cordless telephones could be used for outgoing calls at a lower price than for mobile telephony. CT-2 was primarily considered an alternative to pay phones.

The second system was referred to as digital cellular telephony (DCT), also known as CT-3. It addressed the business market and represented a standard that allowed the user to move about freely within a limited area (the office), handling outgoing and incoming calls.

The next generation, too, has a digital radio interface and should be able to function in different environments – at home, in the office and in urban areas. Two established standards exist today: the European DECT, which is described in more detail in Chapter 2 (Section 2.3), and the Japanese personal handy-phone system (PHS). *Figure B.1.13* illustrates the great expansion occurring in this area, represented by a forecast of the number of cordless telephone users. DECT can also be used for cordless access to N-ISDN and GSM.

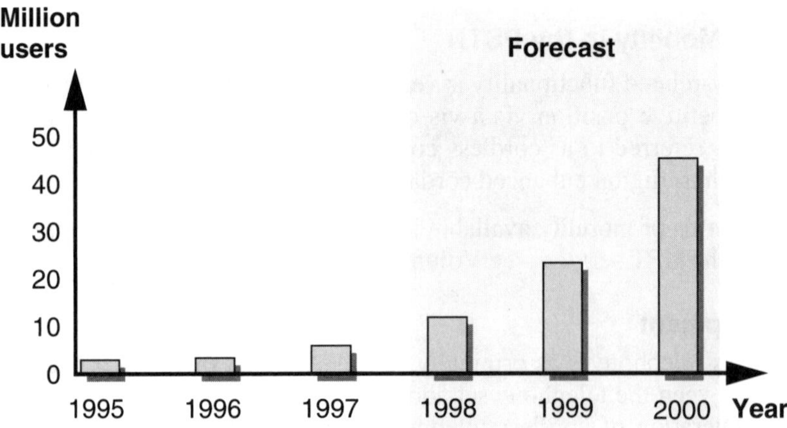

Figure B.1.13 Development of cordless telephone use

Cordless terminal mobility

One possibility presented by DECT is the ability to reach several networks from a single terminal. DECT includes specified interfaces to different networks, and interworking between them can be established through intelligent network (IN) functionality and signalling system No. 7 (SS7). A DECT telephone used in an office could also be used at home and possibly in limited central city areas for cordless terminal mobility (CTM). (See also Chapter 6.)

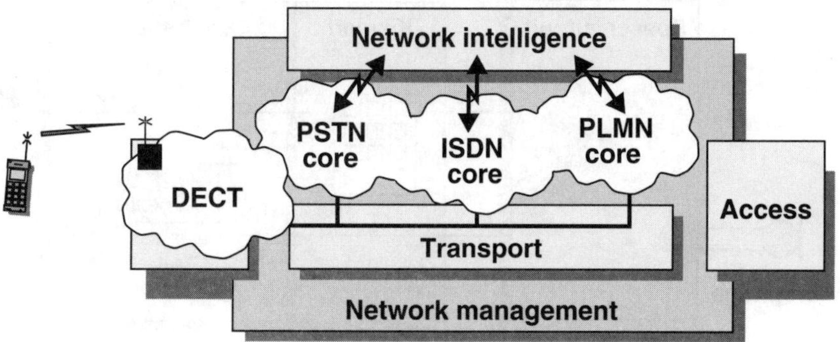

Figure B.1.14 CTM – a single cordless terminal for several networks

1.4 Terminals

Since the PSTN is the oldest and largest network, a multitude of subscriber equipment is available for connection: conventional telephones, text telephones for the deaf and special terminals for medical applications, to name but a few examples. Here we will only concern ourselves with the most common terminals used by residential subscribers and businesses for the transfer of voice, data and video via fixed and cordless connections.

1.4.1 The telephone

In 1876, Alexander Graham Bell applied for a patent for the telephone. The first, simple application consisted of two battery-powered devices placed in separate rooms and connected by one direct line. By turning a crank to generate a current in one of the devices, the user caused a signal to buzz in the other device. One day, Bell's assistant heard not only that signal but also the first words spoken over a telephone: "Mr. Watson, come here; I want you."

Today, the telephone is powered by the local exchange. The schematic diagram in *Figure B.1.15* illustrates the principle of the standard version of the telephone. Somewhat simplified, it can be said to consist of four units:

- the bell and a series capacitor;
- the hook switch;
- the keypad (or dial); and
- the speech circuit with the receiver and microphone.

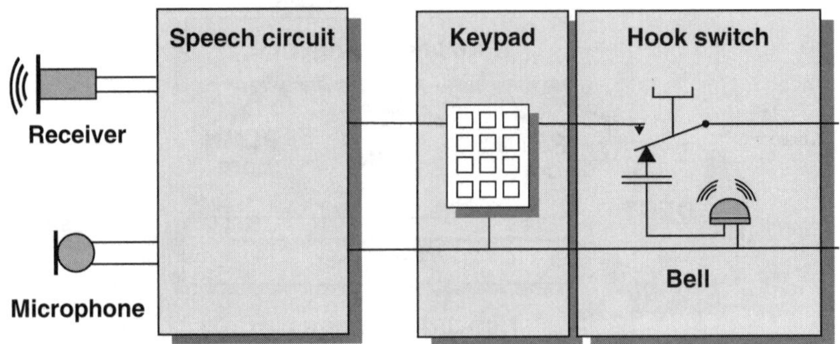

Figure B.1.15 Schematic diagram of a keypad telephone

The bell

The bell is connected via the capacitor when the receiver is resting in its cradle (on hook). When a call is placed to the B-subscriber, the bell is energised via the capacitor by an alternating voltage (approximately 90 V, 25 Hz), producing a ringing signal that notifies the subscriber of the incoming call.

The hook switch

When the A-subscriber lifts the receiver to place a call, the speech circuit and keypad are connected (and the bell is disconnected) via the hook function. This alerts the local exchange that a number is about to be dialled: the B-subscriber number. When the B-subscriber lifts the receiver to answer, the hook switch disconnects the bell in his telephone and instead connects the speech circuit and keypad. Since this closes the subscriber line, current from the local exchange can be fed to the line – an indication that the B-subscriber has answered. The parties can commence their conversation.

The keypad

The keypad of a modern telephone is connected to a tone generator, an electronic circuit that translates keyed inputs to tone codes. Each of the digits and each of the "star" (*) and "hash" (#) function keys is represented by a combination of two tones. The frequency of the oscillators is selected whenever a key is pressed to generate the dual-tone combination unique to the digit or function in question.

Figure B.1.16 illustrates the principle of keypad signalling. The standard is referred to as dual-tone multi-frequency (DTMF). Different combinations of the seven frequencies (the tones) represent the 12 symbols found on an ordinary keypad telephone.

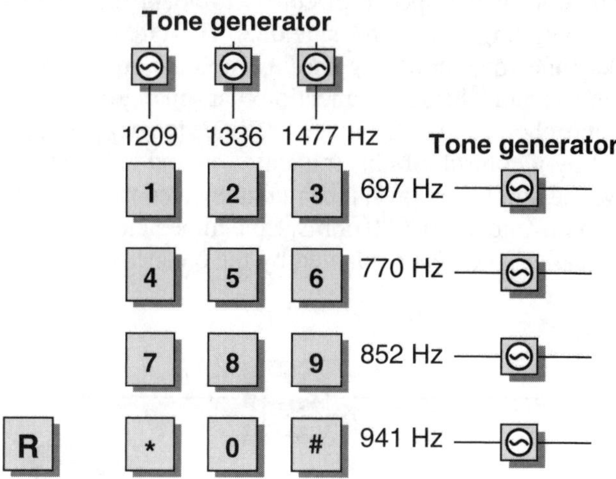

Figure B.1.16 Schematic diagram of a keypad and its frequencies

Some modern telephones also have a function key marked with an "R" (register button). Its function (register recall) is to generate a single pulse. (See Chapter 7, Subsection 7.2.6.)

The dial

Older telephones have dials instead of keypads. Although still common in many countries, these telephones represent just a few percent of all telephones sold today. The principle of the dialling function is of historical interest, so we will briefly discuss it.

The dial creates a pulse train (signals) containing information to the local exchange. The circuit connecting the exchange and the telephone is closed during the entire digit-sending process, but a contact disconnects the speech circuit during each pulse sequence. (The pulses would otherwise be heard as interference, as "clicks", in the receiver.)

The contact connected to the dial consists of a toothed wheel and two contact tongues. When the dial is released (after being wound up), the wheel starts to rotate, alternately breaking and closing the circuit. Every break results in a pulse, and the number of pulses indicates the digit dialled by the subscriber. Each of the digits forms a pulse train that is detected by the local exchange. Interestingly, Sweden is the only country that has zero as the first digit on the dial. The dials of other countries have zero following the nine.

The speech circuit

The primary function of the speech circuit is to adapt the sound level of incoming voice, outgoing voice and sidetone. The circuit comprises two amplifier blocks (one for amplifying the microphone current and one for feeding the receiver) and a bridge connection that separates voice signals to be sent to the microphone and to the receiver. Since the degree of amplification is regulated by a control circuit, transmission and reception distortion can be kept low, and amplification can be maintained constant for subscriber line resistances in the interval 0–900 ohms. Line impedance and the sidetone produced by the caller's voice are adapted by the balance circuit.

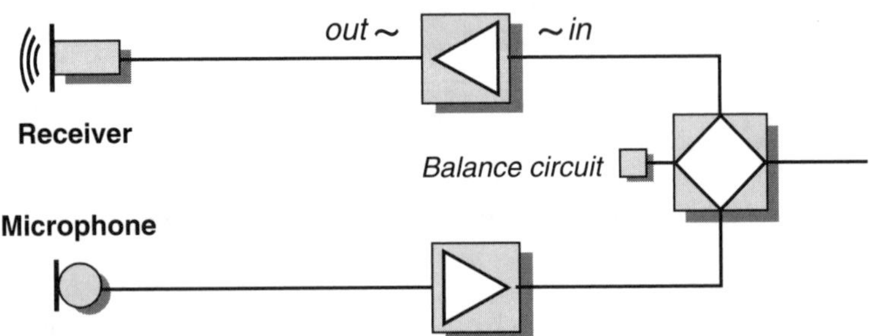

Figure B.1.17 Speech circuit

The speech circuit of older telephones was constructed in a simpler fashion, consisting in principle of only a microphone (usually a carbon-type microphone) and a dynamic receiver. Modern speech circuits provide numerous advantages.

- Sound-level attenuation over long-distance connections is counteracted by line-current-controlled regulation of the speech circuit amplifier.
- Accurate bridge balance and speech circuit impedance enhance sidetone characteristics and optimise the impedance of the apparatus.
- Transmission distortion is negligible.

The receiver

In principle, the design of the receiver is still based on traditional techniques. The current generated by the incoming speech passes through an electromagnet that is constructed around a permanent magnet and connected to a membrane. The oscillations, or movement, of the membrane are converted to sound waves that are perceived by the ear.

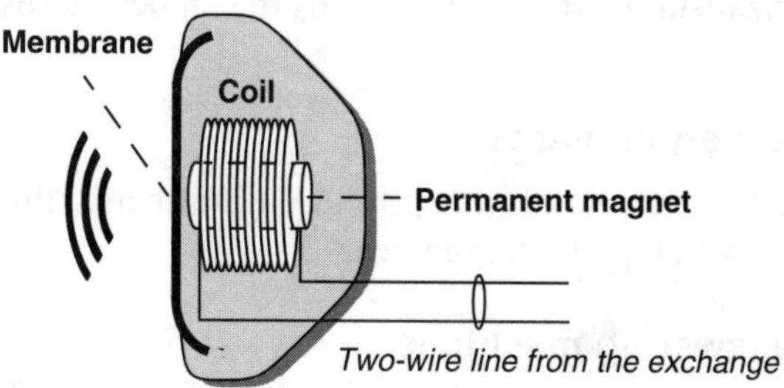

Figure B.1.18 The receiver

The microphone

The old carbon microphones are being increasingly replaced by electret microphones. The material upon which these new microphones are based consists of a thin plastic film, similar to Teflon, that is exposed to a strong electrical field. The film retains its negative and positive charges after the external electrical field is removed – somewhat analogous to the poles of a magnet.

The principle of operation of the electret microphone is illustrated in *Figure B.1.19.* The Teflon film (electret material) is stretched over a fixed electrode. The movable electrode consists of a thin metallic layer covering the electret material.

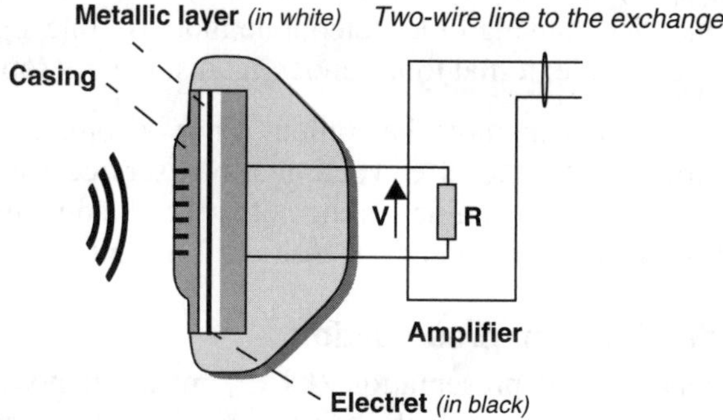

Figure B.1.19 Electret microphone

Irregularities in the surface of the fixed electrode cause a number of small air gaps to arise between the electret and the fixed electrode. The electret microphone can therefore be said to consist of a number of small parallel-connected microphones. The electrical field existing in each of the air gaps is generated by the electret's charge. The movements of the membrane change the size of the air gaps and hence their capacitance. These capacitance variations result in voltage variations that appear across the load resistor, R.

1.4.2 Add-on equipment

A number of add-on terminals that provide subscribers with added functionality have been developed over the years.

Telephone answering machines

The telephone answering machine has a built-in tape recorder which is used by the subscriber to record an announcement to be played back if the call is not answered. As a rule, the caller is also requested to leave a message. The messages can be stored on a variety of storage media, such as standard cassette tapes, microcassette tapes and RAM memory. A common extra feature is the time stamping of incoming calls.

The unit has its own hook function that is normally activated following a couple of ringing signals. After a message has been left, this function automatically breaks and indicates "on hook" to the exchange. The answering function can be set to activate after a number of ringing signals.

Most new telephone answering machines can also be remotely controlled from another telephone. By calling the answering machine, a subscriber can listen to the messages that have been received and, if he so wishes, even record a new announcement.

This remote control functionality involves the transmission of tones from a keypad telephone. When using older telephone models, tone signals can be sent by pressing a small external tone sender against the microphone.

As the price of computer memory has fallen, it has become common since the mid-1990s for operators to offer voice mailbox services; we might call them telephone answering machines in the network. The operation of voice mailboxes is described in more detail in Volume 1, Chapter 6.

Calling line identification presentation

Calling line identification presentation (CLIP) makes it possible for the party receiving a call to see the telephone number of the calling party. A user of this service requires a special display connected to his telephone line.

The CLIP service is described in more detail in Chapter 6, Subsection 6.2.2.

Call meter located at the subscriber

A subscriber who wishes to monitor the cost of his calls immediately can have a call meter connected to his telephone line. The subscriber meter registers the same number of unit charged markings as the call meter located in the local exchange, which requires that meter pulses be transmitted over the subscriber line. The signalling method is described in Chapter 7, Subsection 7.2.3.

Many meters are equipped with two counters: one showing the total of unit charged markings and one that can be reset for each call.

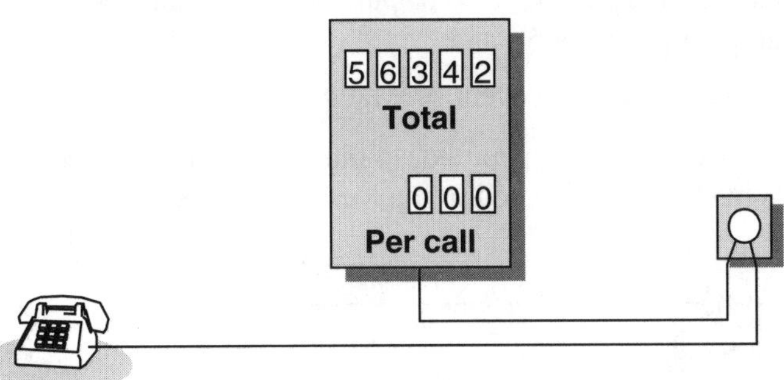

Figure B.1.20 Call meter located with a subscriber

1.4.3 Pay phones

Pay phones (coin-operated and card-operated) are usually owned by the operator running the network. There are also private companies that supply card-operated pay phones.

Emergency numbers can be called from all pay phones free of charge. The same is true for fault reporting and, in some markets, for directory inquiries. Some operators have introduced a service that allows a customer to order a reversed-charge call from a pay phone.

It is also becoming increasingly common that calls can be placed directly to pay phones without the assistance of a telephonist.

Pay phones require call charging information to be transmitted from the local exchange.

Coin-operated pay phones

Figure B.1.21 is a simplified illustration of a coin-operated pay phone.

Coin-operated pay phones are built around a microprocessor that is programmed to recognise different coins. The telephone also has operation and maintenance programs that check functionality and register any faults detected. A preprogrammed telephone number is used to send scheduled reports to the local exchange on the telephone's status, total amount of money collected, the extent to which the coin box is full, and so forth. Alarms are sent to the local exchange if certain types of fault are detected or if vandalism or theft is indicated.

The exchange contains a special line card connected to the pay phone's subscriber line. This card contains functions that

- detect calls and the B-answer (hook detection);
- generate and receive 12 or 16 kHz pulses (for signalling between the exchange and the pay phone); and
- initiate disconnection in the event of a fault.

Meter pulse information is transmitted, in the form of 12 or 16 kHz pulses, from the charging function located in the local exchange.

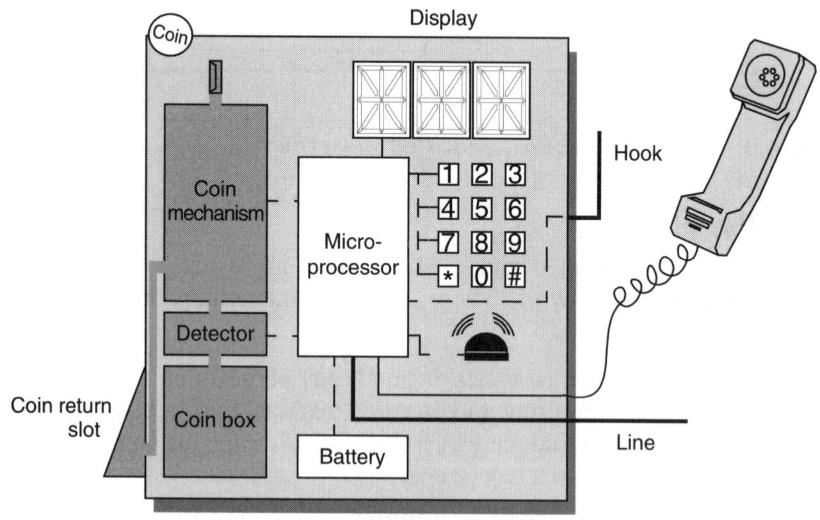

Figure B.1.21 Principle of a coin-operated pay phone

Card-operated pay phone

The majority of new pay phones installed nowadays are card-operated. The coin slot has been replaced by a card reader that reads either credit cards or special telephone cards that are preprogrammed for a given number of unit charged markings. When using a credit card, first the user draws the card through the reader, then enters a personal code. Following the completion of the call, the telephone displays the amount that will be charged to the credit card. Credit-card calls in the PSTN are normally implemented with the help of the IN platform. (See Volume 1, Chapter 6, Subsection 6.2.3.)

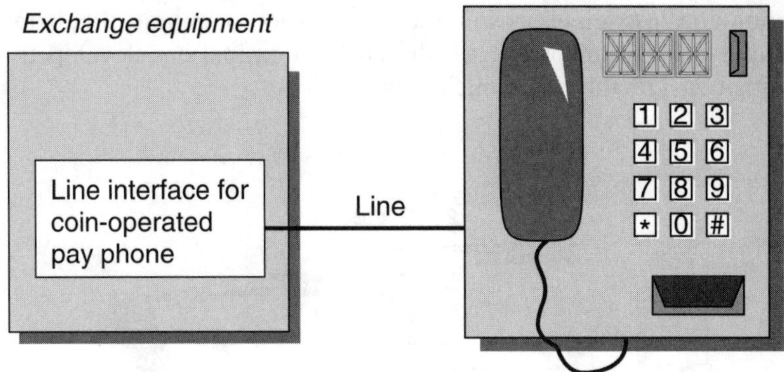

Figure B.1.22 Connecting a coin-operated pay phone to the exchange

1.4.4 Telefax terminals

The term "telefax" (in everyday language "fax") denotes a system for transmitting monochrome images between two telefax terminals. The term also refers to the actual message sent as well as the telefax apparatus. The document to be sent is scanned, point by point, by the fax machine. The resulting information is coded in accordance with an international standard and, after compression, transmitted to the receiving fax via the fax's built-in modem. The receiving unit demodulates the signal, decodes the information and produces a printout. Some systems also produce an acknowledgement on the sending fax; other systems show this acknowledgement on a character display.

Image coding is described in greater detail in Chapter 2, Subsection 2.4.2.

The actual terminal contains many extra functions that supplement the basic service: abbreviated dialling, retransmission if the receiving fax is busy and a queuing system for incoming fax messages.

Many residential subscribers and small companies have terminals that combine telephone and fax functionality (even telephone answering functionality) in one and the same unit.

A fax terminal can also be a personal computer running one of the PC fax programs available today. Faxes are created, sent and received in the form of a file instead of on paper. To be able to send a fax of a document that is only available on paper, a user can attach a scanner to his PC.

1.4.5 Cordless telephones

The following is primarily a study of the DECT terminal. Although the first-generation cordless telephones only offered radio communication between the handset and the telephone set, the DECT terminal has developed into something considerably more intelligent.

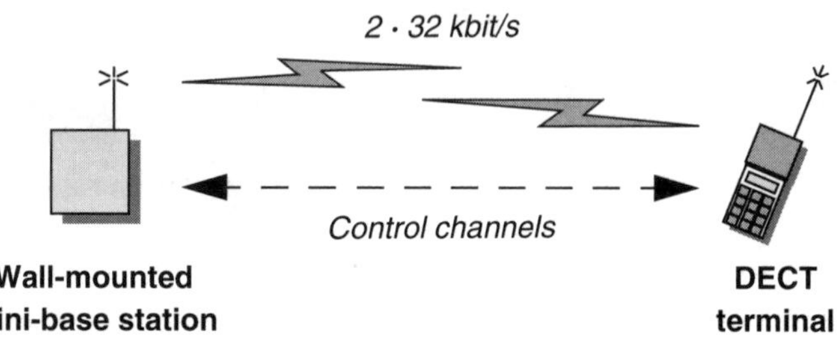

Figure B.1.23 DECT terminal functions

DECT terminals contain some special subscriber features that vary for the different manufacturers, and a number of standard functions.

- A keypad, an antenna and a rechargeable battery (like a mobile telephone); battery power consumption is significantly lower in stand-by mode than when a call is in progress.
- Voice coding and encryption/decryption that provide for secure connections of the same quality as that of a fixed-wire connection.
- Functions that handle signalling to and from the base station.
- Functions for mobile-controlled handover (MCHO). (See Chapter 2, Subsection 2.3.2.)

1.4.6 Combination terminals

It is possible today to build terminals capable of handling air interfaces that conform both to the DECT standard and to different cellular systems, such as GSM. These terminals are referred to as dual-mode telephones. With the help of intelligence in the terminal and in the IN platform, a user can always secure a form of access that works and provides the best price or performance. This generally means DECT access in areas covered by CTM and GSM access when outside of these areas or when moving too quickly for DECT access; for example, when travelling by car.

2 Standards

2.1 Introduction

Many international PSTN recommendations have been developed during the past years, notably by the International Telecommunication Union – Telecommunications Standardization Sector (ITU-T, previously the CCITT). They are not all-inclusive. Traditionally, the PSTN has also been the subject of national standardisation efforts in a number of areas:

- signalling, both in an operator's network and to subscribers;
- the billing and pricing of services;
- service offering and service procedures; and
- the physical access interface.

These local standards have led to a multitude of product versions, so vendors of switching equipment must design their systems to allow for extensive parameterisation. Some parameters can be set to their default values. Nevertheless, operators and vendors must exchange a good deal of information to adapt the equipment for delivery.

For modern systems and networks, like GSM and N-ISDN, the need for parameterisation is significantly less.

2.2 International standards

2.2.1 ITU-T

The ITU-T is the standardisation organisation that has had the greatest influence on the development of the PSTN. The recommendations developed by the various Study Groups used to be published every fourth year in book form, comprising a considerable number of volumes. The books had different colours, recent editions being yellow (1980), red (1984), blue (1988) and white (1992). The recommendations were of particularly great importance in the area of signalling, where SS7 still uses the expressions red, blue and white telephony user part (TUP). Nowadays, due to extremely rapid development in telecommunications, the study groups publish their recommendations as soon as they are complete. (See also Volume 1, Chapter 2.)

The recommendations are subdivided into series designated by a letter (for each of the telecommunications areas) and a number. The most notable PSTN series are:

- Series D: Principles of charging and accounting;
- Series E: PSTN, numbering and routing, service quality, network management;
- Series G: Analog and digital transmission systems;
- Series M: Maintenance;
- Series O: Measurement equipment;
- Series P: Telephony transmission quality;
- Series Q: Switching, value-added services, signalling systems Nos. 4, 5, 6 and 7, R1 and R2, TCAP, IN; and
- Series V: Data communications over the PSTN.

2.3 DECT

DECT is a standard for cordless telephony that was developed by the European Telecommunications Standards Institute (ETSI). The first systems became operative in 1992. DECT contains a number of different specifications and is also described in other chapters of Part B.

- The DECT terminal is described in Chapter 1.
- DECT access functions (both for PBX and for radio in the local loop, in the public network) are described in Chapter 5.
- A brief description of CTM is included in Chapter 6. CTM enables DECT terminals to be used at work, at home and in DECT cells in the central parts of a city.

This chapter will deal with the areas covered by DECT and the various recommendations that together constitute DECT. Since the standard is not specifically intended for the PSTN, we will also be addressing other systems and networks, such as GSM and ISDN.

2.3.1 DECT equipment

DECT access involves three basic units: the radio switch, the base stations and the terminals.

- The radio switch (the common control fixed part) is responsible for the centralised control of the system and is connected to a PBX or local exchange via one or more PCM links. These links can be either digital or analog, which means that DECT can be introduced into older networks.

- A number of base stations (radio fixed part) are connected to the radio switch as needed. Each base station covers one cell. The size of the cells can vary from just under 100 metres to a few kilometres.
- Terminals (cordless portable part), in addition to their functions for voice coding and encryption, contain functions for roaming and handover. (See also Subsection 2.3.2 and Chapter 1.)

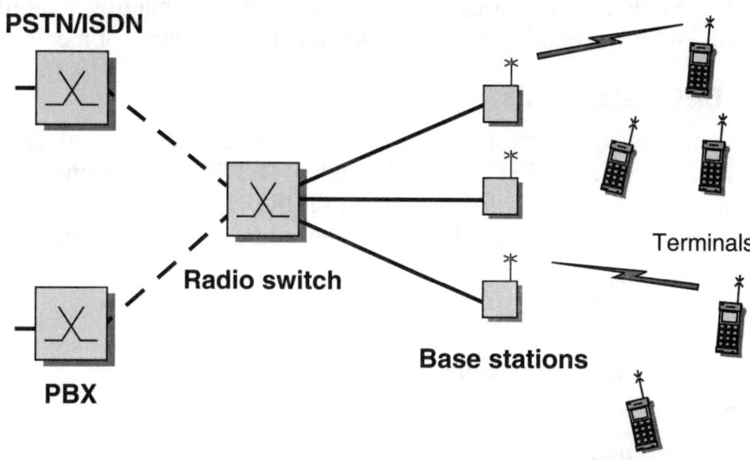

Figure B.2.1 DECT equipment

2.3.2 DECT functions

The first application of DECT was the office environment, where the system was used for cordless access to a company's PBX. This placed certain specific demands on the system.

- It is important to maintain large capacity with respect to the number of simultaneous calls in relation to area coverage.
- The system should allow expansion without requiring extensive planning.
- The radio environment can change quickly (for example, if a fire door is opened or closed) so rapid handover is important.

To meet these demands, DECT contains a few specific functions that we will study in more detail.

Dynamic channel allocation

All base stations can utilise all DECT frequencies but not more than a given number simultaneously. When traffic capacity must be expanded, the operator simply deploys additional base stations.

Mobile-controlled handover

With MCHO, the terminals are responsible for selecting the best channel for transmission. The terminal performs measurements on a continuous basis to determine which channels are disturbed least by channels in adjacent cells. MCHO also contains functions for determining whether handover should be executed, and for executing the handover, during the course of a call.

2.3.3 DECT standards

ETSI names its standards and recommendations in a number of different ways. Three types are ETSI technical standard (ETS), ETSI technical report (ETR) and technical bases for regulation (TBR). The DECT standard consists of some 30 publications. Their contents address the following areas:

- basic standards;
- public and generic access profiles;
- DECT authentication modules;
- DECT profiles;
- test specifications; and
- rules and regulations.

Two standards can be said to form the foundation of DECT, because they cover everything required for the manufacture of DECT equipment:

- the DECT Common Interface (CI), ETS 300 175; and
- the DECT Approval Test Specification, I-ETS 300 176.

The first, which is usually referred to as DECT CI, is a complete overview (in nine volumes) that describes all interfaces, voice coding, transmission, and such. One of the volumes deals with the public access profile, PAP, which describes DECT access to public networks; for example, cordless access to the PSTN.

The DECT Approval Test Specification primarily addresses radio and voice parameters.

In addition to the basic standards, DECT contains a smart card that makes billing more secure and prevents fraud. The card is referred to as the DAM

(DECT authentication module) and is reminiscent of the subscriber identity module (SIM) card in the GSM standard.

Interworking with other networks

As already mentioned, DECT is not a network itself but a standard that deals with accessing other private and public networks. The interface is based on the specification of public and generic access profiles which make it possible to use DECT to access networks such as the PSTN, ISDN, public land mobile network (PLMN) and X.25. A number of DECT profiles have been described in addition to PAP:

- the generic access profile (GAP);
- the DECT/GSM interworking profile;
- the DECT/ISDN interworking profile; and
- the DECT data profiles.

The DECT/GSM profile provides subscribers with cordless access to a fixed GSM network (fixed cellular). This can be a solution for an operator who has a licence for a fixed network only but who hopes to acquire a cellular licence in the future. Subscribers acquire a certain amount of mobility as well as access to the entire range of services offered by the GSM standard.

The DECT/ISDN profile makes DECT the first, and so far the only, radio system that is entirely transparent to ISDN. The profile contains two parts: one that describes the interface between the radio station and the exchange, and one that describes the S-interface between the cordless network terminal and the user terminal.

The DECT data profiles cover the different categories of services having bit rates up to 522 kbit/s, including isochronous services and fax.

2.4 Coding methods

2.4.1 Voice coding in the PSTN

Fixed telephony

For many decades, A/D conversion of voice has been performed employing PCM coding. (See Volume 1, Chapter 2, Subsection 2.7.2.) This is pure amplitude coding that results in a bidirectional connection having a bit rate of 64 kbit/s.

DECT

DECT voice coding makes use of adaptive differential pulse code modulation (ADPCM), which is described in ITU-T Recommendation G.726. ADPCM results in a bit rate of 32 kbit/s with the same information (and thus the same quality) as that resulting from ordinary 64 kbit/s PCM coding. ADPCM, on the other hand, cannot manage higher bit rates (such as 28.8 or 33.6 kbit/s) in data transmission using modems. Instead, DECT uses digital radio transmission and the DECT/ISDN profile.

2.4.2 Image coding

Two image services are available in the PSTN: telefax and video telephony.

Telefax

A transmitting telefax machine has functionality that allows it to scan an image. The information is then coded, compressed and modulated before being transmitted to the receiving fax.

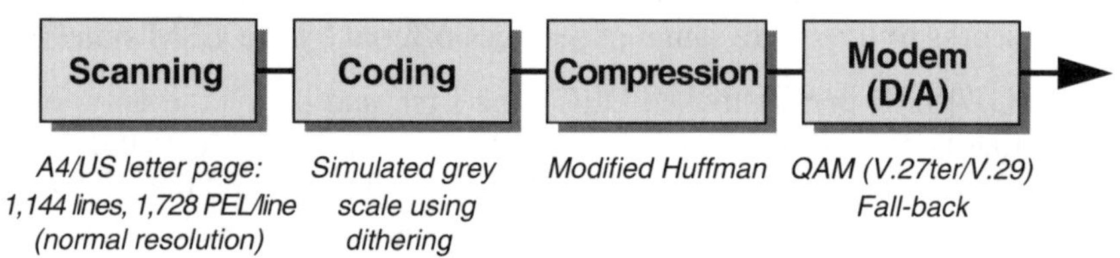

Figure B.2.2 The tasks performed by a Group 3 transmitting telefax

The first telefax standards dealt with analog scanning and were designated Group 1 (1968) and Group 2 (1976). Group 3, the latest fax standard for PSTN transmission, was specified in 1980. Scanning is performed digitally, and the information is then converted to analog signals for transmission over the PSTN.

Group 4 (1984) was specified for ISDN.

Figure B.2.3 shows a comparison of the different standards.

Type	Scanning	Capacity	Introduced	Network
Group 1	Analog	2,400 bit/s	1968	
Group 2	Analog	4,800 bit/s	1976	PSTN
Group 3	Digital	9,600 bit/s (14,400 bit/s)	1980	
Group 4	Digital	64,000 bit/s	1984	ISDN

Figure B.2.3 Telefax standards

Scanning

Scanning starts at the upper left-hand corner of the page. The page is scanned along horizontal lines that are divided into picture elements (PELs). A PEL can be compared to the pixel of a computer screen. Group 3 faxes have a scanning standard of 3.85 lines/mm, giving 1,144 lines/page (both A4 and US letter pages are specified). There are eight PELs per mm, giving 1,728 PEL/line. The scanner registers variations in light intensity reflected from the paper. Each PEL is registered as black (0) or white (1).

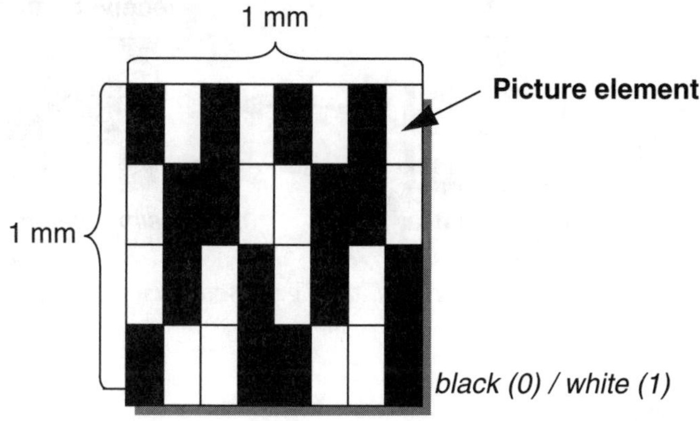

Figure B.2.4 Normal resolution for a Group 3 fax

Although the values shown are for normal resolution, the standard does allow for double resolution, that is, 2,288 lines/page. The resolution can be set on the terminal.

Coding

If all PELs are registered as being either white or black, images containing grey areas will pose a problem. The PELs in an area having a greyness of 49% are coded as being white; consequently, the remaining PELs having a greyness of 51% are coded as being black. This can be controlled by means of a method called *simulated grey scale.*

Dithering is used by Group 3 faxes. The PELs are not compared with a fixed boundary value of 50% greyness. Some PELs are compared with higher values, some with lower. If a given PEL is darker than the boundary value with which it is compared, it will be coded as black; if it is lighter, it will be coded as white. In the example of an area having 49% greyness, 49% of the PELs would be coded as black and the remainder as white.

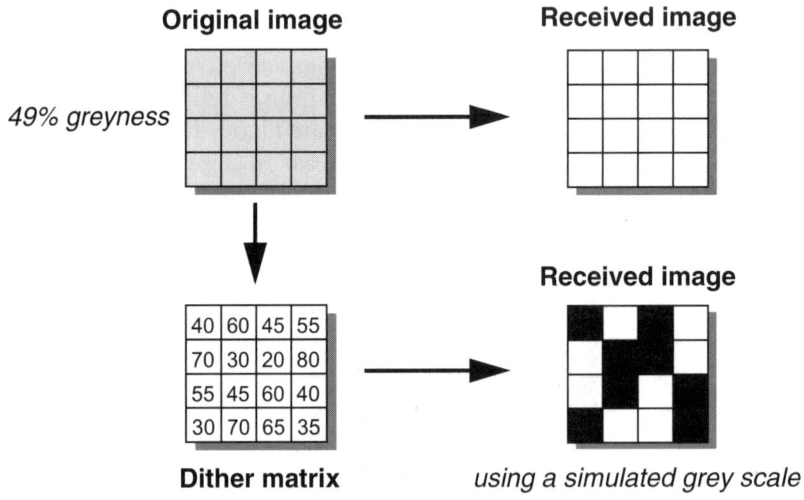

Figure B.2.5 The principle of simulated grey scale using dithering

Compression

Instead of sending long sequences of repetitive ones and zeros (representing white and black PEL values), the fax compresses the information to save time. The method used is a form of variable-length coding (VLC), referred to as modified Huffman. It is based on the statistically most common combinations of a number of consecutive black or white PELs. Common combinations are coded using few bits, unusual combinations using a greater number of bits.

Modulation

Following the compression process, the fax has a bit stream to be transmitted to the receiving fax. In the PSTN, information must be transmitted as analog signals, the task of the fax's built-in modem. The standard used is a type of quadrature amplitude modulation (QAM, see Volume 1, Chapter 4, Subsection 4.4.2), such as ITU-T V.27*ter*/V.29, which contains eight phase and two amplitude positions. It provides a maximum bit rate of 9,600 bit/s. However, capacity has increased since Group 3 was introduced. V.17 is a fax standard that provides up to 14.4 kbit/s. The V.34 standard, which was developed for data communication, provides the same capacity. (See also Subsection 2.4.3.)

Fall-back is always applied, which means that the sending fax starts to transmit using the highest possible transfer rate and then slows down if there are too many errors or if the receiving fax cannot handle the higher transfer rate.

Video-telephony

The transfer of a TV image in uncoded format would require a transfer rate of approximately 200 Mbit/s. To be able to transmit such an amount of information over the PSTN, we would require a compression ratio of 7,000 – which is out of the question if quality is to be maintained. As part of the video telephony concept, we would also like to transmit voice and images simultaneously. But no standard has yet been sufficiently successful to represent a breakthrough in this field. Even so, videophones are available in the market, and ongoing research is aimed at improving quality.

Model coding is a method developed to allow moving pictures to be transferred using narrow bandwidth. It is based on an understanding of the contents of an image rather than on the direct scanning and transfer of the image. For example, let's say that we transfer an original image of the A-subscriber's face and apply it to a model face at the receiving end. Let's also assume that we transmit information as to whether the A-subscriber's mouth is open or closed, whether or not he or she is smiling, nodding, and so forth. Model coding is reminiscent of our manner of describing anything – in this case, a face. Descriptions such as "Peter has light hair, a round face, large glasses, and looks happy" can be said to transmit a significant amount of information in highly compressed form.

The Moving Picture Experts Group is a study group engaged in the creation of a standard for moving pictures – MPEG4 – primarily as applied to the videophone. The bit rate, between 8 and 16 kbit/s, may finally involve a combination of different compression methods.

2.4.3 Data transmission using modems

Data traffic over ordinary, fixed, analog connections must be modulated, because the digital information must be converted to an "audible" signal in the 300–3,400 Hz frequency range. DECT, on the other hand, provides 32 kbit/s digital transmission to subscribers, allowing digital connection.

Modem standards for the PSTN

ITU-T specifies a number of different sets of modem equipment for data communication over the PSTN. The objective is to recommend equipment that is adapted to the network's performance (with respect to signalling, transmission media, interference, and so forth) so that data traffic will be carried securely without interfering with other traffic. At the same time, the equipment should provide the highest possible capacity. Another fundamental consideration of the standardisation effort is to assure compatibility of system parts purchased from different vendors. The following rate classes have been specified by the ITU-T:

ITU-T Recomm.	Bit rate, bit/s	Connection	Line interface 2/4 wire (rate)	Modulation
V.21	300	leased / dial-up	2 (300 baud)	FSK (freq. shift)
V.22	1,200 600	leased / dial-up	2 (600 baud)	PSK (phase shift)
V.23	1,200 600	leased / dial-up	2 (1,200 baud) 2 (600 baud)	FSK
V.26	2,400	leased	4 (1,200 baud)	PSK
V.26bis	2,400 1,200	leased / dial-up	2 (1,200 baud)	PSK
V.27	4,800 4,800	leased	4 (1,600 baud) 2 (1,600 baud)	PSK
V.27bis	4,800 2,400	leased	2/4 (1,600 baud) 2/4 (1,200 baud)	PSK
V.27ter	4,800 2,400	leased	2 (1,600 baud) 2 (1,200 baud)	PSK

ITU-T Recomm.	Bit rate, bit/s	Connection	Line interface 2/4 wire (rate)	Modulation
V.29	9,600	leased	4 (2,400 baud)	QAM (ampl. and phase shift)
V.32	9,600	leased / dial-up	2 (2,400 baud)	QAM
V.32bis	14,400	leased / dial-up	2 (2,400 baud)	QAM
V.34	28,800	leased / dial-up	2 (3,200 baud)	QAM
V.34+	33,600	leased / dial-up	2 (3,200 baud)	QAM

Figure B.2.6 ITU-T modem standards

The interface circuits between a terminal and a modem are selected on the basis of Recommendation V.24. The electrical specifications for such circuits are based on Recommendation V.28, V.10 or V.11.

Network operators can also offer other types of modem, of course. Customers can use even higher bit rates if the PSTN in question has the necessary capacity – primarily a function of distance and the quality of the link. The ITU-T specifies a number of modems for higher speeds (in excess of 48 kbit/s) to be used in the frequency range 60–108 kHz. The standards for these modems are V.36 and V.37.

It is also customary to combine modem standards with a compression standard that suits the specific application (fax or file transfer) to further increase available transmission capacity. V.42*bis* and MNP 5 are two common compression standards. Standards are required for error correction as well. Examples of these standards are V.42, MNP 2-4, MNP 10 and LAPM.

During call set-up, a "handshaking" procedure takes place between the calling and the called modems. The modems exchange information that is necessary for the performance of compression and error-correction, and the bit rate to be used for the transmission is determined. There are standardised methods that ensure maximum connection capacity under prevailing network conditions. Some of these methods are described below.

Line probing

A carrier frequency of 1,700 Hz in the North American network provides good transmission quality; the corresponding frequency in Europe is 1,800 Hz. This leads to compromises in international standards. The best capacity is attained by applying the *line probing* method, which does not specify a fixed carrier frequency and baud rate but allows the modem to probe the line during the connection set-up phase and select the carrier frequency and baud rate that give maximum performance. In most cases, an efficient modem can attain maximum capacity on the first try.

Trellis precoding

The modem contains digital signal processors with high computing capacity. To improve security, the processors make calculations to predict the position of the next modulation point in the coding process. This is referred to as *trellis precoding*.

Adaptive rate system

Modern modems contain a function that makes it possible to continuously adapt the bit rate to a line's signal-to-noise ratio and the received signal level: adaptive rate system (ARS). ARS allows the bit rate to be automatically adjusted either up or down in steps of 2.4 kbit/s.

Data transmission using DECT

DECT uses digital channels at a bit rate of 32 kbit/s for data transmission, so no modulation is required. A number of channels can be combined; for example, five channels are used for ISDN's 144 kbit/s basic rate access. Data transmission rates of up to 522 kbit/s can be achieved by combining a number of channels.

A measure of the quality attained in data transmission with DECT is a BER of $1 \cdot 10^{-8}$ in protected mode.

2.5 PSTN and ISDN standardised interfaces

2.5.1 Introduction

The interfaces between PSTN/ISDN exchanges and access nodes have traditionally been proprietary ones. This has applied to both the commands used and the measurement results obtained in remote testing of subscriber lines, when these tests have been performed by the local exchange. Processor communication between a multiplexer or concentrator and the main exchange is another example.

As increasingly complex electronics and optronics are introduced into today's access networks, operators perceive a growing need to procure access equipment from independent suppliers. But the equipment they purchase from different vendors in the market must also connect to their local exchanges. Reacting to this situation, ETSI developed the V5 interface standard. Though primarily a European standard, it is used worldwide.

Unlike previous proprietary interfaces, V5 does not support the transfer of network management information between the local exchange and the access nodes. This presents the situation depicted in *Figure B.2.7*.

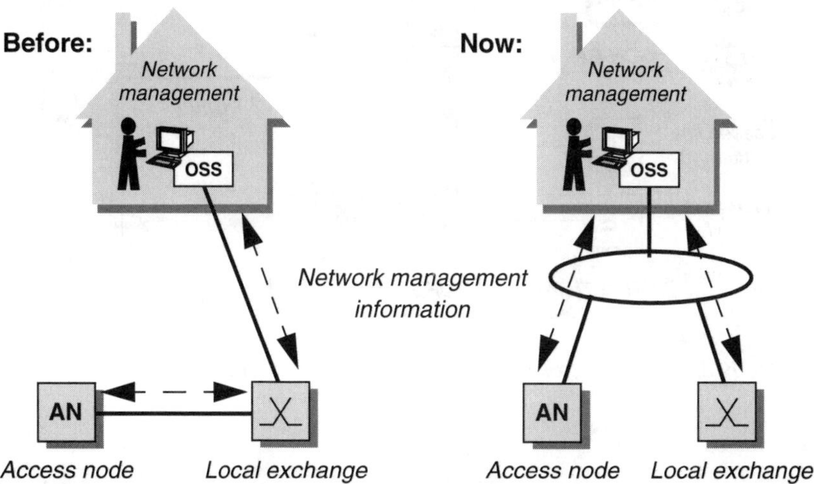

Figure B.2.7 A new situation for the network management of access nodes

There are two versions of the V5 standard: V5.1 and V5.2. The V5.1 version has been defined for the interface between a subscriber multiplexer and a local exchange, while V5.2 is applicable to the interface between a concentrator (a remote subscriber stage) and a local exchange.

2.5.2 V 5.1

The V5.1 interface can be used for non-concentrated traffic between a V5.1 multiplexer and a local exchange, as shown in *Figure B.2.8.* The multiplexer has ports for connecting PSTN and ISDN terminals (2B+D) and can multiplex up to 30 PSTN connections or 15 ISDN basic rate accesses over a 2,048 kbit/s link.

The V5 interface includes separate channels for traffic, signalling (for the PSTN and ISDN) and control. A link access procedure (LAP) V5 protocol is used for signalling and control information. Time slot 16 is selected first, then time slot 15 and, if required, time slot 31 as well. Other channels are used for frame alignment (time slot 0) and for traffic. See *Figure B.2.9.*

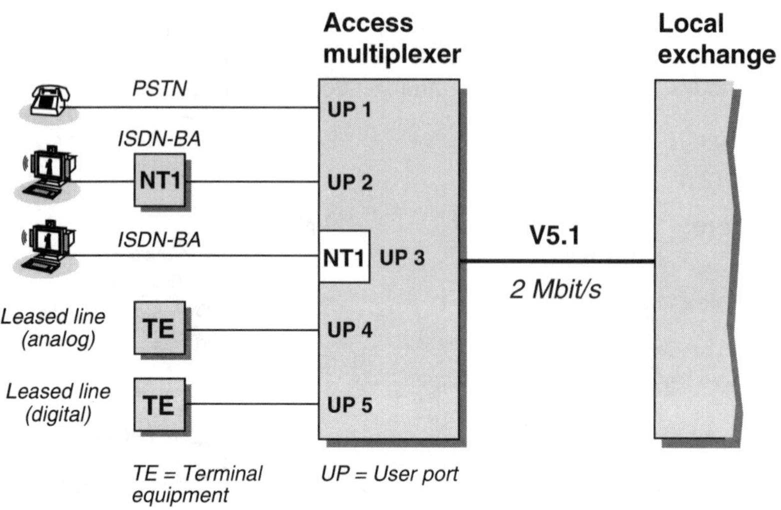

Figure B.2.8 Multiplexer with a V5.1 interface to the local exchange

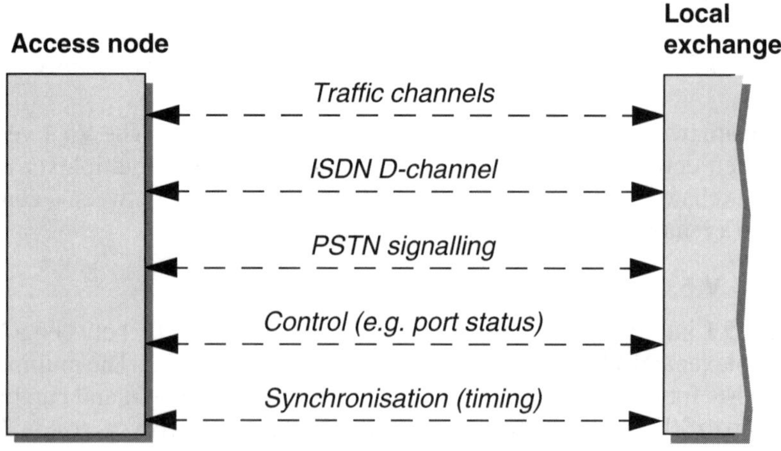

Figure B.2.9 Information on a V5.1 link

2.5.3 V 5.2

The V5.2 interface can be used for concentrated traffic between the access node and the local exchange.

A V5.2 concentrator is capable of concentrating PSTN, ISDN-BA (basic rate access) and ISDN-PRA (primary rate access) traffic. A simpler version, referred to as *single link*, has only one PCM link between the access node and the local exchange. This is sufficient for the concentration of telephone calls from 200–300 subscribers.

A multilink can handle 2–16 2 Mbit/s links. The number of links installed depends on the volume of traffic.

3 Switching and switch control

3.1 Introduction

Switching in the PSTN is based on circuit-switching technique. The type of temporary, bidirectional connection established by means of this technique was originally intended exclusively for the transfer of speech (or "voice" in current terminology). During the long era of analog telephony, the purpose of interconnecting two subscribers was to establish a purely physical contact between their respective lines. In our modern digital switching and transmission, it is the time slots containing the two subscribers' eight-bit voice samples that are linked together to form a logical connection. Consequently, since PCM coding is standard for the A/D conversion of voice over the PSTN, a digital exchange sets up 64 kbit/s connections.

3.1.1 History

In 1878, the first manual exchange was constructed in La Porte, in the United States. At its inception it served 21 subscribers and could connect any two of them together. A ringing signal sounded at the operator's switchboard when any of the subscribers turned the crank of his telephone. (See Note in Chapter 1, Subsection 1.2.5.) Upon answering the signal, the operator was asked to connect the call to one of the other subscribers, which she did manually. She also made a note of who placed the call and when it started and stopped – notes that made it possible to charge for the call.

We can say that the market forces of the early 1890s prompted the development of the first automatic telephone exchange. It was called the "Strowger switch", after its originator Almon B. Strowger. Strowger was an undertaker from Kansas City who, soon after the advent of the telephone, found himself exposed to a serious form of unfair competition. The woman who operated the manual exchange was the wife of Strowger's competitor, and she connected anyone who asked to speak with an undertaker to her husband.

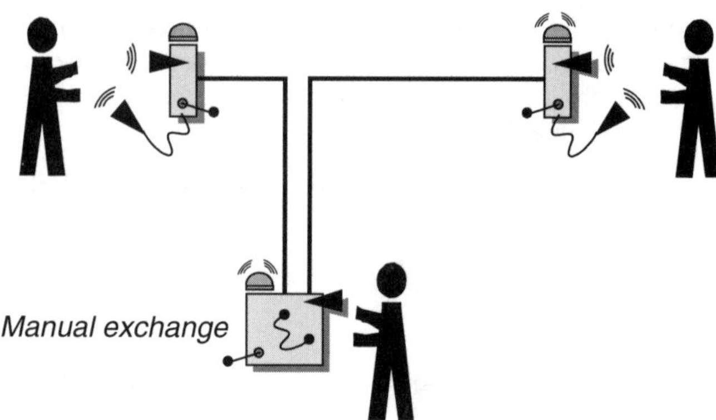

Figure B.3.1 A manual exchange

Many years passed during which electromechanical telephone exchanges were developed and improved. The primary objective was still the same as that of the manual exchange: to detect the A-subscriber's call attempt, to connect him to the correct B-subscriber, and to save data about the call for the purpose of billing. The 1960s and 1970s saw the advent of telephone exchanges that were controlled by processors: stored program control (SPC) exchanges. As a result, new functions could be built into the exchanges – of benefit to subscribers and network operators. These functions enabled the introduction of new types of service and facilitated supervision, charging and the gathering of statistics.

3.1.2 PSTN nodes

Nodes and network hierarchy are described in detail in Volume 1, Chapter 3. A brief summary is provided here.

PSTN nodes can be subdivided into three main categories: local exchanges, transit exchanges and international exchanges. Local exchanges are used for the connection of subscribers. Transit exchanges switch traffic within and between different geographical areas. International exchanges, and other gateway type exchanges, switch traffic to telecommunications networks that belong to other operators.

This chapter will primarily deal with the local exchange. Among its functions are the trunk and signalling functions that are typical of the PSTN.Normally, the PSTN and N-ISDN share the utilisation of hardware in the various exchanges (with the exception of the subscriber stage in the local exchange). A great deal of the contents of the following sections is therefore applicable to N-ISDN as well. The expression "PSTN/ISDN exchanges" is also in common use.

3.2 A present-day local exchange

The primary task of the local exchange is

- to switch calls from the connected subscribers to other subscribers in the same exchange or to some specific type of equipment in the exchange;
- to switch calls between the connected subscribers and other parts of the network; and
- to charge for local and trunk calls and the use of distributed subscriber services.

3.2.1 Local exchange functions

The switching part of today's local exchanges contains two switching points. The first of these is the central group switch. The second is a less complex switch in the subscriber stage to allow common equipment to be located there and to concentrate traffic to the central group switch. The subscriber stage and the lines to other exchanges are connected to the central group switch, as is other equipment that should be connectable, such as signalling terminals.

The set-up of connections is controlled by a real-time processor. This processor also handles charging, which is closely related to the switching function. The control and charging functions, as well as the line interface circuit, will be addressed in this chapter.

From the point of view of traffic handling, the functions of a local exchange can be illustrated as in *Figure B.3.2.*

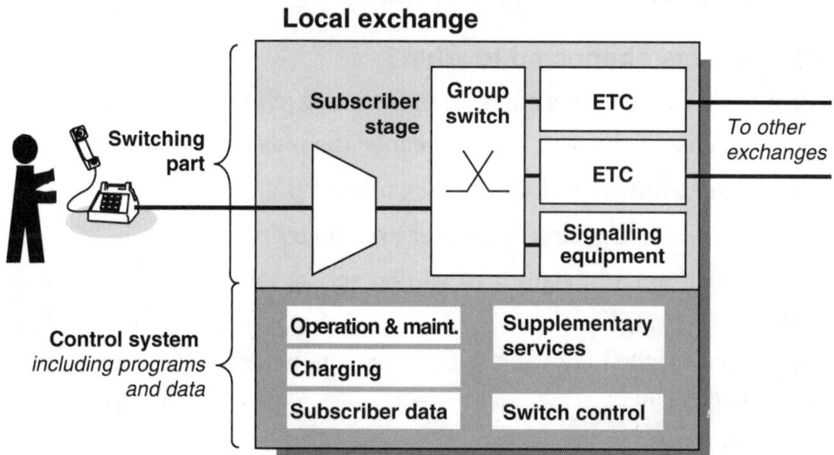

Figure B.3.2 Functional groups of a local exchange

A characteristic feature of modern exchanges is their modular design. This modularity facilitates expansion of capacity and the addition of new functionality. Regardless of their location in the network, all exchanges with switching facilities include a number of basic functions. This system core contains:

- a group switch for switching functions;
- a trunk stage, including exchange terminal circuits (ETCs) that serve as an interface to the transport network;
- signalling functions for communication with other exchanges (using SS7, for example);
- operation and maintenance functions (not used in the connection set-up phase); and
- the control function.

In addition, the local exchange contains the following functions:

- the subscriber stage, whose tasks include current feed of the subscriber's line, A/D conversion, concentration in the direction of the group switch, signalling to and from the subscriber and the control function;
- subscriber service functions, where distributed supplementary services like "call waiting", "call forwarding unconditional" and "automatic call-back" are implemented (network intelligence layer functions);
- functions for the implementation of the centrex service;
- the function for the charging of calls and services (in some cases); and
- Internet access functions (in some cases).

3.2.2 What is connected to what?

A local exchange sets up a connection from one of the local subscribers to

- another subscriber in the same exchange (an internal call);
- a PBX, via a time slot of a PCM link to the PBX;
- a time slot of a PCM link to another exchange;
- the Internet, via a modem pool and an access server (see *Part H – The Internet*);
- equipment for the play-back of recorded announcements (announcement equipment); and
- other equipment in the exchange.

Signalling equipment for the register signals of a channel-associated signalling (CAS) system is connected to the group switch. This equipment generates and receives signals in multi-frequency compelled (MFC) signalling and is connected to the time slot that will later be used by the call. Signalling terminals for SS7 signalling are connected semi-permanently to a time slot dedicated to signalling.

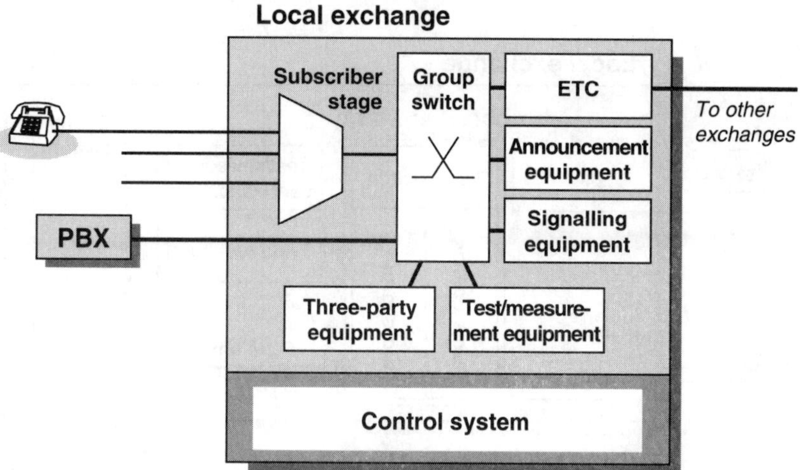

Figure B.3.3 An example of the equipment connected to the group switch

Announcement equipment plays recorded announcements and is used in the event of a fault and in connection with certain subscriber services. The machine is normally connected to subscribers in the same exchange to avoid unnecessary use of resources in the trunk network.

There is also equipment for setting up connections in which more than two subscribers are involved: three-party calls, call waiting, expediting of a call in progress and broadcasting.

In addition, there are test instruments and tone generators used by operation and maintenance personnel. This equipment can be connected to similar equipment in other exchanges; for example, to test telephones and PBXs.

3.2.3 PSTN switching-function requirements

The grade of service (GoS) is an important quality parameter in the PSTN. Placing a call during peak periods can result in congestion in the subscriber stage or on the outgoing line. Depending on the technique used, group switches can also cause congestion during periods of heavy traffic.

In recent years, greater focus has been attributed to GoS due to the increased use of the Internet. Internet traffic has very long holding times in comparison with telephony, which calls for different dimensioning of the exchanges.

3.2.4 The subscriber stage

The line interface circuits (LIC) and a small time switch are the primary components of a subscriber stage. See *Figure B.3.4.*

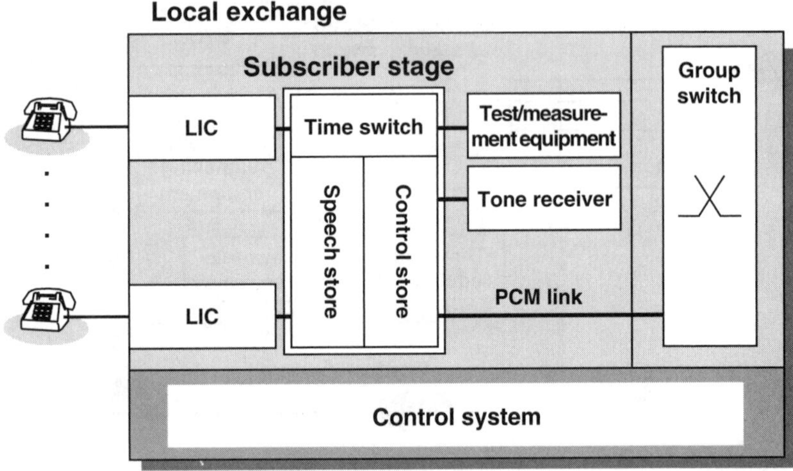

Figure B.3.4 Time switch in the subscriber stage

Every subscriber is connected to a line interface circuit that provides adjustment to the analog voice frequency (VF) interface for subscribers who have traditional fixed access. The LIC is a standardised module employed in all junctions between a fixed, analog subscriber's line and the digital network; for example, in the subscriber stage or in a multiplexer. In old exchanges with an analog subscriber stage, the LIC is located after a "metallic" switch where it can be shared by several subscribers.

An LIC includes:

- overvoltage protection;
- test equipment that can be connected to facilitate automatic measurement and troubleshooting of a subscriber's line (test access);
- ringing voltage to the telephone (alternating current);
- telephone current supply (direct current);

- detection of hook state (off hook and on hook);
- detection of pulses generated by dial telephones;
- polarity inversion (used in signalling to certain coin-operated pay phones and PBXs);
- a hybrid for the junction between two-wire and four-wire sections; and
- an A/D converter (that utilises PCM technique).

The hybrid forms the junction between two-wire and four-wire sections. The hybrid is balanced to the impedance of the subscriber's line to avoid echo. Since the impedance of the line is affected by changes in weather, automatically regulated balancing equipment is available nowadays that bases its operation on scheduled measurement of line impedance. Hybrids are discussed in greater detail in Chapter 4.

The A/D converter operates in both directions. It includes equipment for analog-to-digital conversion in the direction of the subscriber stage, and the corresponding equipment for digital-to-analog conversion in the opposite direction. The result is a PCM code having a bit rate of 64 kbit/s (8,000 eight-bit samples per second) per voice channel in each direction. (A/D conversion is dealt with in Volume 1, Chapter 2.)

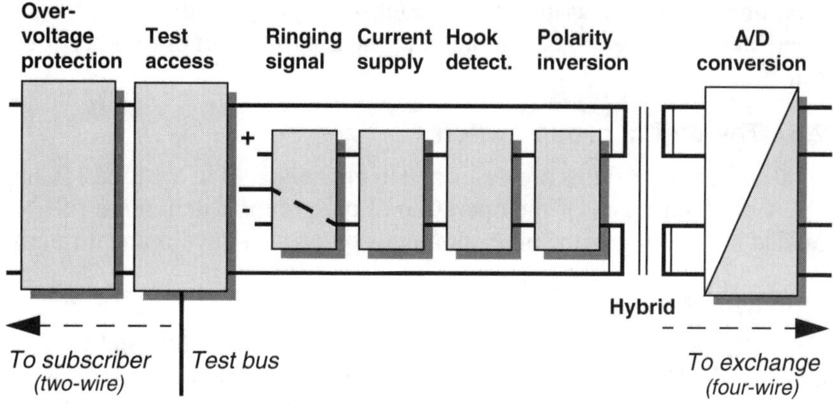

Figure B.3.5 Line interface circuit architecture

3.2.5 The time switch in the subscriber stage

The time switch in the subscriber stage connects subscribers to common equipment, such as digit receivers, information tones and test equipment.

The switch also performs concentration by connecting subscribers to time slots in those PCM links that interconnect the subscriber stage and the group switch.

The degree of concentration – generally in the range 10:1 to 3:1 – is a function of the amount of traffic generated by each subscriber. Given the degree of concentration just mentioned, the number of time slots in the direction of the group switch is between 10% and 30% of the number of subscribers. The great variation is due to the fact that many different subscriber categories are connected. Traffic will be low if the local exchange is situated in a residential area where the majority of subscribers are private persons; this traffic level can allow a concentration of about 10:1. In an exchange situated in a city business district, each subscriber generates a significantly larger traffic volume which may require a concentration of 3:1. Continuous traffic measurement indicates whether the number of lines into the group switch is unnecessarily large or inappropriately small.

The time switch contains one bus for incoming and one bus for outgoing time slots. Each subscriber or other connection has a specific time slot assigned on the buses. When a subscriber makes a call, his time slots contain speech samples; otherwise they are empty. The time switch contains a speech store for intermediate storage of information from the time slots. The control function performs an analysis and determines the order in which the samples are to be read for the desired connections to be established. The corresponding values are written into a control memory. In this way, the subscribers are connected to one another, to the group switch or to other equipment.

3.2.6 The digital group switch

Digital switching systems are described in greater detail in Volume 1, Chapter 3. A brief summary of the operation of the group switch in the PSTN is provided here, along with some comments on present development trends.

Group switch

The unit responsible for establishing connections is still referred to as the group switch. The primary task of the digital group switch is to organise the flow of time slots so that connections can be established between subscribers or between a subscriber and the equipment that is to provide a service.

There are two types of component in the digital group switch: the time switch and the space switch. Two flows of time slots – one for each direction – are connected together. An example of the time-switch-time (TST) structure is illustrated in *Figure B.3.6.*

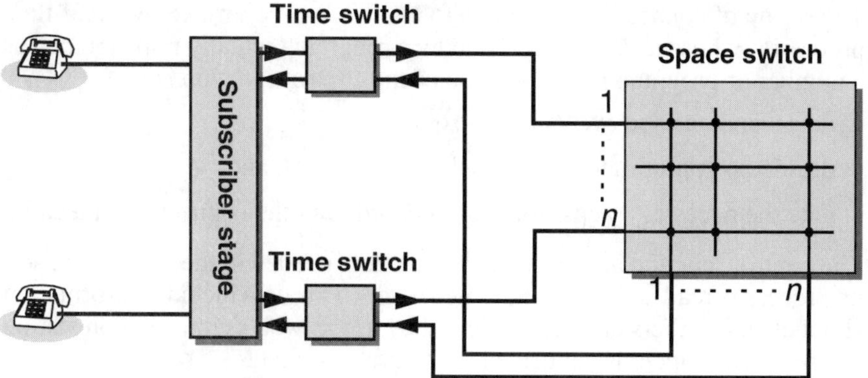

Figure B.3.6 The principle of TST switching

Capacity

Digital group switches are used in small exchanges, located in sparsely populated areas, as well as in the largest international exchanges. Not too long ago it was common for local exchanges to serve 10,000 to 30,000 subscribers – occasionally only a few thousand. An example can be useful. The group switch of a local exchange with 10,000 subscribers, a concentration of 10:1, 20% internal traffic and no transit traffic should be capable of setting up approximately 900 simultaneous connections. There are still some small exchanges, but because of recent advances in the development of access and transmission systems, larger local exchanges that serve more than a hundred thousand subscribers are becoming more common. Large group switches installed in today's PSTNs manage close on 65,000 simultaneous connections (using twice as many connection points).

New requirements

Since the group switch is jointly used by the PSTN and N-ISDN, today's group switches must also include functions that allow for the set-up of connections consisting of more than one time slot, which is referred to as wideband or $n \cdot 64$ kbit/s.

A function that is used more frequently and that affects switching is broadcasting. Broadcasting can be used for services like "today's weather" or "stock exchange quotations", to provide callers with the correct time or for alarm functions. Broadcasting, in this context, means that a connection is set up from a single source – announcement equipment, for example – to many simultaneous listeners.

3.3 The control function

The set-up of connections in a modern exchange is controlled by a real-time processor, whose tasks are regulated by a program (actually implemented as a number of programs). The purpose of the control function is to

- detect and analyse events in the exchange;
- decide on appropriate actions (select a program); and
- take the necessary steps (for example, ordering the connection of a call).

The control function also ensures that the data needed in the connection set-up process is read and modified as necessary. This data includes information about all subscribers and the services they use as well as information stating where all equipment is connected to the group switch.

The capacity of an exchange and its control function is indicated by the number of call attempts that can be handled per hour. This is referred to as busy hour call attempts (BHCA). Capacity is not only a function of the processor power but also of the type of traffic. Today's most powerful control systems, used in the PSTN, can handle more than 1,000,000 BHCA. Ordinarily, processor load is expressed as the total processing time (in milliseconds) per call. This load increases if service offerings are large (and if the services are frequently used) or if advanced signalling is required. For example, SS7 consumes more processor power than CAS signalling.

There are a number of other factors that affect processor load and, hence, system capacity. (See also Volume 1, Chapter 10.)

3.3.1 The control function and the set-up and release of a call

To enable correct connection, the processor performs a number of analyses and then makes a series of decisions. Is this subscriber allowed to place this call? Where is the call to be connected? What should the call cost? To illustrate the analysis and decision process, we will study four phases of the set-up and release of a call.

Phase 1: The A-subscriber lifts the handset

By regularly scanning all subscribers' lines to detect call attempts, the exchange's control system immediately notices that a subscriber has lifted the handset. To determine whether a dialling tone is to be sent – and to prepare for the reception of the B-subscriber number – the control function performs a number of tasks:

- A check is made against the exchange's subscriber database. To begin with, the subscriber may be barred for outgoing calls, but there are also services that affect the set-up of the connection. No dialling tone is to be sent if the *hot line* service is activated. If "call forwarding unconditional" is activated, a discontinuous dialling tone is normally sent to remind the subscriber that no incoming calls will be connected to this telephone.

- A memory area in the control unit is reserved for storing the telephone number dialled by the subscriber. Other information retrieved from the subscriber database and likely to affect the set-up of the connection, such as the subscriber category, is also stored in this area.
- A tone receiver for DTMF signalling is connected through the time switch in the subscriber stage. After this process has been concluded, a dialling tone can be sent.

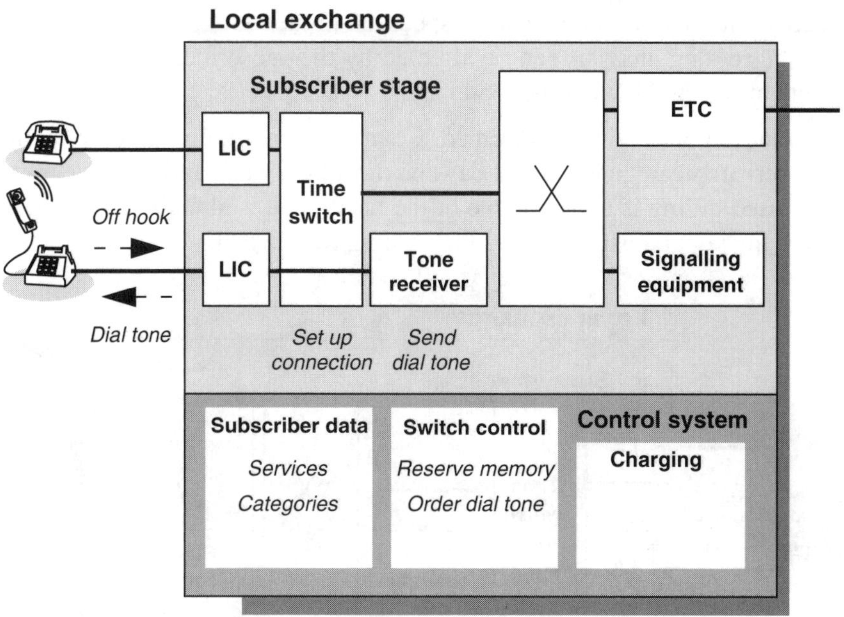

Figure B.3.7 A subscriber has lifted the handset

Phase 2: The exchange receives the B-subscriber number

The B-subscriber number is received by the tone receiver, which sends it to the control function. (The pulses received from a dial telephone are interpreted by the line interface circuit.) The following functions are performed:

- The control function analyses the B-subscriber number to determine a set of parameters, the most important of which are:

- where is the call to be connected (to a local subscriber or to another exchange)?
- which charging method applies?
- what will be the length of the number?

- If the B-subscriber number pertains to a local subscriber, a query is sent to the subscriber database. This database contains information stating the line interface circuit to which the subscriber is physically connected, whether the subscriber is barred for incoming calls and the services he subscribes to. If "call diversion unconditional" or "call waiting" are activated, connection set-up will be affected.
- If the B-subscriber number pertains to a subscriber of another exchange, then a routing analysis must be performed. Depending on subscriber category, alternative routing can be specified in the routing table. The result of the routing analysis can be affected by the subscriber's category, the time of day and many other parameters.
- A charging analysis is performed. Charging is normally affected by the subscriber's category, time of day and day of the week and whether or not itemised billing is applied. One of the tariffs that is already registered as exchange data must be selected for billing for the call.

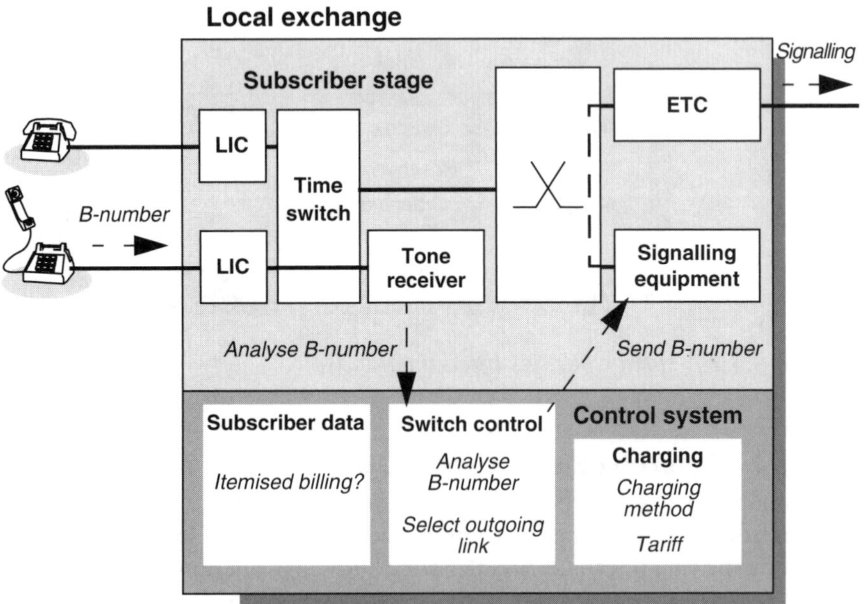

Figure B.3.8 The B-subscriber number is analysed for an outgoing call

- The set-up of the connection is prepared after the analyses are concluded. An outgoing time slot is reserved in the group switch, and, in the case of an outgoing call, the exchange starts signalling to the next exchange. Signalling may take a path different from that taken by the voice transmission if SS7 is used.

Phase 3: The exchange sets up the outgoing call

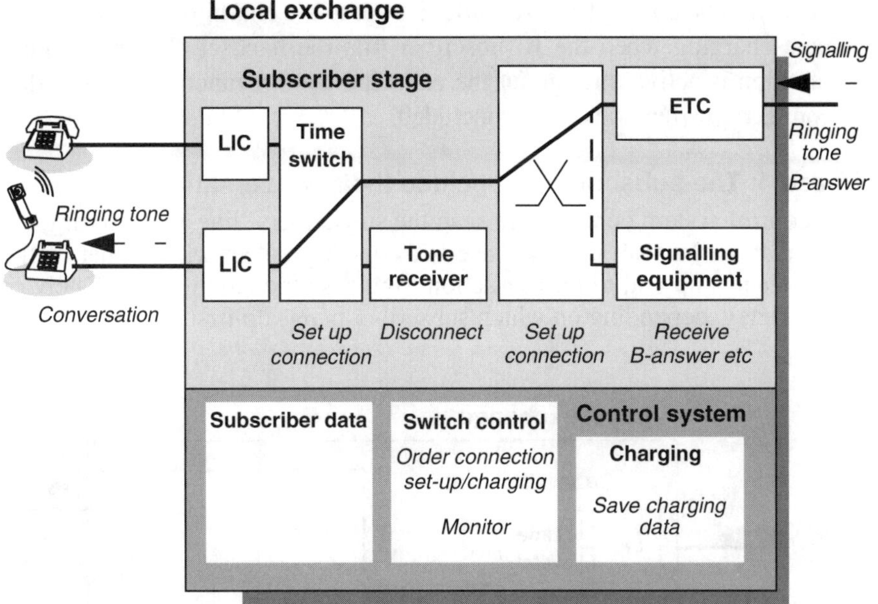

Figure B.3.9 An outgoing call is set up

The control function will use the result of the aforementioned analyses during the concluding phase of the signalling process. Congestion could have been encountered along the path, the B-subscriber number could have been vacant or the B-subscriber could have been busy. However, in most cases the B-subscriber is free, and the exchanges starts to send ringing signals.

- The connection is set up from the B-subscriber's exchange – possibly via other exchanges – resulting in a signal being sent to the A-subscriber's exchange: "B-subscriber free".
- The control function orders the group switch to reserve a path between the subscriber stage and the selected time slot on the outgoing PCM link.

- The control function orders the time switch in the subscriber stage to disconnect the A-subscriber from the tone receiver. The subscriber is instead connected to the selected time slot in the direction of the group switch. A connection has now been established between the two subscribers.
- The B-subscriber's exchange sends a ringing signal to the local subscriber and a ringing tone to the A-subscriber. The ringing tone is sent in the reverse direction over the established connection.
- The control function starts to monitor the connection, primarily to enable the call to be charged for. An order is sent to the charging function to initiate charging when the B-subscriber lifts the handset. The monitoring function is active throughout the call. The control function initiates disconnection when the call is concluded.

Phase 4: The subscribers conclude their conversation

The control system continues to scan the subscribers' lines even during the conversation. Its task in this phase is to quickly detect when either of the parties hangs up and to initiate action to release the circuit immediately or with a delay, depending on which subscriber hangs up first.

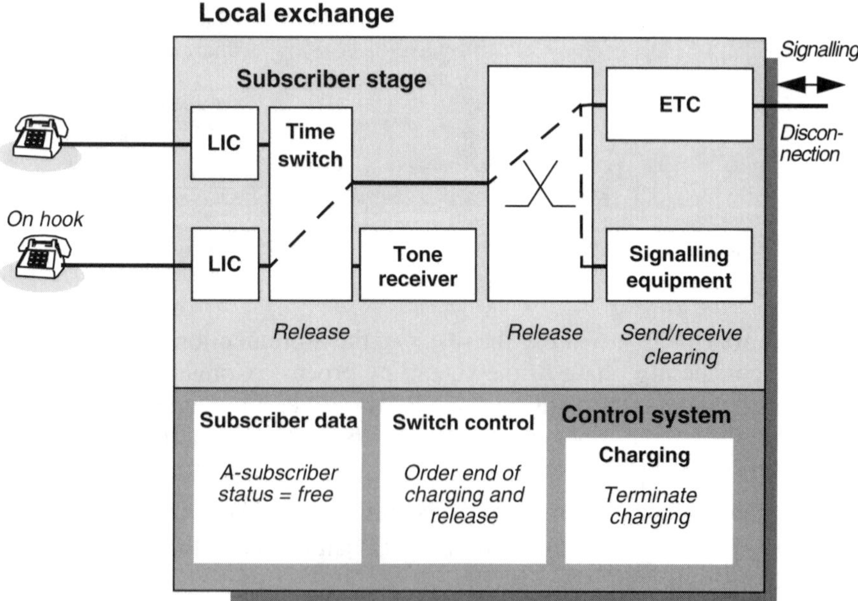

Figure B.3.10 Release of a call

- The call is normally assumed to be concluded when the A-subscriber hangs up, in which case the call is released without any noticeable delay. No time supervision is activated, because the A-subscriber normally pays for the call. The A-subscriber is not to be penalised (charged a higher cost) if, for any reason, the B-subscriber does not hang up.
- It cannot be immediately assumed that a call is concluded because the B-subscriber hangs up first: he may wish to continue the call from another telephone. The exchange will therefore activate time supervision (ordinarily 90 seconds) before initiating release of the call. However, the call will be immediately released if the A-subscriber hangs up at any time during this supervisory period.
- The control function's first action, after having decided to release the call, is to order the charging function to terminate call charging.
- The control function then orders the disconnection of all equipment that was used for the call. This means that time slots are released and can be used by other calls. Signalling is also performed to ensure that all exchanges involved in setting up the call release their equipment.

3.4 Network hierarchy

The different network hierarchies are dealt with exhaustively in Volume 1, Chapter 3. In the following subsections, we will mention some network elements and functions that are relevant to PSTN connection set-up.

3.4.1 Central and remote subscriber stages

As mentioned earlier, the trend is towards increasingly larger local exchanges. Subscribers are often connected via remote subscriber stages which, from a switching point of view, perform exactly the same functions as those performed by centrally located subscriber stages.

Signals are sent to the control function in the local exchange, even in the case of a remote subscriber stage. (See Chapter 7.) However, a function is ordinarily provided for handling internal calls, should there be a break on the links to the main exchange. When these links are down, information about which services the various subscribers have access to is lost and their use cannot be charged for.

The remote subscriber stage is becoming an increasingly common component in access networks.

3.4.2 Alternative routing

In the traditional PSTN exchange hierarchy, traffic has been routed to direct links (high-congestion routes), and, if they are busy, the next higher level in the hierarchy (low-congestion routes) has been used. (See also Volume 1, Chapter 10, Subsection 10.8.5.) New routing functions are now available thanks to SS7 and the TUP protocol. One example is the possibility of preventing rerouting further on in the network and instead trying an alternative route all the way from the originating exchange. Another example is placing subscribers in different categories; emergency services, for example, could have access to a number of alternative routes or even routes designated for their exclusive use.

3.4.3 Semi-permanent connections

A connection which must not be congested and which must have good transmission characteristics can be set up through the group switch using commands. Such connections are referred to as semi-permanent connections and can utilise different paths through the exchange hierarchy.

Semi-permanent connections are used to connect SS7 signalling terminals with their dedicated time slots. The connections run either from one local exchange to another or to an exchange higher up the hierarchy that serves as a signalling transfer point (STP). Semi-permanent connections can also be used to create an internal network for a company by setting up leased lines between the company's PBXs. Leased lines – permanent connections – can also be handled exclusively by the transport network.

The transmission quality of modem data connections can be guaranteed through the use of leased lines. Avoiding the time-consuming connection set-up phase in data transmission is an added advantage of leased lines.

Leased lines not only run from one exchange to the next but can connect many exchanges at different levels in a hierarchy; for example, to link the offices of a single company in several different countries.

4 Transmission techniques

4.1 Introduction

The development of transmission techniques has been advanced significantly by the need to reduce network costs. We have witnessed an evolution from systems employing open-wire lines to multiplexed, analog systems using coaxial or radio links, on to digital fibre-optic systems – based on time-division and wavelength-division multiplexing – with a capacity of tens of Gbit/s per fibre pair. And then there are satellite systems, the first of which were put into operation as early as 1965. The first commercial optical systems came on the scene in 1980.

From the point of view of PSTN transmission quality, this evolutionary process has not been without problems. Digitisation resulted in a heterogeneous analog-digital network, and satellite systems introduced considerable delays.

A completely different aspect is related to the question: What is the PSTN? The introduction to Chapter 1 provides a brief description of "the PSTN model of the 1960s". In the 1960s, the PSTN was *the* network, of which the transmission components, in the form of cables and radio links (employing analog transmission), were integral parts. Today we have a variety of bearer networks and a transport network based on digital transmission, which all the bearer networks have in common, to a great extent. (See Volume 1, Chapter 5.) Pure PSTN transmission exists only in the access part of the network.

We might feel inclined to regard a common transmission network as one large bit transporter, and what the bits actually represent as less important. But that is not the case. As a matter of fact, it should even be possible to link every individual bit to a particular service. Is the bit sensitive to error? To delays? How sensitive? Can the bit stream be manipulated?

The only way to avoid having to consider bit-stream transmission quality is to build completely transparent networks in which bit errors, echo, delays and delay variations do not occur. But such a network is unrealistic; it would be too expensive. We must accept the fact that a balance has to be struck between the quality requirements of the various services, on the one hand, and network costs on the other. The following section will therefore shed some light on the cost-saving transmission techniques that are used in the PSTN and their impact on voice and data traffic.

Quality parameters are discussed in detail in Volume 1, Chapters 4 and 10.

4.2 Cost-saving transmission techniques

The multiplexing and modulation techniques and other methods generally applied to use transmission media efficiently were dealt with in Volume 1, Chapter 4, Section 4.4. Those methods are generally applicable. In the following we will discuss some methods closely related to telephony service.

We will focus on the combination of telephone and analog two-wire in the access network and on methods for using four-wire connections more efficiently by allowing pauses in a telephone conversation to be used by other calls.

4.2.1 The combination of telephone and analog two-wire

It is less expensive to use two copper wires instead of four, but it poses a twofold problem. We introduce attenuation that cannot readily be compensated through amplification as well as frequency-dependent amplitude distortion: the higher voice frequencies are attenuated more than the lower ones.

Two-wire systems are unsuitable for long-distance networks because of this attenuation.

In today's telecommunications networks, many trunk networks are digital and, hence, considered to be attenuation-free. This allows a margin of at least 10 dB at each end for the attenuation of the access network (provided that the telephones are of modern design and have frequency characteristics opposite to those of the copper pair). Earlier, analog two-wire transmission was sometimes used between exchanges, too, but this technique reduces the allowable attenuation of the expensive access network, because the total attenuation between two subscribers must be kept within defined limits. "Loudness rating" (LR) refers to the total attenuation, which is composed of the send loudness rating (SLR) and the receive loudness rating (RLR). LR is generally specified in the transmission plan.

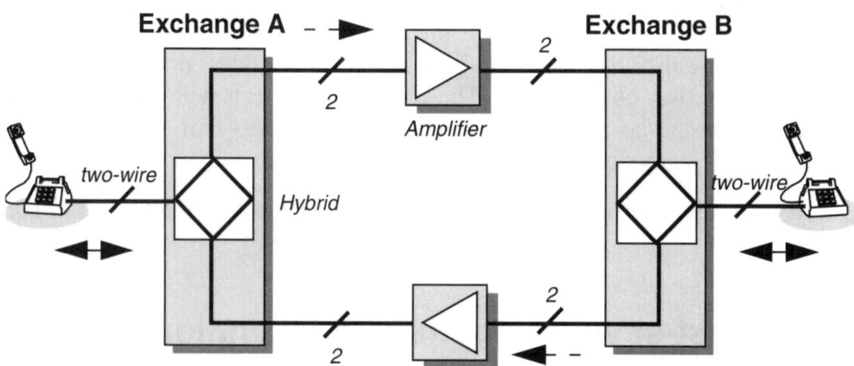

Figure B.4.1 Two-wire connection between subscriber and exchange, four-wire between exchanges

Nowadays, the junction between two-wire and four-wire resides in the local exchange or in a point between the subscriber and the local exchange; that is, in a remote subscriber stage or multiplexer, where the signal is converted from an analog to a digital signal.

Figure B.4.1 illustrates the point of transition between two-wire and four-wire in a local exchange. The figure is a diagrammatic sketch that also explains why the converter used in this point is called a "hybrid".

The hybrid equipment is used to separate the two voice directions of the two-wire connection so that they can be applied to the two pairs of a four-wire connection. Earlier equipment was generally composed of two differential transformers and a line balance, as shown in *Figure B.4.2*.

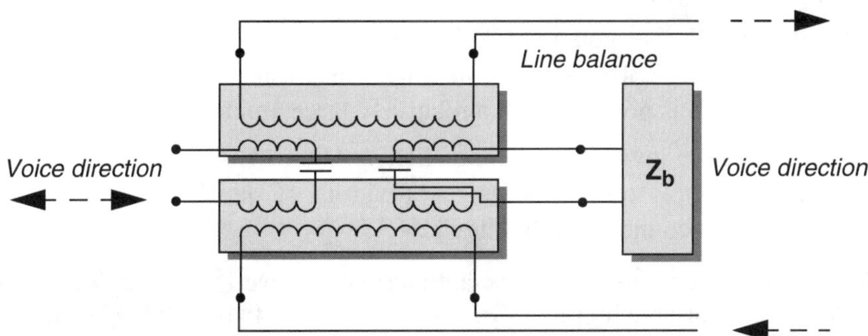

Figure B.4.2 Hybrid

If the impedance of the line balance, Z_b, is equal to the impedance of the line, then no voice energy from the incoming wire pair will leak over to the outgoing pair. On the other hand, the balanced hybrid results in attenuation, because the incoming power is divided into two equal parts. Halving the power means an attenuation of approximately 3 dB. To this must be added the hybrid's own attenuation of approximately 0.5 dB. For every hybrid, the resultant attenuation is thus approximately 3.5 dB.

Nowadays, hybrids are normally built with operational amplifiers (OP amplifiers). These hybrids are equipped with a balance that can be adjusted automatically when the impedance of the subscriber line changes, owing to changes in the weather or because a subscriber has connected new equipment.

4.2.2 DCME

Due to the length and expense of certain transmission media – for example, submarine cables and satellite connections – technicians have researched the possibility of using voice compression to allow many more calls to share each connection. A variety of analog methods have been tested over the years. In the 1980s, digital circuit multiplexing equipment (DCME) emerged as the dominant solution. For telephony services, DCME provides an average compression of 5:1. Other teleservices cannot tolerate such compression, which is one of the reasons why even in today's transport network we need to know which bits deliver a specific type of service.

DCME, described in ITU-T Recommendation G.763, is not a fixed standard: different manufacturers have somewhat different solutions. DCME equipment is connected to an international exchange; the interface for signalling between the DCME and the exchange is described in ITU-T Recommendation Q.50.

DCME includes two compression functions:

- Digital speech interpolation (DSI), based on the fact that all subscribers speak on average 30%–40% of the time. This means that compression by a factor of 2.5 is possible with a relatively large number of lines.
- More effective low-rate encoding (LRE). ADPCM (see Chapter 2, Subsection 2.4.1) is ordinarily used, providing 32 kbit/s for every call. ADPCM is recommended by the ITU-T.

DCME equipment also contains a function for overload handling. It is referred to as variable bit rate (VBR) and allows bits to be "stolen" from the voice connections to create new, temporary channels.

Figure B.4.3 illustrates the functions included in DCME equipment.

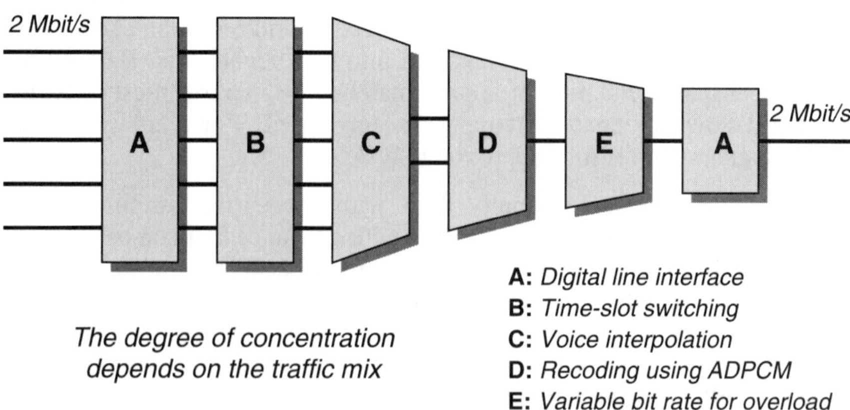

Figure B.4.3 DCME equipment functions

A connection can be routed between two international exchanges, one of which uses the North American standard and the other the European standard. In such cases, the DCME equipment will also perform conversion for the PCM systems, between T1 (1.5 Mbit/s) and E1 (2 Mbit/s), as well as the conversion of voice coding between the μ-law and the A-law. These standards are described in Volume 1, Chapter 2, Subsection 2.7.2. See *Figure B.4.4*, which is somewhat simplified.

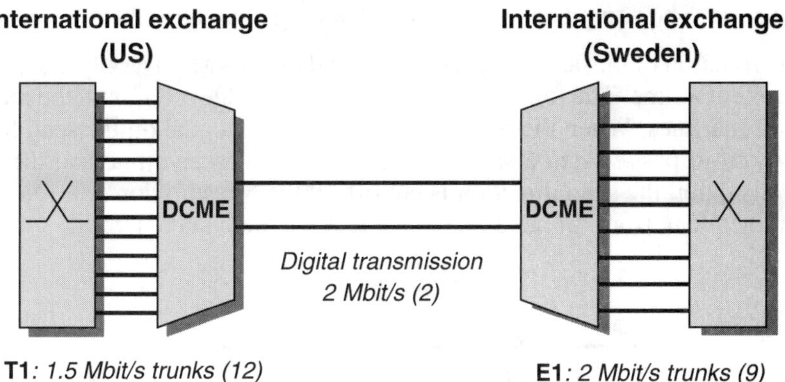

Figure B.4.4 Example of an international connection using DCME equipment

4.3 Managing echo

The cost savings described in the preceding section also have drawbacks. The most serious difficulties are echo and data transmission problems.

4.3.1 The echo problem

Echoes during a telephone conversation are extremely irritating. The fact that one's own speech returns after a few hundred milliseconds makes it difficult to speak in a normal rhythm. The phenomenon of echo is caused by imbalance in the hybrid that handles the transition between the two-wire and four-wire circuits. Previously, echo was noticeable only over long satellite connections where the distance causes long propagation time. One's own speech bounces back in the other subscriber's hybrid and is then returned. The problem has increased during the past years, because even digital telephones (for example GSM) contain voice coders that require a certain amount of time to perform their tasks. These distracting echo problems can be experienced when we are speaking on a GSM telephone with a subscriber who has an ordinary fixed telephone.

The echo effect can be counteracted by carefully balancing the hybrid equipment. If this is not sufficient, the effects can be reduced with the help of a device to limit the echo. There are two types: echo suppressors and echo cancellers.

Echo suppressors

A network echo suppressor (NES) consists of a controllable transmission gate (R) in the send direction and a controllable attenuator (A) in the receive direction. The equipment is controlled by a logic circuit (L).

The function of the echo suppressor is based on the fact that only one person speaks at a time. The logic circuit detects the signal level of both the receive and send lines. When the receive line is quiet, the signal on the send line is allowed to pass. When a signal is present on the receive line and the send line is quiet, the send direction is cut off by the transmission gate. No echo can then leak from the send line to the receive line via the hybrid.

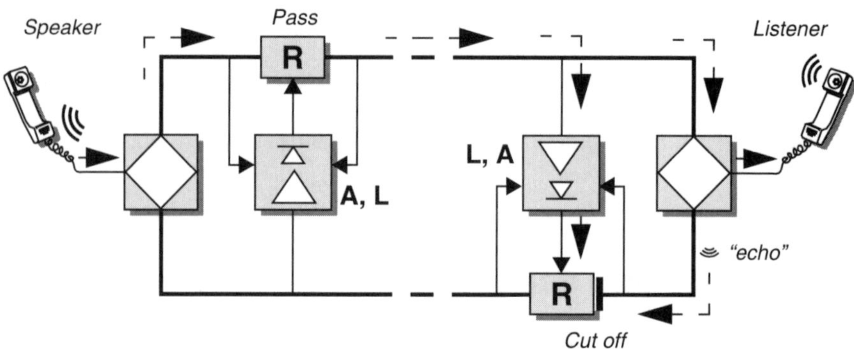

Figure B.4.5 Network echo suppressors in cooperation

The logic circuit can detect the presence of concurrent energy in both directions and can prevent the system from blocking traffic if both subscribers speak at the same time. The echo suppressor is set so that the transmission gate allows the signal on the send line to pass, whereas a balanced attenuator is connected in the receive direction.

Echo canceller

A network echo canceller (NEC) consists of a subtraction circuit (positioned in the send direction) that subtracts from the received signal a calculated replica of the signal's echo. The echo canceller is often augmented by a clipping circuit that blocks signals below a certain, low level. This eliminates any weak echo remaining after subtraction.

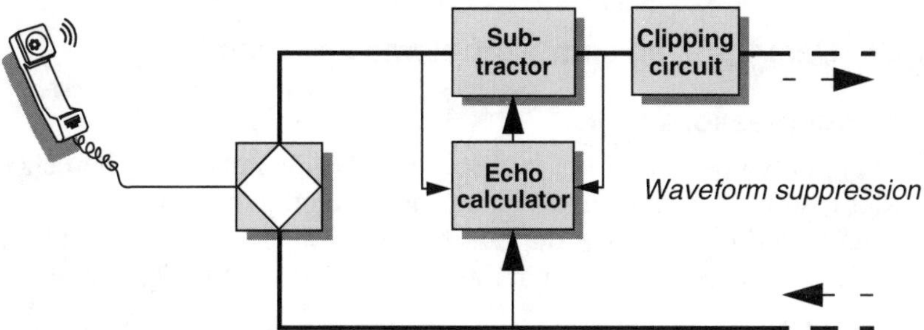

Figure B.4.6 Network echo canceller

The echo canceller is more effective than the echo suppressor, but both can be used together in many applications because they are complementary.

Echo canceller pools

The echo canceller is normally located in international exchanges or in the national transit exchanges of countries having long distances between inhabited areas. Earlier, they were always built into equipment that handled the PCM connection, that is, the exchange terminal circuit (ETC). Nowadays, there is a more flexible solution: a pool of echo cancellers activated when needed. This solutions permits a selective use of the cancellers, which makes them economically viable in lower-ranked exchanges.

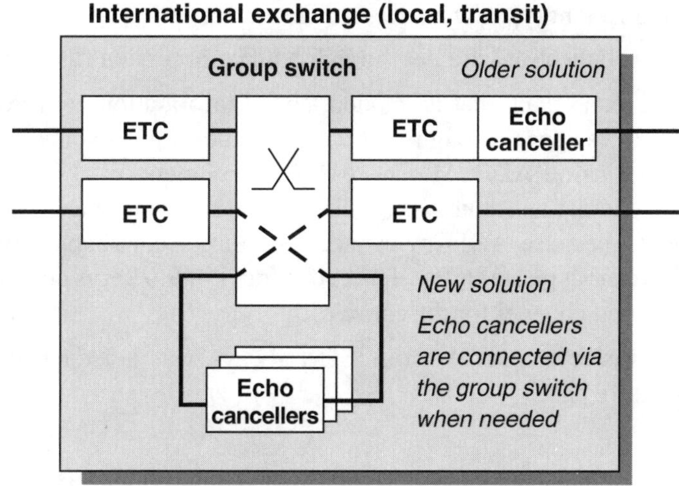

Figure B.4.7 Echo canceller pool

When an echo canceller is required, it is connected via the group switch, to the incoming and outgoing trunk lines.

4.3.2 Data transmission – problems and solutions

Echo suppressors

Echo suppressors should not be used in data transmission. The echo suppressor results in clipping and sudden amplitude fluctuations which interfere with data traffic and make duplex transmission of data impossible. Echo cancellers can cause bit errors in their manipulation of the bit stream.

Unlike ISDN, the PSTN cannot use subscriber signalling to demand different types of transmission for different types of service. To enable echo cancellers to be disconnected in data transmission, modems are equipped with a tone generator in the voice band (usually 2,100 Hz). When an echo canceller detects such a tone, it deactivates itself for the entire call. The modem then handles the echo effects.

The traffic control functions of the exchange are used when echo cancellers are to be disconnected on a permanent basis.

In telefax traffic, echo cancellers are less of a problem and need not be disconnected.

DCME

Data and telefax traffic cannot tolerate the compression performed in DCME equipment. Moreover, the PSTN's transport network is integrated with that of ISDN. DCME equipment must therefore include capability to handle different types of traffic in different ways:

- Voice connections are put through both compression functions.
- Voice-band data, that is, modem-coded information on a PCM connection, never goes through voice interpolation but in some cases is compressed using ADPCM. The ADPCM technique works well for voice-band data up to 4.8 kbit/s. Quality degrades for bit rates of 9.6 kbit/s and higher, because ADPCM cannot code the discontinuous shifts in level that occur at phase shifts. Hence, data rates of 9.6 kbit/s and higher have a dedicated channel for the entire path.
- 64 kbit/s data channels from ISDN always have a dedicated channel for the entire path.

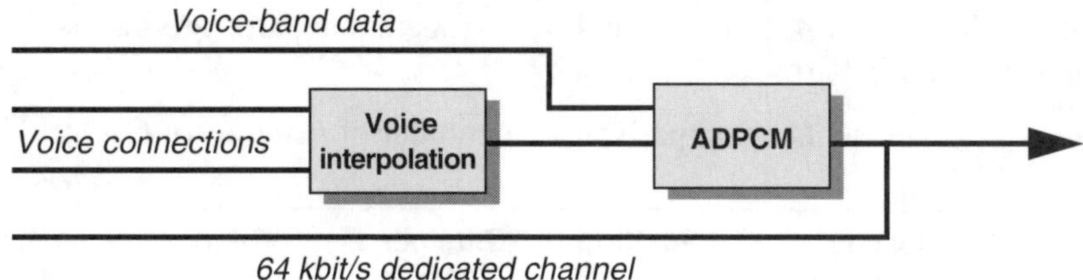

Figure B.4.8 DCME traffic handling

The DCME receives information about which type of traffic is carried by each channel from the exchange. This signalling is referred to as *bearer service selection*. It only operates together with the ISDN user part (ISUP) protocol, which is one reason why ISUP is often also used for PSTN signalling.

Transmission quality and connection set-up

The PSTN has no error-detection or data-retransmission functionality. In the event of a transmission error, it is the end-user's (the modem's or the computer's) task to detect this error and to request retransmission.

Another problem is uneven transmission quality. From a quality point of view, the two-wire section of the PSTN (over copper pairs) is a weak link in a connection. Transfer rates must be adapted to the line quality to limit the BER to an acceptable level. Modern modems are equipped with a line probing function which performs this adaptation in a dynamic fashion. (See Subsection 2.4.3.)

An additional difficulty is the long connection set-up time that the PSTN requires for data-communication applications. As mentioned earlier, leased lines are a means of avoiding the connection set-up phase, but they are still a relatively expensive solution.

Despite these disadvantages, data (notably the Internet) and telefax traffic are increasing rapidly in the PSTN. This is the result of several PSTN enhancements:

- shorter connection set-up time, thanks to SS7 signalling;
- lower BER, due to the increased use of fibre in the trunk network; and
- better equipped access networks, in which the use of fibre is on the increase.

In addition, trends in modem development are promising. Traditional frequency-shift and phase-shift modulation are being replaced by QAM-type amplitude-shift and phase-shift modulation. These methods are described in Volume 1, Chapter 4, Subsection 4.4.2. Modem standards are discussed in Chapter 2 of this Part.

Figure B.4.9 presents a comparison of a number of versions of QAM:

Capacity	Positions	Bits per position	Baud
9,600 bit/s	16	4	2,400
14,400 bit/s	64	6	2,400
19,200 bit/s	256	8	2,400
28,800 bit/s	512	9	3,200

Figure B.4.9 QAM versions for the PSTN

5 Trunk and access networks

5.1 Introduction

When telephony was in its infancy, there was not much difference between the lines that connected a subscriber to the switchboard operator and those that linked the operators together. Today, trunk and access networks are built more or less separately, although the transport technique used in the trunk network is becoming increasingly common in the access network as well.

5.2 The trunk network

The traditional copper trunk network in the PSTN has gradually been supplemented by radio links, satellite systems and optical fibre. The key issue has been to achieve high capacity to economise on expensive cable.

Today's trunk networks include the PDH, SDH and SONET multiplexing hierarchies. Since the trunk network is often shared by many bearer networks, we described it in Volume 1, Chapter 5. Typical connections between exchanges and trunks are described in Chapter 7 of this Part.

5.3 The access network

Subscribers can be connected to a local exchange in different ways. The subscriber stage can be implemented centrally or remotely, and the transmission medium can be fixed or wireless. As a rule, the subscriber cannot tell one medium from the other, at least not when he is using the basic telephony service. However, the availability of services can depend on the access method used. Some old access methods may result in a transmission quality that does not meet the requirements of modern, high-speed modems. Other methods can add value to existing services – a certain degree of mobility, for example.

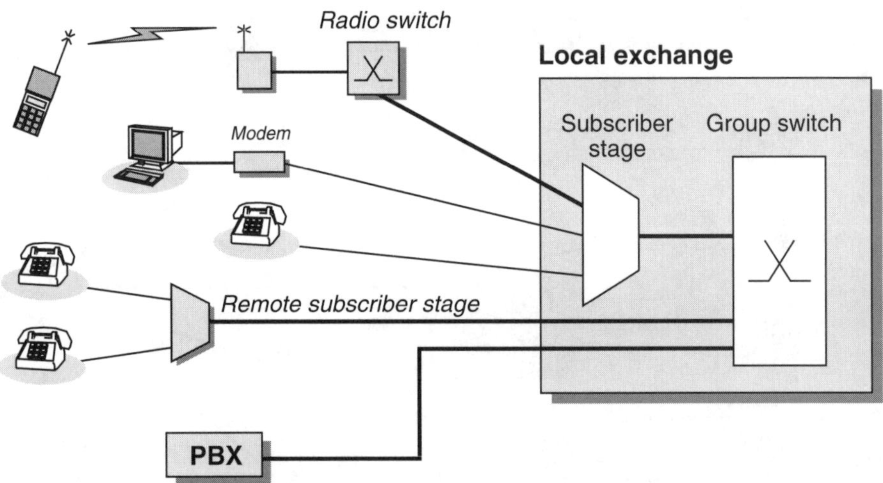

Figure B.5.1 Subscriber lines connected to a PSTN local exchange

Two main categories of subscribers are connected to the PSTN. One of these categories consists of ordinary one-line subscribers who can have several telephones connected to their line. They have one channel for the transmission of a 300–3,400 Hz analog signal and for subscriber signalling. The other category consists of business subscribers who have PBXs equipped with several channels.

The terminals for connection to the PSTN include ordinary telephones, cordless telephones, pay phones, fax machines and modems for data communication. (See Chapter 1 for a detailed description of terminals.)

5.3.1 Digital transmission in the metallic access network

Like the trunk network, the access network is playing an increasingly important role as a common resource for several bearer networks. Increased digitisation (see *Figure B.5.2*) and a common PSTN/ISDN configuration are two notable trends.

An example of a mixed network structure is shown in *Figure B.5.2.*

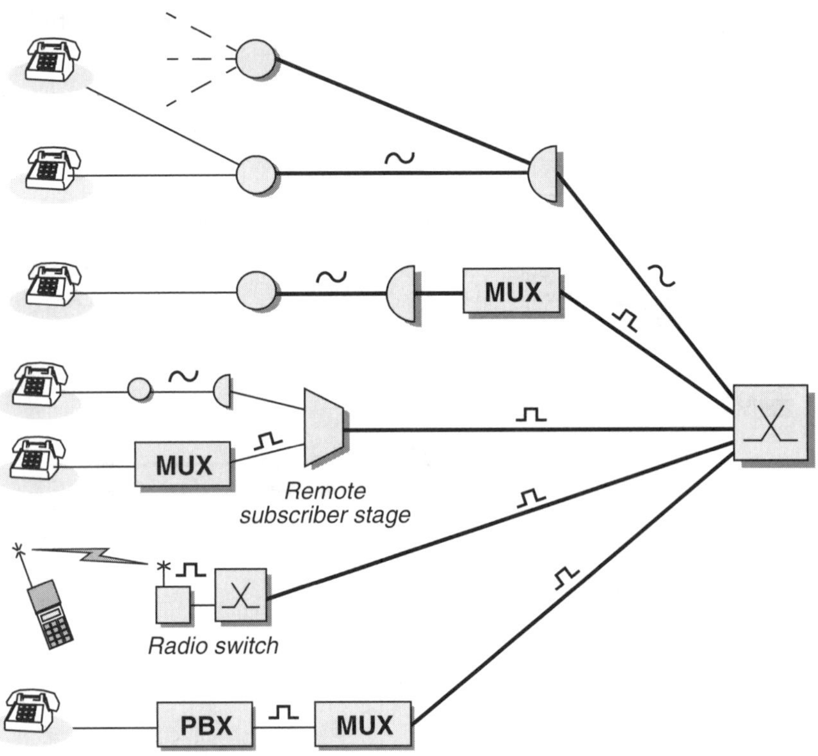

Figure B.5.2 Equipment in the access network

The remote subscriber stage is a key component of this network structure.

The access network has been the last bastion of analog technology to hold out against the onrush of digitisation. There is nothing surprising about that; after all, telephones generate an analog signal. Traditionally, we have used a metallic access network consisting of paired copper cables, run from the exchange in thick bundles and then branched at cross-connection and distribution points. (See also Volume 1, Chapter 5.)

When the PSTN was digitised, A/D conversion of voice was often performed in the local exchange. Today, deploying the digitising function in distribution points in the metallic access network is becoming quite common. However, the trend is towards performing A/D conversion in the subscriber's terminal, and this arrangement has already been accepted as a standard solution for PBXs. The A/D function resides in the subscriber terminal in modern wireless telephony, too.

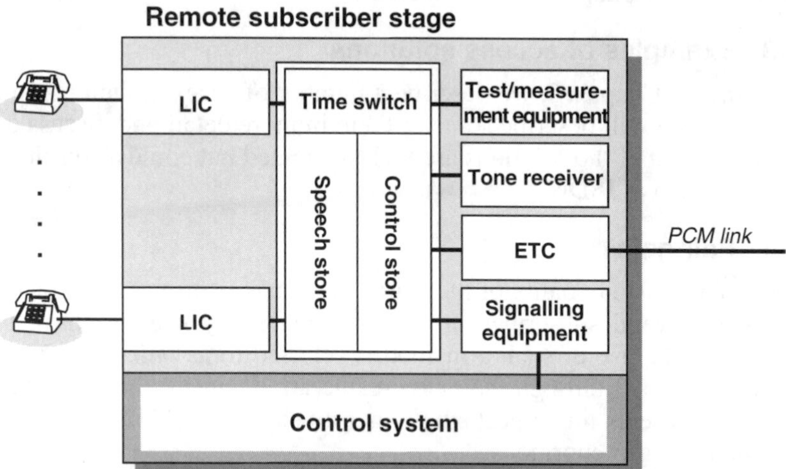

Figure B.5.3 Remote subscriber stage – basic design and connection

The A/D point in the network must have electronic equipment for multiplexing and/or concentration of the digital signals. This requires a suitable environment and a function for supervising the A/D point. The environment is ordinarily implemented as a cabinet or container system that includes equipment for power supply and cooling.

5.3.2 Full-service networks

Digitisation has resulted in a tendency to use different media in the access network much more effectively than originally planned. The following are examples of this tendency.

- Copper pairs can be used at very high frequencies over moderate distances.
- Coaxial cable for cable TV can also be used for interactive services, such as video-on-demand, Internet access and telephony.

- "Fibre to the home" (FTTH) offers an "unlimited" number of new facilities.
- The use of radio access is being extended, enabling 2 Mbit/s connections.

In a full-service network of this type, the PSTN will be just one of many bearer services between subscribers and switching nodes.

Another type of integration between the PSTN and other networks takes place near the switching nodes, where optical SDH rings are introduced. (See Volume 1, Chapter 5, Section 5.12.)

5.3.3 Examples of access solutions

In Volume 1, Chapter 5, we describe a number of access solutions. In this subsection, we will describe some of them in more detail and discuss other solutions. Most of the solutions are PSTN-oriented but could also suit other networks, such as ISDN.

5.3.4 Pair gain

As the transmission quality of the paired cable has improved, new methods that allow several subscribers to share a single physical line have been developed. The use of such a method is referred to as *pair gain,* because capacity is gained through the paired-cable arrangement. Since the access network represents the largest single investment in the PSTN, its potential for economising is enormous.

Today's technology allows at least 12 subscribers to share a single line. The distance from the exchange to a subscriber can be 5–25 kilometres, depending on the type of traffic generated. Today's pair-gain systems use digital transmission and can serve a mix of subscribers in the PSTN and ISDN. The transmission quality is sufficiently high to allow traffic from fax machines and high-speed modems. Since the systems are digital, A/D conversion takes place near or at the subscriber's. Sometimes ADPCM coding is used for the PSTN's analog connections, which gives 32 kbit/s for each subscriber; 64 kbit/s is necessary for fax machines and high-speed modems to achieve full capacity. (See also the description of voice coding in Chapter 2 Subsection 2.4.1.) *Figure B.5.4* illustrates an access network based on pair-gain technique.

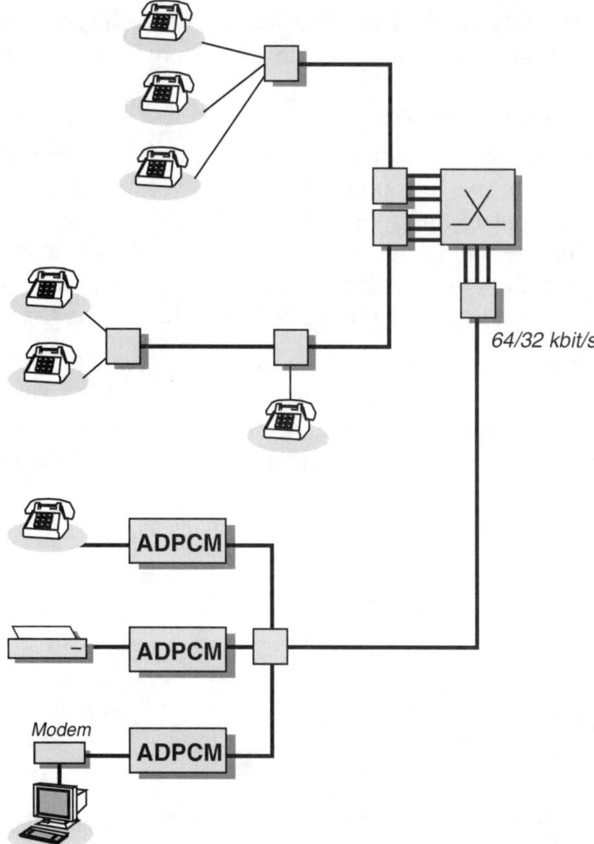

Figure B.5.4 Example of an access network based on a pair-gain system

A line code (2B1Q, for example) is used for the digital transmission. The line can still be used for functions such as power supply to subscribers and for sending meter pulses to pay phones.

5.3.5 Radio access in the PSTN

In some cases, radio access in the PSTN is preferable to copper access. This rule always applies to the connection of subscribers in sparsely populated areas and sometimes to the connection of digital equipment, such as subscriber stages or PBXs. Radio access can also be used when implementing wireless telephony in the PSTN. In fact, because it takes less time to install, radio access can be used to quickly expand a network when many subscribers are waiting to get connections.

A newly established operator in the access network often prefers radio access, since he does not know exactly which residents will sign up for his services nor the locations of the geographical access points.

Point-to-multipoint

There are several radio-based solutions for the connection of single subscribers in sparsely populated areas. We begin by describing a solution called point-to-multipoint (PMP). Analog or digital radio equipment for transmission and reception is installed in or near the subscriber's home. The telephone is connected to the radio equipment, and a local power source is used (instead of power being fed from the exchange).

Radio systems of this type are used in large countries with thinly populated regions, such as Canada, Australia and Sweden. The systems are particularly well-suited for installation in developing countries with low telephone density (perhaps only one telephone for every 100 inhabitants).

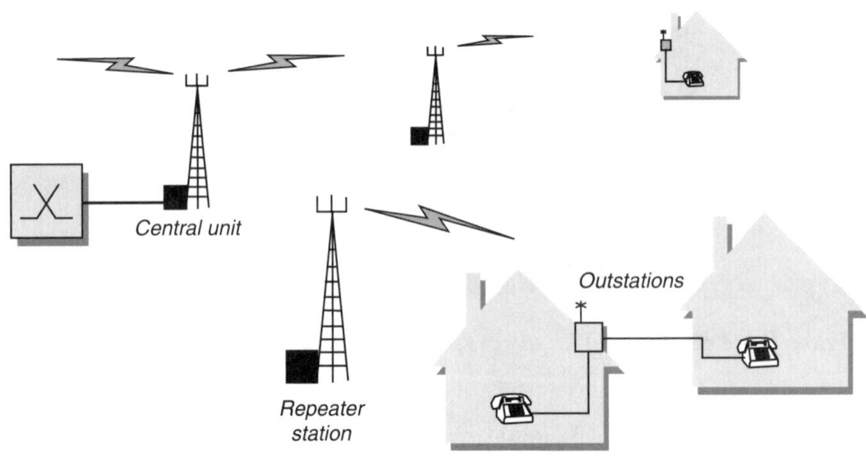

Figure B.5.5 PMP system for sparsely populated areas

A PMP system consists of three parts:

- a central unit;
- an omnidirectional radio transmitter; and
- a number of outstations.

Common frequency ranges are 1.3–2.7 GHz and 10.5 GHz. The use of repeater stations gives a coverage of about 700 kilometres. (A repeater station is an "extra" antenna which receives and forwards signals.) The outstation is continuously polled to check whether any subscribers are ready to send a message; if so, the subscriber is allocated a radio channel. The ratio of subscribers to outstations is usually 6 to 1, and the number of subscribers per outstation may vary from one to roughly 30–40. Today's modern systems can handle digital subscriber lines and set up internal calls. Also, they have built-in operation and maintenance systems.

Satellite systems in the access network

Naturally, satellite systems provide even better area coverage than PMP systems. Satellites are used for access in jungles, archipelagoes, and the like.

Radio in the local loop

An operator can also use radio equipment based on the principles of cellular network traffic (such as NMT or GSM) or wireless telephony (such as DECT) to connect ordinary PSTN subscribers to a local exchange. The radio-in-the-local-loop (RLL) solution provides a replacement for fixed paired copper cable. Access procedures used in cellular systems are dealt with in *Part D – PLMN*, and DECT access is described in Section 5.4.

RLL offers several advantages. The network operator need not build an extensive infrastructure before starting to connect subscribers. And even if radio access implies more expensive subscriber terminals, the inflow of revenues will be speeded up. This is attractive to new operators who have been granted a licence for operation in the fixed telephone network.

If the operator wishes to have wide base-station coverage, cellular systems will be the best choice. Note, however, that a number of factors may favour the use of DECT:

- DECT equipment is cheaper.
- Network planning is simpler because no frequency planning is necessary.
- Capacity is readily expanded by adding new base stations and adjusting the cell sizes.
- DECT capacity per channel is greater than in today's digital cellular systems (32 kbit/s).
- All frequencies for cellular networks may already have been allocated.
- The PSTN and ISDN can share a common access network because transmission is digital.

In terms of switching, radio equipment performs the functions of a subscriber multiplexer. Radio equipment has an interface (in which A/D conversion is performed) to the local exchange, but the local exchange takes full responsibility for the subscriber database and the switching and charging functions.

In practice, the subscriber will not be aware of any changes. He has his radio equipment and its antenna in his home, and although power is not supplied from the exchange, he still perceives the arrangement as a normal telephone subscription. However, radio access can also offer subscribers an extra service in the form of some mobility; for instance, within the coverage area of the nearest mast.

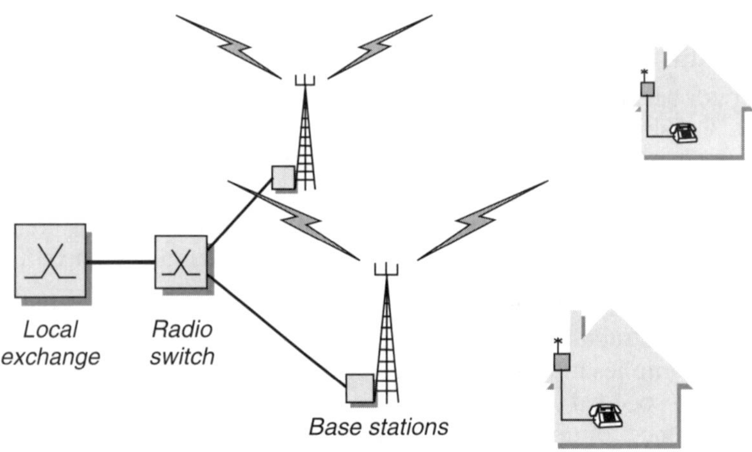

Figure B.5.6 Radio in the local loop

If DECT is used for the air interface, different DECT accesses can also be combined, allowing the subscriber to use the same wireless telephone at work and in the home. This is called cordless terminal mobility and is described in Chapter 2.

Fixed cellular

An operator who is licensed to operate a fixed public telephone network can also opt to configure it using the nodes that we normally find in the PLMN. This means that subscribers are connected to a mobile switching centre (MSC) rather than an "ordinary" local exchange. However, this method – referred to as *fixed cellular* – will not provide the same degree of mobility as a mobile telephone in the PLMN.

From the operator's point of view, the fixed cellular option means being able to commence operations more quickly while facilitating the future construction of a PLMN. If the operator already has a PLMN, he will be able to offer his subscribers the same set of services in both networks. In addition, new services and new equipment introduced in one of the networks can be used in the other network as well.

5.4 DECT

The DECT standard is described in Chapter 2. Here we will study the actual access procedure. DECT has been allocated the 1,880–1,900 MHz frequency range, which in turn is divided into 10 frequencies. Each frequency is in turn divided into 24 time slots according to a method called time-division multiple access (TDMA). Unlike cellular systems, a DECT connection does not occupy two different frequencies. Instead, the first 12 time slots are used for sending information from the base station to the terminal, while the remaining 12 time slots are used in the opposite direction, a method called time-division duplex (TDD). In other words, every frequency can handle 12 calls in duplex mode, which gives a total of 120 channels in the DECT system. All the channels have a bit rate of 32 kbit/s in both directions for subscriber traffic.

Each time slot is divided into fields, as shown in *Figure B.5.7.* The first field is used for synchronisation; the second for identification, control and signalling (control channel); the third for actual traffic (voice or data); the fourth for a checksum for detecting transmission errors. The time slots are separated by short gaps in which no information is transmitted. The purpose of this arrangement is to prevent the time slots from overlapping due to differences in the distance between the base station and the terminals connected.

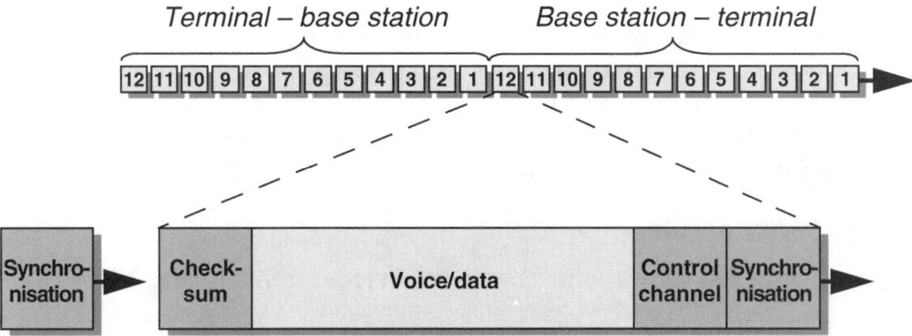

Figure B.5.7 The TDMA/TDD frame for DECT

6 Network intelligence and value-added services

6.1 Introduction

The introduction of computer-controlled telephone exchanges was an incentive for operators to create new, completely different subscriber services in the network. The prime driving force during the 1970s and 1980s was not to meet subscriber requirements but to enable operators (monopolistic telecommunications administrations) to make more money on the existing network. Neither marketing nor the establishment of a company image was high on the agenda in those days.

Today it is much easier for an operator to create a distinctive image for himself and to increase revenue. Some services are charged for, others are free. Many of the free services help to increase the number of successful calls, which in turn generates revenue.

Network operators also sell services to other service providers, who can either charge their customers – the end-users – or offer services free of charge.

The new services have given the PSTN a face-lift. Despite extensive investments in other, more sophisticated technology, the development of services in the PSTN will always have top priority because of the large number of subscribers that are connected to this network.

6.2 Distributed supplementary services

6.2.1 Introduction

Distributed supplementary services are implemented in the local exchanges of the network. This deployment has been chosen mainly because the services are frequently used and because many of them were introduced long before the technology for centralised supplementary services (IN technology) was developed.

6.2.2 PSTN services

The following list shows some common services offered by the PSTN.

- *Do not disturb*
  Calls are connected to a recorded message or tone information.

- *Wake-up/reminder service*
  The subscriber enters on his keypad telephone the hour at which he wants to be called. The telephone exchange calls him at that hour and connects him to a recorded message.
- *Call forwarding*
  This service reroutes incoming calls to another number. The subscriber enters the forwarding number (also called the C-number) on his keypad telephone and is then charged the cost for the additional call path. The caller pays only for the call to the original number. Calls can be forwarded to any number in the PSTN, PLMN and ISDN.
  Call forwarding is available in different variants. "Call forwarding unconditional" means that all incoming calls are to be forwarded. The subscriber can also choose "call forwarding on no reply" or "call forwarding on busy". A recent variant called "selective call forwarding" means accepting calls from one or more predetermined numbers and forwarding all other calls.
- *Callback (completion of call to a busy subscriber)*
  If the called subscriber is busy, the caller can order the callback service, which means that he is queued for connection to the busy number. When the number becomes free, the caller will receive a signal and when he lifts the handset, his telephone will automatically make a new call attempt.
  A variant of this service orders callback if the called subscriber does not answer. In this case, the next time the called subscriber uses his telephone and replaces the handset, the calling subscriber's local exchange will make a new call attempt.
- *Last number redial*
  The last number dialled is stored in the local exchange and can be redialled by means of a simple code.
- *Services for old PBXs*
  A small, simple PBX that has no services of its own can be equipped with special types of call forwarding.
- *Remote control of services*
  A subscriber can use a telephone other than his own to order services such as call forwarding for calls made to his home telephone.
- *Queuing of calls*
  Simultaneous calls – mainly to companies, government authorities and institutions – can be queued.

- *Three-party conference*
  Three parties can communicate with each other over the same connection. If such a conference connection is ordered through a telephonist, more than three parties can participate.
- *Abbreviated dialling*
  Subscribers can enter a list of abbreviated numbers in the local exchange. This service is practical for a company whose PBX has no function for internal abbreviated numbers.
- *Call waiting*
  A special signal is generated during a call in progress to indicate that a third party is trying to reach you. This caller receives an ordinary ringing tone. You can terminate the ongoing call and answer the new one or continue the ongoing call, in which case the new caller will receive a busy tone after several signals. You can also alternate between the two calls.
- *Calling line identification presentation (CLIP)*
  Also called "caller ID", this service allows a called party to see the telephone number of an incoming call on a display connected to the telephone line. The local exchange is kept updated on which subscribers have signed up for this service.
- *Calling line identification restriction (CLIR)*
  This service allows a subscriber to order the system not to display his number. CLIR can be activated on a permanent or temporary basis. Legislation in most countries stipulates that the service must be offered in combination with CLIP.
- *Hot line*
  This service allows the subscriber to be automatically connected to a programmed number merely by lifting the handset. Two variants are available: The number is called directly or after a few seconds. The delay enables the subscriber to call a number other than the programmed one.
- *Malicious-call tracing*
  Subscribers who are subjected to harassment over the phone can order tracing of all incoming calls, which means that the caller is identified. Some old signalling systems may limit the use of this service because they lack functions for transferring the A-number to other exchanges. In that case, clearing can be delayed so as to enable manual tracing.
- *Barring services*
  Certain types of outgoing calls can be barred in different ways, for example, by trunk discrimination. It is also possible to bar specified numbers

(such as premium rate numbers) or to define open numbers and bar the rest. However, as yet no service exists that bars certain types of incoming calls. To effect such call screening, the subscriber has to use the CLIP service or selective call forwarding.

6.2.3 Standardisation

In Europe, ETSI is working on the standardisation of all services in the network. The purpose of this work is to determine which services should be offered and to specify the relevant procedures for access and control. Unfortunately, progress has been slower than expected. Many of the services have been introduced in several countries, but local adaptations abound, and some services have been developed for use in a specific market. This has created problems for the manufacturers of telecommunications systems and – to some extent – even for subscribers.

Service codes

Service codes are used to access and control services via the telephone. ETSI has chosen the code 21 (*21*) for "call forwarding unconditional", to name one example. It has also been agreed that

- * is used at the beginning of a procedure for starting or activating a service;
- # is used at the beginning of a procedure for disconnecting or deactivating a service;
- *# is used at the beginning of a procedure for inquiries about a service;
- * is used as a punctuation mark in a procedure; and
- # is used to end a procedure.

6.3 Centralised supplementary services and value-added services

6.3.1 IN services

The range of supplementary services has expanded considerably as a result of the introduction of IN services in the PSTN. The term "centralised network intelligence" is also used in this context.

IN services are available to all subscribers, including those connected to old exchanges. To be able to choose among different service options, all a subscriber needs is a keypad telephone. Some IN services without options are also available to subscribers with dial telephones.

Freephone (the called subscriber pays for the call) is an example of an IN service used mainly by companies.

Another example is *universal access number*: A multisite company is assigned the same access number for all its branch offices nationwide.

Number portability, which can also be implemented as a distributed service, is becoming increasingly important. Full number portability means that the subscriber can

- change operators;
- move within a geographical area, for example, a city, or region; or
- change from one bearer service to another (for example, from the PSTN to ISDN)

without having to change telephone numbers.

6.3.2 PSTN-specific value-added services

We provide a detailed description of a number of value-added services in the PSTN in Volume 1, Chapter 6, Section 6.3.

6.3.3 Voice and fax mailboxes

The answering machine service is frequently used in the fixed network, whereas it has proved impractical to connect an answering machine with telephones used in the PLMN. For this reason, mobile-network operators have introduced "voice mailboxes". The operator has a large, central answering machine to which subscribers can connect as required. Services such as "call forwarding on no reply" can be used to connect the voice mailbox. Similar systems for storing faxes are also available. Voice mailboxes offer more services than an ordinary answering machine, and the cost is often very low.

The success of this type of service in mobile networks has resulted in PSTN operators also offering it. Combinations with UPT can create flexible services for users who are always on the move. This reduces the need for user equipment in the form of answering machines and telefaxes, because these facilities are provided by the PSTN infrastructure. Moreover, a fax mailbox offers additional advantages. The subscriber can fetch faxes received at any time and have them printed out on the nearest telefax machine. Voice and fax mailboxes can also be combined with different types of retrieval service (such as paging and automatic calling) to inform the subscriber that messages have been received.

The voice mailbox service is increasingly being offered in developing countries. Private persons or families subscribing to this service need not have a telephone subscription of their own but can nevertheless keep in touch with a relative who is working elsewhere, perhaps in a far-away country.

6.3.4 Controlling the services

In the PSTN, the subscriber and the network can communicate in several ways: voice mode, tone signals or pulses. The subscriber uses his own voice and the tone keys (or dial) on his telephone. The network is equipped with announcement equipment to send recorded messages and tone senders for tone signals.

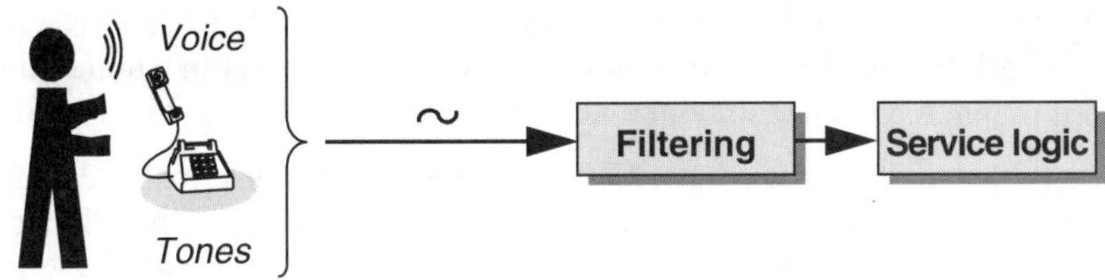

Figure B.6.1 Tones and voice messages control the services

This restricts the user interface for services: Information to the user is given in the form of voice messages. And if a user receives an excess of information, he might not remember all of it. In such a case, the service is not user-friendly.

This problem has been solved through "menus". A menu first prompts a user to press a key to select the service he wants to use, after which he is offered additional options. A limited amount of information in each "branch" makes it easier for the user to remember the alternatives available.

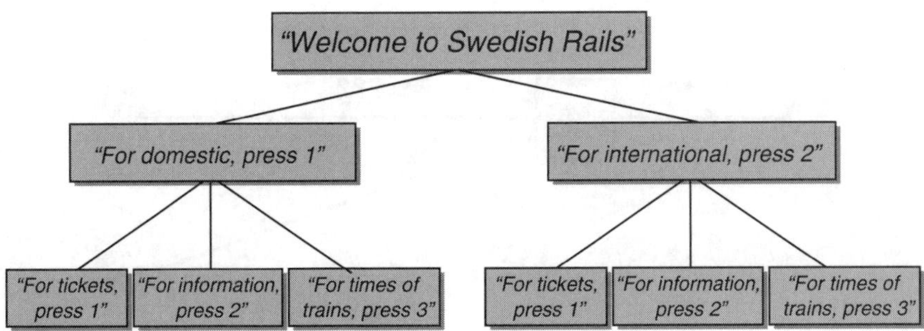

Figure B.6.2 Menu options in a user–service dialogue

Many systems allow users to press their option before the voice message ends. In this way, frequent users of a service do not have to listen to messages they know by heart.

The most modern type of control utilises a function called speech recognition. For example, if you say the word "connect" after the directory inquiry service has given you a subscriber's number, the system will automatically connect you to that number.

6.4 Service interaction

A problem facing today's PSTN operators is that the network was not originally designed for the wide range of services now available. There is a risk that, in certain situations, two or more services will interact in a quite unexpected manner. This phenomenon is referred to as service interaction (SI).

Assume that two services have been activated for a subscriber: "call forwarding on busy" and "call waiting". How is the exchange to handle a call attempt to this subscriber if he is already engaged in a call? Since the two services contradict each other, they cannot be executed at the same time.

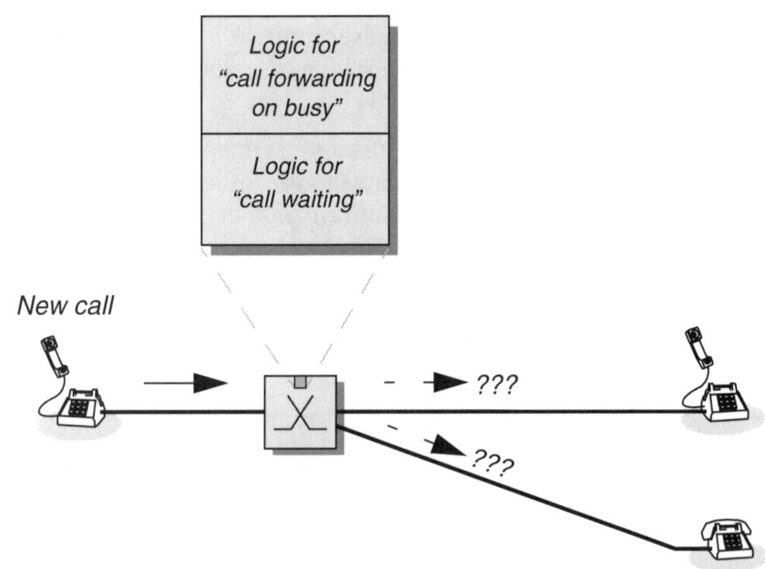

Figure B.6.3 Call forwarding or call waiting?

To avoid this problem, the network operator must decide which of the two services should have priority.

Another example: Call forwarding may create loops in the network and cause it to be totally blocked. Let's assume that A has ordered his calls to be forwarded to B, who lives in another town, and that B has forwarded *his* calls to A. If there were no control functions and no restrictions, a call could be set up back and forth between A and B and seize all lines between the two towns.

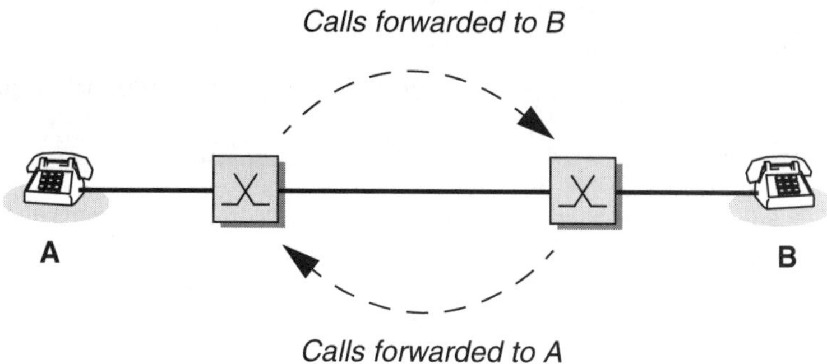

Figure B.6.4 All lines between two towns are seized

As countermeasures against this kind of technical hitch, the operator can install a barring function in the exchange and provide the signalling system with special mechanisms. Both variants are used in today's PSTN.

The number of possible service combinations increases exponentially as more services are added. Therefore, it is difficult to predict whether service interaction between distributed and centralised services is liable to occur. Even if only distributed supplementary services are involved, testing all possible cases is no easy task.

6.5 Operators' telephonist services

6.5.1 Traditional telephonist services in the PSTN

The PSTN has a long tradition of telephonist-handled services. Not so long ago, we could not make an international call without the assistance of a telephonist. Connecting a person-to-person call is still a common service provided by telephonists. Other traditional telephonist services are:

- *Absent-subscriber service*
  The telephonist answers calls to an absent subscriber.
- *Call booking*
  The telephonist connects a call to the desired number at the desired time.
- *Person-to-person call*
  The telephonist ensures that the caller is connected to the person he wants to communicate with.
- *Serial call*
  The subscriber can ask the telephonist to set up several calls.
- *Telephone conference*
  The telephonist can set up a conference connection with up to 30 participants.
- *Directory enquiries service*
  Modernised versions of this service include recorded messages and speech recognition.

6.5.2 New telephonist services

Recently, more and more operators have realised how important telephonist services are in a world of ever-increasing automation. Many callers hang up when they hear an answering-machine message – they want to communicate with a human being. Thus, personal answering services are suitable for small businesses that cannot afford to employ a telephonist.

6.6 Business services

6.6.1 Centrex

Network operators use the centrex service to simulate a PBX by means of software installed in the local exchange. This service was developed in the US but is now used in many other countries. The following features make it attractive to small and medium-sized businesses:

- The customer need not invest in a PBX of his own, nor does he have to bear the cost of operation and maintenance.
- The operator is solely responsible for providing the necessary competence as far as exchange functions are concerned.
- The customer has access to new services without having to upgrade an existing PBX or buy a new one.

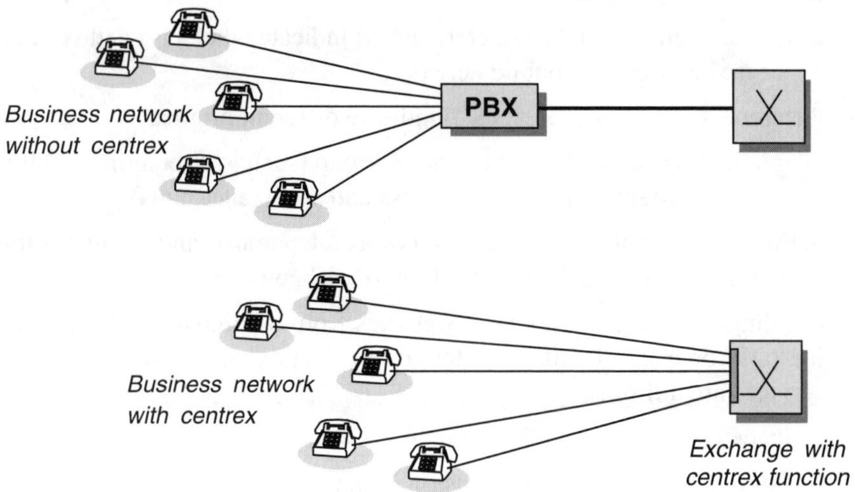

Figure B.6.5 Centrex streamlines business communications

The customer has a separate numbering plan for internal communication. As in an ordinary PBX, a special number (for example, 0) must be dialled for outgoing calls. Centrex groups at different sites can be interconnected, in which case special extension numbers are used for inter-group traffic. Since switching takes place in the ordinary public network, the centrex function translates the extension number into the actual subscriber number.

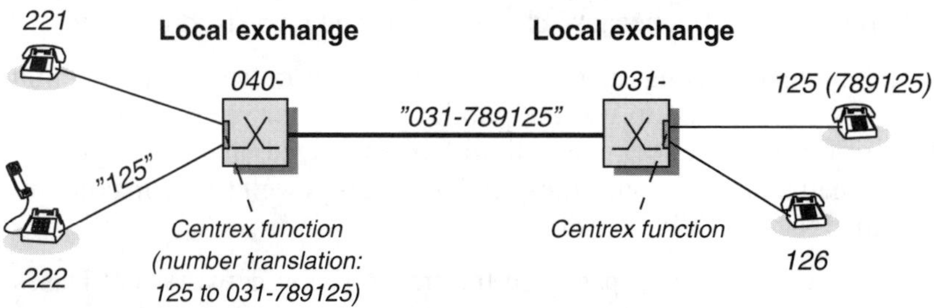

Figure B.6.6 Centrex in two towns

Although centrex cannot match the features of the most advanced PBXs, it offers many of the services provided by ordinary PBXs. Examples include:

- call pick-up, which means that an incoming call to a specific extension can be answered by another extension;
- different ringing-signal characteristics to indicate whether a call is internal or dialled from the public network;
- different "call waiting" signals to indicate different origins;
- telephonist services within the centrex group (such as expediting a call in progress, transferring a call in progress and conference calls);
- defining the telephone that is to serve as telephonist, and changing this definition by commands or according to a schedule;
- enabling the operator to gather statistics from a company (for instance, the ratio of internal calls to external, and the extent to which different services are utilised);
- callback on busy, and callback on no answer; and
- transfer of calls to another extension in the company.

6.6.2 Telephone traffic between business units

Traffic between business units refers to communication between different offices connected to PBXs or to centrex groups. Three basic telephony solutions are available:

- leased lines;
- virtual private networks (VPN); and
- the public network (the PSTN, ISDN).

In peak-traffic situations, the simultaneous use of all three solutions might be the most economical way of communicating, while leased lines are better suited for low traffic, because charging is based on a fixed rate.

For a long time, leasing lines in the PSTN was the only option for a multisite company that needed to use the public network for internal telephone and data traffic. Leased lines are still widely employed, and although they are not defined as an IN service they lend themselves well to use in combination with the IN-based VPN service.

The operator reserves capacity in the transmission network and leases this capacity to customers. A circuit can be run through the exchanges, or the group switch of the exchange can set up a permanent connection between the input channel and the output channel.

Customers are usually offered analog lines and digital $n \cdot 64$ kbit/s and 2 Mbit/s lines. Some operators can offer higher rates from specific parts of the network.

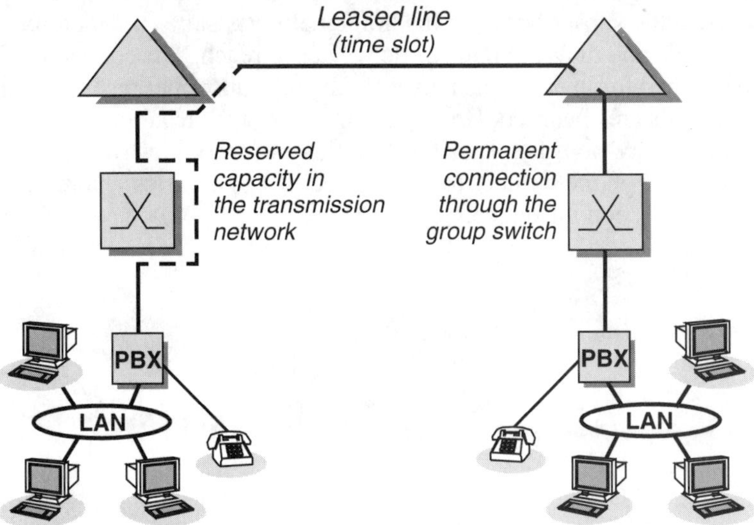

Figure B.6.7 Leased line running through the PSTN of a country

There are arguments for and against leased lines:

- *Advantages*
  Transmission quality is predictable. The price is low provided the customer makes efficient use of the service. Availability is high.
- *Disadvantages*
  Setting up a leased line through the network can take weeks. The price will be high if the service is underutilised. Line capacity is restricted.

6.6.3 Virtual private networks

We describe the VPN service, which is an alternative or a complement to leased lines, in Volume 1, Chapter 6, Subsection 6.2.3. Being based on IN, a VPN is a much more flexible solution that permits more rapid introduction. It can also provide the company and the operator with valuable statistics showing, for example, the extent to which services are utilised.

Whether or not the VPN service is attractive to companies depends on the price, but the risk of congestion may also be a decisive factor.

6.6.4 Make calls abroad – pay when you get home

For a couple of years now, several international telecom operators have been offering services that make it easier to phone from abroad. This applies to charging routines as well as to the troublesome international prefixes. To use this service, the subscriber calls his home network, states his identity and a personal code and dials the number he wishes to reach. The connection is set up and charged for in the home network, and the subscriber receives a bill on which all calls are specified. He will thus be saved the trouble of using coins or having to pay high hotel tariffs. For this purpose, most operators have assigned a Freephone number to the service in all countries where that type of number has been introduced.

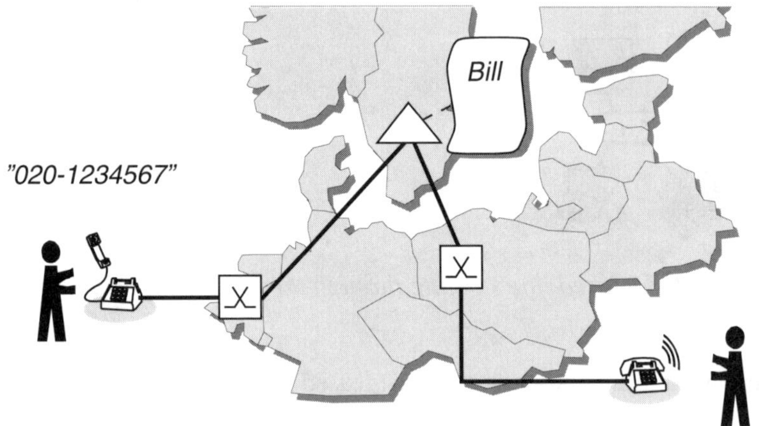

Figure B.6.8 Calls made abroad are charged on the telephone bill at home

As an alternative, a user can call a telephonist in the home country and ask for help setting up a connection. This will work in the same way as the service we have just described – only with that little extra human touch.

6.6.5 Remote access to PBX networks

Large companies with extensive private networks can use a variant of the service described in the previous subsection. An employee calls the company's private network from outside and identifies himself by dialling a code. After the code has been received and verified, the user receives a new dial tone and can make calls within the company's network as if he were directly connected to it. Both international abbreviated numbers and the company's leased lines can be used.

This service is vulnerable from the point of view of security. If numbers and codes get into the wrong hands, they can be used for unauthorised long-distance calls, resulting in congestion of traffic as the company's lines are seized.

6.6.6 Mobility implemented in PBXs

A database that keeps a constant check on every employee's whereabouts can be used to route calls to the right address, regardless of whether an employee is in his summer cottage, at the wheel or in the office. This can be seen as a variant of UPT except that the company's PBX serves as the base. Consequently, companies without a PBX cannot access the service but will use UPT in the PSTN.

6.6.7 Wide area paging

The wide area paging (WAP) service is becoming increasingly popular. It is described in detail in Volume 1, Chapter 6.

WAP is a network in its own right but many users sign up for a combined WAP and PSTN subscription. This means that they can use one of the "call forwarding" variants to have their calls connected to the paging receiver.

7 Signalling

7.1 Introduction

Interacting network elements communicate by means of signalling. Many generations of terminals (especially telephones) and telephone exchanges, with varying intelligence and communication capability, have been designed over the years. (See our description of the situation in the 1960s in Chapter 1, Section 1.2.)

To all these generations of technology must be added the diversity in the area of standardisation, with a large number of local variants. Clearly, therefore, we cannot present even a fraction of the "history of signalling" in this chapter. What we *can* do, on the other hand, is declare that the current trend is towards international harmonisation.

Three key factors have been driving this development: first, network operators want to be able to choose among several suppliers; second, there is a need for short "time to market"; and third, different network operators need to cooperate in different roles.

On the whole, signalling has developed into pure data communication between the processors of the interacting network elements. (Humans are still trusted to serve as processors for ordinary telephones.)

To make it easier to understand the importance of signalling, and its main principles, we will first describe signalling between a subscriber and his local exchange and then go on to describe signalling between exchanges.

The third case – signalling between exchanges and network intelligence nodes – is dealt with in Volume 1, Chapter 7, Section 7.8. The associated signalling between subscribers and the local exchange is described in the following.

7.2 Subscriber signalling

7.2.1 Signalling to and from the subscriber

To start a telephone call, the A-subscriber lifts the handset. As a result, the hook switch of the telephone closes the circuit, thus enabling the local exchange to detect the call attempt as a direct current on the subscriber line.

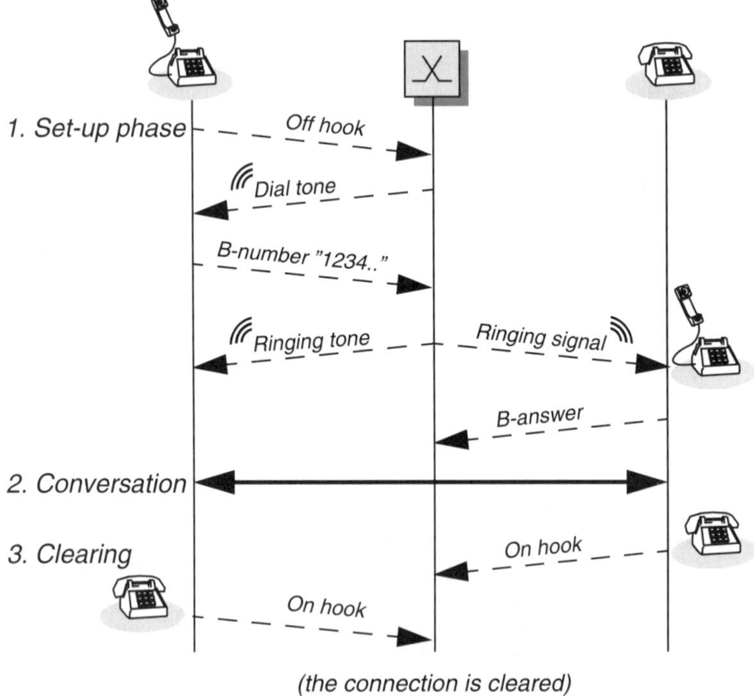

Figure B.7.1 Subscriber signalling for a telephone call

After making certain checks and preparations, the local exchange acts on the call by sending a dial tone to the A-subscriber, who can now continue the set-up procedure by dialling the B-subscriber's number.

If a keypad telephone is used, the B-subscriber's number is transferred in the form of DTMF tones generated by the caller's telephone. The DTMF receiver of the local exchange translates the received signals into internal signals that are forwarded to the control system.

After a connection has been set up to the B-subscriber's exchange, this exchange sends a ringing tone to the A-subscriber and a ringing signal to the B-subscriber (provided, of course, that the B-subscriber's telephone is free). If B answers, the two parties can start communicating. To avoid seizing more equipment than necessary, other information tones – busy, congestion and interception – are sent to the A-subscriber from his own exchange.

The signalling equipment also has a tone sender that sends DTMF signals to the subscribers; for example, if the B-subscriber uses the CLIP service.

In other words, the subscriber connection carries hook-state information, DTMF signals, information tones, ringing signals and the actual traffic (voice, fax or data).

7.2.2 Signalling for calling line identification presentation

A special display is connected to subscriber lines that use the CLIP service. The A-subscriber's number is sent from the local exchange before the ringing signal. The signalling protocol for number transfer is usually a combination of DTMF and pole reversal. Before the first ringing signal is sent, the B-subscriber's CLIP function is activated by the local exchange reversing the polarity for the DC feed on the subscriber line. Then the A-number is sent in the form of DTMF signals to the B-subscriber's display, where it is displayed and stored in memory. Only then is the ringing signal sent to the B-subscriber.

Phase-shift signalling is another method used for CLIP. As yet, no common standard has been defined for signalling to terminals that use this service.

7.2.3 Meter-pulse signalling

The local exchange sends meter pulses to call meters installed at the subscriber and to pay phones. Let's study the call meter as an example.

The exchange has separate equipment for pulse sending. Every unit charged marking recorded by the exchange results in the generation of an outgoing pulse. The subscriber lines represent one of the conductors, while the other is earth. The subscriber terminal has similar equipment for receiving the pulses, which – after rectification – activate a counter. The older 50 Hz pulse rate is usually replaced by the method illustrated in *Figure B.7.2*, which is based on sending 12 kHz or 16 kHz pulses, that is, above the voice band. (No common standard is available.)

The same principle (using the same frequencies) applies to signalling between an exchange and a pay phone.

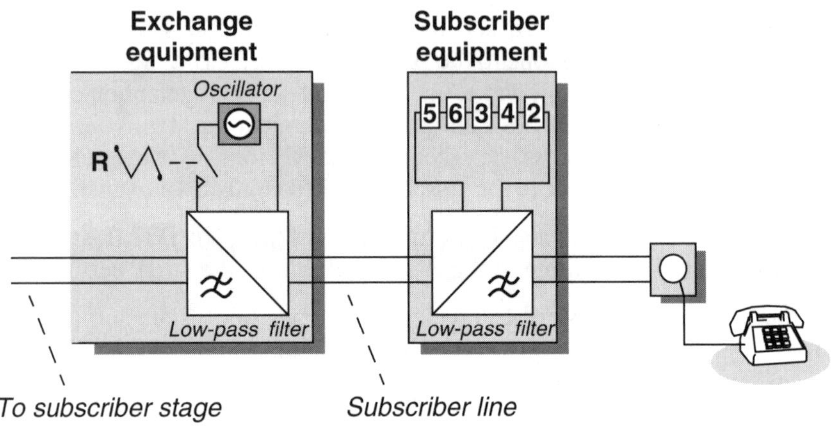

Figure B.7.2 Basic meter-pulse transfer

7.2.4 Signalling between a multiplexer and the local exchange

A 2 Mbit/s link (ITU-T Recommendation G.703) is used for transmission between the subscriber multiplexer and the local exchange. A special signalling time slot (usually time slot No. 16) and the voice time slot of each subscriber are used for subscriber signalling.

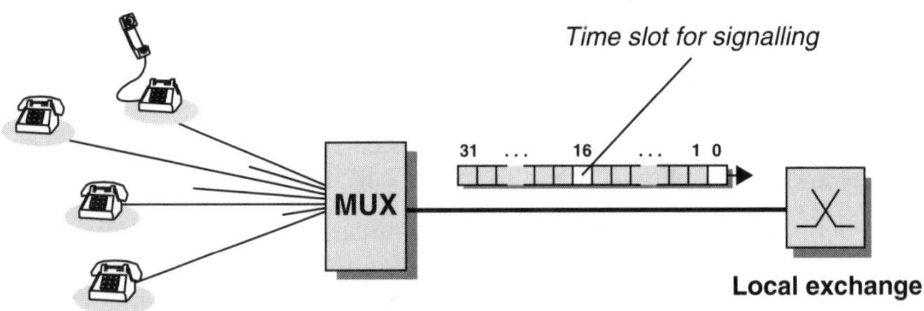

Figure B.7.3 Signalling between multiplexer and local exchange

In the direction of the local exchange, the signalling time slot is used to inform the local exchange about the hook state (off hook or on hook) of the connected subscribers. It is also used for transfer of the B-number if the subscriber has a dial telephone. In this case, the digits are sent on the analog subscriber line in the form of pulses (timed breaks in the DC feed). In the subscriber multiplexer, every digit is translated into a binary code which is transferred in the signalling time slot.

For pay phones (coin-operated or card-operated), the signalling time slot is also used for sending charging information.

In the direction of the subscriber, the signalling time slot is used for ordering the subscriber multiplexer to generate and send a ringing signal to the called subscriber or to transfer pulses for private call meters.

In many cases, the signalling time slot has also been used for the transfer of internal operation and maintenance information between the multiplexer and the local exchange. No international standards exist for this type of information, making it difficult for operators to buy equipment from different suppliers. The new ETSI V5.1 standard for the interface between the subscriber multiplexer and the subscriber stage also covers signalling and does not allow any operation and maintenance information in the signalling time slot. V5.1 (which corresponds to the US standard TR008) is described in Chapter 2.

The voice time slot is used for transferring address information (the B-number or supplementary services) directly to the local exchange if the subscriber has a keypad telephone with DTMF signalling.

In other words, the address information is detected by the local exchange. Information tones (dial tone, busy tone and the like) are also generated in the local exchange and sent in the voice time slot.

A subscriber multiplexer can also be adapted to be able to connect analog PBXs. Subsection 7.3.4 deals with PBX signalling.

7.2.5 Signalling between an RSS and a local exchange

Signalling between a remote subscriber stage and a local exchange can be compared to internal signalling between a subscriber stage in the local exchange and the processor system of that exchange. Thus, internal signalling (software signalling) is used for all communication related to events that occur or measures that are taken in the subscriber stage.

Signalling between a remote subscriber stage and a local exchange can be based on different signalling concepts. SS7 is a typical example. A time slot in a 2 Mbit/s connection is reserved for this signalling. Even the address information (the B-number) is transferred in the time slot for signalling – not in the time slot for the voice connection, as in signalling from a multiplexer.

ETSI standard V5.2 for the interface between a remote subscriber stage and the connection to the local exchange includes signalling. As with V5.1, no operation and maintenance information is allowed in the interface. V5.2 (which corresponds to the US standard TR303) is described in Chapter 2.

7.2.6 Subscriber signalling for supplementary services

Supplementary services, such as abbreviated dialling, call forwarding and callback, are available to subscribers connected to digital local exchanges. The subscriber usually activates these services by lifting the handset and then pressing a "star-digits-hash" combination. Also, the register button (R) is used, for example, when alternating between calls and for three-party calls. The system usually confirms the execution of a service by sending a tone or a recorded message.

This means that a supplementary service is activated by direct DTMF signalling between the subscriber and the local exchange.

Pressing the register button results in a short break. The equipment of the line interface circuit that senses the hook state also receives this signal.

7.2.7 Subscriber signalling for value-added services

The telephone is an extremely efficient tool for a subscriber who wishes to send a message to a computer (calling in sick, for example) or make a financial transaction.

The PSTN treats such services as any other telephone connection: It sets up the connection after the subscriber has dialled the number of the service. When the call is answered (by announcement equipment connected to the computer handling the service), direct contact with the computer is established. The announcement equipment prompts the subscriber to state, for example, a personal identity number and other information. The keypad telephone's DTMF signalling is the tool used for transferring information from the subscriber directly to the computer over the established connection.

Another typical example of a value-added service is telebanking, which allows us to make bank transactions by means of a keypad telephone.

When we have established contact with the bank by dialling a predetermined number, announcement equipment tells us what transactions are available and which buttons to press for accessing them. Then we make our transactions by using the keypad of the telephone. We communicate directly with the bank's computer by exchanging DTMF signals over the established telephone connection.

Services of this type are usually classified as value-added services because they are not provided by the PSTN and do not fall under the heading of voice transmission. They are rather a form of telephone-operated, simple data communication.

7.2.8 Subscriber signalling for IN services

As far as subscriber signalling is concerned, access to IN services is regarded as regular call set-up operations. A keypad telephone with DTMF signalling is used. Also, voice recognition is being developed and should grow. (See also Chapter 6, Subsection 6.3.2.)

7.2.9 Subscriber signalling for telefax

To fax a document we dial the B-subscriber's number in the usual manner. The number is temporarily stored in the memory of the fax machine and shown on a display. If the number is correct, we press the SEND button to transfer the number by DTMF signalling to the local exchange. The set-up procedure along the path to the B-subscriber's line is exactly the same as for an ordinary telephone call.

.When the called fax machine answers, the two machines exchange a number of parameters (resolution and so forth) and then determine the transfer rate. This procedure, called "handshaking", is performed by the modems of the two fax machines.

A fax machine of the Group 3 type can have a built-in modem based on the V.29 standard and – to be able to cope with poor transmission quality – a modem based on V.27*ter* with automatic bit-rate adaptation. With this equipment, the transfer rate will be up to 9600 bit/s; poor transmission quality can reduce that figure to 4800 or 2400 bit/s. High-speed Group 3 fax machines are also available. During the handshaking phase, the quality of the connection is checked, and the highest possible transfer rate is selected. Such a fax machine also has a modem of the V.21 type (300 bit/s) for use during the initial handshaking phase.

If the B-subscriber's fax is engaged, a busy tone is sent to the A-subscriber's fax. Most machines are equipped with a function that redials the number at regular intervals until contact is established.

One page is transmitted at a time, with the receiving machine acknowledging each page. Transmission can be interrupted by serious transmission errors; for example, if the receiving machine fails to acknowledge a page.

The transmission is terminated by the receiving machine when it acknowledges receipt of the last page. Both subscribers' faxes are then disconnected, and the connection is cleared as for a normal telephone conversation.

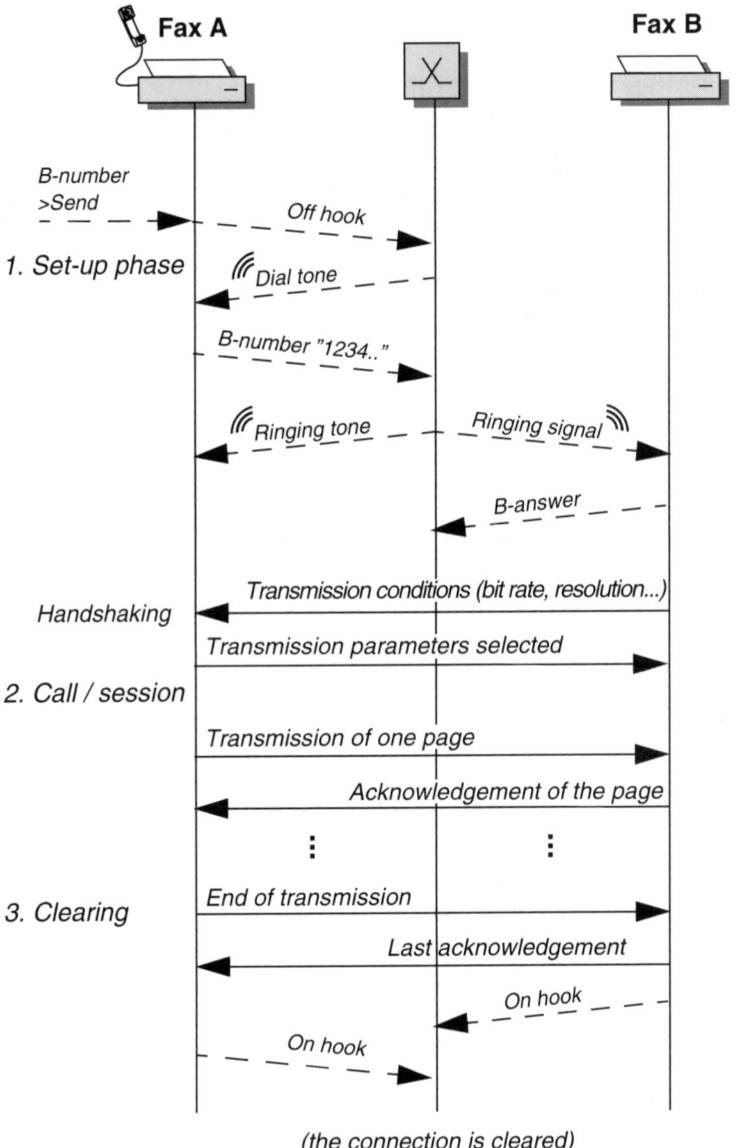

Figure B.7.4 Subscriber signalling for a fax connection

7.3 Interexchange signalling in the PSTN

If more than one local exchange is involved in setting up a connection or in activating a supplementary service, these exchanges must interchange information.

Several hundred systems for interexchange signalling are available. Most of them were developed for national use only, whereas a few have been accepted and defined by the ITU-T or ANSI as standardised signalling systems.

Channel-associated signalling

Most of the systems for interexchange signalling are based on the principle of CAS. (See Volume 1, Chapter 7.) Signalling systems No. 5, R1 and R2 are examples of CAS.

CAS is divided into line signalling and register signalling. This division is also reflected by separate signalling functions in the exchange.

Line signalling handles the exchange of information showing the line state of the trunks between two exchanges, such as seizure, answer, clear forward and clear back. This routine information is used in the same way for all connections.

Register signalling handles the exchange of routing information (B-number, A-category, B-status, and the like) and is thus unique to each call.

Common-channel signalling

The most modern form of interexchange signalling on circuit-switched connections is common-channel signalling (CCS). SS7, which belongs to this category, is predominant in modern digital networks. (See Volume 1, Chapter 7.)

CCS requires a separate signalling network; that is, the signals have a bearer service of their own. Because the signalling network executes this bearer service, it can be accessed by users other than the PSTN. Other typical users are the ISDN and PLMN. The network is described in *Part E – The signalling network.*

Information interchange

All signalling systems, regardless of type, transmit three main categories of information between exchanges:

- information for set-up, supervision and clearing;
- service-related information (such as call forwarding and callback, as well as charging); and

- information showing change in status (such as congestion in the switching equipment of neighbouring exchanges or in the transmission network).

7.3.1 Exchange equipment

There are three main types of interexchange signalling:

- analog connections (trunk circuits) using CAS;
- digital connections using CAS; and
- digital connections using CCS.

CAS is mostly used for connecting analog exchanges still in the network.

Analog trunk circuits

In old-type networks, a trunk circuit could be seized from one direction only (one-way seizure). With the introduction of better signalling methods, the trunk circuits could be treated as two-way circuits allowing seizure from both directions. In *Figure B.7.5,* exchange A and exchange B are interconnected by three trunk circuits. Trunk circuit 1 is intended for seizure from A to B, trunk circuit 2 for seizure from B to A, and trunk circuit 3 can be seized in either direction.

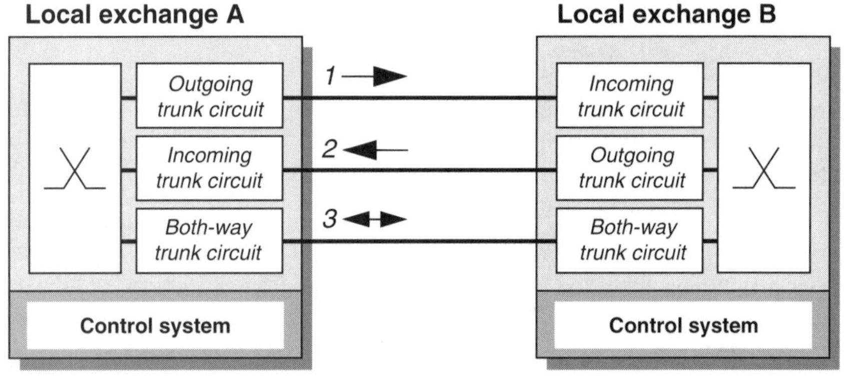

Figure B.7.5 Seizure of analog trunk circuits

The signalling equipment in the exchanges is referred to as outgoing trunk circuit, incoming trunk circuit and both-way trunk circuit, as shown in *Figure B.7.5.*

Digital connections

We will now add two digital paths between the exchanges in *Figure B.7.6.*

- The first one is a 32-channel PCM system with CAS. Time slot 16 is used for the line signalling of the 30 voice channels. Code senders and code receivers are connected to send and receive register signals.
- The second one, too, is a 32-channel PCM system but with CCS. The signalling need not use the same path as the traffic but, in this case, a dedicated time slot on the same PCM link is used. This signalling is handled by a signalling terminal in each exchange which is always connected to the dedicated time slot.
- The PCM systems are connected by means of a printed board assembly called exchange terminal circuit (ETC).

Figure B.7.6 shows a line unit with all these components for signalling on analog as well as digital circuits.

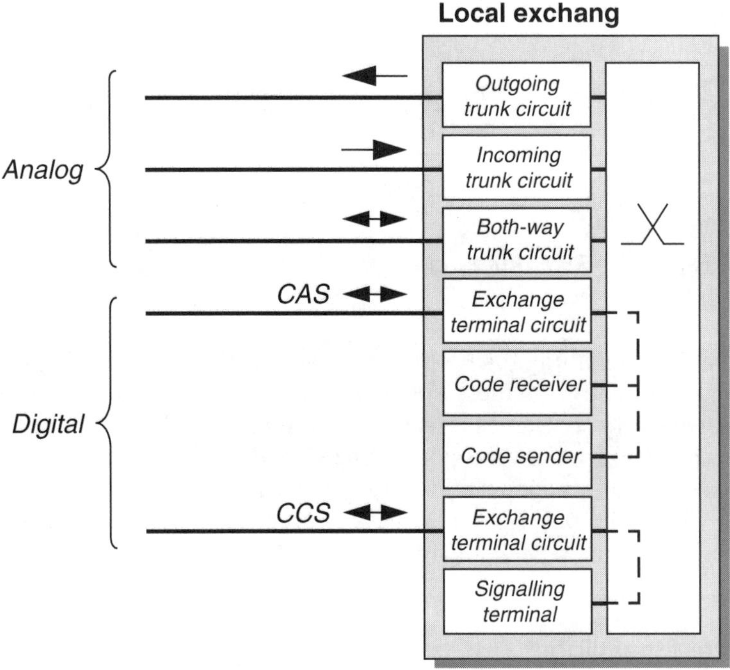

Figure B.7.6 Line unit with different types of termination

7.3.2 Channel-associated signalling

Line signalling

Traffic in time slots 1–15 and 17–31 in a 2 Mbit/s PCM circuit uses time slot 16 for line signalling.

Two voice time slots at a time can send line signals in time slot 16. The use of time slot 16 is shared by the traffic time slots in a 16-frame continuous sequence (one multiframe). In the first frame, time slot 16 is used to indicate the beginning of a new multiframe (multiframe alignment). Thus, 15 frames will be needed to allow all voice time slots to send line signals.

Consequently, every voice channel has 2 kbit/s for the transmission of signalling information. (Each time slot corresponds to 64 kbit/s. One time slot in every 16 frames gives 64/16 = 4 kbit/s. Two channels at a time share the signalling space of a time slot, which gives 4 kbit/s / 2 = 2 kbit/s for each channel.)

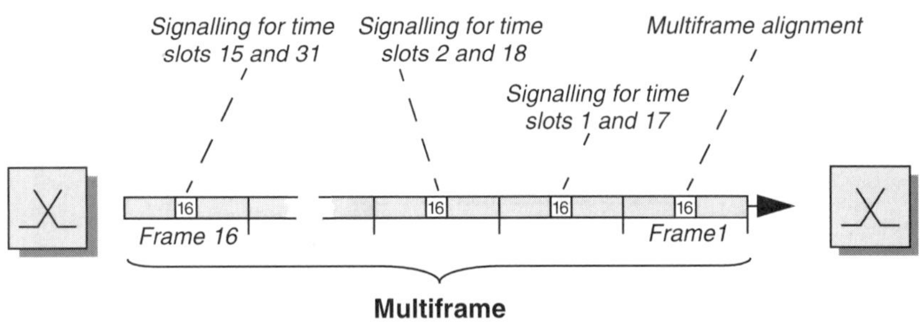

Figure B.7.7 Line signalling in time slot 16

Note that line signalling for 1.5 Mbit/s PCM circuits (24-channel systems) is designed differently. On these circuits, the least significant bit of each voice time slot of every six frames is used for line signalling. In other words, these systems have no special time slot for line signalling. The transfer rate in digital transmission is reduced to 56 kbit/s, since only seven of the eight bits are reliable (7/8 • 64 = 56). However, the least significant bit in every six frames has no effect on the perceived voice quality in a normal telephone conversation.

Register signalling

Register signals can be transmitted in different ways, but the most common method is based on multi-frequency signalling, in which two out of, say, six frequencies are combined to form 15 different signals representing digits or categories.

The exchange equipment for this system is code senders and code receivers. The concept, which was originally intended for analog exchanges and networks, has been developed into a digital version for use in networks with digital exchanges and digital transmission. The register signals are sent and received by the code senders and code receivers in the time slots reserved for each call.

The code senders and code receivers constitute a common resource in an exchange, which means that they are connected in a given voice time slot only during the register-signalling phase. This corresponds to an average holding time of two to four seconds per connection. The holding time will depend on three factors: how fast the subscriber dials the number, the number of digits being dialled and whether the equipment is used as a code sender or code receiver.

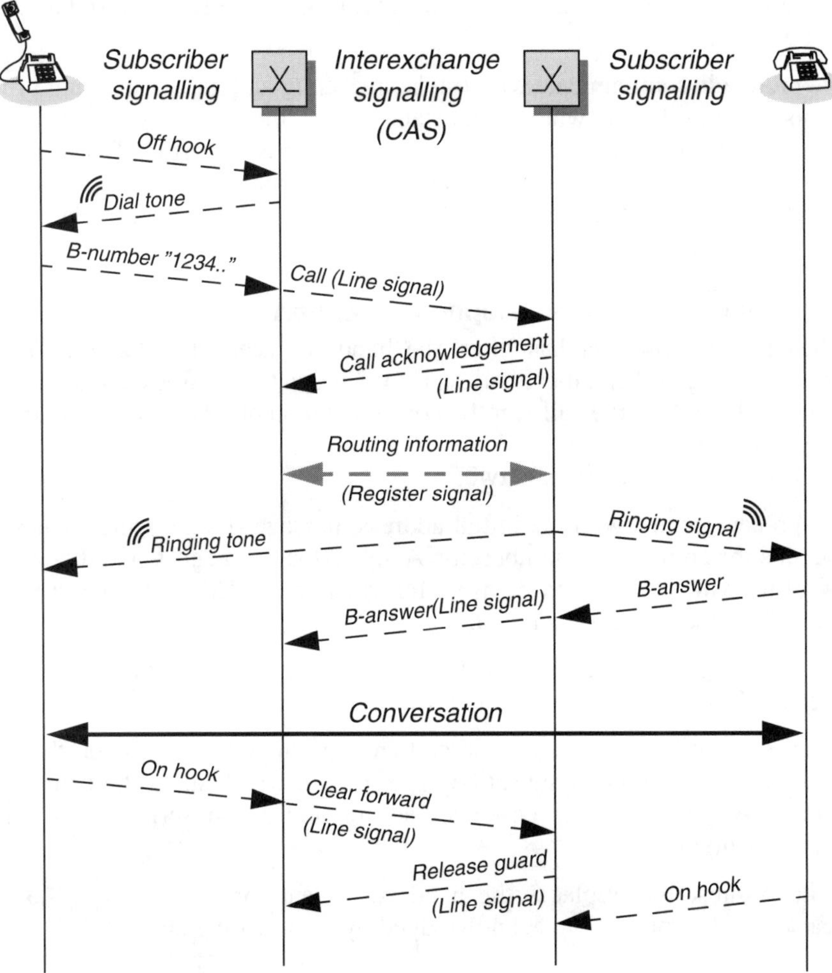

Figure B.7.8 CAS for a trunk call

A common register signalling system is MFC R2, a standard defined by the ITU-T. Multi-frequency compelled (MFC) signalling involves the sender requesting an acknowledgement from the receiver before it stops sending one pair of tones and starts sending the next pair. The receiver sends its acknowledgement after it has received the pair of tones for 200 ms. This means that the method allows a maximum of five digits to be sent per second.

7.3.3 Common-channel signalling with SS7

In SS7, the protocol called TUP (corresponding to layers 4-7 in the OSI model) contains all the signals required to handle telephone connections in the national network. Today, these connections in the PSTN can also be handled by ISUP.

The protocols communicate with traffic-analysing and traffic-handling programs in the exchange, which initiate and receive the necessary signals. The protocols also communicate with the message transfer part (MTP) in SS7. MTP carries the signalling packets and is responsible for error-free transfer of signal messages between two exchanges. MTP is described in *Part E – The signalling network*.

Call set-up based on the telephony user part

When the A-subscriber has lifted the handset, received a dial tone and started dialling, a B-number analysis is initiated in the local exchange. If the analysis shows that the call is to be connected to another exchange, an outgoing trunk circuit is selected. *Figure B.7.9* illustrates the procedure, assuming SS7 is used in the trunk network.

The process begins with the initial address message (IAM), which usually contains the complete B-number, the A-subscriber's category and the identity of the voice channel to be used. Information needed for the control of echo suppressors is also included.

The receiving exchange responds by sending an address complete message, when the B-subscriber has been identified and can receive the incoming call.

If the B-subscriber has a free line and answers the call, an answer charge message is sent to the A-subscriber's exchange, which starts the charging process. A connection has now been set up, and the subscribers can start communicating.

If the A-subscriber replaces the handset, a clear forward signal initiates clearing of the connection, acknowledged by the release guard signal.

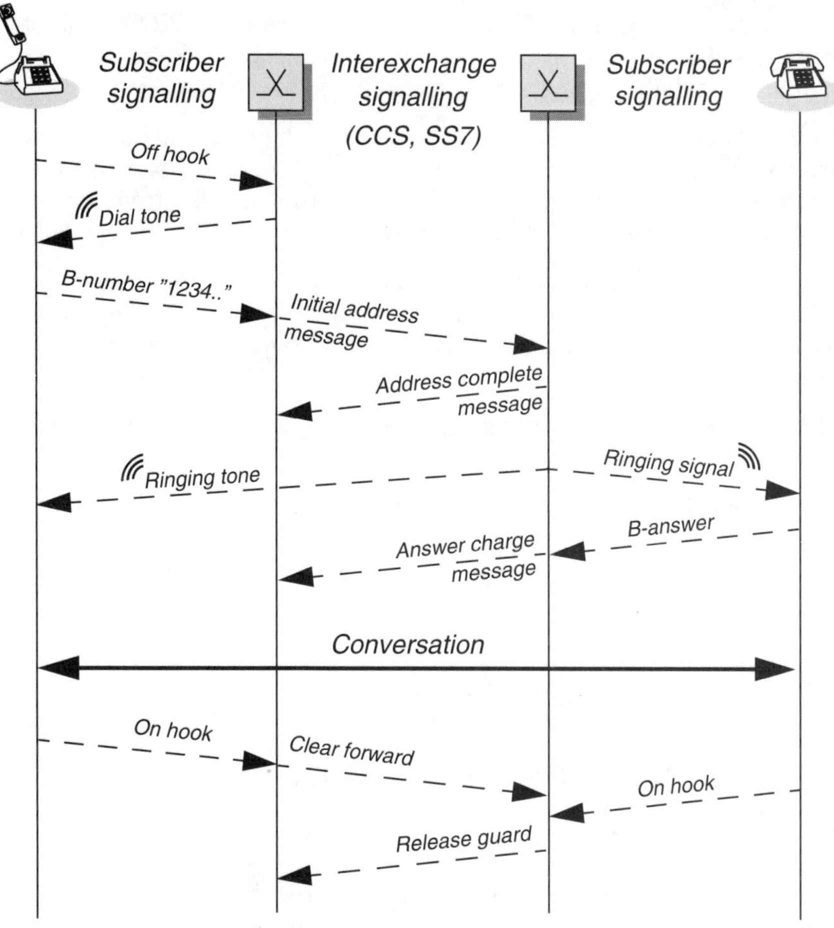

Figure B.7.9 SS7 signalling for a trunk call between two exchanges (TUP)

If the B-subscriber replaces the handset first, a line signal – clear back – is sent backwards through the network. This signal starts time supervision in the charging exchange (usually A's local exchange). The supervisory period is normally 90 seconds, allowing the B-subscriber to change telephones or connect the current one to another jack. When the supervisory period expires, the connection is cleared. If the A-subscriber also replaces his handset within 90 seconds, the connection is cleared immediately.

7.3.4 Signalling between a PBX and a local exchange

Many different signalling systems are used between PBXs and local exchanges. This is because a PBX can be either analog or digital and provide anything from basic to very sophisticated functions and services.

A PBX is connected to a public local exchange by outgoing and incoming circuits. Incoming circuits are often required to permit direct dialling-in, which means a subscriber can dial a PBX extension number from the public network and be connected directly without the assistance of a telephonist.

From the functional point of view – and not least with regard to signalling – a PBX can therefore be compared to a small local exchange. Ordinarily, a PBX and its local exchange communicate through some form of inter-exchange signalling.

MFC-R2 is one of the signalling systems employed. For analog PBXs of an older type, DTMF or decadic pulsing can also be used.

Other protocols for signalling between PBXs are digital private network signalling system No. 1 and the Q-point signalling system.

SS7 can serve as a bearer of these signalling protocols through the public network.

8 Network management

8.1 Introduction

A large portion of PSTN equipment (such as transmission equipment, the signalling network and the IN platform) is shared by the PSTN and other networks. The PSTN, too, can make use of the two telecommunications management network (TMN) and simple network management protocol (SNMP) standards for centralised operation and maintenance.

But there are also PSTN-specific entities: the subscriber database, the charging functions and the functions that handle switching within the exchange and through the network. A typical network architecture with centralised operation and maintenance is shown in *Figure B.8.1.* The following abbreviations are used in the figure:

- OSS (*operations support system*);
- OMC (*operation and maintenance centre*); and
- NMC (*network management centre*).

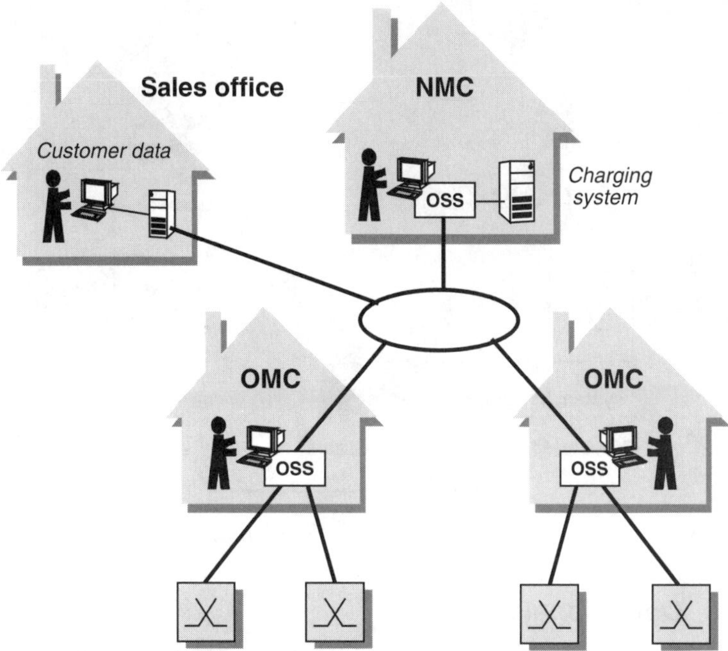

Figure B.8.1 Centralised operation and maintenance in the PSTN

8.2 Operation and maintenance functions

A general description of operation and maintenance (O&M) functions is given in Volume 1, Chapter 8.

PSTN exchanges contain a number of functions aimed at facilitating O&M work. Examples include equipment for line measurement (test access) and equipment for rearranging connections (distribution frames).

The computerised control system of a modern exchange is connected to an input/output (I/O) interface for communication with O&M personnel. Terminals are connected to the I/O system to allow command-initiated execution of O&M functions. All operations that can be performed from these local terminals can also be remotely controlled from special OMCs, which are connected to the I/O system of the exchange via a data network, such as X.25.

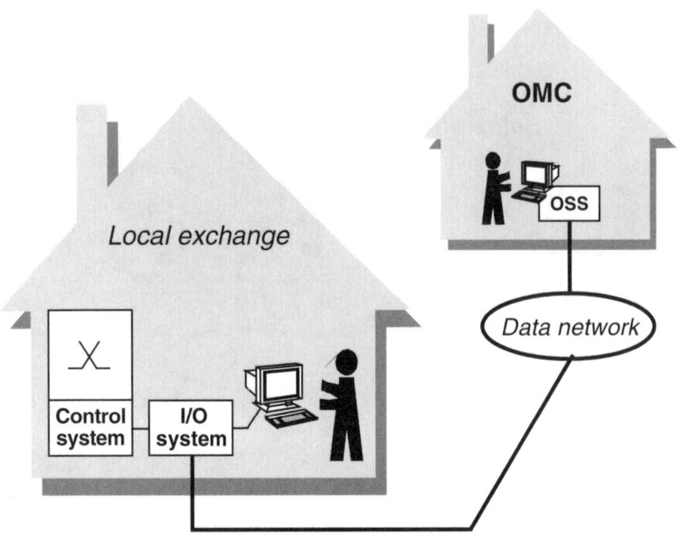

Figure B.8.2 Connecting a terminal for operation and maintenance

8.2.1 Operational functions

Operational functions can be divided into two categories: functions for gathering statistics and administrative functions. Statistical data are required when planning a network. They answer a number of questions, such as:

- From where and to whom do subscribers call?
- What are the holding times for different types of equipment?
- What percentage of the traffic on a given circuit will encounter congestion?
- How many calls are involved in an IN service?
- What IN services are popular?

Administration is a collective term for functions that enable the network operator to add, change or remove data. They also allow an operator to order printouts showing the current state of:

- *the subscriber database* where the operator can add or remove subscribers, change the availability of services, introduce restriction classes and alter subscriber categories;
- *trunk circuits and signalling* where the operator can connect or disconnect PCM links, alter signalling systems and add signalling equipment;

- *group switch and switch control* where the operator can add or remove number series, alter routing alternatives and set up leased lines; and
- *IN services* where the operator can alter existing services and introduce new ones, add new users, alter menus and messages and so forth.

Needless to say, the network operator must be able to make modifications while the network is in service and without interfering with traffic. This is important in the PSTN, because the network is circuit-switched and carries isochronous services that are sensitive to interference.

8.2.2 Maintenance functions

The introduction of SPC exchanges allowed operators to automate many maintenance functions. In most cases, the network operator sets limit values for supervisory functions: an isolated fault that does not disturb traffic need not trigger an alarm, but personnel are alerted if things get worse. Alarms are usually divided into different urgency classes. Programs are provided for troubleshooting, fault diagnosis and, possibly, fault correction. Hardware faults are isolated, and faulty units are taken out of operation.

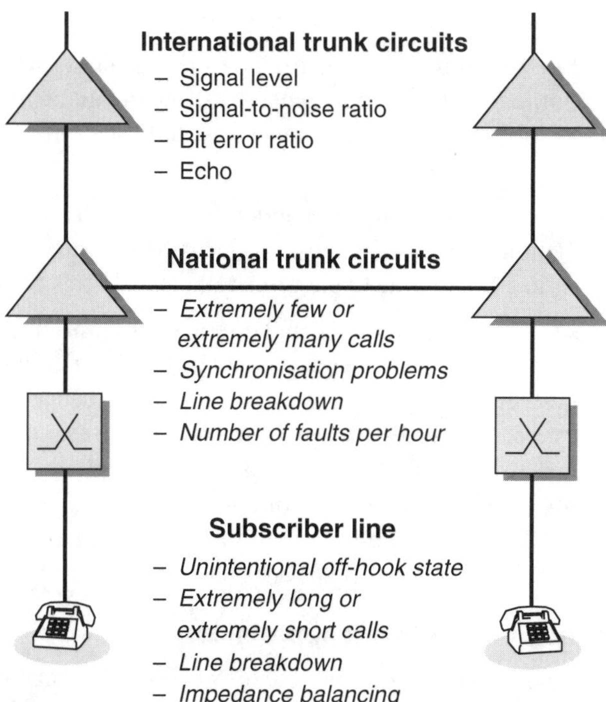

Figure B.8.3 Supervision of subscriber lines and trunk circuits

Vital functions are always backed up by some form of redundancy. For example, the hardware of the group switch can be duplicated. In other cases, such as SS7 signalling, alternative routes can be provided.

Supervision of subscriber lines and trunk circuits are important maintenance functions. Special supervisory equipment is provided for international trunk circuits because they extend long distances, some via submarine cable or satellite link. *Figure B.8.3* illustrates a few supervisory functions.

Test equipment connected to the exchanges is also used in supervision. By assigning such equipment a B-number, maintenance personnel can call it from other parts of the country to test the network's in-service performance and transmission quality.

8.2.3 Control system functions

In certain circumstances, the control system must have access to special O&M functions:

- A fault in the control system must not cause a stoppage in the exchange. This is prevented by the operator providing hardware redundancy, separate control systems for diagnostics in serious situations, backup functions for software and other contingency measures.
- The control system must never get overloaded. Functions that limit the total processor load when it approaches 100% are available. In such a situation, some subscribers may not receive a dial tone when they lift the handset.
- A system for setting priorities is mandatory. When serious faults occur, essential functions must have higher priority than traffic functions. In normal operation, traffic must take priority over statistics collection.
- It must be possible to correct faults and upgrade programs and data during operation. This requirement can be satisfied by hardware redundancy. In a distributed system other processors will take over. In the case of a central-processor system, the processors can be duplicated, so that the two central processors work in parallel. Another solution is an operating system which permits the simultaneous use of two versions of the same program and which has functions for phasing out the old version after the new one has taken over all operational functions.

8.2.4 Functions for network supervision

The state of the home exchange is not the only object of supervision. Traffic originating in the exchange must also be supervised to permit detection and correction of faults in other nodes. Several parameters are measured:

- number of call attempts (seizures) per voice channel and hour;
- the percentage of traffic that meets with congestion, in the home exchange or further along the switching path; and
- the ratio of the number of call attempts to the number of answers.

The operator sets limit values for the parameters used, and the system takes action as soon as a limit value is exceeded (or not reached). A high percentage of congestion or a low percentage of answers indicates the presence of problems in the network (such as a broken PCM link or an overloaded exchange). Alerting the maintenance personnel and waiting for them to alter the routing tables manually in every exchange would take at least a couple of minutes. Instead, the operator programs alternative routing tables from the beginning, thus allowing the exchange to activate them automatically in a few seconds.

Time slot 0 in the PCM frame is used for frame alignment and one other task: to convey information relating to the status of the nodes and other network management data. The time slot is used alternately – that is, in every other frame – for frame alignment and O&M information.

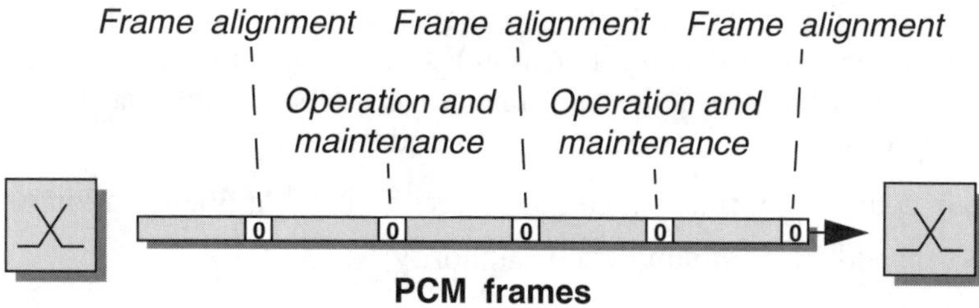

Figure B.8.4 Information in time slot 0

9 Interworking between networks

9.1 Introduction

For a long time, the PSTN was the only telecommunications network. As time went by, other networks were added, mainly because the PSTN's abilities were not adequate to the demands for quality, capacity and functionality.

This has led to a growing need for interworking between networks. Actually, several factors have contributed to making it a key issue:

- The PSTN is optimised for voice connections and supplementary telephony services.
- The new networks that have been developed interact with the PSTN and sometimes even use it as a transport network.
- As a result of recent deregulation, most markets are served by several operators.

9.2 Interworking between operators

Many countries are now in the middle of a process aimed at liberalising their PSTNs. The traditional operators have owned all parts of the existing access network (dominated by paired cable) and the transport network. Some of these monopolies have been split into a network operator and a service provider.

In the US, which has a long history of liberalisation, the powerful AT&T was split up because its monopoly position violated the Unfair Competition Act. Today, several companies operate transport networks in the US, and subscriber service is divided into regions. This situation necessitates the establishment of general rules and standards for physical interfaces and signalling and for handling emergency calls and the like.

In many countries, three official bodies are involved in liberalisation:

- a postal and telecommunications authority;
- an anti-trust agency; and
- a government authority for allocating frequencies.

Another area that requires interworking between networks is interconnection of private and public networks, briefly described in Chapter 5, Trunk and access networks, and in Chapter 7, Signalling. Yet another area concerns the interconnection of networks that apply different standards; for instance, North American and European networks. (See Chapter 5.)

9.2.1 Accounting

Accounting means balancing different operators' revenue and expense flows. The accounting function has long been used in international traffic but is now also required at the national level. Accounts are settled with the help of counters which record the following data for every destination:

- number of calls;
- total duration of calls; and
- total number of charging pulses.

The reading of counters and accounting vis-à-vis other administrations take place at regular, agreed intervals. In Volume 1, Chapter 9, we discuss some of the problems that may arise when entering into such agreements. Accepted standards govern the traditional settlement of accounts between international operators.

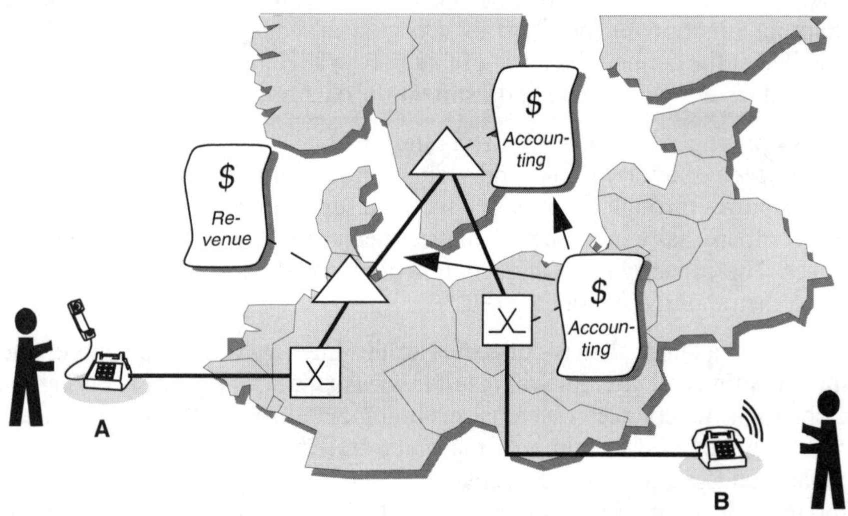

Figure B.9.1 Settlement of accounts in international traffic

9.3 Traffic between bearer networks

9.3.1 Telephony

Voice traffic can be coded in different ways in different networks. Here we will use GSM to exemplify a mobile network with digital access. Voice coding in GSM gives 13 kbit/s (or half that figure), which must be converted into 64 kbit/s to allow switching in the PSTN. The GSM network performs this code conversion.

In ISDN, voice traffic is usually coded in the same way as in the PSTN.

9.3.2 Fax and data traffic

In the handshaking procedure in fax traffic, the sending and receiving terminals agree on a maximum common bit rate. ISDN has larger capacity, and PLMN standards usually have smaller capacity than that provided for fax communication in the PSTN. But it is the task of the terminals – not the network – to make the necessary adjustments.

In data traffic, different types of interconnection can be used. The PSTN subscriber uses a modem that provides a certain capacity on a line that is either dialled up or leased. Then, dedicated PCM links interconnect the PSTN and the data network. If the data network is packet-switched, an adapting function in the form of a packet assembly/disassembly will be installed at the connection point of that network. Hence, as for fax traffic the PSTN does not perform any adjustment for data traffic.

Not surprisingly, Internet access via the PSTN is a remarkable growth area for this type of interworking. Individuals and small businesses can buy their subscriptions through a company that has a server connected to the Internet. The company has a modem pool that connects incoming calls to this Internet server. The capacity of a connection depends on the modem capacity at the subscriber and in the modem pool.

As long as a subscriber is connected to the Internet via his telephone line, any incoming call attempt will result in a busy tone. One way of solving this problem is to connect conversion equipment through the group switch, which applies GSM coding of the voice traffic. A computer with microphone, loudspeaker and the necessary software can then be used as a telephone while the modem is connected to the Internet. The telephone connection is digital and uses only 13 kbit/s of the total modem capacity. This solution is also treated in *Part H – The Internet*.

9.4 Integration with ISDN and the PLMN

From the outset, the ISDN standard was designed to allow this network to be physically based on the PSTN. PLMN standards form the basis of separate networks, but some areas are common to mobile networks and the PSTN. This means that the networks can no longer be regarded as completely monolithic. The following areas support integration of the PSTN, ISDN and PLMN:

- signalling
  signalling system No. 7 (SS7) is used with the common bearer called MTP;

- transport
  the trunk circuits are often multiplexed to form a common system (PDH, SDH/SONET) which carries traffic from different networks on the same physical circuit;
- numbering
  the number series of networks that provide telephony services are coordinated;
- services
  the IN platform can be used to provide subscribers with the same services in all three networks; and
- access
  the DECT standard for wireless telephony can be used in networks that support telephone traffic; a subscriber can have a terminal that functions in different networks by means of the CTM service.

10 Network planning

10.1 Introduction

If the PSTN is to survive in the long term, it must have an adequate base of services. Today, prospects seem rather bright, especially in countries with digitised networks.

- Although "fixed telephony" is facing tough competition from mobile telephony, we must remember that mobility can also be introduced in the PSTN to a certain extent (DECT, UPT, CTM).
- Telephony, as a service, has never been better. Quick set-up and excellent voice quality are properties unmatched by mobile systems.
- Gradually increasing modem rates favour telefax and data transmission, especially Internet access.
- The PSTN can provide many supplementary services; for example, through IN.

However, there is one problem:

- Growth of Internet traffic is a positive factor as long as the volume is small compared with telephony traffic. In the future, though, the situation will be reversed as the PSTN becomes overloaded because of longer holding times. A telephone subscriber uses his terminal during a fraction of a 24-hour period, whereas an Internet surfer's holding time can be 5–10 times longer. Moreover, as we have already mentioned, it is impossible to contact the surfer by phone while he is connected unless special equipment is introduced.

The following description of network planning for the PSTN roughly coincides with the presentation in Volume 1, Chapter 10, except for some points that are specific to the PSTN:

- digitising;
- network architecture;
- fundamental technical plans; and
- dimensioning.

In the following we will also discuss some issues that the PSTN has in common with other networks, such as N-ISDN:

- location of supplementary services;
- new operators' network architecture;
- network equipment; and
- operational functions.

10.2 Network architecture

10.2.1 Digitisation

Only a few countries in the world have fully digitised telephone networks, but development is accelerating because of the ever-increasing cost of maintaining analog circuits and exchanges. Another factor that speeds up the digitisation process is the growing proportion of Internet traffic in the PSTN.

10.2.2 Exchange hierarchy

In addition to setting up calls between its own subscribers, the local exchange establishes long-distance connections upwards through the exchange hierarchy. Normally, the local exchange also handles the charging of calls. The next higher level is the transit exchange, and the top level is the international exchange. A traditional six-level hierarchy, as recommended by the CCITT (the ITU-T's predecessor), is described in Chapter 3 of Volume 1.

Today's network capacity in terms of transmission and exchange performance is considerably larger than yesterday's. In addition, network management systems contain more sophisticated functions, thus flattening the PSTN's architecture. A modern network can resemble the one shown in *Figure B.10.1,* with only a few hierarchical levels and modern transmission between the local exchange and the remote subscriber stages.

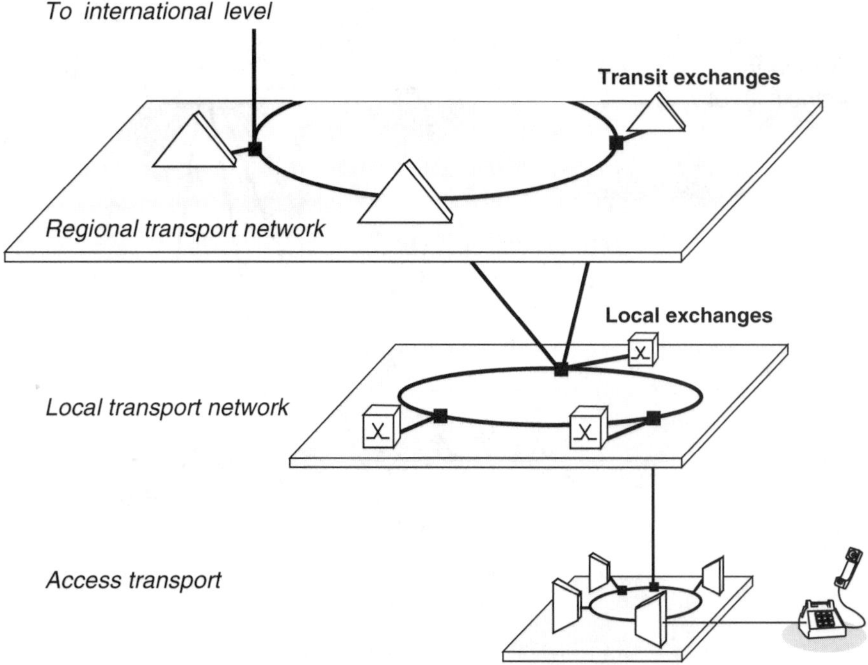

Figure B.10.1 PSTN with a flatter exchange hierarchy

10.2.3 Metropolitan area networks

The architecture of a metropolitan area network can be based on three models: a network with direct routes, with tandem exchanges or with a combination of direct routes and tandem exchanges.

Tandem exchanges set up calls between the local exchanges of a defined geographical region, such as a metropolitan area. They are often built in pairs to provide the necessary redundancy. Such a network may also have direct routes between the local exchanges.

In very big cities, network operators may have to install many interconnected exchanges. A big city can also be divided into several tandem areas.

Tandem and transit functions can be integrated in the same exchange, provided the exchange has sufficient capacity. If separate exchanges are used, there can be routes between tandem and transit exchanges. These routes are only used as stand-by paths in case of malfunctions in the normal connections between a local exchange and the transit level.

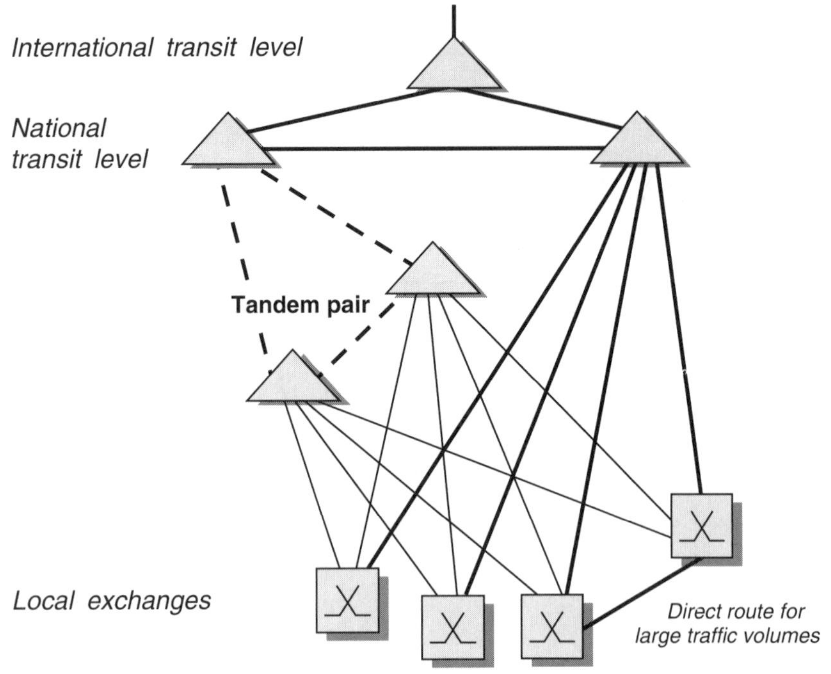

Figure B.10.2 Tandem pair in a metropolitan area

10.3 Fundamental technical plans

In Volume 1, Chapter 10, we describe the fundamental technical plans that form the basis of network planning. The requirements specifications used in the purchase of equipment are also based on these plans. Some of the plans are applicable to several networks, while others are more or less network-specific.

- The *numbering plan* is normally common to the PSTN and ISDN. As a rule, the PLMN is accessed using a special code.

- The *transmission plan* is common to the PSTN and several other networks. (However, this does not apply in countries where many analog exchanges are still in use.)
- The *routing plan* is largely common to the PSTN and ISDN.
- The *signalling plan* is PSTN-specific as far as old-type signalling systems are concerned. It is common to the PSTN and ISDN, in many respects, when SS7 is used.
- The *synchronisation plan* is common to interconnected digital networks.
- The *charging plan* is unique to the PSTN or coordinated with the ISDN. However, it can be coordinated to include a PLMN if both networks are run by the same operator.
- The *network management plan* is unique to the PSTN or coordinated with ISDN. Service quality requirements depend on the amount of fax and data traffic. O&M work can be coordinated with that for other networks.
- The *frequency plan* is common to all networks which use radio for transmission in the trunk or access network.

10.3.1 Alternative routing

Basic routing theory is discussed in Volume 1, Chapter 10.

The different types of traffic in the PSTN – telephony, fax traffic and data traffic – make different demands on transmission quality. Consequently, they are sometimes routed over different paths in the network. *Figure B.10.3* shows three possible paths from exchange A to exchange B. Traffic on one of these paths passes an analog exchange.

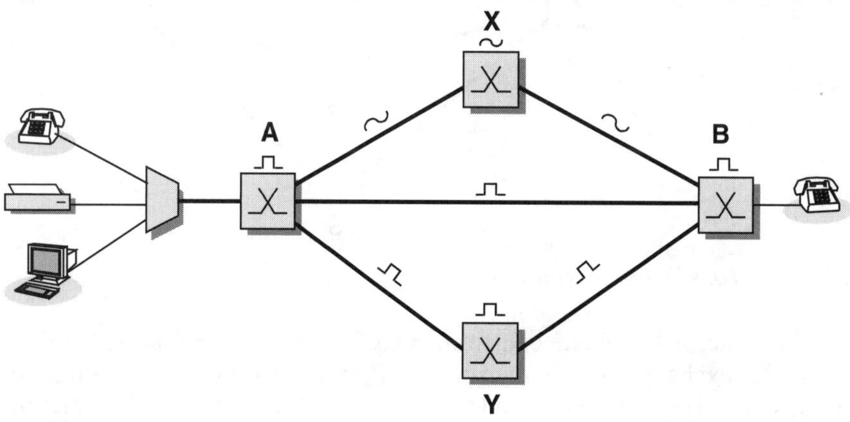

Figure B.10.3 Alternative routing

The subscribers implied in our example can be divided into different categories. The result of the B-number analysis indicates routing which uses the subscriber category to determine the appropriate alternative routing.

- For subscribers belonging to the "telephony" category, the direct path to B is the first-choice route. If congestion is encountered on that route, the traffic is distributed between the paths that pass through exchanges X and Y; for example, each of these paths will carry 50% of the traffic.
- The direct path to B is the first-choice route even for subscribers in the "fax" or "computer" category. If congestion is encountered on that route, the route through Y is selected. But the route to exchange X is never selected for these categories, because analog transmission on the route means inferior quality.

Dynamic routing

Dynamic routing is a more advanced routing function. This means that the exchange learns from its mistakes, so to speak. If a high-usage route (direct connection) is available, it is always selected first. If congestion is encountered on that route, the last successful alternative is selected.

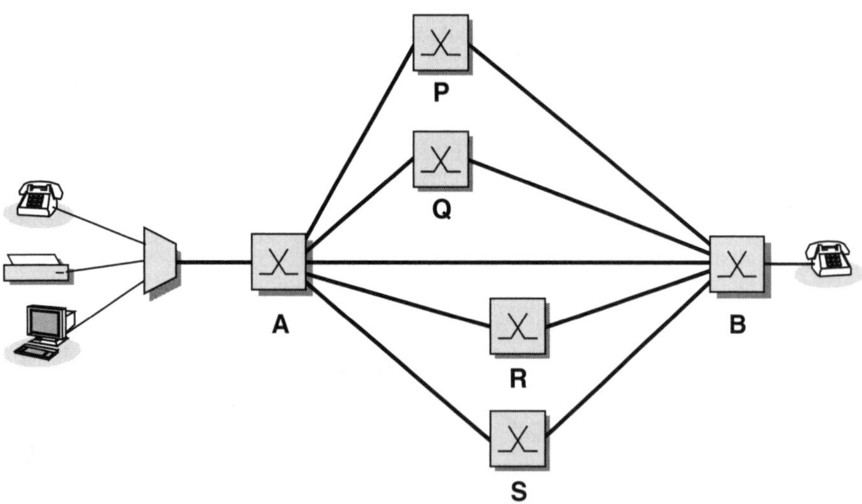

Figure B.10.4 Dynamic routing

For example, A telephone call from A to B meets congestion on the direct path. The exchange selects the route to P, but this route is also congested, because exchange P is overloaded. Selection of the route to Q results in a successful set-up attempt. The next time a call meets congestion on the direct route between A and B, the system "remembers" the path through Q being open last time and selects that route first. In this way, the system avoids making an unsuccessful attempt to switch the call through P, if it is still congested.

Even more advanced functions for dynamic routing are on the drawing board. In such a concept, each network node records information about the load in other nodes and can take this circumstance into account when selecting a route.

10.3.2 Location of supplementary services

Most functions in digital exchanges are implemented in software, because software is cheap when mass-produced. Functions which – for reasons of economy – used to be placed high up in the network hierarchy so that they could be shared by a large number of subscribers have been moved down to the local exchange level. Even rarely used exclusive functions can be moved downwards through the hierarchy without becoming costly.

At the same time, the IN platform has been developed with a view to allowing centralisation of services with large amounts of data. This platform also makes it possible to offer all types of service to subscribers who are still connected to old-type analog exchanges.

Supplementary services are normally implemented as follows:

- Local deployment: Simple services that only concern individual subscribers (call forwarding, wake-up service, call waiting) and services that generate traffic peaks (such as televoting).
- Central deployment: Services that require flexibility (frequent modification) or large amounts of data (such as Freephone); services that interconnect different networks (such as VPN); and services that require sophisticated equipment (such as speech recognition).

10.3.3 Network architecture for new operators

We have got used to seeing new mobile-network operators on the scene, but the deregulation of markets has also attracted new operators of fixed networks. A new operator's network planning differs from that of an "old" one. The existing network belongs to the competitor, and interworking and shared use of equipment are usually regulated by an independent government authority.

The new operator builds his network around his own switching equipment, which includes a subscriber database and charging functions. It is also common for new operators to have their own network management systems, even if such systems can be leased.

Important questions in network planning are:

- How should the subscribers be connected?
- How should transport be arranged?

Figure B.10.5 shows an example of a network run by a new operator whose operations cover two towns. We will now take a closer look at the way access and transport problems have been solved.

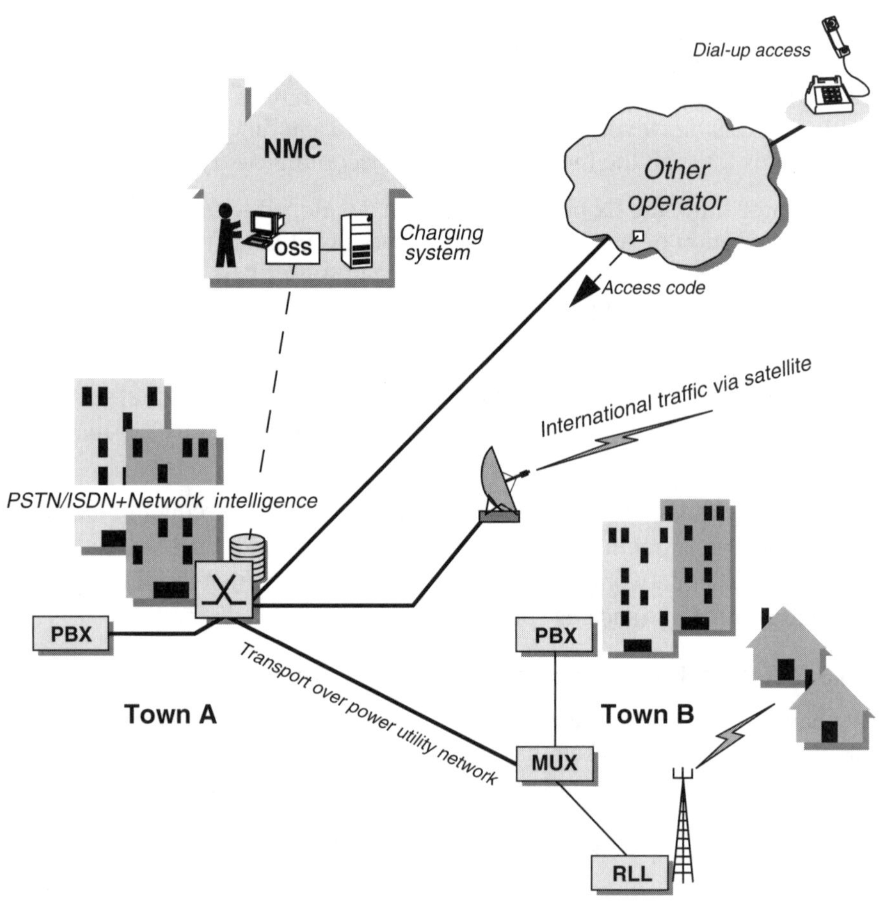

Figure B.10.5 Example of a new operator's PSTN

Connection of subscribers

Basically, subscribers can be connected in two different ways: by installing a separate access network or by using dial-up connections.

Separate access networks are mainly intended for companies and usually consist of one or more PCM systems, installed between the companies' PBXs, and a switching node which belongs to the operator. Of course, the operator can install his own fibre-optic or copper circuits, but the quickest method in most cases will be to use either radio links or existing network equipment – leased from local authorities, power utilities, cable-TV operators or the like. By using high-capacity multiplexers, the operator can also extend his network to areas where he has not yet established switching nodes.

Radio access will be the most profitable solution if the operator builds an access network for connecting residential subscribers. The time won and the possibility of connecting subscribers without knowing in advance their exact location will compensate for the higher connection cost per subscriber (compared with paired cable).

The other alternative open to the operator – dial-up access – means that subscribers are connected to a local exchange in the previous monopoly network and that a special number for access to the new operator has been defined. When the subscriber dials this access number, a connection is set up, and a new dial tone is generated. As a rule, the new operator's switching node must have IN functionality to handle this procedure. Access codes, number series and the distribution of revenue are regulated by an independent government authority.

Transport networks

We now turn to a brief examination of the transport network in the context of new operators' network planning. New operators can choose between circuits of their own and leased capacity in an existing network. If the former monopoly agency still owns the transport network, rules can be established to govern how capacity should be made available to new operators and how much it should cost. Railway companies, power utilities and TV companies also lease capacity in their transmission networks to new operators. If a fibre-optic network is used for transmission, many new operators install SDH equipment to connect their nodes to the transport network. They might also need that type of equipment for the access network, if it covers considerable distances.

Many new operators focus their resources on international traffic. A new operator can opt to enter into agreements with one or more "colleagues" in other countries to be allowed to connect his network to theirs. In this way, he will not have to share the revenue from international traffic with competitors in the home market.

10.4 Dimensioning

The fundamental principles of telephone network dimensioning are dealt with in Volume 1, Chapter 10. They are based on the traffic theory developed by the Danish mathematician A.K. Erlang at the beginning of this century. Operators can use this theory when estimating the amount of equipment required to offer subscribers a certain service level, provided they know the traffic demand.

The dimensioning of equipment is based on two different principles. A subscriber either meets congestion if all equipment is occupied (loss system) or is queued for the necessary resources to become available (delay system).

- Equipment that has been dimensioned as a loss system is active for almost the whole of the call. It is also referred to as *traffic-carrying equipment.*
- Equipment that has been dimensioned as a delay system is active only for a short time (usually during the set-up phase) and is then released to be used for other calls. This equipment is referred to as *common equipment.*

Let us first take another look at the equipment of a local exchange and the systems that are used to perform the different functions.

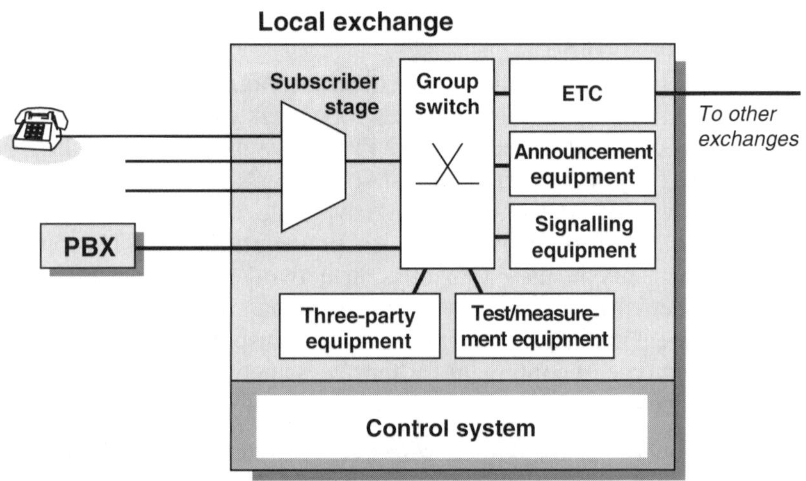

Figure B.10.6 Functions of a local exchange

10.4.1 Traffic-carrying equipment

The term "traffic-carrying equipment" refers to exchange equipment that functions as a loss system, as explained above. It includes:

- links from the subscriber stage to the group switch;
- links from other exchanges;
- announcement equipment;
- equipment for multiparty calls and broadcasting functions; and
- switching equipment (the group switch and the time switch of the subscriber stage).

10.4.2 Common equipment

The following exchange equipment is only used during a short part of each call, which means that it functions as a delay system:

- tone receivers for DTMF signalling to and from subscribers;
- code senders and code receivers for register signalling (CAS) to and from other exchanges;
- signalling terminals for SS7;
- equipment for signalling to and from PBXs; and
- the control system (processors).

10.5 Operational functions

Other important factors that affect the service level are the dimensioning of the control system (processor capacity), whether or not the system has built-in redundancy and whether the need for spare parts is satisfied. In addition, the operator's planning must include the processes for power supply and cooling, as well as an alarm system designed to warn of any events outside the exchange that may affect its operation.

10.5.1 Power supply

The PSTN operates on electricity, so it needs some form of power supply.

- The telephone sets connected to the exchange must be powered.
- The exchange equipment as well as the equipment between exchange and subscriber (multiplexers and remote subscriber stages) must be powered.

The exchange is connected to the power mains. Rectifiers and transformers convert AC power to DC power and check that the right voltage is applied. To be able to cope with a mains outage, all exchanges have some form of backup power. This equipment often consists of a set of accumulators which receive trickle charge from the rectifiers. In many cases, the operator also has diesel-powered, stand-by electric generators, depending on the applicable requirements for safe operation and the reliability of the mains.

10.5.2 Cooling

The need for cooling increases in step with the miniaturisation of exchange components, because as components become more compact, more heat is generated per unit of volume. Printed circuit boards must be placed so that the heat generated does not exceed the capacity of the cooling equipment. While water tanks or air-conditioners were sufficient for cooling the air in previous systems, some of today's cabinets are equipped with built-in fans.

10.5.3 External alarms

Conditions and events outside the network may affect network operation, so exchange installations contain an alarm system for external equipment. The equipment that can be connected to the alarm system includes:

- power supply equipment;
- cooling equipment (temperature alarms);
- alarms indicating extreme humidity or flooding;
- alarms indicating earthquakes and other natural disasters; and
- burglar alarms on doors and windows.

All these alarms can be handled by the exchange itself and sent to O&M personnel over the regular O&M network.

Part C – N-ISDN

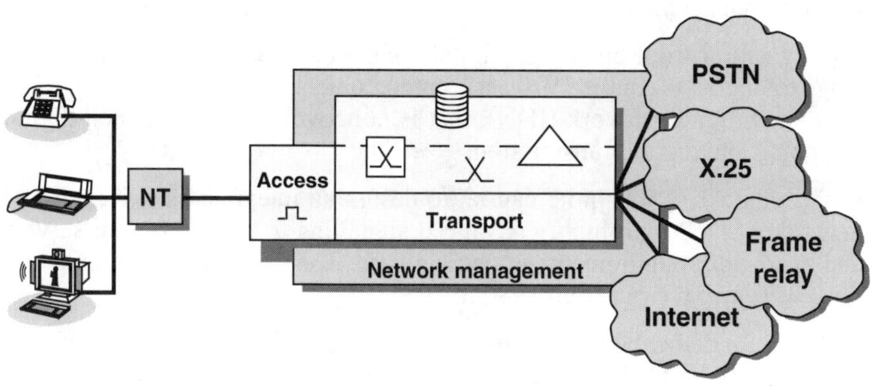

Figure C.0.1 Reference model

1 User services and terminals

1.1 Introduction

The traditional network layout has one network for telephony, a second for telex, a third for packet-switched data traffic and so on. In other words, basically one network for each service category. This is no longer an ideal situation from a network operator's point of view, considering today's cost of network management.

The transition from analog to digital technology has posed another challenge to operators. In the 1970s, a common objective was the creation of an integrated digital network (IDN), that is, a network with integrated digital switching and digital transmission.

In this context, it was quite natural to design an integrated services digital network (ISDN) with highly advanced signalling to meet different service and bandwidth requirements in one network. The first ISDN recommendations were worked out from 1980 to 1984.

ISDN is fundamentally a circuit-switched network. In the 1990s, circuit switching began to face competition from the cell-switched ATM technology with a broadband ISDN (B-ISDN). Accordingly, the first ISDN concept is called N-ISDN, for *narrowband*.

In the following, we will use the abbreviation ISDN to refer to N-ISDN unless otherwise specified.

The ITU-T defines ISDN as follows:

- ISDN is a service-integrated network for digital connections between user interfaces;
- it gives access to all services via one or a few well-defined interfaces;
- it allows separate development of networks on the one hand and services on the other;
- it presupposes digital transmission even in the subscriber access part; and
- it is usually based on the IDN for telephony.

The ISDN network structure is interwoven with the public switched telephone network (PSTN) structure, and PSTN/ISDN can therefore be seen as a "dual network" with common exchanges and network management systems. The difference between the PSTN and ISDN is most obvious in the way they handle local access, especially in subscriber terminals.

As we can see, the ITU-T's definition of ISDN covers both technical aspects and services. It is interesting to note the distinction made between network and services.

ISDN's basic bearer service is called *64 kbit/s unrestricted*. This means that the network can transmit any kind of digital code – digitised images as well as data and digitised speech. In other words, ISDN is ideally suited for multimedia services. It also allows new services to be developed without requiring redesign of the existing network – provided that the signals are digital and that the transfer is based on applicable ISDN protocols. The bandwidth can be 30 • 64 kbit/s = 1,920 kbit/s.

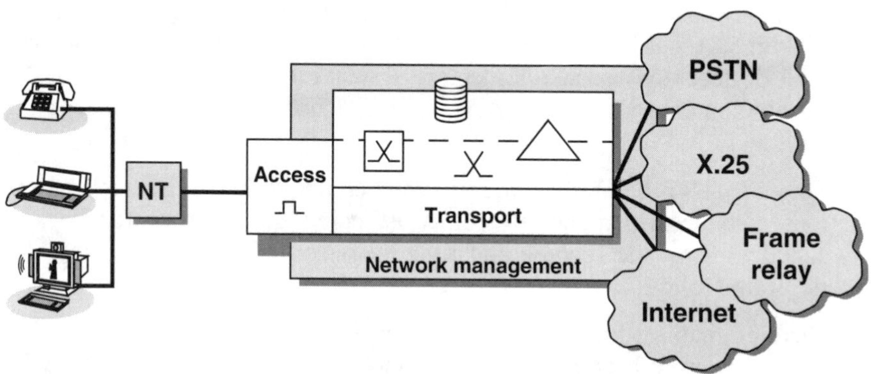

Figure C.1.1 Digital transmission on the path to the subscriber

ISDN was originally characterised by limited mobility or no mobility at all. In recent years, mobility has been enhanced through the introduction of wireless access – digital enhanced cordless telecommunication (DECT) systems – and network intelligence, such as number portability and universal personal telecommunication (UPT). In spite of ISDN's great potential, its introduction has been a slow business in many countries. One reason is that ISDN was long regarded as "a solution in search of a problem". ISDN has offered no attractive subscriber services, except in countries where network operators have introduced standard supplementary services in ISDN instead of in the PSTN and where the need for these services has forced the pace of development.

Another reason has been the lack of standards. To some extent, ISDN technology has differed between countries, which has made it necessary to adapt the design of telephones and other equipment to the requirements of individual countries. Thus, international communication has been problematic.

Today, ISDN is close to a breakthrough because several new "ISDN-friendly" applications are available: Internet access, videoconferencing and others.

In addition, a common standard now governs ISDN traffic in Europe: the Euro-ISDN standard (see Chapter 2).

1.2 Services in ISDN

1.2.1 ISDN's service potential

In theory, ISDN can handle all services that require a bandwidth of up to 1,920 kbit/s. According to the Euro-ISDN standard, the network has a large number of decentralised supplementary services and can use advanced, IN-based supplementary services even more efficiently than they are used in the PSTN.

Although ISDN is basically a circuit-switched network, the first recommendations also described the possibility of using the network for packet-switched traffic. The recommendations also comprise one more transfer mode: frame relay.

Powerful signalling functions – in the form of digital signalling system 1 (DSS1) – are used between subscriber and exchange. The same is true for signalling between exchanges, which employs the ISDN user part (ISUP) of signalling system No. 7 (SS7).

This description seems to indicate that ISDN should be an important and attractive network service, comparable with the PSTN and mobile telephony. But the picture has a number of complex elements, especially as far as residential users of the Internet are concerned. Today, many telecom subscribers are connected over copper cables used for the PSTN. One of the basic ideas of the ISDN concept is that these PSTN subscribers should have no trouble "trading in" their present network for ISDN. For this application, a specially designed access is available: basic rate access, with a maximum switched bandwidth of 128 kbit/s. Although this is quite sufficient for most services, it limits the use of advanced Internet services and most video services, thus involving ISDN's basic rate access in a struggle on two fronts:

- The enhancement of the PSTN's modem standards is an ongoing process, and a bit rate of 64 kbit/s may soon be possible.
- Wideband alternatives – for example, asymmetrical digital subscriber line (ADSL) – are being developed for Internet access above PSTN's capacity. (See Volume 1, Chapter 4, Subsection 4.4.3.).

The difference in price between available technologies will have a great impact on development. With competitively priced services, ISDN could well fulfil its outstanding potential.

1.2.2 ISDN terminology

The standardisation of ISDN has made it necessary to introduce a number of new terms. Some of them have proved useful even outside ISDN, such as bearer service, teleservice and supplementary service, which are frequently used in Volume 1 (see Chapter 1, for example). Other terms are used mainly in connection with N-ISDN:

- B-channel;
- D-channel;
- basic rate access (BRA);
- primary rate access (PRA); and
- terminal adapter (TA).

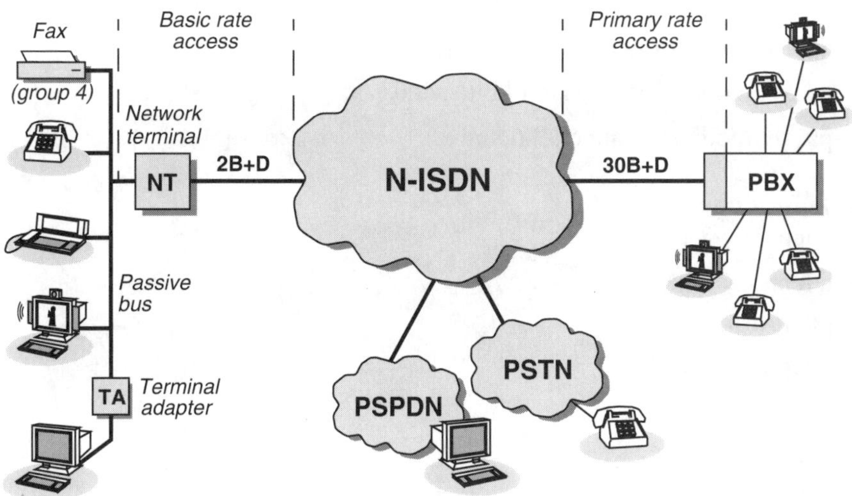

Figure C.1.2 Basic ISDN concepts

Two types of channel are used in ISDN:

The B-channel (64 kbit/s) is the regular traffic channel for transparent transmission of subscriber information through the network.

The D-channel (64 or 16 kbit/s) is mainly used for signalling but also for packet traffic.

BRA is defined as "2B+D" (2 •64 kbit/s + 16 kbit/s). It employs a special "minitransmission system", of the plesiochronous digital hierarchy (PDH) type, which usually has a bit rate of 160 kbit/s. "2B+D" requires 144 kbit/s, 13 kbit/s is used for synchronisation, and 3 kbit/s for network management.

PRA is defined as "30B+D" (30 • 64 kbit/s + 64 kbit/s). It uses a standard 2048 kbit/s pulse code modulation (PCM) system. 64 kbit/s is used for synchronisation and network management.

The terminal adapters handle adaptation between standard terminals and ISDN's interfaces for connection. Adapters are often used to increase the rate up to the B-channel's 64 kbit/s by means of dummy bits.

1.2.3 Services as perceived by the operator

Euro-ISDN specifies a number of bearer services and teleservices. In addition, individual operators offer their own service portfolios.

Bearer services

ISDN provides three types of circuit mode bearer service: 3.1 kHz audio, 64 kbit/s unrestricted and speech. (See Chapter 2, Subsection 2.2.2.)

Other examples of bearer services are:

- packet mode B-channel, 64 kbit/s; and
- packet mode D-channel, 9.6 kbit/s.

Teleservices

- telephony 3.1 kHz;
- telephony 7 kHz;
- telefax group 2/3;
- telefax group 4;
- videotex; and
- video-telephony.

1.2.4 Teleservices as perceived by the user

Companies, first and foremost, are interested in ISDN. Small companies can get the same communication facilities as large ones without having to pay for leased lines or separate networks. Some of the services may also be useful to individuals, such as teleworkers and Internet surfers. For teleworking and PBX applications, ISDN is a competitive alternative for large companies.

Telephony

ISDN can be used for regular telephone traffic, but in most countries telephony is "part of the bargain" when subscribers acquire ISDN for other purposes. In countries where most of the supplementary services for telephony have been implemented in ISDN but not in the PSTN, telephony has been the service most in demand. A telephone connected to ISDN works like an ordinary telephone, and calls are usually charged at regular tariffs.

Telephony with higher speech quality can be offered but only between two subscribers who have access to the teleservice called "telephony 7 kHz".

Private branch exchanges

The connection of a private branch exchange (PBX) to ISDN offers more powerful signalling than with the PSTN. The IN service virtual private network (VPN) enables a company to interconnect several PBXs to form a single network without having to lease lines from operators.

Telefax

The group 4 fax is specially designed for use in ISDN. This fax uses a bit rate of 64 kbit/s, which corresponds to the capacity of one B-channel.

A group 3 fax can be connected to ISDN through an adapter which increases the bit rate to 64 kbit/s. The effective bit rate for a group 3 fax is normally 9,600 or 14,400 bit/s. A group 4 fax can communicate with a group 3 fax, in which case the bit rate for group 3 will be used.

Videoconferencing and video-telephony

ISDN can be used for video-telephony, desktop conferencing and videoconferencing.

One BRA – that is, two B-channels – gives a relatively good picture and good sound. In video-telephony and PC-based desktop conferencing, the quality is usually considered acceptable.

More than two B-channels (usually six or 30 channels) may be needed to get good picture quality in videoconferencing.

PRA – 30 B-channels – gives about the same quality as a regular telecast. Telemedicine may serve as an example of an application. Six B-channels give 384 kbit/s, which is sufficient for videoconferencing in most cases and cheaper than 30 channels.

So far, there is no complete standard for desktop conferencing systems. The quality of sound and video transferred between different makes of equipment is acceptable, but collaborative working in a common document requires the communicating parties to use the same make of equipment.

High-quality sound

High-quality sound can be transferred in coded form via BRA. In the coding process, a sound signal of CD quality is compressed in the send direction and decompressed to roughly the original quality in the receiver.

Data communication, including Internet access

Data can be transferred at rates up to 2 Mbit/s (30 B-channels). If the transferred data volumes are large, and if they must be transferred at a very high rate, leased lines or ATM transfer is a better alternative.

File transfer

Large data files, high-quality images and CAD/CAM files can be transferred over ISDN.

LAN Interconnect

ISDN is a flexible alternative for LAN interconnect. More B-channels can easily be added as the need for capacity increases. The initial cost is relatively small, and the network service and routers with ISDN interfaces are rather cheap.

ISDN may also be suitable in configurations with uneven traffic load. In these cases, ISDN is used to handle peak traffic that leased lines or VPNs are unable to carry.

ISDN is also used as backup for leased lines.

Remote connection to LAN

ISDN BRA is a practical alternative for connecting teleworkers to their company's LAN. Most applications include a server connected to the LAN and to a client in the local computer. Both server and client are ordinarily composed of a printed board assembly and software installed in a PC. The server is often installed on a separate computer to improve performance. The clients are connected using a BRA. The server can be connected using a number of BRAs or one PRA, depending on the number of clients and the frequency and duration of their sessions.

Remote supervision and alarms

ISDN is a low-cost method for remote supervision of road traffic and underground stations. Both video and sound can be transferred over the network.

1.2.5 Combinations of teleservices

Teleworking, office in the home

ISDN can supply all the communication facilities needed in teleworking and home-office applications. However, a prerequisite is that the network is generally accessible and that there is a decline in the price of equipment and subscriptions. For most teleworkers, the capacity provided by BRA is sufficient.

Distance education

As we stated in the introductory part of this volume (*The telecommunications services market*), videoconferencing and desktop conferencing are valuable tools in distance education, and ISDN is an excellent choice for this purpose. The ISDN access can be used for file transfer, fax, telephony and access to the Internet.

Collaborative working

ISDN is ideal for collaborative working; it lends itself equally well to desktop conferencing, file transfer, telephony and fax.

Graphics production

The graphic arts industry has long used ISDN for telecommunication. Wideband solutions may be attractive in the future, but they are not yet generally available (besides being too costly for most companies).

Telemedicine

ISDN is used in medical applications – such as in the transfer of X-rays. Many county councils in Sweden have made considerable progress in this area.

1.2.6 Special business services in ISDN

See *Part B – PSTN*, Chapter 1, Subsection 1.3.7.

1.2.7 Mobility in ISDN

See *Part B – PSTN*, Chapter 2, Sections 2.3 and 2.4, which deal with DECT, and Volume 1, Chapter 6, Subsection 6.3, where UPT is presented.

1.3 Terminals

The left side of *Figure C.1.2* shows typical BRA with network terminations and several subscriber terminals. The right side shows typical PRA with a PBX and connected terminals.

1.3.1 Network terminations

Network terminations (NT) are used to connect ISDN equipment to the public network. NT1 and NT2 have slightly different functions. (See Chapter 2, Subsection 2.2.4.) *Figure C.1.3* shows two examples of NTs.

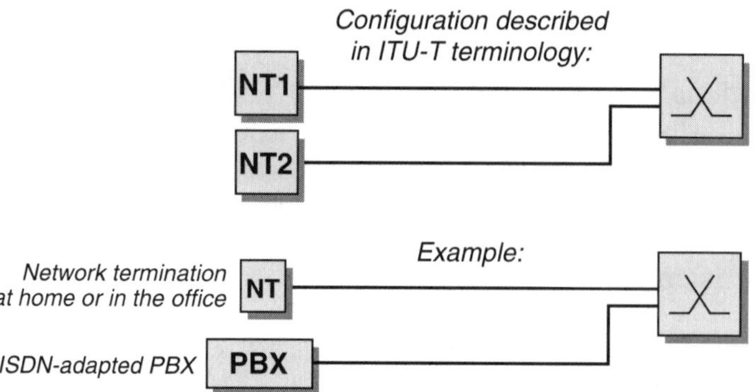

Figure C.1.3 Examples of network terminations for access to ISDN

1.3.2 Terminal equipment

The terminal unit installed at the subscriber's is called terminal equipment (TE). Two types of terminal can be connected to ISDN:

- TE1, terminals with a built-in ISDN interface; and
- TE2, terminals of other types (for example, V.24 or X.21).

Figure C.1.4 shows a type of terminal equipment (TE1) connected to NTs. Examples of terminals are also shown in the figure.

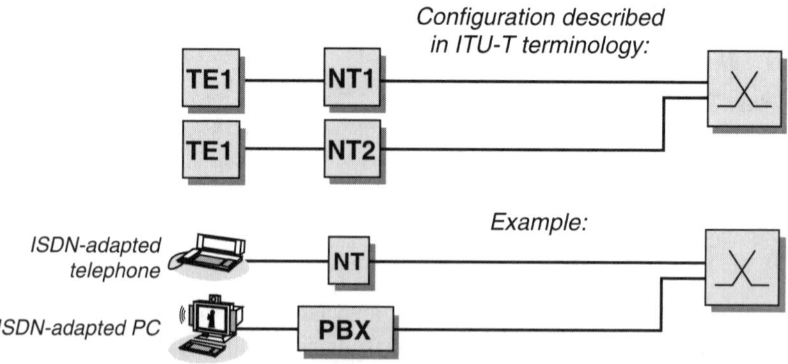

Figure C.1.4 Terminals for connection to ISDN

1.3.3 Subscriber equipment

Terminal adapter

Terminal adapters (TAs) are used to connect non-ISDN terminals to ISDN. There are adapters for BRA and PRA:

- adapters for PCs, mainframes and servers;
- adapters for X.25 data terminals (this application requires a packet mode bearer service in ISDN); and
- adapters for X.21 data terminals (this application requires a circuit mode bearer service in ISDN).

Figure C.1.5 shows how a terminal adapter can be connected to an ordinary personal computer.

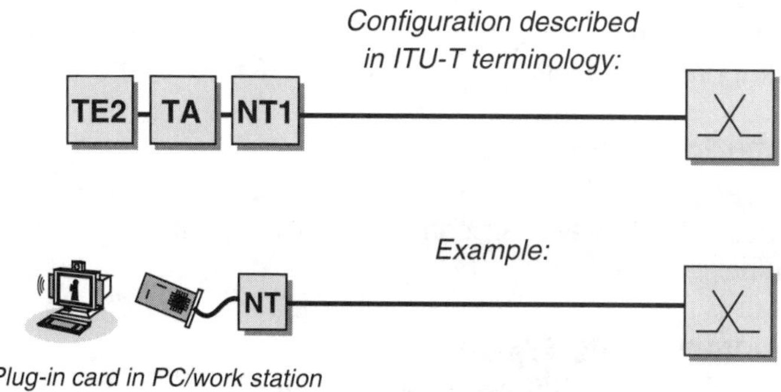

Figure C.1.5 Connection of non-ISDN-adapted equipment

Telephones

Special digital telephones (always with a display) can be connected directly to ISDN. An ordinary analog telephone be connected using a TA.

Private branch exchanges

A PBX can either have primary or basic rate access. A PBX with ISDN functionality is a common type of PRA.

DECT terminals

DECT terminals can be connected for wireless access to ISDN. The very first applications have been wireless connection to a PBX, but wireless access to the home is also possible. Each channel has a digital transmission capacity of 32 kbit/s; a combination of five channels gives BRA.

The DECT system is described in detail in *Part B – PSTN*.

PCs with ISDN cards

Most PC cards are intended for BRA, but PC cards with interface for PRA are also available. The standard used is called H.320.

PCs fitted with an ISDN card are growing in importance as terminals. Examples of new applications are file transfer, remote connection to LAN, desktop conferencing systems, group 3 and group 4 faxes via PC, telephone answering services and remote supervision.

However, not all cards can communicate with all suppliers' routers.

Video-telephony

There is no uniform standard for video-telephony. A videophone connected to ISDN can use either a single channel or several channels depending on picture quality requirements.

Videoconferencing equipment

Videoconferencing equipment with ISDN interface is available in the market. The H.320 standard ensures compatibility between equipment from different suppliers.

Desktop conferencing system

See under "PCs with ISDN cards" above. The H.320 standard is applied here, too.

Group 4 faxes

A fax connected to ISDN closely resembles the faxes connected to the PSTN (see *Part B – PSTN*), but ISDN applications require no modem equipment because digital transmission is used throughout. A group 4 fax is almost seven times faster than a group 3 fax of the type that can handle a bit rate of 9.6 kbit/s.

Inverse multiplexer

If the network cannot set up $n \cdot 64$ kbit/s (multirate) connections for wideband service, a number of B-channels can be set up individually but are handled as a single unit ($n \cdot 64$ kbit/s) by means of an *inverse multiplexer*. (See *Figure C.1.6*.)

Figure C.1.6 Inverse multiplexer, 384 kbit/s

2 Standards

2.1 Standardisation bodies and interest groups

ISDN standardisation is an extensive task. It comprises signalling, switching, transmission, network architecture, operation and maintenance and services. Standardisation is a continuous process resulting in new designs and improvements to existing specifications.

2.1.1 The ITU-T and ETSI

ISDN standardisation is primarily carried out by the International Telecommunication Union – Telecommunications Standardization Sector (ITU-T) and the European Telecommunications Standards Institute (ETSI). In Europe, the EU Commission has carried out standardisation work aimed at mandatory adaptation to certain standards and European norms.

2.1.2 Euro-ISDN

Previously, ISDN was implemented in different ways in different countries. The resulting incompatibility affected services and the interworking between equipment from different manufacturers. To solve this problem and to establish a uniform European norm for ISDN, 26 network operators in 22 European countries signed an ISDN Memorandum of Understanding (ISDN-MoU) in 1989.

On the basis of this ISDN-MoU and the ISDN standards established by ETSI in 1988, a very ambitious attempt at coordination – called Euro-ISDN – was made in December 1993. Euro-ISDN is designed as a common ISDN implementation that all European operators are planning to adopt. Euro-ISDN is available in several new versions presenting new ISDN services.

Many new applications and expanded cooperation between manufacturers and operators of ISDN equipment have widened the range of products compatible with Euro-ISDN. The resulting drop in prices should have a positive effect on the acceptance of ISDN applications in the market. Euro-ISDN is also being adopted outside Europe (in South Africa and Israel). The goal is global acceptance of Euro-ISDN.

2.2 Established recommendations

As far back as 1988, the ITU-T specified a first set of thoroughly worked-out recommendations, which in practice are regarded as international standards. ISDN is specified in the Series I recommendations and structured as shown in *Figure C.2.1*.

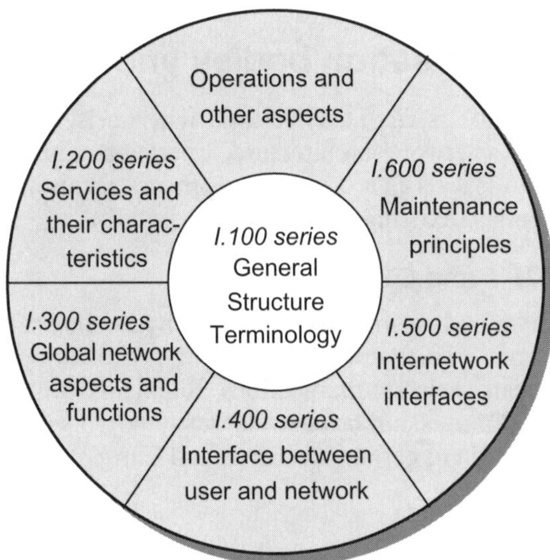

Figure C.2.1 Series I recommendations

2.2.1 The I.100 series – General, structure, terminology

The I.100 series includes a number of recommendations that describe and define the principles and the terminology used in ISDN.

2.2.2 The I.200 series – Services and their characteristics

Like other networks, ISDN offers two main types of service: bearer services and teleservices. The bearer services, which are described in Recommendation I.211, transfer digital information between two points in a network or between two different networks.

ISDN has three types of standardised, circuit-mode bearer service:

- *3.1 kHz audio*, used in modem traffic and in intercommunication with non-ISDN networks;
- *64 kbit/s unrestricted*, providing a transparent 64 kbit/s connection, which means that no echo suppression or bit manipulation is performed; and
- *speech*, for 64 kbit/s voice connections; transparency is not guaranteed.

The teleservices are based on the bearer services and adapted to different applications. A typical feature of a teleservice is that it offers "complete" communication between users, including terminal functions. Most of the teleservices are described in the ITU-T's Recommendation I.212.

The following are examples of teleservices:

- telephony 3.1 kHz;
- telephony 7 kHz;
- telefax group 2/3;
- telefax group 4;
- videotex; and
- video-telephony.

There are also a number of supplementary services – defined in Recommendation I.250 – which can be used with bearer services and teleservices. Recommendations I.252–I.258 describe the supplementary services in detail.

The following are examples of supplementary services in ISDN:

- calling line identification (CLIP);
- calling line identification restriction (CLIR);
- direct dialling-in (DDI);
- multiple subscriber number (MSN); and
- terminal portability (TP).

New, ETSI-compatible supplementary services are being developed continuously.

2.2.3 The I.300 series – Global network aspects and functions

The I.300 series deals with network functions for bearer services and teleservices. In this context, the term "network functions" refers to channel structure, flow control, frame synchronisation, multiplexing, addressing, routing and fault management.

I.310 – Functional principles of the ISDN network

Recommendation I.310 describes the functional principles of the ISDN network.

I.320 – Reference model for protocols

Recommendation I.320 describes a reference model for ISDN protocols. The three-dimensional model, which is presented in perspective, is very complicated.

I.330 – Numbering and addressing principles

Recommendation I.330 describes ISDN's numbering and addressing principles. An ISDN address consists of a country code and a national ISDN number plus an ISDN subaddress, where applicable. (See *Figure C.2.2.*) The address can be of variable length.

Country codes are defined in the ITU-T's E.163 standard, a numbering plan is described in Recommendations E.164 and I.331 and connection types are specified in Recommendation I.340.

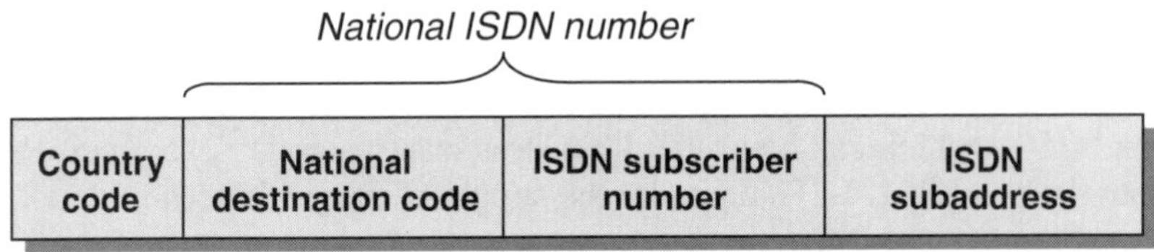

Figure C.2.2 ISDN address according to ITU-T I.330

2.2.4 The I.400 series – Interface between user and network

I.400 is the largest part of the I series. The recommendations worked out by the ITU-T so far are mainly concerned with standardisation of the user interface. The cornerstone of this work is the preparation of a reference model for the connection of subscriber equipment.

I.410 – General aspects

I.410 contains general comments on and principles for the recommendations of the series. Its contents include reference configurations for functionality in network connection points and user equipment.

I.411 – Reference models

I.411 describes reference models and exemplifies a number of possible configurations by means of terminating function blocks and reference points. The function blocks TE1, TE2, NT1, NT2 and TA are also defined here. *Figure C.2.3* is a survey of different reference configurations for subscriber connections.

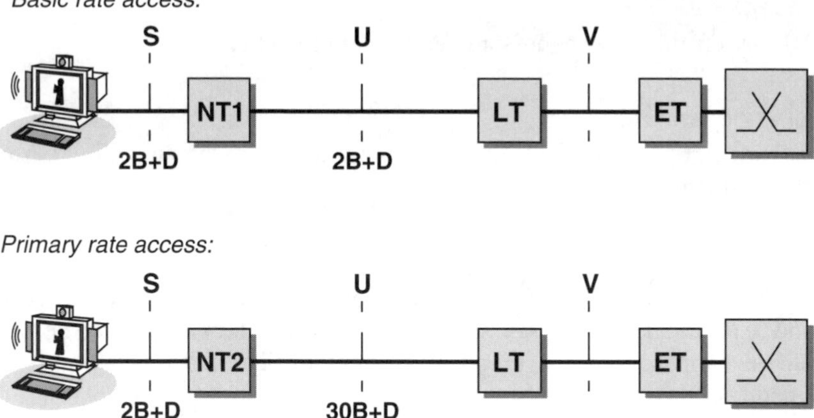

Figure C.2.3 Reference configurations for subscriber connections to ISDN

Network terminations

- NT1: Network termination 1 with functions corresponding to layer 1 of the open systems interconnect (OSI) model. NT1 is the physical and electrical termination of the subscriber line.
- NT2: Network termination 2. In addition to layer 1 functions, it may contain functions for layers 2 and 3 of the OSI model. NT2 could be a PBX, for example.

Terminal equipment

Subscriber terminal with functions corresponding to layers 1–7 of the OSI model. Two types of TE have been defined:

- TE1: Terminal type 1. Terminal with an ISDN interface, for instance a digital telephone or an integrated speech and data terminal.

- TE2: Terminal type 2. Terminal which has a different interface – for example, X.21 or V.24 – and which requires special adaptation to the ISDN interface.

Terminal adapter

TA: Terminal adapter to adapt TE2 equipment to the ISDN interface.

Line terminal

LT: Line terminal. Exchange-side equivalent to NT1.

Exchange terminal

ET: Exchange terminal with functions for adapting to the switching system of the exchange.

Reference points

Note that points R, S, T, U and V are reference points and need not correspond to physical interfaces. Two or more function blocks can often be combined to form a common piece of equipment. The reference points are defined as follows:

- reference point R indicates the interface between TA and TE2;
- reference point S indicates the interface between NT and TE, or TA;
- reference point T indicates the interface between NT1 and NT2;
- reference point U indicates the interface in the connection network, between the exchange and NT1; and
- reference point V indicates the interface between LT and ET in the exchange.

I.412 – Channel structures and connection alternatives

The B-channel

A 64 kbit/s B-channel can be divided into a number of subchannels (8, 16 and 32 kbit/s). But even if the channel is divided it must be addressed to one destination only. The channel can be used for both circuit mode and packet mode services.

When a B-channel sends data at a bit rate below 64 kbit/s, rate adaptation functions are provided. This means converting the users' data, which is usually sent at a rate of 2400, 4800 or 9600 bit/s, in two steps. In the first step, the data stream is converted into a subchannel level bit rate, which is then increased to 64 kbit/s through so-called bit/byte repetition.

The D-channel

The D-channel is used for signalling during the set-up and clearing of connections on the B-channels. Between these two phases, data traffic is carried on the D-channel without disturbing the signalling function.

Dynamic allocation is performed by the link protocol between the terminal (or NT2) and the network. The protocol is called *link access procedure on the D-channel* (*LAPD*) and is of the *high level data link control* (*HDLC*) type.

For a detailed description of D-channel signalling, see Chapter 7, Section 7.2.

The H-channel

Unlike the B and D-channels, the H-channel is not a separate channel. It consists of different combinations of B and D-channels, which together provide large transmission capacity.

Examples:

- B = 64 kbit/s
- D = 16 or 64 kbit/s
- H0 = 6B = 384 kbit/s
- H11 = 23B+D = 1536 kbit/s (the US and Japan)
- H12 = 30B+D = 1920 kbit/s (the rest of the world)

I.420 – Interface for basic rate access

See Chapter 1, Subsection 1.2.2.

I.421 – Interface for primary rate access

See Chapter 1, Subsection 1.2.2.

I.430 – Specification of basic rate interface for physical layer

Recommendation I.430 describes the interface of the BRA, with reference configurations, terminating devices, connectors and contacts, as well as the multiplexing of the two B-channels and the D-channel. The recommendation also describes different applications of the interface, line codes and channel access procedures.

I.431 – Specification of primary rate interface for physical layer

The interface of the PRA, which was specified to allow connection to PBXs, is only intended for point-to-point configurations. The channel structure is dealt with in Chapter 1, Subsection 1.2.2. The H-channels ($n \cdot 64$ kbit/s) are used for wideband services.

I.440 and I.441 – Specification for the link layer

Recommendations I.440 and I.441 describe the LAPD protocol. (I.440 and I.441 were originally called Q.920 and Q.921 respectively, because they were worked out by another study group.) Recommendation I.441 describes the structure of the information frames, as well as commands and responses. Together these recommendations specify a general signalling system for digital access signalling.

I.450 and I.451 – Specification for the network layer

The network layer is specified in Recommendations I.450 and I.451, which were originally called Q.930 and Q.931 respectively. These recommendations describe how the terminals and the network communicate over the D-channel for the ordering of services.

I.460-I.466 – Support for other interfaces

Recommendations I.460–I.466 deal with multiplexing, rate adaptation and support for other interfaces, such as support for X.21 terminals in I.461, support for X.25 terminals in I.462, and support for terminals with V-interface (V.110) in I.463.

2.2.5 The I.500 series – Internetwork interfaces

Interworking functions (IWF) are used to meet the great need for interworking between ISDN and other networks. I.500 describes a scenario and a structure for the recommendations of this series. The recommendations have been divided into four levels:

- General level – I.510, I.515, the X.300-series
- Scenario level – I.515–I.570
- Functional level – I.515, I.520, I.530, I.462, I.332, X.81, X.31
- Protocol level – Q.120–Q.180, Q.251–Q.300, Q.310–Q.490

I.500 also refers to many recommendations in other series, such as:

- X.75 – IWF for packet-switched networks
- Q.700 – Network protocol

I.510 describes the principles that govern IWF and gives some examples of interworking between networks.

- ISDN – PSTN
- ISDN – CSPDN (circuit switched public data network)
- ISDN – PSPDN (packet switched public data network)

- ISDN – private network

The I.600 series – Maintenance principles

This series deals with the principles that govern subscriber access and subscriber installation. It also defines functions for fault tracing and other types of maintenance relating to subscriber accesses and installation.

3 Switching and switch control

3.1 Introduction

As we have mentioned in Chapter 1 (and in *Part B – PSTN*), ISDN and PSTN are usually combined to form a dual network in which they use the same resources to a certain extent. The switching equipment provides us with a typical example of this way of making rational use of resources. Since both the digitised PSTN and ISDN use 64 kbit/s circuit switching, the two networks can share subscriber switches as well as group switch equipment.

This chapter will focus on the switching and switch control functions of the local exchange. We apply the reasoning used in Volume 1, Chapter 10, Subsection 10.8.4, in that we see the exchange as a platform having a number of network applications. (See *Figure C.3.1.*)

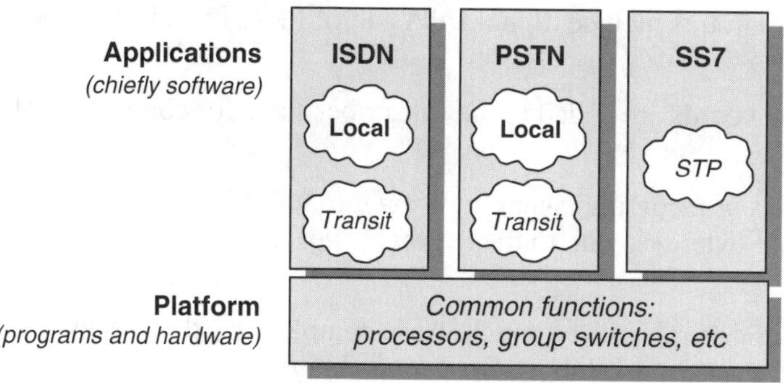

Figure C.3.1 Outline of a PSTN/ISDN exchange (with signal transfer point function)

Figure C.3.2 is an example of the traditional way of illustrating a local exchange in the PSTN/ISDN.

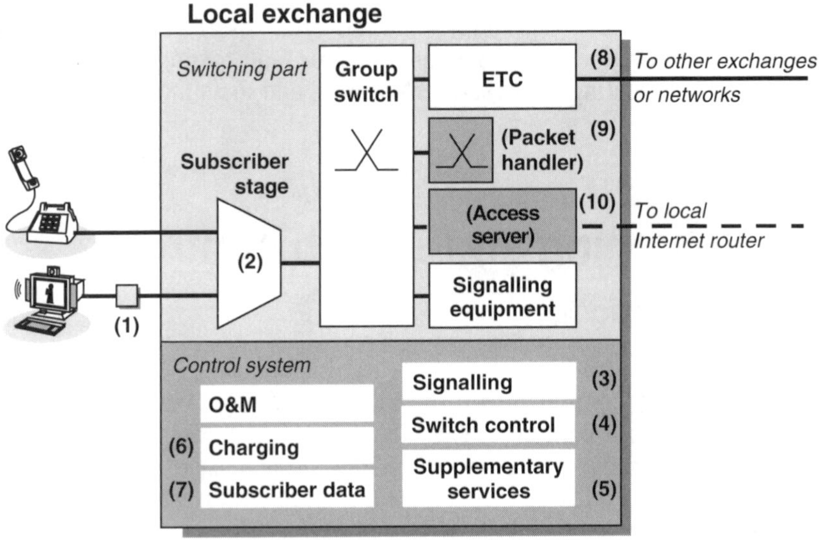

Figure C.3.2 Local exchange in the PSTN/ISDN

Let us now see what equipment must be added to a local exchange in the PSTN to create a PSTN/ISDN local exchange according to *Figure C.3.2.*

1. The access circuits include digital BRA and/or PRA, in addition to analog access.

2. Digital line boards are added to the subscriber stage for connection of the digital accesses.

3. The analysis of incoming signalling from the subscriber or trunk side will be much more extensive due to the "verbal" capacity of the signalling systems in ISDN.

4. The switch control will be much more complex, partly because of the many bearer services in ISDN, such as n • 64 kbit/s.

5. ISDN has other supplementary services, such as closed user group for data communication.

6. ISDN's charging functions are more complicated.

7. ISDN needs more subscriber data to be able to handle the different types of terminal that can be connected.

8. ISDN must be connectable to other ISDN exchanges, PSPDN, PSTN (analog and digital) and possibly to other types of network, which requires a wider range of adaptation facilities than in the PSTN.

9. Some ISDN exchanges are equipped with packet handlers for X.25 traffic on the B or D-channel.

10. Some ISDN exchanges contain equipment for access and statistical or static multiplexing of 64 or 128 kbit/s Internet traffic. This equipment is usually connected to the trunk side of the group switch. Modems are not required, as they are in the PSTN.

Additional comments on item 8. above: ISDN is digital, by definition, and has its own signalling systems (DSS1 and ISUP). Unless all the aforementioned requirements concerning the environment of ISDN exchanges are met, there is no "ISDN network", and the functionality offered to subscribers is reduced in principle to the PSTN level. (See *Figure C.3.3.*) An exception is the switching of calls between two ISDN-connected subscribers who belong to the same local exchange.

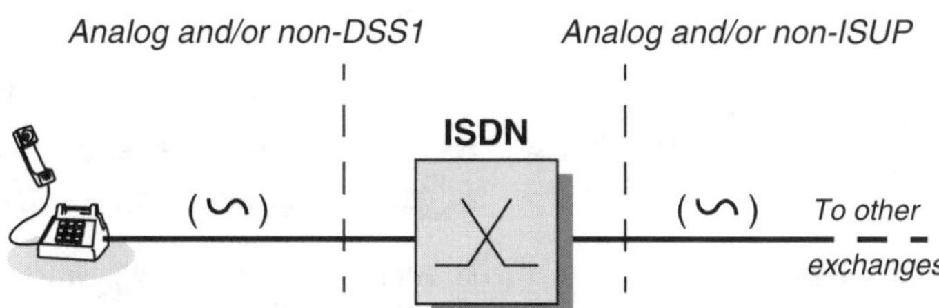

Figure C.3.3 A non-ISDN environment reduces functionality

If the digitising of the network is behind schedule, it is still possible to build an ISDN network, but the result will be a separate, thin overlay network. For an individual connection, ISDN functionality can also be retained by means of routing (see Subsection 3.3.4).

3.2 The subscriber stage

Several types of circuit can be connected to a combined PSTN/ISDN subscriber stage:

- An analog PSTN circuit is connected to an analog line circuit. (See *Part B – PSTN*, Chapter 3, Subsection 3.2.4.)

- BRA is connected to a digital line circuit for 2B+D.
- A "generic" subscriber line multiplexer is connected to a V5.1 line circuit.
- PRA is connected to a digital line circuit for 30B+D.

The V5.1 interface is dealt with in *Part B – PSTN*, Chapter 2, Subsection 2.5.2. It usually contains a combination of PSTN and ISDN accesses (2B+D).

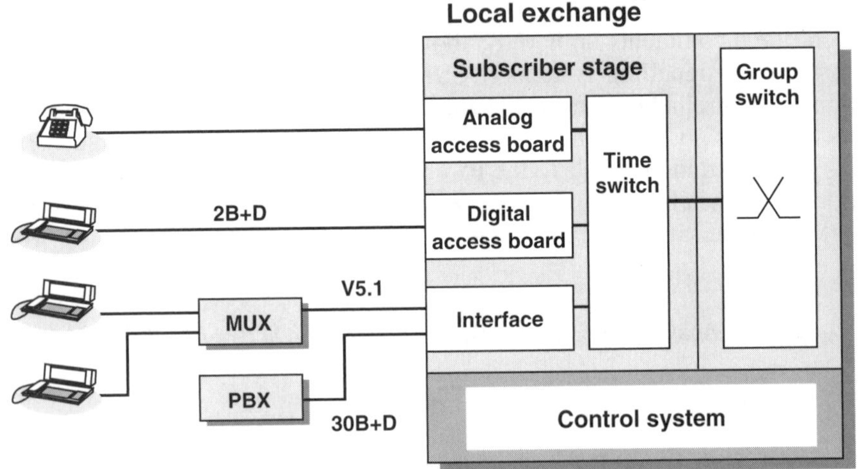

Figure C.3.4 Connection of basic rate access and primary rate access to a local exchange that can handle both PSTN and ISDN

As in the case of PSTN subscribers only, the time switch will concentrate PSTN/ISDN traffic on the path to the group switch. There is often a substantial share of business traffic on ISDN connections, resulting in high average traffic intensity per channel. The number of 2 Mbit/s links to the group switch is dimensioned depending on traffic and grade of service.

3.2.1 Handling of D-channels

The main task of the D-channels in ISDN is to carry signalling between the subscriber's terminal and the ISDN exchange. They can also carry packet mode data traffic between a subscriber and a packet-switched data network. In other words, a D-channel performs two functions that the exchange must be capable of handling in different ways:

- When a D-channel is used for signalling, the control system of the exchange uses the information for switch control.

- When a D-channel is used for packet-switched data traffic, the information is sent to a co-located or remote packet handler, and then on to the packet data network.

The signalling terminals (ST) of the ISDN exchange perform the separating process. In the opposite direction – from the exchange to the subscriber – the signalling terminal ensures that both the signalling information and packet data can be loaded onto the D-channel to the subscriber. *Figure C.3.5* shows an example of implementation.

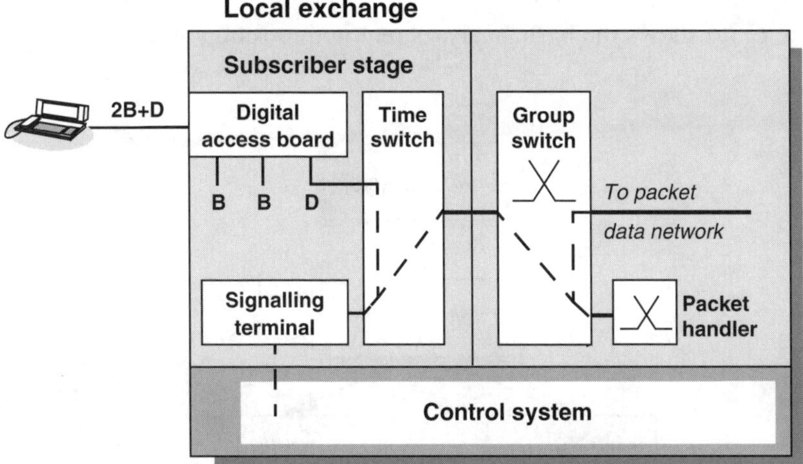

Figure C.3.5 Local exchange paths for signalling messages and D-channel packet data

Signalling and data traffic are separated by means of the service access point identifier (SAPI) in the subscriber signalling. (See Section 3.6.)

3.3 Switch control

Switch control in an ISDN network is very complicated because of the hundreds of parameters required to control switching through the exchange. In this section, we will discuss some fundamental control principles.

3.3.1 Parameters for information transfer – Analyses

The parameters for information transfer include

- transfer mode;

- bearer service – including bit rate and transparency (audio, unrestricted, speech);
- signalling protocol;
- teleservice with higher-layer protocol (for checking compatibility);
- A-number and B-number; and
- A-category and B-category.

The parameters may either form part of the SETUP signalling message or be stored in the exchange.

Figure C.3.6 shows the basic analyses required to set up an ISDN connection.

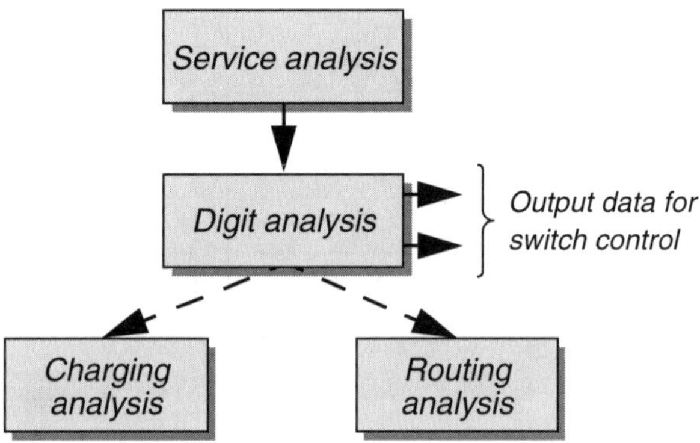

Figure C.3.6 Basic analyses for setting up an ISDN connection

3.3.2 Service analysis

An ISDN subscriber calls the network by sending a SETUP message. The contents of the message are determined by the service (or services) that the subscriber or his terminal wants to use. The connection is handled in different ways, depending on the type of service to be provided. If the subscriber requests a supplementary service in ISDN – such as "call forwarding unconditional" – the service analysis will detect that request. The relevant software will then be activated and, for a short period, provide the logic that controls the call.

Teleservices or bearer services require a different type of service analysis. The purpose of this analysis is to check if the network can offer the requested service and what requirements the network must satisfy to execute it. The information is used to control the switching and, to some extent, the communication phase. For example, if the subscriber requests the bearer service "64 kbit/s unrestricted digital", then the network will ensure that services of the "call waiting" type do not interrupt the communication. The "call waiting" service is only compatible with the teleservice "telephony".

The service analysis also provides information for the compatibility check performed in the B-subscriber's local exchange.

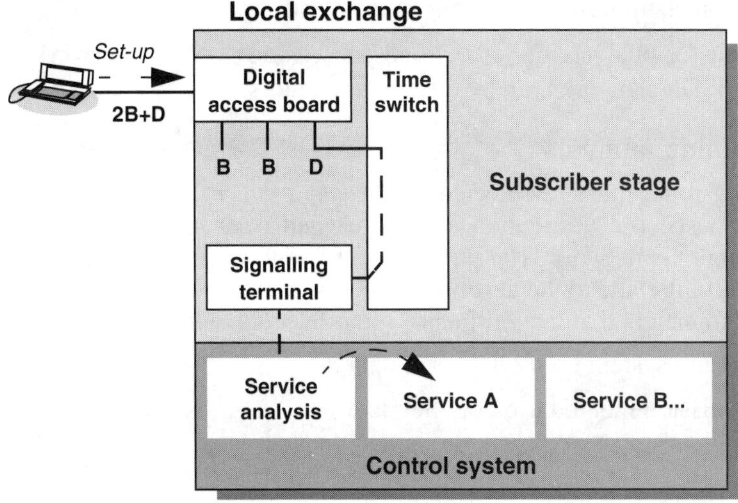

Figure C.3.7 Service analysis at the initial stage of an ISDN connection

3.3.3 Number analysis

Once the service analysis is finished, the number analysis can start, which means that the B-number is analysed. There are also other types of number analysis – for example, analysis of the A-number to verify that it has been accepted – and analyses that provide charging data.

The number analysis may encompass several numbering plans. The X.25 network uses a numbering plan according to Recommendation X.121. PSTN is based on E.163, and PSTN/ISDN on E.164.

When an ISDN subscriber connects his terminal to a data network, the digits are fetched from another numbering plan. To facilitate the digit analysis, each numbering plan has a unique code called *numbering and addressing plan indicator* (*NAPI*).

The number analysis results in a large amount of output data, which mainly consists of input data for other types of analysis. Some information from the number analysis is saved and used for connection control and for supervising the established connection.

The following are examples of key results of the number analysis:

- input data for routing analysis of outgoing connections to other parts of the network or to other networks;
- input data for charging analysis;
- information about terminating connections; and
- input data for analysis of restrictions concerning service interworking between ISDN networks run by different operators.

3.3.4 Routing analysis

An outgoing route must be selected to connect a call to other exchanges. Ordinarily, a specific destination can be reached over several alternative routes through the network. The purpose of the routing analysis is to find a suitable outgoing route to the destination addressed by the subscriber. ISDN has more parameters that may influence route selection, such as:

- the signalling system used on the route; or
- the transmission method used on the route.

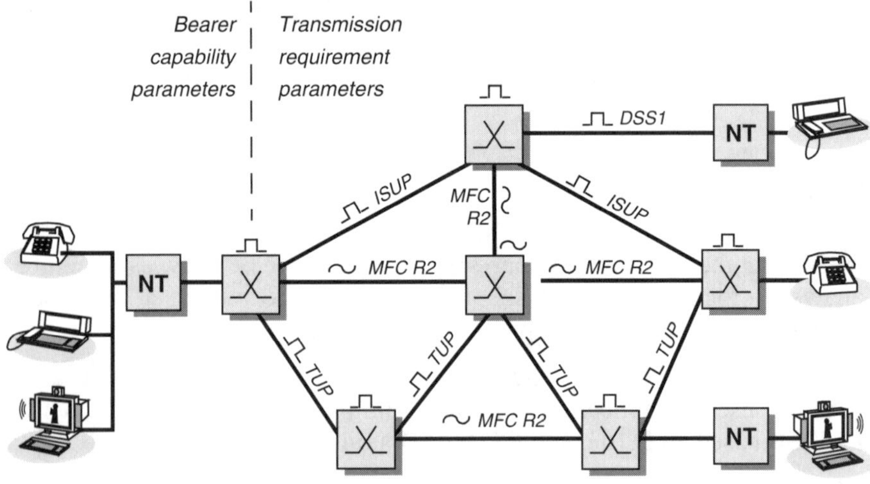

Figure C.3.8 Examples of parameters that influence route selection

All important requirements to be met by the bearer service are given in DSS1's SETUP message (bearer capability) and in the ISUP's initial address message (transmission requirement). If a subscriber requests the service "64 kbit/s unrestricted digital", an ISDN connection must be set up all the way to the called party. If the subscriber has requested the telephony service, the call can also use the PSTN.

Figure C.3.8 shows an example of a network whose exchanges are interconnected by both analog and digital routes.

3.3.5 Charging analysis

As in the case of the PSTN, network operators can set tariffs for ISDN that take into account the distance between the A-subscriber and the B-subscriber. Traditionally, this has been the only possible charging method and is still an important component of the charging principles for the PSTN and ISDN.

Both networks can also introduce a large number of supplementary services. (See Chapter 6.) ISDN-specific services include user-to-user messages, which can be sent during the set-up and communication phases. Another special data communication service is interworking with a PSPDN by means of packet handlers. The network operator may choose to charge a fixed fee, no fee at all or a usage-based fee.

The address information produced by the number analysis is essential to the charging analysis. This is usually called a charging case. Other input data for the charging analysis are:

- the subscriber service used and the result of its use (for example, unsuccessful activation of call forwarding should not be charged);
- the origin of the call (the type of subscriber that initiated it);
- services associated with the call; and
- any adaptation equipment connected, such as a packet handler.

The charging analysis uses a large number of tables, each having a specific function. The use of several tables ensures greater flexibility both for the manufacturer of the system and for the network operator who is to load data into the installed exchange. The following are examples of output data generated by the charging analysis:

- the exchange in the network that will handle the charging function;
- the party that will pay for the call (A-subscriber or B-subscriber);
- the charging method applied; and
- the tariff to be used for the call.

3.4 Network hierarchy

The ISDN network hierarchy is described in Volume 1, Chapter 3, Section 3.8, and in *Part B – PSTN*, which means that ISDN contains

- centrally and remotely installed subscriber switches;
- local exchanges;
- transit exchanges; and
- international exchanges.

All these network elements must be digital, of course, and all exchanges must be equipped with SS7 including ISUP. In most cases, all network elements are designed for both PSTN and ISDN applications.

Subscriber switches and local exchanges are dealt with in Sections 3.1–3.3. In the text that follows, we will add transit exchanges and international exchanges to the list.

3.4.1 Transit exchange, international exchange

A transit exchange can be completely transparent to ISDN in terms of signalling and transmission provided the interconnected circuits use the same signalling system. Exchanges with different ISUP signalling, with charging or gateway functions or with data processing of the signalling message are referred to as "filtering" (non-transparent) exchanges. An international exchange is normally of the filtering type. Other functions – notably in international exchanges – include the connection of echo suppression or echo cancellation and the use of digital circuit multiplication equipment (DCME).

3.5 Wideband/Multirate connections in ISDN

Standardised wideband bit rates are 2 •64 kbit/s, 6 •64 kbit/s, 24 •64 kbit/s and 30 •64 kbit/s, but many systems offer additional transfer rates. Wideband connections can be semipermanent or set up on demand, and all belong to the *unrestricted* class.

3.6 Packet traffic and packet switching in ISDN

Packet traffic (X.25) can be carried by both B-channels and D-channels in BRA and PRA. If the bit rate of packet traffic is below the 64 kbit/s of the B-channels and the 16 kbit/s of the D-channels, flags are inserted as fillers. The subscriber needs an adapter for this purpose. If the B-channel is used for BRA, the bit rate of packet traffic is limited to 9.6 kbit/s. *Figure C.3.9* shows how packet traffic is routed in BRA.

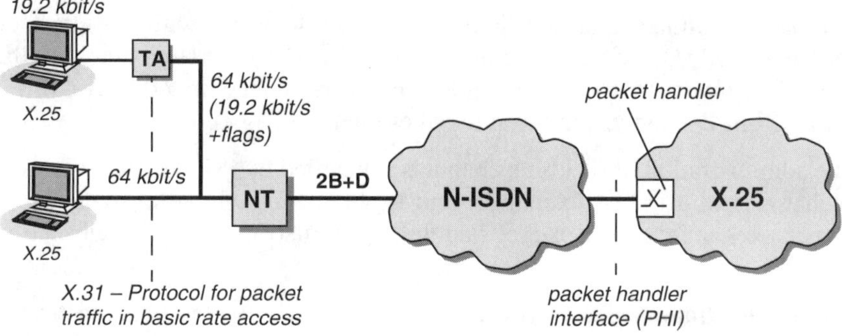

Figure C.3.9 Possible path for packet traffic in the case of basic rate access

The packet handler can be installed physically adjacent to an X.25 node, an ISDN node or as a stand-alone node.

Let's assume that the packet handler is connected to an ISDN transit exchange. Packet-traffic handling in the local exchange might then be as shown in *Figure C.3.10.*

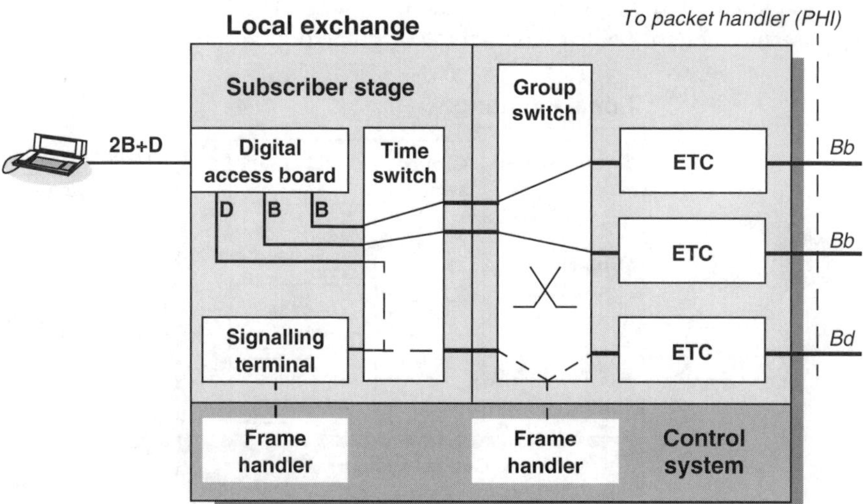

Figure C.3.10 Packet and frame handling in ISDN

As shown in *Figure C.3.10*, frame handling functions are provided in the subscriber stage control part and in the group switch control part. The frame handling functions concentrate the traffic on the D-channels, while traffic on the B-channels passes transparently through the switching stages.

The packet handler interface (PHI) is basically identical with the interface for PRA, 30B+D. Some B-channels in the PHI (Bb) are B-channels in the subscriber interface, too, while others (Bd) carry concentrated traffic originating from D-channels in the subscriber interface.

The administration of 64 kbit/s channels is handled by ISUP between a local exchange and a transit exchange, and by D-channel signalling between a transit exchange and a packet handler. (See also Chapter 7, Subsection 7.2.3.)

The administration of packet traffic in the Bd channels is handled by the address field in layer 2 of the packet frame, which unambiguously relates a subscriber access to a virtual channel in the PHI.

The address field also includes the SAPI, which separates X.25 traffic from signalling, and a terminal equipment identifier (TEI), which identifies the terminal.

3.7 Internet traffic in ISDN

When B-channels in BRA and PRA are used for Internet traffic, no A/D conversion via modem takes place, as it does in the PSTN. Consequently, ISDN requires no modem pools to extract the original, digital Internet traffic.

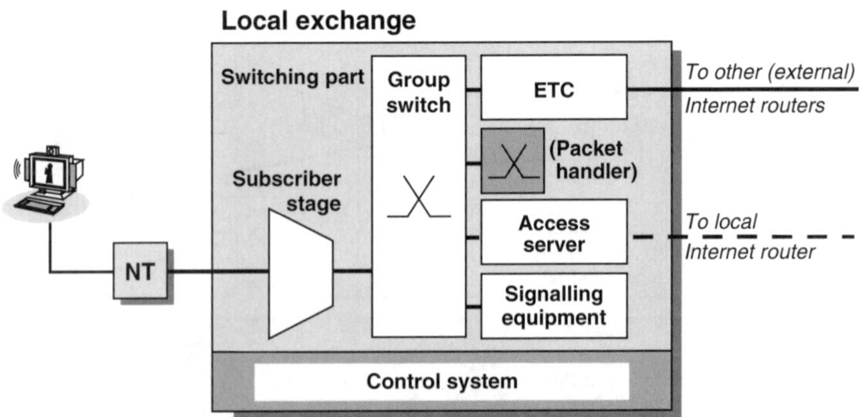

Figure C.3.11 ISDN local exchange with Internet access

ISDN exchanges used to extract Internet traffic can be equipped with ports to an access server. This server adapts Internet traffic to a LAN that includes an Internet router or converts the traffic into a statistically multiplexed bit stream, for transfer to a remote router. (See *Part H – The Internet*, Chapter 5, Subsections 5.4.1 and 5.5 for a description of intermediate access.) Frame relay, or sometimes ATM, is used for statistical multiplexing.

4 Transmission techniques

4.1 Transmission in ISDN

As far as transmission techniques are concerned, ISDN differs from the PSTN in a few basic respects.

ISDN requires digital transmission throughout the path between two subscribers.

ISDN uses *multiple access,* which enables the ISDN subscriber to connect a good deal more terminals to the access line than the line has capacity for. This could also be a disadvantage: If eight terminals have been connected to a two-channel access, then at least six terminals must be inactive all the time.

As we mentioned in Chapter 1, Subsection 1.2.2, PRA uses a 30B+D standard PCM system, 2048 kbit/s. BRA, on the other hand, uses a digital "mini-transmission system" of the PDH type with a capacity of 144 kbit/s, which corresponds to 2B+D. No international standard has been specified for the transmission system itself, but a common type uses a bit rate of 160 kbit/s and line code 2B1Q. This system is described in more detail in Subsection 4.1.1. ISDN accesses operating in a narrower band and designed according to a special standard are used for radio transmission. The B-channel's bit rate is reduced to 9.6 kbit/s in GSM systems, and to 32 kbit/s in DECT systems.

The standard ISDN design is used for ISDN transmission over copper pairs, optical fibre and coaxial cable.

In the following, we will deal first and foremost with transmission techniques for BRA 2B+D over copper pairs.

4.1.1 Reference points S and U

The introduction of ISDN involves some new aspects of transmission that relate to the digitisation of subscriber lines. In Chapter 2, we mentioned that the ITU-T has defined a number of reference points for subscriber connections in ISDN. This subsection describes the techniques for information transfer in reference points S and U. (See *Figure C.4.1.*)

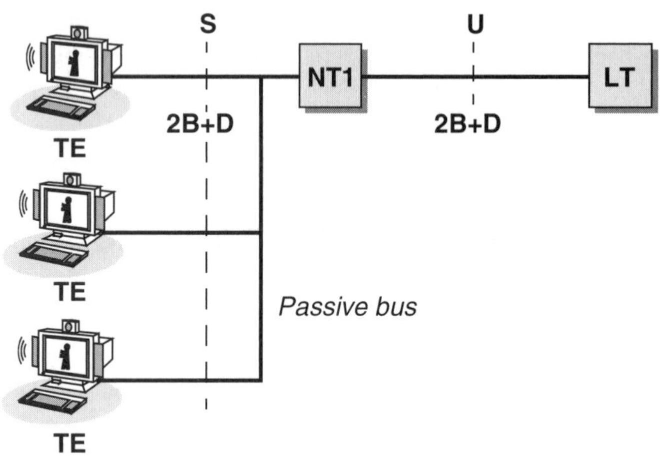

Figure C.4.1 Reference points S and U

The S-interface

The interface between TE and NT – called the S-interface – transfers information on four wires, two in each direction. The line coding method used in the S-interface is called pseudo-ternary alternate mark inversion (pseudo-ternary AMI). The following rules apply to this coding variant:

Pseudo-ternary rules:

- A binary "one" is always represented by no voltage, that is, 0.
- A binary "zero" is represented by voltage, -1 or +1.

AMI rules:

- Voltage -1 and +1 is to be sent alternately.

The result is a code form with no DC component. (See *Figure C.4.2.*)

The bit rate in the S-interface is 192 kbit/s in each direction. The information is transferred in 48-bit frames. The capacity available for information is restricted to 144 kbit/s because 12 of the 48 bits are used for frame synchronisation, terminal access, DC voltage equalisation, and other functions. *Figure C.4.3* shows how the 48 bits are used.

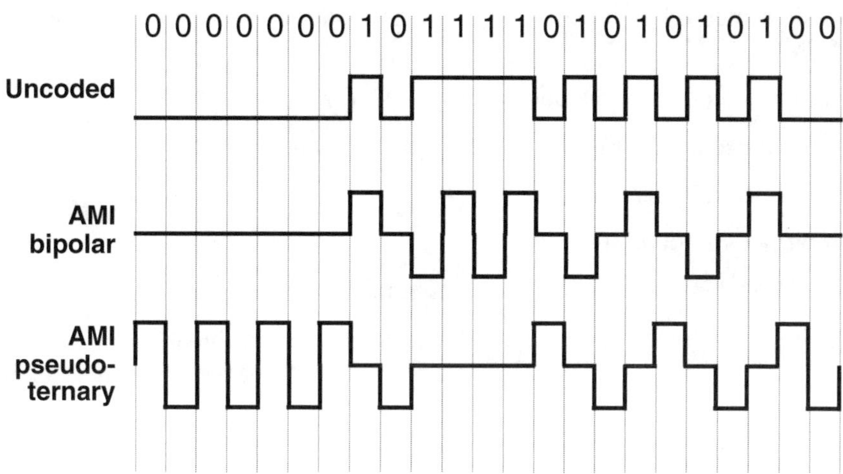

Figure C.4.2 Pseudo-ternary AMI code

Up to eight terminals may want to use a B-channel at the same time, so a specific access procedure has been prescribed for this channel. The procedure (*collision detection*) prevents multiple terminals from sending simultaneously.

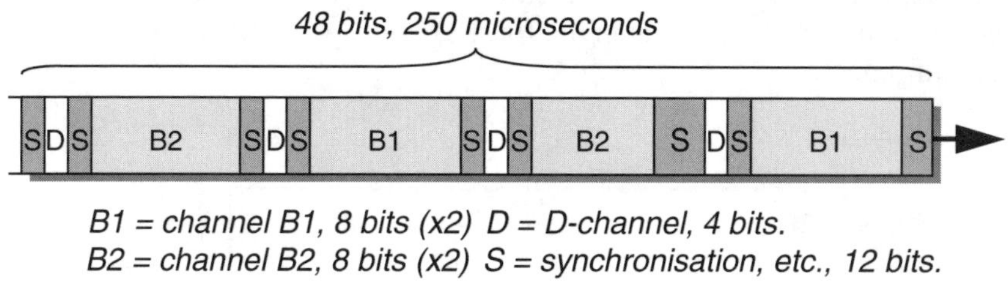

Figure C.4.3 Frame structure in the S-interface

The U-interface

Another important interface is the U-interface between LT and NT. The information transfer on the U-interface makes use of existing two-wire connections in the access network. The bit rate is 160 kbit/s, which includes 2B+D, frame synchronisation, and so on. Since no standard for transmission on the U-interface has been specified, several methods can be used. Two possible methods are echo cancelling and time compression multiplexing (TCM).

Echo cancellation is characterised by:

- simultaneous transmission in both directions (full duplex);
- elimination of echo; and
- a bit rate of 160 kbit/s.

The TCM method, which is less common, is characterised by:

- half duplex, that is, alternate, high-speed transfer of "bursts"; and
- a bit rate of 360 kbit/s.

Echo cancelling and line code

Due to imperfections in hybrids, the send signal from the user's transmitter will generate an echo signal that might disturb the received signal. The purpose of the echo canceller is to neutralise this disturbance. The principle applied is that of eliminating the echo by means of a compensating signal. *Figure C.4.4* shows the block structure of an echo canceller.

Since the echo signal looks different depending on the cable used, it must be possible to control the echo cancellation function to permit adaptation to the connection involved.

Echo cancellation is more effective than TCM but is also more complicated because it needs intelligence in the form of microprocessors in the terminating equipment.

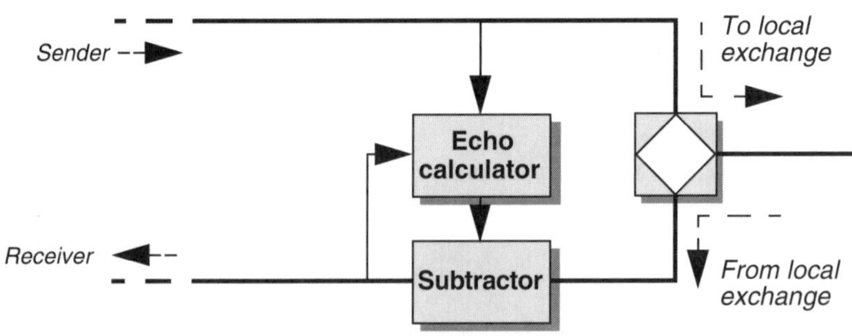

Figure C.4.4 The principle of echo cancelling

The line code used (2B1Q) is a four-level bipolar code where each signal element corresponds to two transmitted bits. Since the two-bit representation is called QUAT, the abbreviated form 2B1Q is interpreted as "two bits on one QUAT". The transfer rate is 160 kbit/s. (See *Figure C.4.5.*)

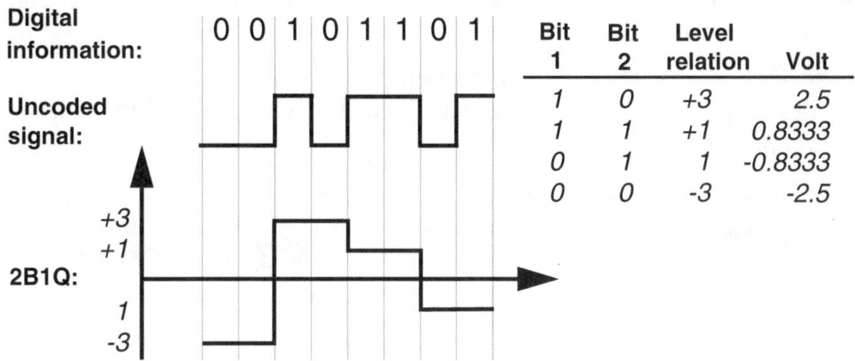

Bit 1	Bit 2	Level relation	Volt
1	0	+3	2.5
1	1	+1	0.8333
0	1	1	-0.8333
0	0	-3	-2.5

Figure C.4.5 Line code 2B1Q

The frame structure of 2B1Q code is shown in *Figure C.4.6*. The frame contains a total of 240 bits. Eighteen of these are used for synchronisation, and six for operation and maintenance. The remaining bits form 12 18-bit words for the B and D-channels.

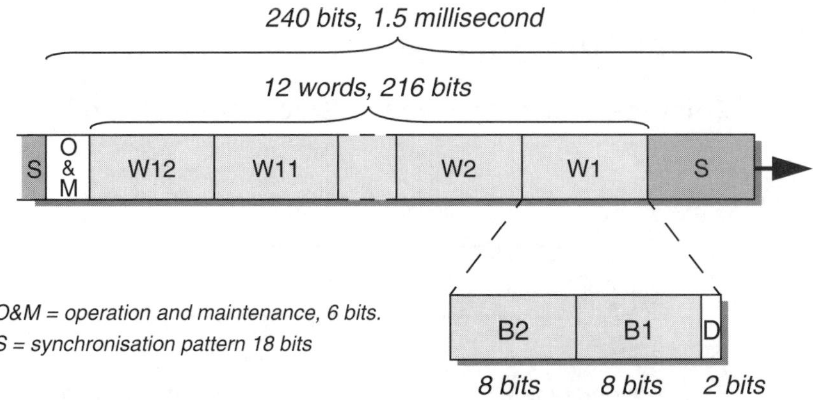

Figure C.4.6 Frame structure of the 2B1Q code

5 Trunk and access networks

5.1 Introduction

The PSTN and ISDN transmit voice and data, so they make more or less the same demands on the trunk and access networks. Thus, most of Chapter 5 of *Part B – PSTN* applies to ISDN as well, but some important differences must be emphasised.

- ISDN is totally dependent on the digitisation of the network. Some countries have only recently begun to digitise exchanges and transmission equipment.
- ISDN can offer a higher bit rate. This paves the way for the introduction of more advanced services, many of which require high transmission quality. One example is Internet traffic, with a bit rate of 128 kbit/s.
- The fact that ISDN has more advanced signalling functions facilitates the control of echo cancellers and DCME equipment. The result is flexible adaptation of network functions to the transferred services: telephony, data, fax and so on.
- The range of BRA transfer over ordinary copper pairs is somewhat restricted. Nevertheless, a conductor diameter of 0.4 mm will usually allow a distance of at least 4 or 5 km from the subscriber switch to a network termination.

Some reference configurations for BRA are described below.

5.2 Configurations

5.2.1 Point-to-point connection between terminal and NT

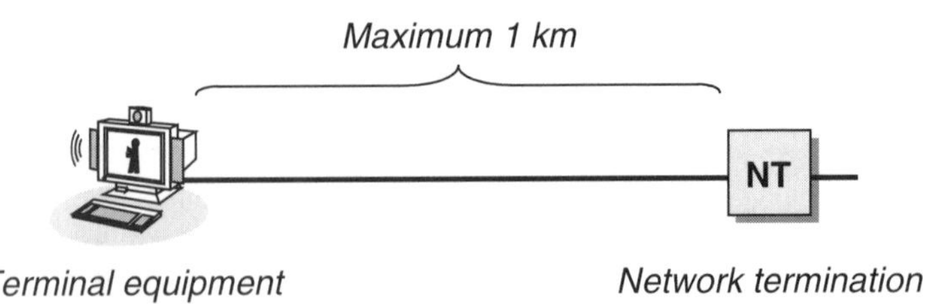

Figure C.5.1 Maximum point-to-point distance

A simple example of a BRA installation is the connection of a data or telephony terminal to the network termination (NT1), a so-called point-to-point connection. An NT may have several connections of this type arranged in a star configuration. The factor that restricts distance is the permissible attenuation (6 dB), which corresponds to a distance of about 1 km from the NT to the TE.

5.2.2 Passive bus

An alternative way of connecting terminals to the network termination is to use a passive bus that can connect up to eight terminals. (See *Figure C.5.2.*)

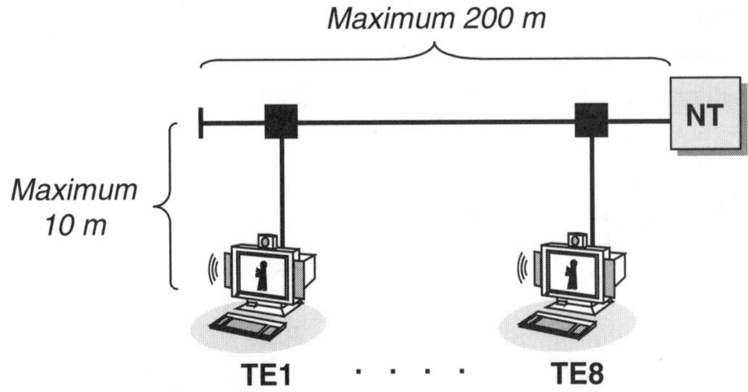

Figure C.5.2 Passive-bus configuration

The range of the S-interface, between NT and TE, is very short, not more than 200 m. The points to which TE is connected must be connected in series, and the distance between a connection point and a terminal must not exceed 10 m. These restrictions seldom pose any problems but they may complicate the connection of several terminals in a star-shaped network. Other types of equipment (with no S-interface) may also be connected to the bus via a TA.

The network allows operators to allocate up to eight different addresses to each BRA. These addresses can be used either for routing a call to a specific terminal or for giving a terminal several addresses. In other words, terminals can be given unique numbers as though they had separate connections to the network, However, the subscriber has access only to his two B-channels, which means that if calls are in progress on two telephones on the passive bus, he cannot use another service that requires a B-channel. But he can use the D-channel (provided it is idle) to set up a packet-switched data connection. The individual numbers are programmed in each terminal.

5.3 Some access variants

Figures C.5.3–C.5.5 show examples of typical ISDN accesses.

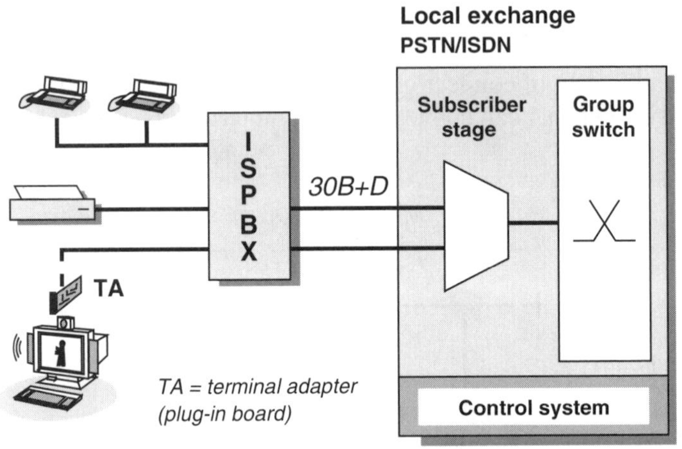

Figure C.5.3 Connection of an ISDN-adapted PBX to primary rate access

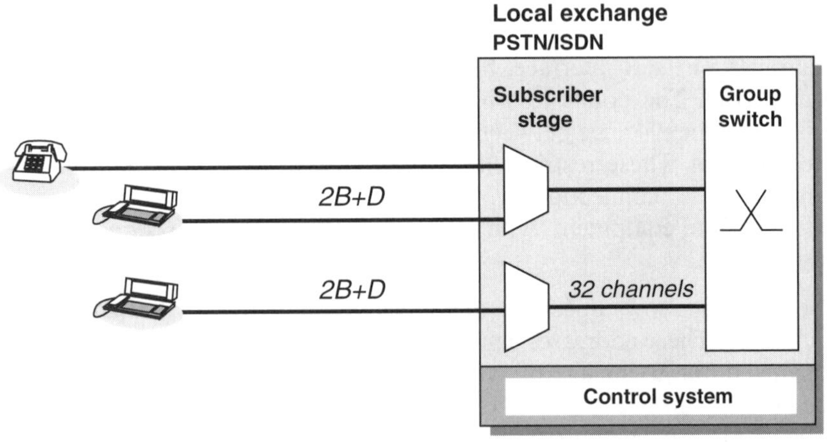

Figure C.5.4 Connection of basic rate access installed within a few kilometres of the local exchange

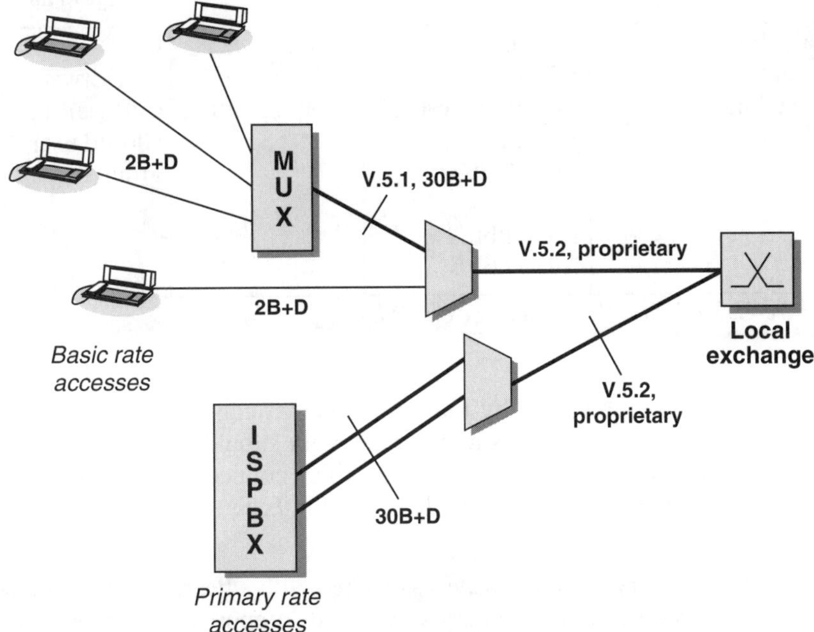

Figure C.5.5 Different ways of connecting basic rate and primary rate access in the access network

6 Network intelligence and value-added services

6.1 Introduction

As we mentioned in Chapter 2, Subsection 2.2.2, ISDN services fall into three basic categories: bearer services, teleservices and supplementary services. *Figure C.6.1* illustrates this division and gives examples of different types of service.

ISDN services			
Teleservices	**Bearer services**		**Supplementary services**
Telephony Telefax Mixed mode Videotex	*Circuit mode* 3.1 kHz audio 64 kbit/s unrestrict. Speech 2 •64 kbit/s 384 kbit/s 1,536 kbit/s 1,920 kbit/s	*Packet mode* X.25 User signalling	CLIP Call forwarding Call waiting Closed user group

Figure C.6.1 Examples of services in ISDN

A teleservice is represented by the terminals that can be connected to the NT. A bearer service indicates how the network should transport the information. The basic service in ISDN is a 64 kbit/s connection, which can also be provided in multiples. For example, 1,536 kbit/s equals 24 64 kbit/s channels.

Supplementary services are always associated with a bearer service or a teleservice. A specific supplementary service can support several teleservices and/or bearer services.

On the whole, ISDN offers the same supplementary services as the PSTN plus a few additional ones. For example, the service closed user group (CUG) is an ISDN supplementary service that originated in data networks. Different countries and operators have introduced different supplementary services.

The PSTNs of some countries have not included standard supplementary services for telephony (such as call waiting and call forwarding). Instead, these services have been offered by ISDN, thus contributing to its expansion. In other countries, they have been available in the PSTN but not in ISDN.

One problem has been the lack of standards for supplementary services in ISDN, which has resulted in varying methods of implementation.

Supplementary services are implemented either locally, in the nodes to which the subscribers are connected (distributed implementation), or in special network intelligence nodes (centralised implementation).

Network service functionality can be layered as shown in *Figure C.6.2.*

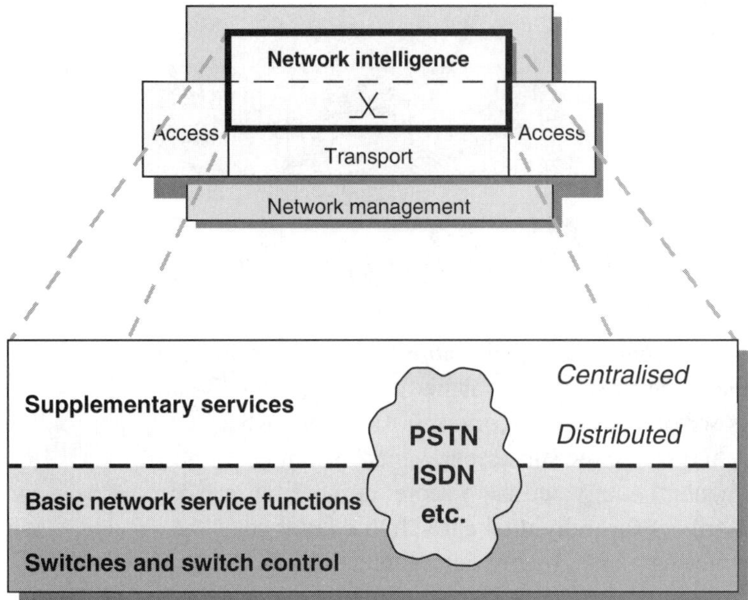

Figure C.6.2 Layering of network service functionality

6.2 Distributed supplementary services

6.2.1 Euro-ISDN

As mentioned in Chapter 2, Euro-ISDN has been adopted for use in Europe. A number of supplementary services – associated with the bearer service 64 kbit/s unrestricted – have been defined. They can also support other circuit mode bearer services, and some of them can support packet mode bearer services.

Like teleservices and bearer services, supplementary services are introduced in stages.

Supplementary services, Stage 1

Euro-ISDN1 includes five supplementary services:

- *CLIP*: *calling line identification presentation* allows the A-subscriber's number to be displayed on the B-subscriber's terminal.

Figure C.6.3 Calling line identification presentation

- *CLIR*: *calling line identification restriction* allows the A-subscriber to prevent the presentation of his number on the B-subscriber's terminal. This service is very important in situations where CLIP is prohibited by law, and where the subscriber wants his number to be secret. CLIR can be permanently activated for a secret number but can also be used by other subscribers for individual calls. In the latter case, the service is activated by entering a code before communication starts.

Figure C.6.4 Calling line identification restriction

- *DDI: direct dialling-in* makes it possible to call a PBX extension without operator assistance.
- *MSN: multiple subscriber number* allows up to eight numbers to be associated with one BRA.
- *Terminal portability* means a user can move his terminal from one jack to another during a call in progress.

Supplementary services in Euro-ISDN2

- *UUS: user-to-user signalling* allows a user to send and receive a limited amount of user information over the D-channel either before or during a call.

Figure C.6.5 User-to-user signalling

The following variants are available:
- UUS-1: message transfer during the set-up phase
- UUS-2: message transfer when the B-subscriber receives ringing signals
- UUS-3: message transfer during a call in progress

- *SUB: subaddress* allows a user of an access to be identified by adding digits to the subscriber number.
- *CUG: closed user group* is a group whose members are not free to make calls to addressees outside the group. Access to the group can also be barred.
- *COLP: connected line identification presentation* allows the A-subscriber to see the B-subscriber's national ISDN number, including extension and MSN.
- *COLR: connected line identification restriction* allows the B-subscriber to prevent presentation of his national ISDN number.

Supplementary services in Euro-ISDN3 or later stages

- *UUS-2 and UUS-3*, see above.
- *AOC: advice of charge* allows the A-subscriber to be advised of usage-based charging
  - during call set-up (*AOC-S*);
  - during the call (*AOC-D*); or
  - at the end of the call (*AOC-E*).
- *Call waiting* informs a user during a call in progress if another subscriber is trying to call him. The user can either accept or reject the new call. In Euro-ISDN, this service is available for BRA only.
- *CCBS: completion of call to busy subscriber* automatically sends a call-back signal to the B-subscriber when his line becomes free.

- *Conference call* is a telephone call between three or more parties.
- *MMC: meet me conference* books a conference call in advance.
- *CFU: call forwarding, unconditional,* allows calls to be connected to another number. CFU may be restricted to a specific teleservice; for example, activation of the telephony service will not affect the telefax service.

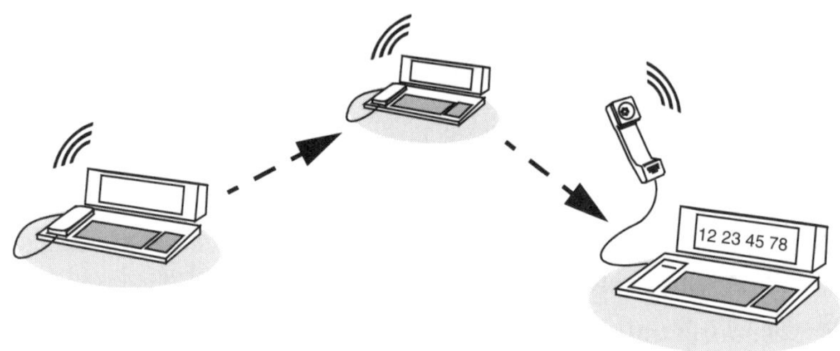

Figure C.6.6 Call forwarding, unconditional

- *CFB: call forwarding busy* forwards all calls (or only “speech” calls) to another number if the called subscriber is busy. This service, too, can be restricted to a specific teleservice.
- *CFNR: call forwarding no reply* forwards incoming calls to another number if the caller receives no answer. This service can also be restricted to a specific teleservice.
- *CD: call deflection* allows the addressed party to answer the call or let it be forwarded.
- *3PTY: three-party service* allows the user to communicate with two persons at the same time or alternate between two calls.
- *CH: call hold* allows the user to hold a call, make a new call, finish the new call and then return to the call he put on hold.
- *MCI: malicious-call identification* allows a subscriber to order the network to record the A-number of an incoming call for later identification. The A and B-subscribers’ subaddresses can also be recorded.

Implementation

All supplementary Euro-ISDN services described here are usually distributed, that is, installed in local exchanges.

6.2.2 Other distributed supplementary services

- *ADI: abbreviated dialling* simplifies dialling of long numbers and numbers that are frequently called.
- *ICB: incoming call barring* bars specific types of incoming calls.
- *Call diversion protection* or *incoming diverted call barring* is activated by a subscriber to stop all incoming, forwarded calls. This protective function can be defined per teleservice and be controlled by the subscriber.

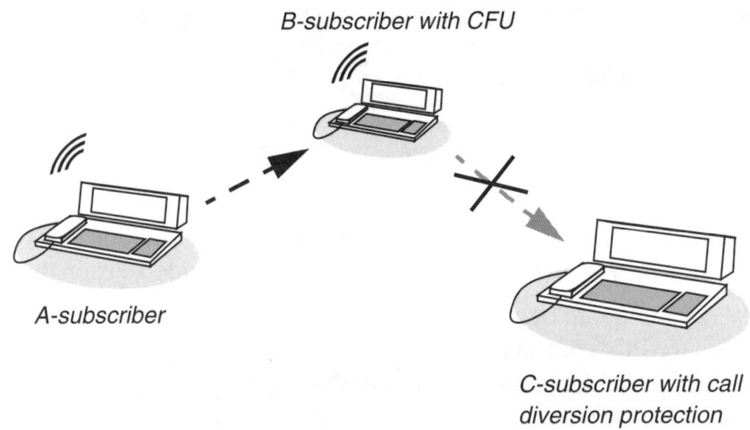

Figure C.6.7 Call diversion protection

- *FDC: fixed destination call* automatically connects the call to a predetermined number, either directly or after a short delay. If the subscriber dials another number during the delay, the service is deactivated and the subscriber can use his telephone in the usual manner.
- *OCB: outgoing call barring* bars all or some types of outgoing calls. The service is user-controlled (UC) or fixed (F).
- *Call forwarding to fixed announcement* allows an ISDN subscriber to forward incoming telephone calls to a recorded message.
- *PRI: priority* assigns subscribers with this service priority when the exchange is overloaded. This service can also affect the selection of outgoing routes in that the subscriber has priority in overload situations.
- *Interception service* reroutes calls to absent subscribers to recorded messages or to a telephonist.

- *TH: trunk hunting* has the system search for an idle channel according to a predetermined method. The purpose of trunk hunting is to obtain even distribution among the channels that connect user equipment.
- *LH: line hunting* distributes incoming calls among free extensions.

6.3 Centralised supplementary services

This section describes some of the supplementary services for ISDN subscribers that are implemented in IN technology. Most of them are available to PSTN subscribers, as well, but often with less functionality than in ISDN. (The services are also described in Volume 1, Chapter 6.)

- *Freephone* can have greater functionality – such as statistics of the number of calls from different types of terminal – in ISDN. A user can opt to have only the freephone number presented and not the actual B-number.
- *Televoting* allows calls of a specific category to be put through; the staff at a TV station may want to put through calls from, say, video terminals only.
- *Credit-card call* can be used for data communication, as well, in ISDN. Requests for PIN code and other data can be sent in the form of text messages (instead of spoken messages) to the ISDN terminal. The network operator can offer extra accounts with different tariffs for different teleservices and terminals (such as fax, telephony or data).
- *UPT: universal personal telecommunication* grants access for an ISDN subscriber using an ISDN terminal to the same supplementary services all the time (for example, user-to-user signalling and charging information).
- *UAN: universal access number* allows the presentation of the universal number alone – not the actual B-number – to the calling and the called party. The number can be the same for telephony, fax and data. The system routes the call to the desired access.
- *Freefax* is the fax variant of *freephone*.
- *Number portability*. (See *Part B – PSTN*, Chapter 6, Subsection 6.3.1.)

6.4 Value-added services

ISDN subscribers can be offered more bandwidth for value-added services than PSTN subscribers. This means that ISDN may capture a large market share as far as access to information services over the Internet is concerned.

7 Signalling

7.1 Introduction

As is evident from Chapters 1 and 6, ISDN is an extremely flexible network with many bearer service variants offering different bandwidths and with many supplementary services. This level of flexibility requires powerful signalling between subscriber and exchange as well as between exchanges.

Subscriber signalling (D-channel signalling) is typical of and unique to ISDN, but a simplified form of the interexchange signalling (ISUP signalling) used in ISDN is being introduced in the PSTN.

Subscriber signalling is carried by *LAPD links,* while interexchange signalling is carried by the message transfer part (MTP) of the SS7 network; see the description in *Part E – The signalling network.*

The centralised supplementary services (see Chapter 6, Section 6.3) also require the dialogue handling protocol mentioned in Volume 1, Chapter 7, Section 7.8, and in *Part E – The signalling network*, namely the transaction capabilities application part (TCAP).

Quite a few signalling variants are used in ISDN: both old and new ISUP protocols and national and regional ISUP variants. This makes translation between different ISUP protocols necessary, especially in international exchanges.

ISDN signalling has a unique characteristic in that it can carry a limited amount of user information between subscribers – user-to-user messages, for example – and signalling (such as Qsig and DPNSS) between PBXs.

7.2 Subscriber signalling

7.2.1 Survey

The D-channel is used for signalling between user and network. In other words, the D-channel serves as a means of transport for the signalling messages that control communication on the B-channels.

The protocols for the D-channel follow the OSI model's division into layers 1–3. They have been standardised by the ITU-T and form DSS1, specified in Recommendation Q.931. Since DSS1 has a common signalling channel for several traffic channels, it is a common-channel signalling (CCS) system.

The following describes the standard that applies to the S-interface for BRA 2B+D.

Layer	ITU-T recommendation
3	I.451 – Network layer protocol
2	I.441/Q.921 – Link access protocol
1	I.430 – 2B+D, physical layer

Figure C.7.1 Protocols for the basic rate interface in reference point S

Like SS7, the D-channel carries packet mode messages. The packets are distributed on D-channel bits in the physical layer of the S-interface. The D-channel bits are separated by octets from the B-channels (B1 and B2) as shown in *Figure C.7.2*.

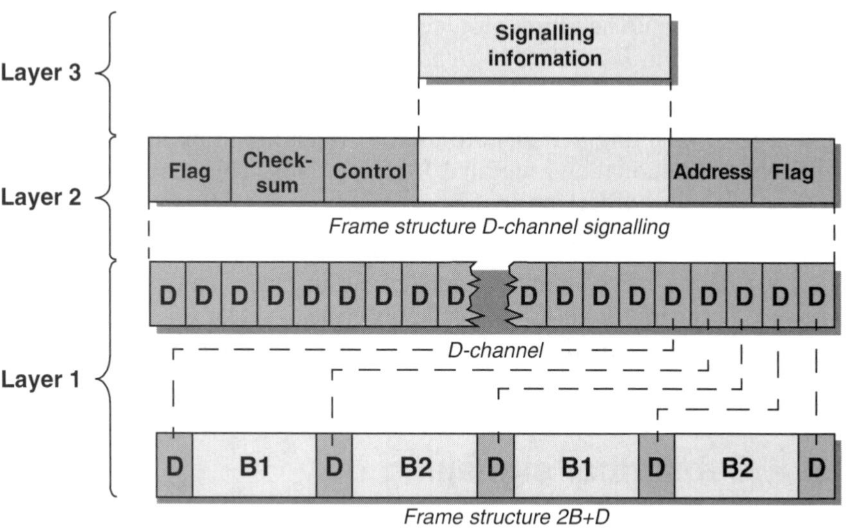

Figure C.7.2 Relationships between D-channel protocols for OSI layers 1–3

Layer 3: The network layer protocol specifies procedures for the set-up and disconnection of calls between users. A "procedure" in this context is a number of messages on the D-channel. Recommendation I.451 defines the composition of signalling messages.

Layer 2: The ITU-T has defined LAPD as the link access protocol for the D-channel. Recommendation I.441 defines:

- set-up and disconnection of data links;
- flow control;
- sequence control;
- fault management; and
- frame synchronisation and frame structure for signalling messages on the D-channel.

Layer 1: This is where the physical layer for the 2B+D basic rate interface is specified. Recommendation I.430 describes the following layer 1 functions:

- bit flow and frame structure for the multiplexing of the B1, B2 and D-channels; and
- activation procedures for the bus between TE and NT.

The following is a somewhat simplified description of the protocols in the three layers. (See also *Figure C.7.2*.)

- Layer 3 gives guidelines for the composition of signalling messages.
- Layer 2 gives a frame structure for the transport of signalling messages using the D-channel bits.
- Layer 1 provides a flow of information bits of 64+64+16 kbit/s for the 2B+D information (including signalling information).

7.2.2 Layer 3 – Signalling message of network layer protocol

The structure of the signalling message is shown in *Figure C.7.3*. It always begins with the three fields *protocol discriminator*, *call reference* and *message type*, followed by the actual signalling information.

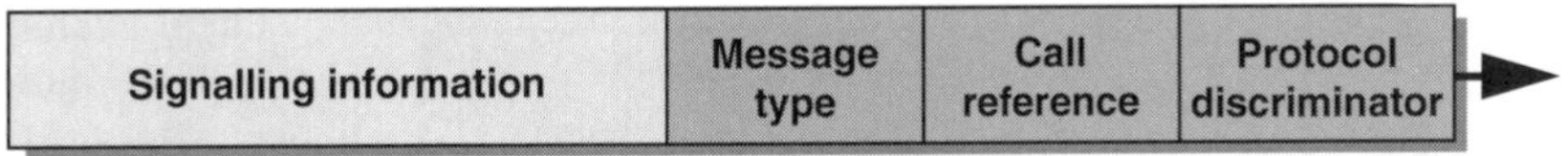

Figure C.7.3 The main components of a signalling message

Protocol discriminator

This field instructs the receiver in the choice of protocol, thus making it possible to use other protocols for layer 3, such as X.25 or a national protocol. The field length is one octet.

Call reference

This field is used to identify the call to which the signalling message belongs. The field can be one or more octets long. Call reference is preceded by an octet indicating the field length (number of octets).

Message type

This field indicates the type of message to be sent. The field is always one octet long. Four groups of message types have been defined:

- messages for call set-up;
- messages sent during the information phase;
- messages for disconnection; and
- other messages.

Signalling information

The signalling information is composed of information elements. An information element may consist of one or more octets.

The complexity and variability of the signalling information are reflected by the parameters included in the first message type, SETUP, which is sent to the local exchange when an ISDN connection is to be established. (See *Figure C.7.4.*) The parameters concern B-number information, supplementary services and transmission requirements to be met by the network, for example, unrestricted digital transmission. Such transmission requirements are included in the bearer capability part of the SETUP message.

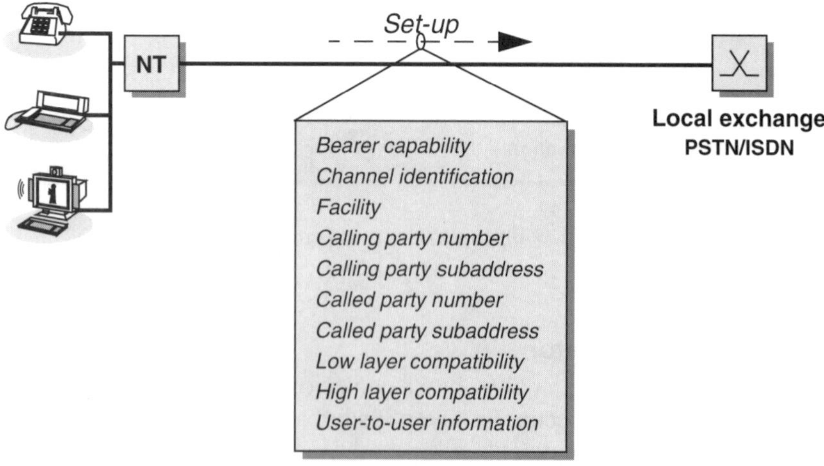

Figure C.7.4 SETUP message with parameters

7.2.3 Layer 2 – LAPD frame

The signalling message is placed in the information field in frames provided by layer 2 (see *Figure C.7.5*). The following terms recur frequently in layer 2 protocols:

- HDLC: *high-level data link control* is an example of a bit-oriented layer 2 protocol;
- LAP: *link access procedure* is a general designation for the ITU-T's recommendation for layer 2 protocols;
- LAPB: *link access procedure balanced* is an example of a layer 2 protocol for X.25;
- LAPD: *link access procedure on the D-channel* is an example of a layer 2 protocol for the D-channel.

LAPD is the focus of our discussion here. See also Part F1, Subsection 2.2.2.

Frame structure

The frame structure in layer 2 is shown in *Figure C.7.5*. The number of octets may vary. A unique bit pattern (a flag) indicates where a frame begins and ends.

Two formats are used: type A, without an information field, and type B, with an information field. The frame also contains an address field and a control field.

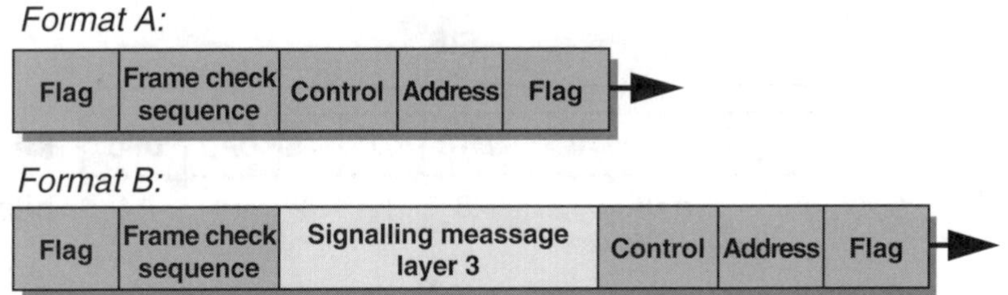

Figure C.7.5 Frame structures

Address field

The address is composed of two octets:

- the SAPI indicates the desired type of service (signalling or a packet data service); and
- the TEI identifies the terminal.

Control field

Layer 2 has three types of frame structure. The control field indicates the type of message concerned.

- Information format: This frame is used for signalling messages from layer 3.
- Supervisory format: This frame is used for the transfer of acknowledgements, requests for retransmission, and messages reporting that the receiver is not ready.
- Unnumbered format: This frame is used for setting up and disconnecting data links.

Frame check sequence

Frame check sequence (FCS) contains a checksum which is the result of a calculation made on the bits from "address" up to and including "information". The field consists of two octets.

7.3 Interexchange signalling for ISDN

As we have already mentioned, the ISUP uses the MTP in the SS7 network as a bearer. The SS7 network is very reliable and includes functions to ensure that only noncorrupted ISUP messages are received.

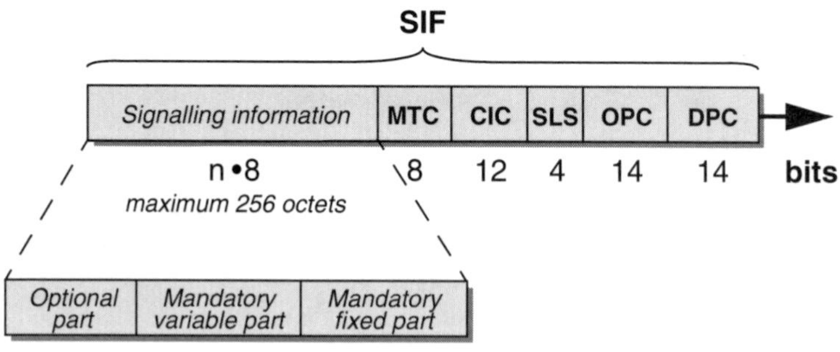

Figure C.7.6 Signalling message in ISDN

The format of signalling messages in ISDN differs somewhat from that of PSTN messages. (See *Part E – The signalling network*, Chapter 2, Subsection 2.2.3.) The actual ISUP information consists of message type code (MTC) plus signalling information in the signalling information field (SIF).

This is the equivalent of H0/H1 plus signalling information in the telephone user part (TUP). The labels also differ slightly. In ISUP, the signalling link selection (SLS) field is separated from the circuit identification code (CIC) field. As *Figure C.7.6* shows, the signalling information field in ISUP consists of a mandatory fixed part, a mandatory variable part and an optional part (described in Section 7.3.2).

ISUP is described in the ITU-T's Recommendations Q.761–Q.764.

7.3.1 Message type code

The message type code (MTC) indicates the type of message that follows. *Figure C.7.7* shows examples of message types defined by the ITU-T.

Message	**Code**
Address (IAM)	00000001
Address complete	00000110
Response	00001001
Information	00000100
Release	00001011

Figure C.7.7 Message type codes

7.3.2 Signalling information

The signalling information consists of a number of parameters, such as B-number, charging data and the service requested. The length of the parameters can be fixed or variable; parameters of variable length also have a length indicator. They are sent in a predetermined order and located in three "parts".

- The *mandatory fixed part* contains parameters of a fixed length, which means that their length need not be indicated; nor is it necessary to indicate the parameter names, because each message type always sends the parameters in a predetermined order.
- The *mandatory variable part* contains parameters of varying length (number of octets). Pointers are used to indicate the first octet of each parameter. All pointers are sent first. No name is needed because the message type determines the order of their appearance. Each parameter begins with a length indicator.

- The *optional part* contains any additional parameters. Since these parameters are sent in arbitrary order, names and length indicators must be included.

Figure C.7.8 shows examples of parameters defined by the ITU-T.

Parameter	**Code**
B-subscriber number	00000100
A-subscriber number	00001001
Additional number	00000101
User-to-user information	00100000

Figure C.7.8 Codes for signalling information

7.3.3 Setting up interexchange connections in ISDN

All the information required to set up a connection between two ISDN subscribers is contained in the initial address message (IAM). Much of this information originates from the SETUP message used in subscriber signalling.

Transmission requirements from the bearer capability part of the SETUP message are translated into transmission requirement parameters in ISUP. Such ISUP parameters could relate to echo suppressors and satellite hops. The objective is high-quality of data calls (no echo suppressors) and of voice connections (not more than one satellite hop).

See also *Figure C.3.8* which shows the relationship between routing on one side and signalling and transmission requirements on the other. IAM contains basic data for routing to the B-subscriber's ISDN exchange and for setting up a connection to that exchange.

Let's assume that we are going to set up a connection between exchanges 1 and 5 via the nodes 2 and 4, as shown in *Figure C.7.9*. The nodes 1, 3 and 5 are exchanges as well as signalling points (SP) in the signalling network, and the nodes 2 and 4 are signal transfer points (STP). The description below gives a simplified illustration of the set-up procedure. In reality, the procedure involves the exchange of a number of messages, such as call, set-up request and acknowledgements.

- *Node 1.* An IAM is created and sent to node 2. A voice or data channel is set up between node 1 and node 3.

- *Node 2*. The IAM's routing label information is analysed. The IAM is sent on to node 3.
- *Node 3*. The IAM's routing label and B-number information are analysed. A voice or data channel is set up between node 3 and node 5. A new IAM is created and sent to node 4.
- *Node 4*. The IAM's routing label information is analysed. The IAM is sent on to node 5.
- *Node 5*. The IAM's routing label and B-number information are analysed.

A connection has now been set up between node 1 and node 5.

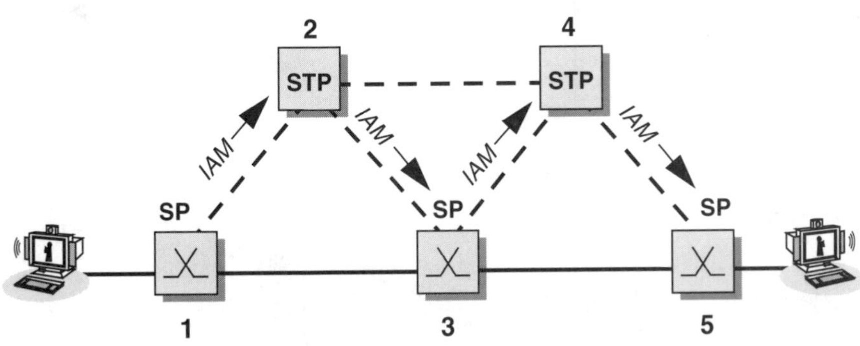

Figure C.7.9 Procedure for setting up a connection between ISDN local exchanges

7.3.4 Example of subscriber signalling for ISDN call set-up

We will now describe the signalling required when an ISDN subscriber (A) is to communicate with an ISDN subscriber (B) belonging to another local exchange. See *Figure C.7.10*.

After the A-subscriber has dialled the B-number and pressed the send key, a SETUP message is sent on the D-channel to the local exchange. If, after analysis, the message is found to contain all the necessary information, a CALL PROCEED signal is sent to the A-subscriber's terminal. This means that no more set-up information can be given.

When the A-subscriber's local exchange has selected an outgoing circuit, an ISUP message – IAM – is sent to the B-subscriber's local exchange. This message contains all initial data about the connection. After the IAM has been analysed, a SETUP message is sent on the D-channel to the B-subscriber's terminal. If the message is correct and complete, the terminal actuates a ringing signal and sends an ALERT message to its local exchange (indicating that the ringing function is being applied at the called terminal).

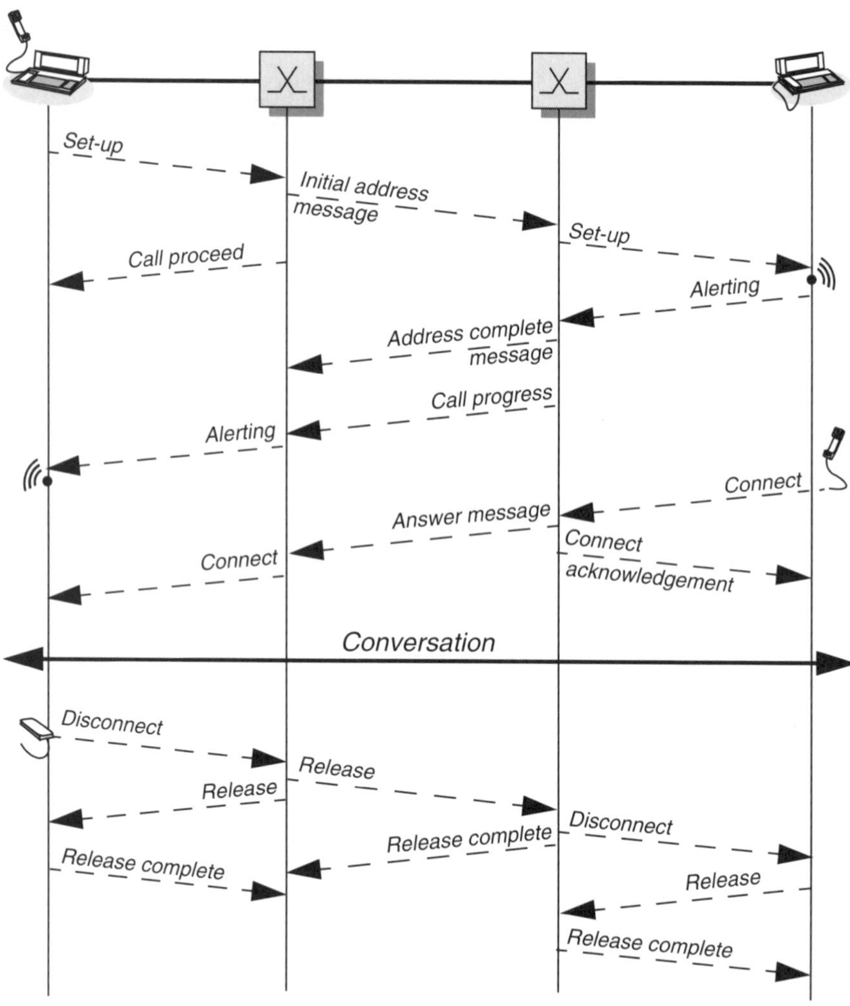

Figure C.7.10 Signalling required when setting up and disconnecting an ISDN connection

Local exchange B now sends an "address complete" message (ACM) to local exchange A, thus indicating that the B-subscriber is free. In response to the received ALERT message, exchange B sends an ISUP "call progress" message (CPG) to exchange A. When this message is received by the A-exchange, an ALERT message is also sent (on the D-channel) to the A-subscriber's terminal, which responds by generating a ringing tone.

If the B-subscriber answers, his terminal sends a CONNECT message on the D-channel. This message (CONNECT ACK) is acknowledged by exchange B, which also sends it on to exchange A in the form of an "answer" message (ANM). Exchange A, in turn, sends a CONNECT message (on the D-channel) to the A-subscriber's terminal, which also acknowledges that message. A connection is thus set up and the charging process has started.

The disconnect phase starts when the A-subscriber hangs up. (Note that in some systems the B-subscriber can also initiate disconnect.) If the A-subscriber hangs up first, his exchange sends a "release" message (REL), which starts the release process. Once the B-subscriber's exchange has released the connection, it answers by sending the "release complete" message (RLC).

Figure C.7.10 shows the ISUP signals and how they relate to the signals sent in DSS1 messages to the subscribers.

8 Network management

8.1 Introduction

A general description of the operation and maintenance functions is found in Volume 1. A large portion of the equipment in ISDN – such as the switching hardware equipment and the IN platform – is shared with other networks. As in other networks, the telecommunications management network (TMN) and simple network management protocol (SNMP) standards can be provided for centralised operation and maintenance.

Specific ISDN management objects are the ISDN subscriber database, the charging function and the switching functions. A typical network architecture with centralised operation and maintenance is shown in *Figure C.8.1,* where the following abbreviations are used:

- operations support system (OSS)
- operation and maintenance centre (OMC)
- network management centre (NMC)

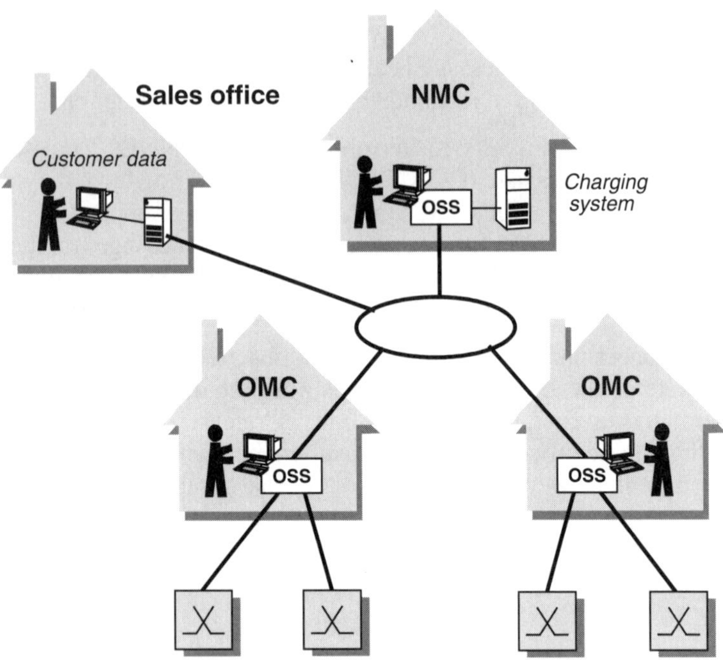

Figure C.8.1 Example of organisation for network management in ISDN

The higher degree of complexity in ISDN compared to the PSTN makes stricter demands on both customers' and network operators' understanding of how the different services function. To this end, we need a customer support centre with information about parameter settings, call procedures, intercommunication between different networks and so on.

Operations disturbances in the network are recorded regionally and by the customer support centre. All disturbances are documented, and all faults are corrected, either by regional staff or by the network management centre.

Different units will have a varying degree of experience and skills in ISDN operation, but the purpose of the network management centre is to concentrate experience and to serve as a backup source of technical know-how.

8.2 ISDN equipment

The subscriber's terminals and, to some extent, the interface to NT are the most frequent sources of problems due to the fact that customers' equipment and the network are not always fully compatible. To avoid these problems, it is essential that the subscriber terminals be approved according to applicable standards.

Access equipment such as multiplexers have built-in operation and maintenance functions for supervising and controlling subscriber lines. The multiplexer is monitored regionally but can also be called up from the customer support centre or the network management centre when a fault has to be corrected.

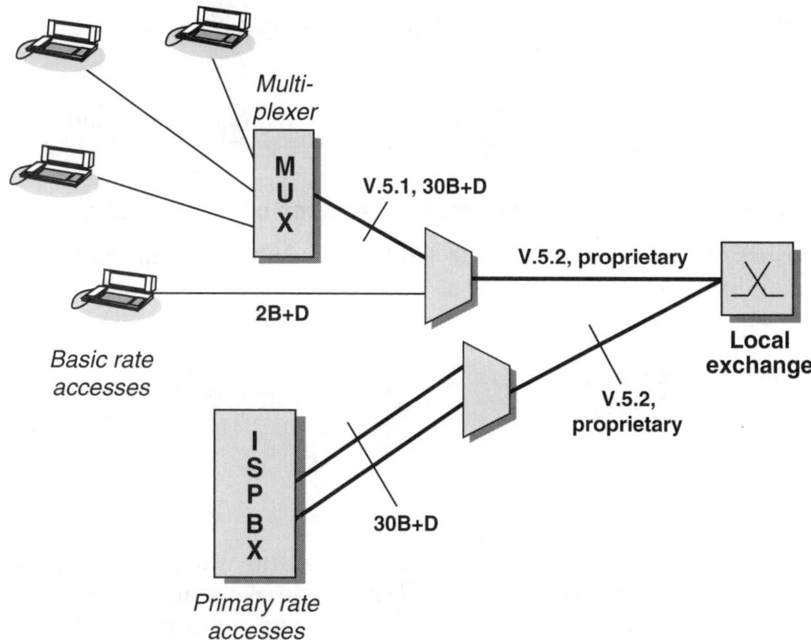

Figure C.8.2 Network elements for basic rate and primary rate access

8.3 Operations functions for subscriber access

The operations functions for subscriber accesses comprise:

- connection and disconnection of subscriber lines;
- transfer of data between network elements;
- collection of traffic data;
- fault and disturbance supervision;

- continuous fault correction;
- fault tracing; and
- quality checking.

ISDN is better equipped than PSTN in the following respects:

- transfer of data;
- quality testing of subscriber connections through echo analysis on different sections of the subscriber's digital switching path; and
- fault tracing.

The following subsections will focus on fault and disturbance supervision and quality testing by means of echo analysis.

8.3.1 Disturbance supervision of subscriber line sections

Statistics of disturbances are collected for each subscriber line and for each type of disturbance; for example

- line activity disturbance;
- return of sent message;
- loss of frame (LOF);
- incorrect checksum; and
- other signalling faults.

Disturbances on subscriber lines actuate an alarm when a preset limit is exceeded. Such disturbances may come from external sources, mainly in the form of impulse noise produced by electric motors and strip-light fittings.

8.3.2 Fault supervision of subscriber line sections

Four clearly defined sections of the digital path (DIP) are supervised by monitors:

- PBX to NT;
- NT to LT;
- ET to NT (ET is an exchange terminal for a PBX connected directly to the group switch); and
- LT to NT.

There is a bit error counter for each DIP section.

Supervision of bit error ratio

The number of erroneous bits in time slot zero is divided by the number of checked bits. The result is a value indicating the bit error ratio (BER). Each DIP has a separate BER supervision function.

Supervision of the passive bus

Fault indications are sent from the network termination over the D-channel of the subscriber connection. The following faults are supervised:

- voltage faults on the passive bus; and
- LOF on the passive bus.

Supervision of the D-channel

Protocol errors for the link layer or return of sent messages are recorded. For the network layer, the number of status and restart messages is counted.

An alarm is actuated when the predetermined tolerance level is exceeded.

Supervision of signalling units

The D-channel's signalling unit is supervised continuously. If a fault is detected, all traffic that uses the affected equipment is rerouted, and an alarm is actuated. The function is tested every five minutes to see if the fault has been corrected.

Alarm indication signal (AIS) is the most serious fault on the list. The following faults are supervised (top priority first):

- AIS;
- LOF;
- consecutive severely errored seconds (CSES); and
- remote alarm indication (RAI).

8.3.3 Quality testing and supervision of subscriber connections

BRA can be tested – one section at a time – through continuous echo analysis and fault tracing. Echo analysis is performed by a separate test module which can test three sections of the subscriber line part:

- the digital line interface circuit of the subscriber part: line circuit clock, power supply;
- the network termination of the subscriber part; and
- terminal equipment.

The test board sends a random bit sequence for one second and then compares the echo with the sequence sent. Before each echo test, the test board performs a self-check by sending a bit stream to itself via the time switch. Subscriber equipment can be tested only if it is equipped with the necessary test functions.

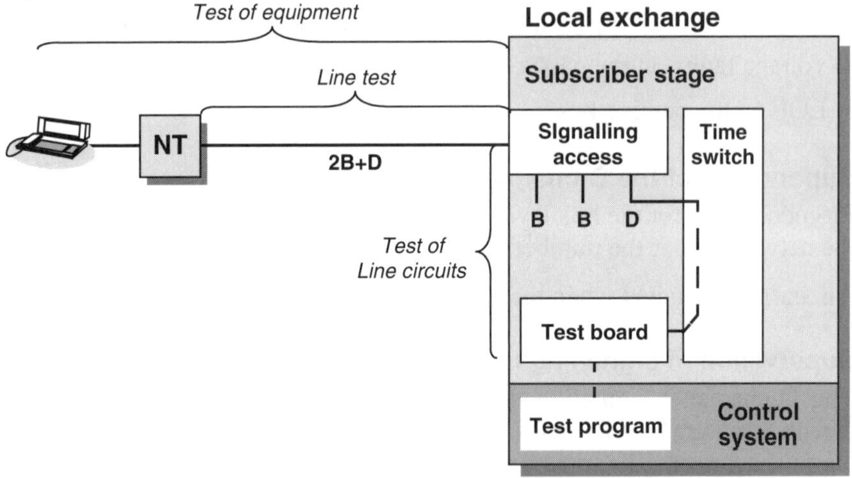

Figure C.8.3 Configuration for echo analysis in ISDN

All testing and supervision is done by the test board, but manual testing is also possible.

The echo tests generate an alarm if one of the following limits is exceeded:

- *Degraded minutes (DM)*: if there is more than one error in 1,000,000 bits (10^{-6}) during a one-minute interval;
- *Errored seconds (ES)*: if bit errors occur in more than 8% of a one-second interval;
- *Severely errored seconds (SES)*: if bit errors occur more than once in 1,000 bits during a one-second test; and
- *Unavailable seconds (US)*: if availability is insufficient during a 10-second period. Blocking is initiated by the occurrence of 1 bit error in 1,000 bits every second during a 10-second interval. The blocking is not reset until no bit error in 1,000 bits has been recorded for any second during a 10-second interval.

8.3.4 Alarm system

Recurring faults on a subscriber line or a subscriber circuit result in blocking, which in turn triggers an alarm.

A special function in the exchange handles the supervision of blocked and fault-marked subscriber sections. Normally there are two alarm levels. An alarm relating to a predetermined number of subscribers can be actuated at a higher level of the maintenance system hierarchy.

9 Interworking between networks

9.1 Introduction

Originally, ISDN was designed to replace all other data and telecommunication networks. This ambition was admirable but will not be achieved.

ISDN's relative smallness increases the need for interworking with other networks.

ISDN belongs to the same network family as the PSTN and PLMN, with 64 kbit/s PCM-coded speech as a backbone service in local exchanges and in the surrounding network. Interworking between networks is no problem as far as the voice service is concerned.

When it comes to interworking between networks for the handling of data services, ISDN tends to take on the role as access network for other networks (with the Internet as a major driving force). Other interworking networks are X.21, X.25 and frame relay.

Interworking between networks in the data services area requires special adapters and interworking units (IWUs), which serve as gateways, for example between ISDN and PSPDN.

9.2 Standardisation

Three main standardisation bodies govern the development of interworking between networks: the ITU-T, ETSI and the Internet Engineering Task Force (IETF). The IETF is the Internet's body for producing Requests for Comments (RFCs).

Basic principles for interworking between ISDN and separate data networks are found in the ITU-T's Recommendation X.300 and in ETSI's ETR 030.

9.3 Minimum integration

"Minimum integration" means that all terminals in one network become connected (in the logical sense of the word) to the other network and follow the numbering plan of the other network, either with a fixed number (as in X.21 or X.25) or with a temporary number (as in the Internet).

D-channel signalling is used for switching through ISDN to a port (interworking unit) or to an Internet gateway in the interworking network. The set-up procedure can be automatic (hot line) or initiated by the subscriber dialling an access code.

If the interworking network is the Internet, the next step will be initiation of the "IP phase" between the client – who is connected to ISDN – and the server in the Internet. The corresponding phase for interworking with X.21 networks is illustrated in *Figure C.9.1.*

Traffic can be carried from a subscriber in X.21 to a subscriber in ISDN, provided the IWU is treated as a subscriber in ISDN. The ISDN subscriber is given a number in the X.21 network, and number translation takes place in the IWU. (See *Figure C.9.1.*)

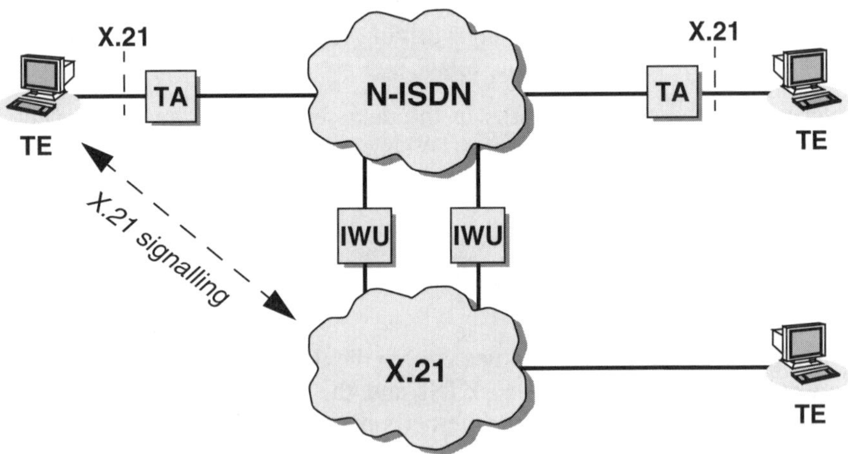

Figure C.9.1 Interconnection between ISDN and an X.21 network – minimum integration

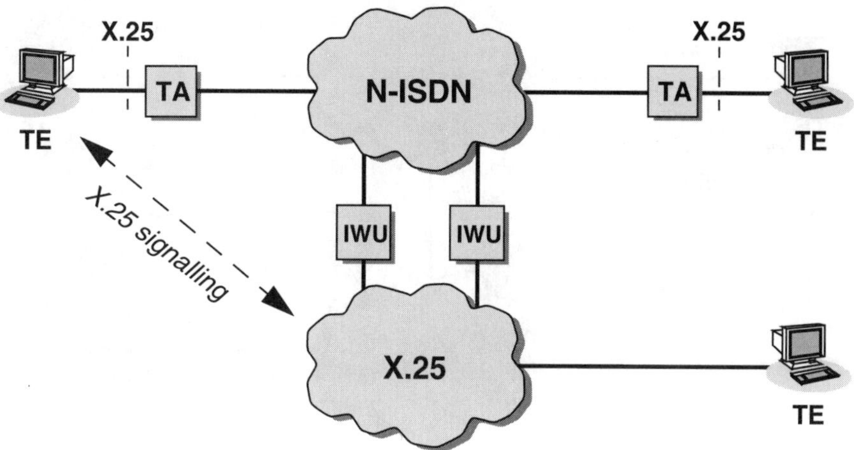

Figure C.9.2 Interconnection between ISDN and a packet-switched data network – minimum integration

Minimum integration interworking between ISDN and X.25 is illustrated in *Figure C.9.2*. This method supports traffic only on the B-channel.

9.4 Maximum integration

During the set-up of a call from an ISDN-connected subscriber, ISDN takes more active part in the set-up process than in minimum integration.

Maximum integration is used between ISDN and X.25 networks.

In this case, ISDN has built-in functions for packet-switched data traffic. When a call is set up from a terminal in ISDN, a 64 kbit/s connection is established between TA and a packet handler (PH) connected to the ISDN exchange. This connection is then used for X.25 signalling.

The packet handler in the ISDN exchange checks whether the B-subscriber is connected to ISDN or to the packet network. If the B-subscriber is connected to the packet network, X.75 signalling is used between the networks. See *Figure C.9.3*.

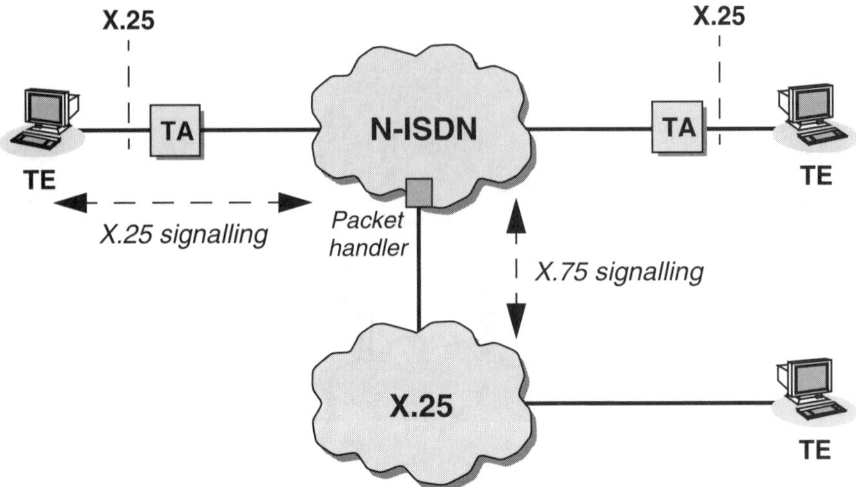

Figure C.9.3 Interconnection between ISDN and a packet-switched data network – maximum integration

9.5 Communication between data subscribers

For this kind of interworking between networks, the same type of modem is connected to the data terminals in ISDN and the PSTN, respectively. The analog signal from the modem is A/D converted by means of PCM coding: for ISDN, before connection to the S-interface, and for PSTN, in the subscriber switch of the local exchange.

10 Network planning

10.1 Introduction

In Chapter 1 we mentioned that

- ISDN usually has IDN for telephony (that is, a digitised PSTN) as a backbone structure;
- the network structure is interwoven with the PSTN structure; and
- ISDN has been regarded as “a solution in search of its problem”.

The first two items seem to favour the planning of PSTN/ISDN instead of only the PSTN or only ISDN. As for the last item, the solution should be Internet access, teleworking and videoconferencing – applications that have become popular in the 1990s. Because ISDN is a product of the 1980s, its slow growth during the first decade was quite natural. But even at that time, applications were available, such as connections to companies that had installed ISPBX (PBXs with ISDN).

In the following sections, we will pay special attention to the planning of ISDN for Internet access, but integrated planning of PSTN/ISDN will also be discussed in brief.

With this approach to the Internet, the supplementary services in ISDN (both IN services and distributed supplementary services) will be of less interest to the network planner, because ISDN will often serve as a network for access to other networks.

Much of the contents of Volume 1, Chapter 10, is applicable to ISDN.

10.2 ISDN as a carrier of Internet traffic

Some of ISDN's characteristics favour its use in Internet traffic.

Residential subscribers usually have a copper pair connected to their homes. This copper pair can be used either for the PSTN or for ISDN (BRA). The cost of an ISDN channel is comparable to the cost of a telephone circuit.

ISDN has a larger bandwidth than the PSTN and is better adapted to data traffic than the PSTN, with its analog access.

Both the PSTN and ISDN have a traffic-concentrating function in the subscriber switch. This gives the PSTN the advantage of shared use of the modems required to "redigitise" Internet traffic in the Internet entry point. But ISDN has an even greater advantage in that it needs no modems at all. Both the PSTN and ISDN benefit from the concentration of traffic in the form of better transmission economy.

On the other hand, ISDN and the PSTN have some characteristics that are not very Internet-friendly:

Although the subscriber switch has a traffic-concentrating function, good transmission economy will not be achieved unless statistical multiplexing of the bursty Internet traffic is performed. Circuit-switched networks cannot manage such multiplexing.

Besides, circuit-switched networks cannot handle the IP protocol, which is necessary to ensure correct routing of Internet traffic.

When weighing these pros and cons, we find that ISDN is well-suited as a carrier of Internet traffic over paths of limited length; for example, between a subscriber and a remote subscriber switch or between a subscriber and a local exchange (or transit exchange). The basic rule is: The more Internet traffic ISDN carries, the shorter the distance.

10.3 ISDN access

10.3.1 Copper section for basic rate access

To ensure high-quality transfer of telephony and data, the length of the copper section must not exceed a certain maximum value. This limit varies depending on factors such as conductor diameter, type of cable, required margin. A rule of thumb is 4 to 5 km. The copper section is connected to a PSTN/ISDN exchange, a remote subscriber switch, or – in exceptional cases – to a special ISDN multiplexer.

10.3.2 Primary rate access

For PRA, the trend is towards *fibre to the office (FTTO)* which will ensure more or less high-quality access to all types of service.

10.3.3 Radio access

Radio access, which was specially designed for mobile or fixed telephony, is becoming more and more common. The shortage of available frequency bands has necessitated highly effective voice coding (32 kbit/s, 13 kbit/s and lower). For Internet traffic, this leads to a corresponding reduction in capacity when such channels are used.

Radio access is dealt with in detail in *Part D – PLMN* and *Part B – PSTN.*

10.4 Fundamental technical plans

10.4.1 Numbering plan

The numbering plan for the ISDN network is based on the numbering plan for the telephone network. Since 1997, all subscribers in the world must have been able to use an international ISDN number containing up to 15 digits. When ISDN was commercially introduced in 1990, the requirement was

0 + 8 digits to allow calls from an ordinary telephone subscriber to an ISDN subscriber. The number of digits has increased gradually.

An ISDN address can also contain a subaddress which is transferred transparently through the network. The subaddress can be used on the terminal side to identify a specific terminal. See *Figure C.10.1*.

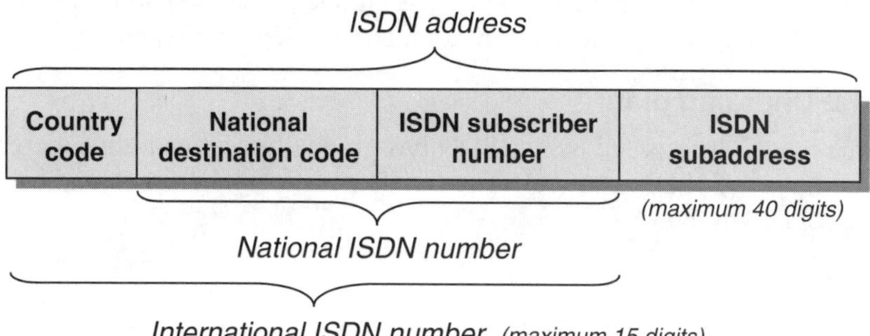

Figure C.10.1 ISDN subscriber number

In theory, BRA can have up to eight numbers on the same connection. This is quite practical if the subscriber has different types of equipment on a single access or if he wishes to direct a certain type of call to a certain terminal.

In the configuration shown in *Figure C.10.2*, the number 0483-1234 is common to both telephones. However, calls to 0483-1236 will be directed only to the telephone at the top of the figure.

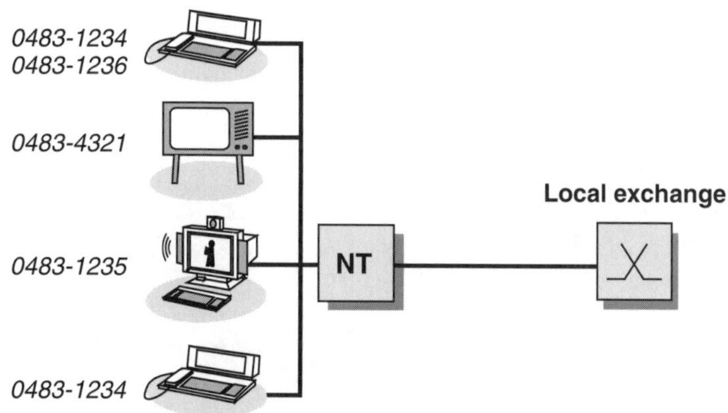

Figure C.10.2 Example of numbering

The number 0483-4321 reaches the videoconferencing equipment in the figure, while the computer answers to 0483-1235.

The numbers are programmed into the terminals, which thereby receive their own address as if they had a dedicated connection to the network. The subscription is limited to the two B-channels in BRA, though. If both telephones are busy, for example, the videoconferencing equipment cannot contact the network. However, a person can call one of the telephones from the other telephone; that is, use BRA as an internal telephone system.

10.4.2 Charging plan

On the whole, the cost of using ISDN has gradually declined, thus increasing demand for ISDN services. The tariffs per channel are comparable to those applied in the PSTN.

10.4.3 Synchronisation plan

Together with the PSTN, ISDN is synchronised according to one of the methods described in Volume 1, Chapter 10, Subsection 10.8.5.

10.5 Recommendations for network structuring

The ITU-T has published a series of five generally formulated recommendations for the structuring and implementation of ISDN:

I.310 Network functional principles;

I.320 Protocol reference model;

I.330 ISDN numbering and addressing principles;

I.335 ISDN routing principles; and

I.340 ISDN connection types.

Part D – PLMN

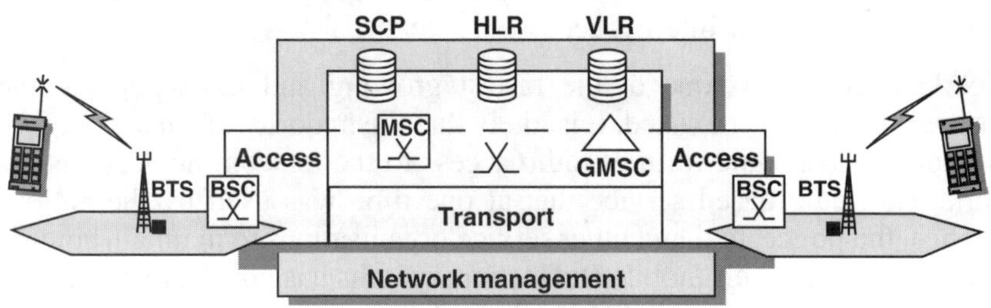

Figure D.0.1 Reference model

1 User services, terminals

1.1 Introduction

A public land mobile network (PLMN) is a telecommunications network for mobile units, referred to as mobile stations or mobile phones.

Mobility is the hallmark of a PLMN. What is more, a PLMN can enhance the capability of other networks to provide mobility; for example, when it serves as a bearer for Internet access.

Mobile telephony is one of the fastest growing and most popular teleservices that has ever existed. It is likely that the majority of subscribers will eventually have some form of radio access to the telecommunications network. The radio-based service that at one time was used by the national defence, the police, taxi and other service organisations to maintain communication between their mobile and stationary units has now developed into a tool that many business professionals find natural to use and, lately, a tool for the average person.

One important reason for the fast growth of mobile telephony is the fact that the service is an extension of the world's most widespread teleservice – fixed telephony. Apart from being able to communicate with one another, subscribers of mobile telephony services are also able to communicate – via PSTN/ISDN gateways – with those who have fixed teleservice subscriptions.

The advantages of increased accessibility experienced by mobile users are attracting an increasing number of new subscribers. This, in turn, places great demands on the capacity of network radio elements – demands that operators have to meet through more efficient use of existing frequencies and by making new frequencies available.

Technically, the development of mobile telephony has progressed from analog to digital mobile systems. Terrestrial systems have also been complemented with satellite systems. The cordless technique – originally a mobile radio access technique for office environments – continues to develop, and the boundary between *cordless* and *cellular* is becoming less distinct.

Mobile telephony is advancing worldwide at a time when liberalisation is in full swing. For the majority of countries, deregulation and privatisation increase competition as the number of operators increases. Different systems, aimed at promoting mobility, operate in parallel in the same geographical area or in the same market. Analog and digital mobile systems, cordless systems and satellite systems are all able to satisfy user demand for mobile telecommunication in various ways.

1.1.1 Mobility

Mobility in a public telecommunications network is no unequivocal concept. (See Volume 1, Chapter 6, Subsection 6.2.4.) We differentiate between portability, movability and (complete) mobility.

Portability represents the simple case in which only the terminal is moved and then connected again at another point in the network. Movability implies that the subscriber moves his personal access; for example, when logging onto a data network from different network positions. Mobility refers to the state of complete ambulatory capability in which both the terminal and subscriber access can be moved, while the network automatically keeps track of all movement. In other words, this means both terminal and service mobility.

Mobility requires radio access via base (or radio base) stations. The physical access in a mobile network is arranged to enable a terminal to connect itself anywhere in the network and move about while a call is in progress. (Of course, the subscriber's subscription must be available at all access points.) This movability presupposes specially designed access ("cells" instead of connection points). It also requires that the terminal be able to maintain continuous radio contact with the network.

1.1.2 Primary PLMN functions – Main network elements

It is necessary to be somewhat familiar with the specialised terminology to understand mobile networks and their functions. Examples of basic concepts include location updating, roaming, handover and paging. To elucidate these concepts and the handling of mobile traffic, we should have used animated illustrations. For practical reasons, we must leave the animation to the reader's imagination when we refer to *Figure D.1.1,* which illustrates the salient elements of a fixed network and of a PLMN.

Mobile networks require functions for network intelligence, even when handling "ordinary" calls. *Figure D.1.1* shows two of these functions: the home location register (HLR) and the visitor location register (VLR). The figure also makes clear that access to the PLMN is significantly different from access to fixed networks. Each base station controller (BSC) includes a switching function allowing it to switch to another base station as the terminal moves (roaming). In the figure, imagine the terminal having moved from location area 1 (LA1), through LA2, to LA3, where it has been called via the associated BSC. The next destination is LA4. Such movement also involves a number of mobile switching centres (MSCs).

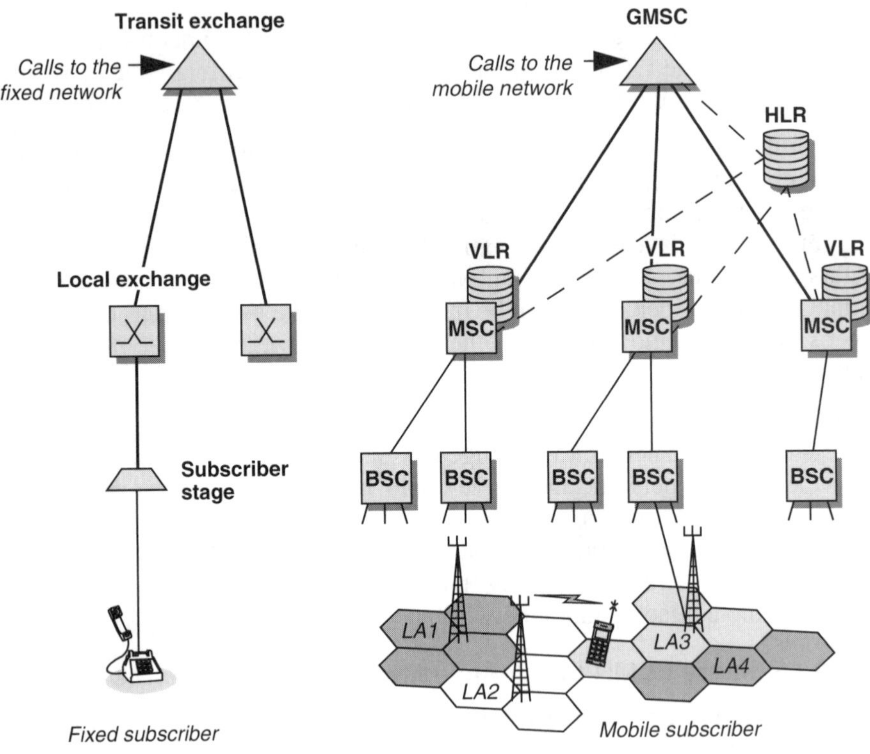

Figure D.1.1 Comparison of a fixed network and a PLMN having cells grouped in location areas (LA)

1.1.3 An orientation – Common concepts

The following concepts are described in this section:

- Cells and base stations – Multiple access
- Radio channels between base stations and mobiles – Control channels and traffic channels
- Attachment and detachment
- Roaming
- Registration and paging – Location area
- Locating and handover

The various network elements – MSC, BTS, HLR, VLR – are clarified in more detail in Chapter 2, Section 2.3.

Cells and base stations – Multiple access

Radio access offers subscribers a number of radio channels for communication. However, radio channels are in short supply. To effectively utilise the frequency spectrum allocated for use by mobile subscribers, every radio channel should be reusable, which requires well-defined and separate geographical areas that have access to a range of frequencies. Such areas of service are referred to as cells. The nomenclature has given rise to the term *cellular system,* that we find in a system name such as personal digital cellular (PDC).

The number of radio channels in a cell is significantly less than the number of mobiles, since – in the normal case – only a minority of the mobiles are active at the same time. The technique used to assign idle traffic channels to calling or called mobiles is referred to as *multiple access*. (See also Volume 1, Chapter 5, Section 5.10.) Three variants of multiple access are described in Chapter 4, Subsections 4.3.5 – 4.3.7, of this part.

Base stations use either omnidirectional or directional antennas. The antenna of an omnidirectional cell radiates (more or less) an equally strong signal in all horizontal directions, thereby covering a circular area. A mobile station located in this area will normally experience good radio contact with the base station. The circle's radius can be modified by changing the output power of the base station, which in most cases is done in connection with cell planning (see Chapter 10, Section 10.5). Maximum cell size is normally determined by the mobile's available output power.

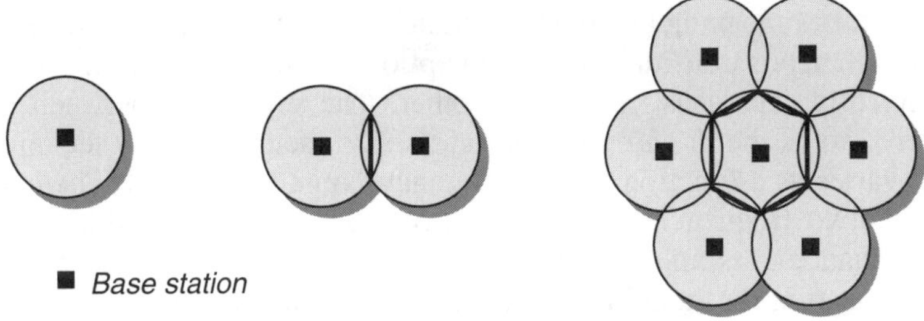

Figure D.1.2 Hexagonal patterns are easy to work with

Figure D.1.2 shows a system made up of omnidirectional cells. The figure also demonstrates the origination of the well-known hexagonal pattern. Hexagonal patterns are easy to work with: graphically, geometrically and logically. However, since the hexagonal model provides an idealised representation of coverage one must always complement this model with actual coverage measurements.

A base station that uses three directional antennas, where each antenna covers an angle of 120°, has three sector cells around it. *Figure D.1.3* illustrates the appearance of the corresponding cell pattern.

It is not always necessary to have three sector cells together. Occasionally, one sector cell will suffice; for example, when covering a section of a road or highway.

The transmitters of each of the cells have their own frequencies. Cell pattern planning is closely related to the use and reuse of frequencies. (See Chapter 5, Subsection 5.2.1.)

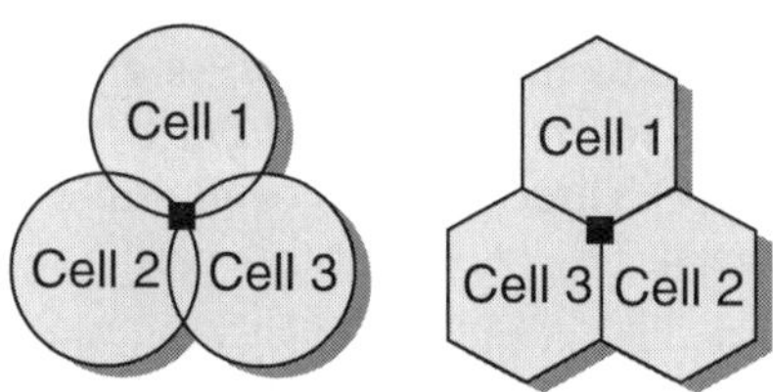

Figure D.1.3 Three sector cells

Radio channels between base stations and mobiles

The mobile telephony service is assigned special operating frequency ranges (that vary depending on the country and the standards employed). These frequency ranges are in turn subdivided into radio channels, commonly 25–30 kHz wide (channel separation). Duplex mode is employed for traffic over radio access, meaning that the base stations and the mobiles must be capable of simultaneous transmission and reception, requiring two frequency ranges sufficiently separated from one another. The separation between them is referred to as the *duplex separation*; its size, determined by technical factors, varies as a function of the frequency range being used. The combination of two frequencies (or portions of frequencies) constitutes a duplex radio channel. As an example, *Figure D.1.4* shows frequency assignment and utilisation for the NMT 450 mobile telephone system.

The channels of a mobile network are divided into two primary groups: control channels and traffic channels.

- Every cell employs at least one channel as a control channel, on which the base station continuously transmits an identifying signal that is used by the mobiles to lock into that particular cell. Control channels are also used for paging calls; if the called mobile is in the cell, it will respond over the same (or another) channel. The number of control channels in a cell varies as a function of the access technique employed and the expected call intensity.

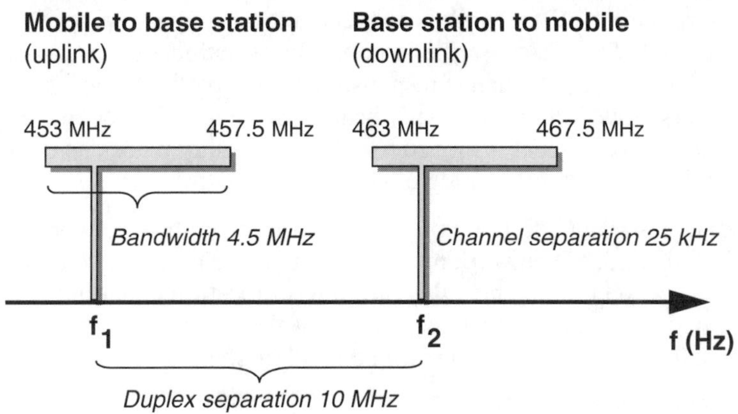

Figure D.1.4 Frequency range for NMT 450

- After having completed call connection signalling, the mobile is assigned another channel – a traffic channel – for the call. The number of traffic channels in a cell varies with the cell's expected traffic intensity.

Control channels and traffic channels are also referred to as *logical channels.* These logical channels are mapped onto physical channels.

A physical channel can be a radio broadcasting frequency, a pair of frequencies (including duplex separation) in an analog mobile system or a time slot on a pair of frequencies in a digital mobile system.

Traffic channels are addressed in greater detail in Chapter 4, Subsection 4.3.5. Control channels are described in Chapter 7.

Attachment and detachment

As soon as a mobile is turned on, it establishes contact with the network. It thus has "access" to the network, and the network registers its movements.

A user can turn his mobile off occasionally to conserve battery power. Since it would not make much sense to attempt to call an idle mobile, the system includes functionality to keep track of whether the mobile is ON (attachment) or OFF (detachment).

Roaming

Regardless of its location, a mobile that is turned on must maintain constant radio contact with the network. Both the network and the mobile include special functionality for this purpose: the roaming function.

Location updating and paging – Location area

A terminal in a fixed network is connected to a fixed access point, which is also associated with a subscriber number. Information about this association is stored in the local exchange responsible for the particular access point. If a terminal is moved, it will normally be assigned a new number depending on which local exchange it is moved to. This movability places no demands on the network in terms of routing or connection control.

Fixed access points do not exist in the world of mobile networks. When a mobile is called, the network must be able to determine its position, and that requires special intelligence. Registration (or location updating) is the intelligent network function that keeps track of the mobile's position. Paging is the actual search operation performed in all or some of the network cells.

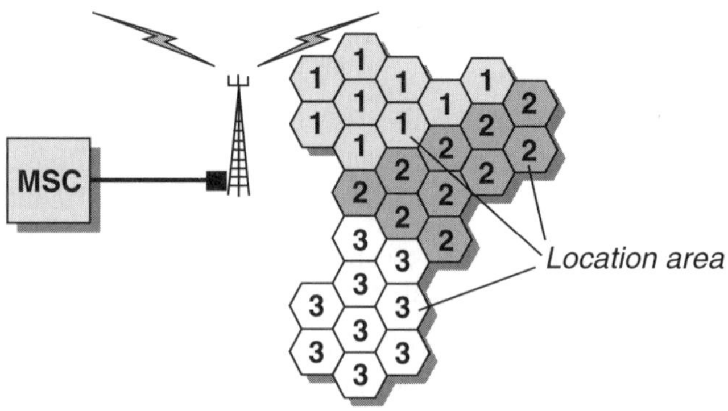

Figure D.1.5 Location area

Radio resources would be greatly overworked if, for every incoming call, the paging function were activated to locate the position of the called mobile all over the network. The solution lies in forcing the mobiles to report their positions, that is, to register. The question is: How often should a mobile report – upon entering a new cell or less frequently? The size of the area within which the mobile need not register becomes a trade-off between location updating and paging. Updating locations per cell would load the network with too many registrations, while a large area – for example, an MSC service area – might very well load the network with too many "paging assignments". The group of cells in which a mobile need not register is referred to as its *location area.* The location area can correspond to a BSC service area (as shown in *Figure D.1.5*) but can also consist of cells from several different BSC service areas located in the same MSC service area.

While the use of a traffic channel is related to specific, non-adjacent cells, call channels are a common resource for a given location area. A location area must not be made so large as to allow the number of calls in the area to cause call-channel congestion.

Since the registration and paging functions require network intelligence, they are also addressed in Chapter 6, Section 6.2.

Locating and handover

The channel used for a call – or for control – must be capable of being switched from cell to cell as the mobile traverses the cells. The system must be able to detect whether or not switching is necessary (normally coinciding with the fact that signal strength has dropped below a given value or the signal-to-noise ratio has become unsatisfactory). This function is referred to as *locating*. The technical term for actually switching from cell to cell – which preferably occurs without the user noticing it – is *handover*.

Handover is addressed in greater detail in Chapter 3 (switching aspects) and in Chapter 5 (transmission aspects).

1.2 Services

The basic idea of mobile services is to offer the moving subscriber the same services that are offered to fixed-network subscribers. Subscriber movement requires sophisticated solutions to maintain service continuity throughout the network. Information on the individual subscriber's access to a specific service and on the status of this service must be transmitted between the exchanges of the mobile network in step with the movement of the subscriber.

1.2.1 Telephony

The most important function of a mobile network is the creation of a good and dependable telephone service. Under favourable radio transmission conditions, the quality of the telephone service is comparable with fixed-network telephony. Digital mobile networks are capable of delivering telephony of varying quality, depending on the voice-coding method employed over radio access. The GSM digital mobile system uses the terms "full-rate coding" (13 kbit/s) and "half-rate coding" (6.5 kbit/s).

1.2.2 Data

The speed normally used by GSM is 9.6 kbit/s, but higher speeds are being developed (see Chapter 2, Subsection 2.4.4).

The use of modems enables analog systems to offer data services with bit rates up to 19.2 kbit/s.

1.2.3 Telefax

All larger mobile systems support Group 3 telefax.

1.2.4 Supplementary services

Mobile network supplementary services are similar to their counterparts in the fixed network, even if services such as call barring require a greater number of variations. A subscription for official use can be barred so that incoming calls are not accepted; for instance, when the mobile is used on an assignment in another country. This protects the company against the risk of having to pay the high cost of private calls being made from home to the mobile.

1.2.5 Emergency call services

Many mobile networks offer an emergency call service. All the user has to do in an emergency situation is contact an emergency centre – no knowledge of the telephone numbers of different centres in the area is required. Even black-listed mobiles and mobiles that are ordinarily unable to pass authentication can use this service.

1.2.6 Messaging services

Messaging services are particularly important in increasing accessibility in a PLMN, because terminals can be turned off or can be in an area where buildings or hills create radio shadows. Voice mail, telefax and short message service (SMS) are examples of messaging services.

SMS allows callers to leave short text messages (GSM allows up to 160 characters). A message that cannot be delivered immediately will be stored in a short-message service centre until the mobile can be reached.

1.3 Service development

As is evident from Subsection 1.2.2, mobile networks have little data transmission capacity. Today's analog mobile systems can have greater capacity than their digital counterparts (19.2 kbit/s for analog and 9.6 kbit/s for digital systems). The explosive development of mobile communication and Internet-type data communication has led to demand for significant enhancement of the data communication capabilities of mobile systems.

The need for video transmission including high resolution can lead to demands for even greater capacity, up to 384 kbit/s or 2 Mbit/s. In principle, this would result in mobile systems made up of three transfer-rate classes:

- Today's systems, which are optimised for the transfer of voice.
- Upgraded versions of today's systems having significantly improved data transfer capacity – slightly more than 100 kbit/s.
- New systems that complement existing systems. One example is the universal mobile telecommunication system (UMTS).

The aim of the UMTS is to enable mobile access to offer the same range of services as those offered by fixed access while providing the same quality. The UMTS and the upgrading of today's systems are addressed in more detail in Chapter 2 (see Section 2.6 and Subsection 2.4.4).

1.3.1 Intelligent mobile terminals

A mobile system is ordinarily considered as simply a "transporter of bits" as far as data communication is concerned. Any intelligent communication with an Internet Web server, for example, is managed by a computer connected to the mobile system. This situation will change as "smarter" mobile terminals appear on the market. The advent of small hand-held computers having built-in communications ability is a step in this direction.

The trend just described implies that the PLMN – from a data communications point of view – will develop from being a bearer network into a network that includes built-in, highly advanced teleservices and value-added services; for instance, services that allow a mobile to be used as a handy tool for making payment transactions. (See also Section 1.5, in particular *Figure D.1.7*.)

1.4 Security

Networks that utilise radio communications are especially sensitive to unauthorised use of terminals and to tapping along the radio path. Mobile networks therefore require the institution of special security measures. Both the user and the network operator must be protected against any unauthorised intrusion by a third party. This protection can either consist of a supplementary service selected by the user; for example, a smart card (with a personal code) for systems that use such cards, or of various network functions such as encryption and authentication.

The following functions have been enhanced to protect the network:

- authentication system that protects against unauthorised use of the network's services;
- encryption to protect against unauthorised tapping of radio access;
- terminal identification that protects against the use of stolen mobiles; and
- temporary telephone numbers that protect against unauthorised access to a mobile's identity.

Security is addressed in greater detail in Chapter 6, Section 6.4.

1.5 Terminals

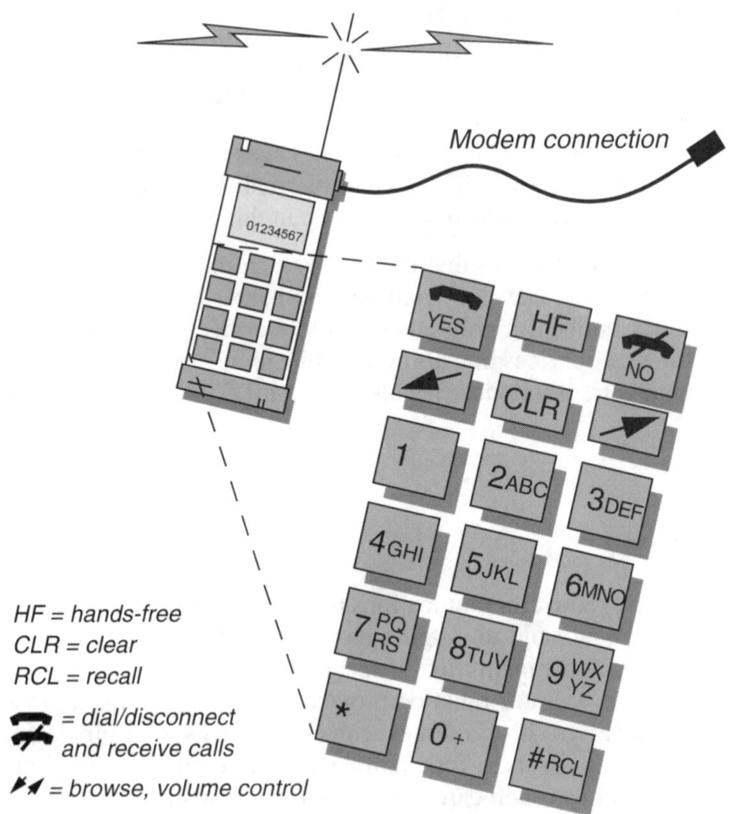

Figure D.1.6 The most important key functions on a mobile telephone

The development of the mobile telephone has been characterised by two dominant trends: size reduction and increased intelligence. Both trends have the same origins, namely the endeavour to make components ever smaller and more advanced and the constant development and refinement of the design. Also, the mobile telephone has already passed three initial phases: the car-mounted model, the portable model and the current pocket model.

In digital networks, the mobile assists in the handover process by continuously measuring base station signal strength and then reporting the measured values to the network. The mobile's ability to control the handover process (mobile-controlled handover) will mark the next step in its development (see Chapter 5, Section 5.4).

A pocket telephone has a number of facilities. The most common are:

- alphanumeric display;
- memory for many abbreviated numbers;
- signal strength indicator;
- battery indicator; and
- electronic lock.

The mobile office is a concept that has developed in step with the increase in teleworking. In addition to the mobile telephone, an important tool is the laptop PC which can be equipped with a modem card. The laptop can then be connected directly to a mobile telephone's modem port. The portable fax is another terminal that can be used over a PLMN.

The development towards more advanced terminals as described in Section 1.3.1 is illustrated in *Figure D.1.7.*

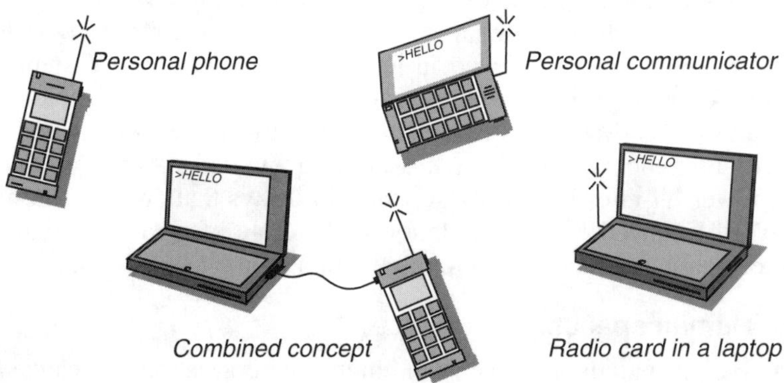

Figure D.1.7 The development of PLMN terminals from simple mobile telephones into intelligent mobile terminals

2 Standardisation

2.1 Standardisation organisations

The most important standardisation efforts in the field of mobile systems have been made by the ITU-T, which has published a large number of mobile network recommendations. Recommendation Q.1001, "General aspects of Public Land Mobile Networks", provides an overview of the definitions, architecture and services related to a public, nationwide, mobile network. Recommendations also deal with other important areas, such as numbering plans, grade of service (GoS), signalling and interworking between networks. ITU-R, the ITU's "radio sector", discusses and regulates the use of the radio frequency spectrum, a limited natural resource required by mobile networks for their operation.

Another influential standards organisation in the field of mobile systems is European Telecommunications Standardisation Institute (ETSI). ETSI has developed a specification for the global system for mobile communication (GSM) and has specified a digital system for cordless telephony, digital enhanced cordless telecommunications (DECT), and a paging system referred to as European radio message system (ERMES).

Other important standardisation organisations are the Japanese RCR and TTC and the North American ANSI, EIA and TIA. North American operators are assigned frequencies by the Federal Communications Commission (FCC).

2.2 Voice coding in mobile networks

Due to the scarcity of available frequency bands, all digital mobile systems use some hybrid form of coding that enables bit rates to be reduced to a level far below the 64 kbit/s achieved in PCM coding. Hence, all systems use voice-block coding instead of pure waveform coding. Each voice block (20 milliseconds in GSM) is analysed and compared with the subsequent block (and with references), and then parameterised and coded. The long blocks enable lower bit rates but they also result in delays that create echo problems. Well-balanced echo cancellation is therefore of great importance to the voice quality in connections involving digital mobile systems.

2.2.1 Human speech

Human speech contains a great deal of redundant information. We can reduce this redundancy through the use of speech analysis and transfer only that portion of speech required to reproduce the information at the receiving end.

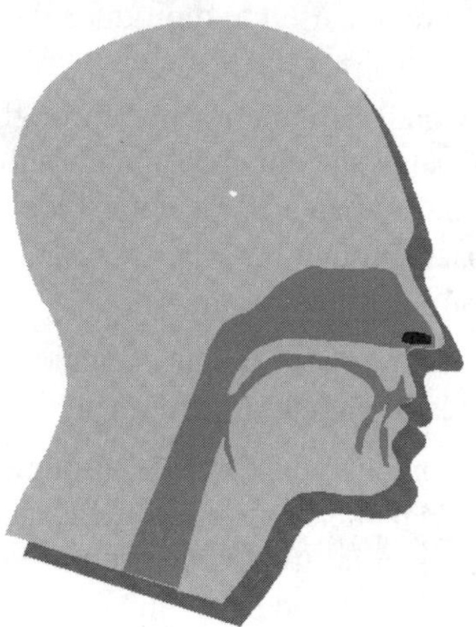

Figure D.2.1 A model of the human organs of speech

The vocal cords vibrate and create sound of varying frequencies. The sound is modified when passing through the organs of speech, which function as a frequency filter.

2.2.2 GSM voice coding

The following is a brief description of the voice coding employed by the mobiles of a GSM system. A number of electronic filters are used to simulate the operation of the human organs of speech and to extract the vocal cords' original frequencies, called *excitation sequences*.

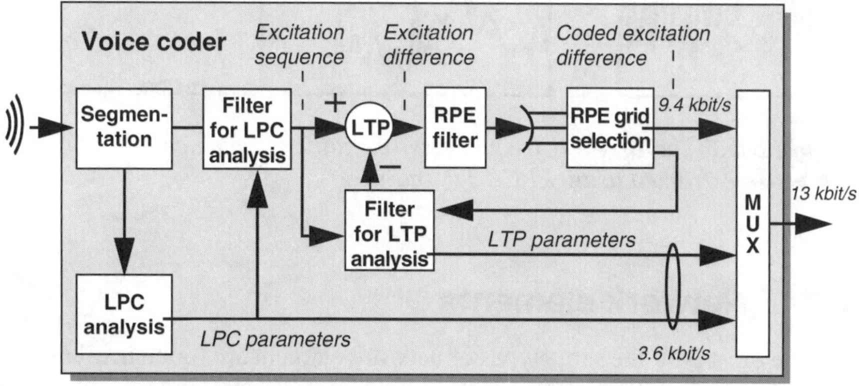

Figure D.2.2 GSM voice coding

Information about the filter characteristics and the excitation sequences is sent to the receiver, where it is used to reproduce the original signal. *Figure D.2.2* and *Figure D.2.3* illustrate the principle.

- The first step of the analysis is performed through linear predictive coding (LPC). The LPC analysis unit is designed as the inverse of the speech organs' filtering model. When a 20 ms voice block from the segmentation unit is allowed to pass through the filter for LPC analysis, this filter will deliver the excitation sequence for the sample.
- Since two consecutive blocks have similar excitation sequences, the difference between them is calculated with the long-term prediction (LTP) methods.
- The resulting excitation difference passes through a low-pass filter and is then input to the residual pulse excitation (RPE) grid selection unit, which is a waveform coder (similar to the one used in PCM). The filtered excitation difference is sampled and every third sample is coded. The resulting bit stream is 9.4 kbit/s.
- The RPE bit stream and the LPC and LTP parameter values are transferred to the receiver, where the original speech is reproduced through a reverse process.

The LPC and LTP parameter values generate 3.6 kbit/s, making the total bit stream from the voice coder 13 kbit/s (260 bits per 20 ms sample).

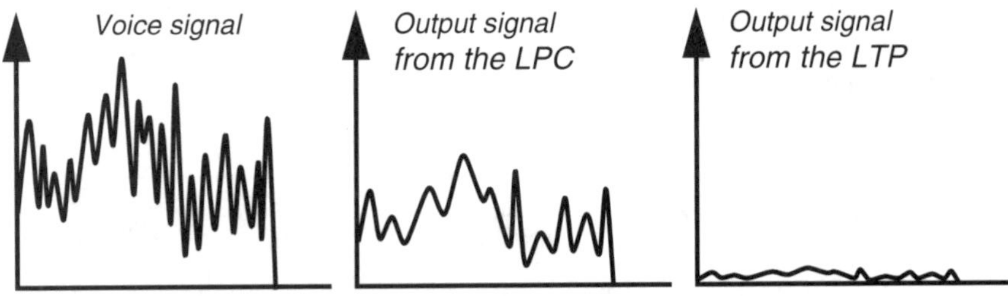

Figure D.2.3 The original frequencies (excitation sequences) of the vocal cords are extracted using LPC/LTP analysis

2.3 Network elements

For the most part, the same types of network element are found in all mobile networks, even if they are named differently in different standards. In *Figure D.2.4,* we use GSM as an example.

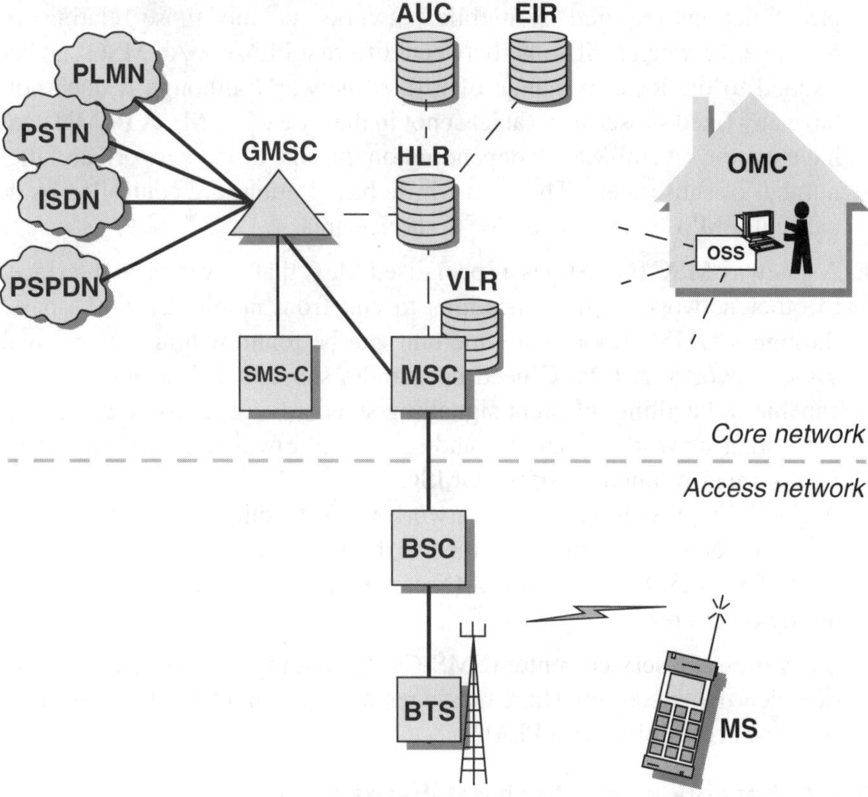

Figure D.2.4 GSM network elements

2.3.1 Network elements for (user) traffic

- MS: A mobile station can be a mobile telephone, a fax having radio access or a laptop computer equipped with a radio modem.
- BTS: A base transceiver station contains equipment for transmission and reception, antennas for one or more cells, plus equipment for encryption/decryption and signal strength measurement and for communication with the BSC.
- BSC: A base station controller, also referred to as the radio exchange, sets up the radio channels for traffic and for signalling to the MSC (see below) and monitors the access network portion of the connection. A BSC also performs traffic concentration and handles handover between the base stations that it controls. BSCs are only found in the GSM standard. In other standards, the MSC also handles radio exchange functions.

- MSC: A mobile switching centre is a switching node having the specialised functions required by mobile networks, notably those relating to handover between MSCs and between different PLMNs. An MSC can be likened to the local exchange of a fixed network, although it does not have any fixed subscribers (at least not in the case of GSM). A PLMN can have one or several MSCs, depending on the size of the network and the number of subscribers. The cells whose base stations are controlled by a particular MSC constitute an MSC service area.
- A gateway MSC (GMSC) is a specialised MSC that serves as an interface to other networks. All connections to and from mobile networks pass through a GMSC (more than one unit can be found within one and the same network). A GMSC need not handle subscriber data but must be capable of handling different signalling standards for its communication with other networks. Charging and settlement of accounts between networks are also functions of the GMSC.
  A GMSC represents a mobile network vis-à-vis other networks. Fixed-network connections are performed at the national or international level of the PSTN/ISDN, where a PLMN can be identified in the same manner as any other operator network.
- Short message service centre (SMS-C): Messaging systems (in the form of voice mailboxes for short messages and fax mailboxes) are used to increase accessibility in a PLMN.

2.3.2 Network elements as databases

- HLR: Mobile subscribers must be permanently registered somewhere in the system. In a fixed network, every subscriber belongs to a local exchange; a mobile subscriber belongs to the network. That is why mobile networks include one or more databases (HLRs) for permanent storage of subscriber data. The HLR keeps continuous track of the location of the subscriber – whether he is in an MSC service area or in a different PLMN. This information is used by the GMSC when receiving a call from another network. An HLR can be a stand-alone network element or built into an MSC.
- VLR: An MSC only handles temporary subscribers, namely those who happen to be in the MSC service area at a given point in time. Data pertaining to these subscribers is stored in a VLR, which can be a stand-alone network element used by several MSCs. Ordinarily, though, each MSC has its own VLR. The VLR keeps track of the service area cells within which a mobile can be located and is constantly informed of whether the mobile is ON or OFF.

- AUC: The Authentication centre stores security information – for example, encryption keys – for all subscribers of the network. The AUC is also used for encryption/decryption.
- EIR: The equipment identity register stores information on the identity of every mobile. The EIR is used to check that a mobile is not reported as stolen or barred for some other reason.

2.3.3 Network elements for additional network intelligence

As in the case of the service control points (SCPs) and service switching points (SSPs) of fixed networks, PLMN operators also have need of such network intelligence nodes. This intelligence enables them to maintain short lead times when creating new services and customer-specific applications.

2.3.4 Network elements for operation and maintenance

The operation and maintenance centre (OMC) accommodates two network elements: an operations support system (OSS) and a network management system (NMS). Both are connected to other network elements in the core and access networks via a separate X.25 network.

2.3.5 Network elements for signalling

Since a GSM network utilises signalling system no. 7 (SS7), either integrated or stand-alone signal transfer points (STPs) are required.

2.3.6 Network elements for transport and transmission

With the exception of transmission over radio access, mobile network standards contain no guidance as to how network elements are to be interconnected from a transmission point of view. Ordinarily, plesiochronous digital hierarchy (PDH), synchronous digital hierarchy (SDH) or synchronous optical network (SONET) systems are used.

2.4 Mobile telephony standards

The following main features distinguish the different types of PLMN from one another:

- the technique used for radio access (TDMA, FDMA, or CDMA – see Chapter 4, Subsections 4.3.5 – 4.3.7);
- the disposition of functionality between the network and the mobile (for example, whether the network or the mobile is responsible for channel selection); and

- the design of the access network (in some networks, the control of access network resources and of the air interface resides in the access network; in other networks, these functions reside in the MSC).

There are currently seven different cellular mobile network standards: three analog and four digital.

2.4.1 Analog mobile networks

Analog mobile networks are characterised by the fact that control channels and traffic channels are analog. Both voice (commonly at 3 kHz) and data are frequency-modulated on a carrier. Today's analog network standards are:

- NMT – Nordic mobile telephony;
- AMPS – American mobile phone system; and
- TACS – Total access communication system

Standard	NMT 450	AMPS	TACS	NMT 900
System start	1981	1984	1985	1986
Frequency band *uplink*	453–457.5 MHz	824–849 MHz	890–915 MHz	890–915 MHz
Frequency band *downlink*	463–467.5 MHz	869–894 MHz	935–960 MHz	935–960 MHz
Channel capacity	180/359	832	1000	999/1999

Figure D.2.5 Analog mobile network standards

NMT

NMT was specified by the Nordic telecommunications administrations and was the first commercially operated public mobile network (1981). Two variants exist: NMT 450 and NMT 900. The numbers relate to the frequency bands used. NMT 900, introduced in 1986 as a result of the fact that the number of NMT 450 channels was insufficient, also offers some international roaming functionality. NMT has been implemented in Europe, the Middle East and Asia.

AMPS

AMPS is a notable mobile network standard that was specified by the US consortium TIA/EIA/ANSI. The air interface standard is referred to as EIA/TIA-553. The first AMPS network became operational as early as 1984 in the US, and 1988 the standard was expanded to contain a wider frequency band, E-AMPS. AMPS networks are found in the Americas, Australia and in Asia.

TACS

TACS is a modified version of AMPS; its frequency band is somewhat higher. The modification was made with the British market in view, where the standard was operational in 1985. TACS also received a wider frequency band in 1988, E-TACS. Since that time, TACS has spread to many countries around the world.

2.4.2 Digital mobile networks

Digital mobile networks are primarily characterised by their digital traffic channels, which means that the speech they carry is coded. However, they can include both analog and digital control channels.

Examples of systems include:

- GSM, global system for mobile communication;
- PCS, personal communications services (IS-95, IS-136, and others);
- D-AMPS, digital AMPS, referred to earlier as ADC, American digital cellular; and
- PDC, personal (Pacific) digital cellular, referred to earlier as JDC, Japanese digital cellular.

Standard	PDC	D-AMPS	GSM 900
Frequency band *uplink*	940–956 MHz 1429–1441 MHz 1453–1465 MHz	824–849 MHz	890–915 MHz
Frequency band *downlink*	810–826 MHz 1477–1489 MHz 1501–1513 MHz	869–894 MHz	935–960 MHz
Channel separation	25 kHz	30 kHz	200 kHz
Multiplexing	3 (6)-channel TDMA		8 (16)-ch. TDMA
Bearer *(bits per frequency channel)*	42 kbit/s	46.6 kbit/s	270 kbit/s

Figure D.2.6 Digital mobile network standards

GSM

Both the traffic and control channels of a GSM system are digital. GSM was specified by ETSI and went into commercial operation in 1992. The acronym GSM originally stood for *groupe spéciale mobile* – the ETSI group which, in 1982, was assigned the task of specifying a digital mobile system that should include international roaming, open interfaces between network elements, better voice quality and certain ISDN functionality.

Three different frequency bands – 900, 1800 and 1900 MHz – are available for GSM systems. By and large, the corresponding standards (called GSM 900, GSM 1800 and GSM 1900) follow the same specification. GSM 1800/1900 is chiefly intended for areas of high mobile density and is one of many ways to utilise the limited frequency range available to mobile telephony. That is why GSM 1800/1900 makes extensive use of microcells within umbrella cells (see Chapter 10, Subsection 10.4.4) and why the output power from its terminals and base stations is low.

GSM networks are found all over the world.

D-AMPS

D-AMPS is a version of AMPS that has been extended to employ digital traffic channels. Thanks to the access technique used (TDMA, three time slots) one 30 kHz channel has capacity for three traffic channels at full coding rate. The extended standard, referred to as IS-54, thus enables D-AMPS to include both analog and digital traffic channels in one and the same network, indeed, even in the same cell. Users of such a mobile network experience the best GoS if their mobiles can shift between analog and digital traffic channels even during handover. D-AMPS became commercially available in 1991–1992 and has about the same area of distribution as AMPS.

The extension of D-AMPS to include a digital, physical control channel that occupies one time slot has since been specified in IS-136 rev. 0. In much the same way as in GSM, logical control channels are mapped onto the time slot. (See Chapter 7, Subsection 7.3.4.) The new standard also includes the two older standards. Hence, a D-AMPS network in accordance with IS-136 rev. 0 can contain both analog and digital traffic and control channels. Following an additional extension – with IS-136 rev. A – D-AMPS is currently specified for 1900 MHz and is referred to as 1900-AMPS. Mobiles that use 1900 MHz need not be capable of handling analog channels, but they should be able to use both the 800 and 1900 MHz bands (dual band).

PCS

Personal communications service (PCS) is a very open standard; it mainly specifies a service interface. A PCS system can either be analog or digital, using cellular or a combination of cellular and cordless techniques. Digital access can be based either on TDMA or on IS-95 (CDMA).

PDC

PDC was specified by RCR in Japan, in cooperation with 11 manufacturers, three of whom were non-Japanese enterprises. The system became commercially available in 1993–1994. The air interface is open and similar to that of D-AMPS, while the network architecture and services are more like GSM. For the time being, PDC is only available in Asia.

2.4.3 Cordless systems

Cellular systems are not the only means of providing mobile telephony. Another large group is also worth mentioning in this connection, namely cordless systems. They have not yet been used to build complete logical networks but are primarily employed in private networks and, increasingly, as a PSTN access method. The appellation "cordless" has its origin in the technique that made it possible for subscribers to connect a small base station to their telephones, thereby attaining a limited degree of mobility (within a radius of a few kilometres). CT-1 denotes *cordless telephony 1st generation*.

Third generation cordless technology (CT-3) has seen the introduction of a radio exchange that can be connected to either a PBX or to a local exchange. A number of base stations connected to the radio exchange will provide the extensions with free mobility within the area covered by the exchange. A CT-3 system can be based on DECT, which uses TDMA for its radio access. The system requires no actual cell planning.

2.4.4 Data communication in digital mobile networks

The demands for greater data communication capacity in mobile systems is briefly addressed in Chapter 1, Section 1.3. In the case of GSM, a number of different techniques are emerging:

- An increase of channel capacity, from 9.6 to 14.4 kbit/s, as a result of new channel coding.
- The use of data compression in accordance with ITU-T Recommendation V.42*bis* or V.42. This technique is most useful and effective when transferring text files.
- Concatenation of up to eight time slots. This technique can be used for *n* •9.6 kbit/s or *n* • 14.4 kbit/s. The concatenation technique is referred to as high-speed circuit switched data (HSCSD) and can also be used for video transmission, see *Figure D.2.7*.

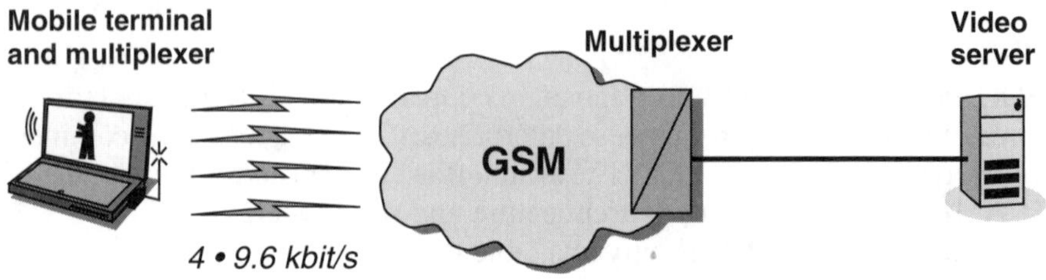

Figure D.2.7 Concatenation of time slots in GSM

- Packetising data in combination with the installation of a packet switch. This method, called general packet radio system (GPRS), is illustrated in *Figure D.2.8*. The combination of GPRS and HSCSD can provide capacity exceeding 100 kbit/s.

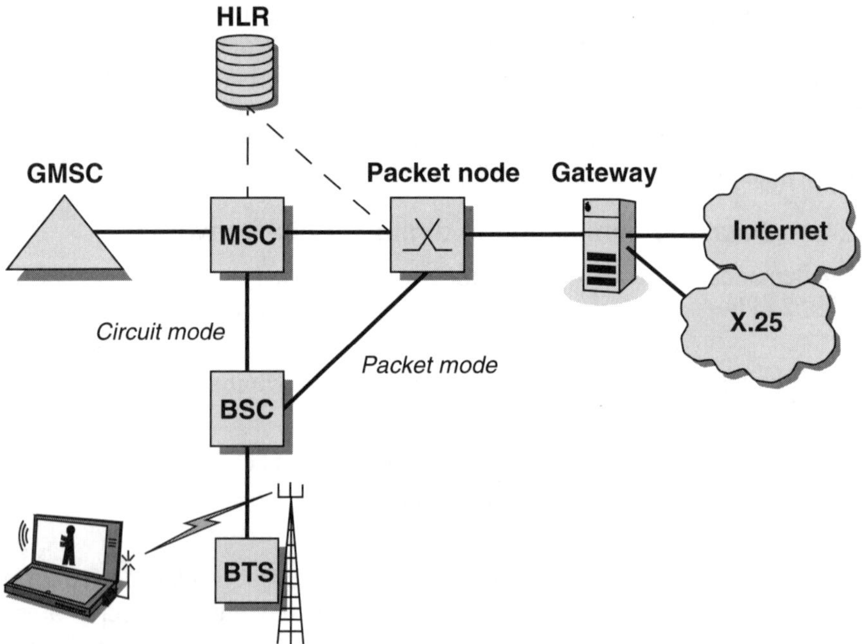

Figure D.2.8 Packet nodes implemented in GSM

2.5 Related standards

2.5.1 Wide area paging networks

As mentioned earlier, ETSI has standardised ERMES for WAP. The first ERMES network was brought into operation in 1993. ERMES operates using 16 different carriers with a bit rate of 6.25 kbit/s and includes international roaming between the different WAP networks (WAPN). The recipient of a call in ERMES can also transmit a response message. (See Volume 1, Chapter 6, Subsection 6.3.3.)

2.5.2 Mobile data networks

An example of a mobile data network – the packet-switched Mobitex – is described in the following. Mobitex was specified by Televerket, the former National Swedish Telecommunications Administration, and became operational in 1987. It is now available on the American and European continents.

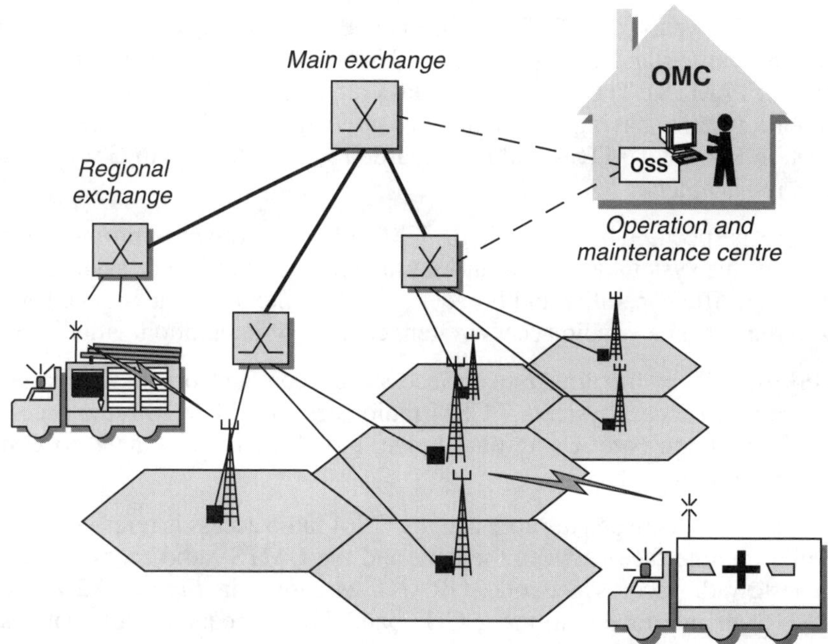

Figure D.2.9 A mobile data network

The network is cellular and in most cases nationwide. It provides the possibility of creating closed user groups (CUGs), regarded as highly advantageous by the system's most customary users – police departments, ambulance services, fire departments and shipping and forwarding agents. Since the network is packet-switched, individual users do not have their own physical channels connected during "calls", which means that there is no need to dimension base station capacity in accordance with ordinary traffic theory.

Mobile users can be connected to fixed computers via regional exchanges. Since messages do not generally exceed 40–50 characters, and since connection set-up times are significantly shorter than is the case in a circuit-switched network, communication is extremely fast.

While en route to a fire, fire-engines can receive information about the situation at the site of the fire, ambulances carrying injured persons can receive blood-group information on the way to the hospital, truck drivers can be directed in real time to the right distribution centre in an unknown city etc.

2.6 Future standards

For several years, the ITU-T has been conducting a project aimed at setting future mobile standards: future public land mobile telecommunications systems (FPLMTS). The project, nowadays referred to as IMT 2000, addresses mobile systems having broadband characteristics. UMTS is the designation used in Europe. UMTS should be regarded as an extension to GSM and not as a replacement.

UMTS is specified by ETSI and the UMTS Forum. The most prominent features of the system are a new air interface for symmetrical or asymmetrical packet traffic capability and broader and more flexible bandwidths. UMTS will thus be a new radio access system capable of integration with GSM.

GSM/UMTS is structured into an access and a core network, having two different radio access systems – GSM radio access and UMTS radio access – and a common core. Using dual mode, mobiles can be adapted to GSM, UMTS or both.

The interface between the core and the GSM radio access is referred to as A, while the interface between the core and the UMTS radio access is called generic radio access network (GRAN), as shown in *Figure D.2.10.* The UMTS air interface is in the 2 GHz band. Three frequency alternatives – 900, 1800 and 1900 MHz – are available to the A-interface.

It is believed that data transmission will account for an increasing portion of traffic and that its destination will often be the Internet. (See *Figure D.2.10.*)

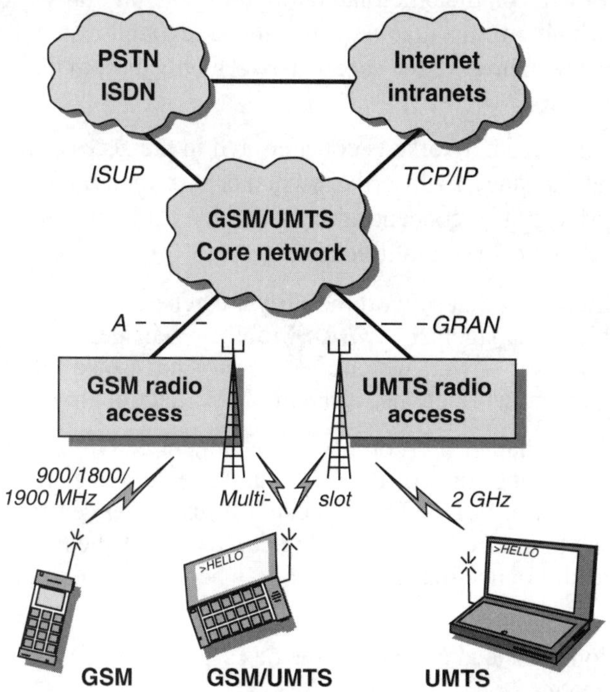

Figure D.2.10 GSM/UMTS architecture

3 Switching and switch control

3.1 Introduction

Mobile network functions for switching and switch control use the same switching technique as that used in PSTN/ISDN but differ in some other respects from the corresponding fixed-network functions.

- An MSC in a mobile network only has temporary subscribers – visiting mobiles – that have no fixed numbers in the MSC's service area.
- Routing between MSCs is based on temporary numbers associated with the visitor for the duration of a call. This number is referred to as the roaming number.
- In a fixed, circuit-switched network, routing is performed only once, and the connection normally remains established until the call is terminated.

In the PLMN, on the other hand, mobiles generally move during ongoing calls, which means that new routing and handover can be required. Handover can involve the access network only or both the access network and the MSCs.

- Traffic in fixed networks is concentrated in the access network, either in the local exchange's subscriber switch or in a stand-alone concentrator. In the PLMN, traffic concentration is mainly performed over the air interface with the help of multiple access.

Network functions that support mobility are generally summarised under the term mobility management (MM). Mobility management requires a good deal of processor power, which the operator must take into account when dimensioning network elements having MM functionality.

As stated in Chapter 1, mobility management requires centrally located intelligence (in the form of the HLR) and special registers integrated with the MSC (VLRs). Mobile IN calls can also use other central network intelligence. We therefore find it more logical to address the topic of mobile call set-up and disconnection in Chapter 6, where network intelligence is discussed.

This section is instead devoted to the description of:

- switching network elements in GSM;
- the network architecture of large mobile networks; and
- switching during an on-going call.

3.2 Switching network elements in GSM

Let us base the discussion on *Figure D.3.1.* This figure illustrates the network architecture of a small GSM network that includes two MSCs plus their respective VLRs, one GMSC and one HLR. In addition, four access networks are included. The network interworks with a PSTN and another PLMN.

Most mobile networks consist of two hierarchical levels: the MSC and the GMSC levels. Transit nodes can also be found in large mobile networks (see Section 3.4). Small networks can have GMSC functions integrated into their MSCs, which results in a "flat", meshed structure.

The traffic channels of the access and core networks differ. The access network handles 13 kbit/s traffic channels, and the core network 64 kbit/s channels. Voice recoding between 13 and 64 kbit/s is performed in the BSC. Encryption equipment is normally located in the base stations.

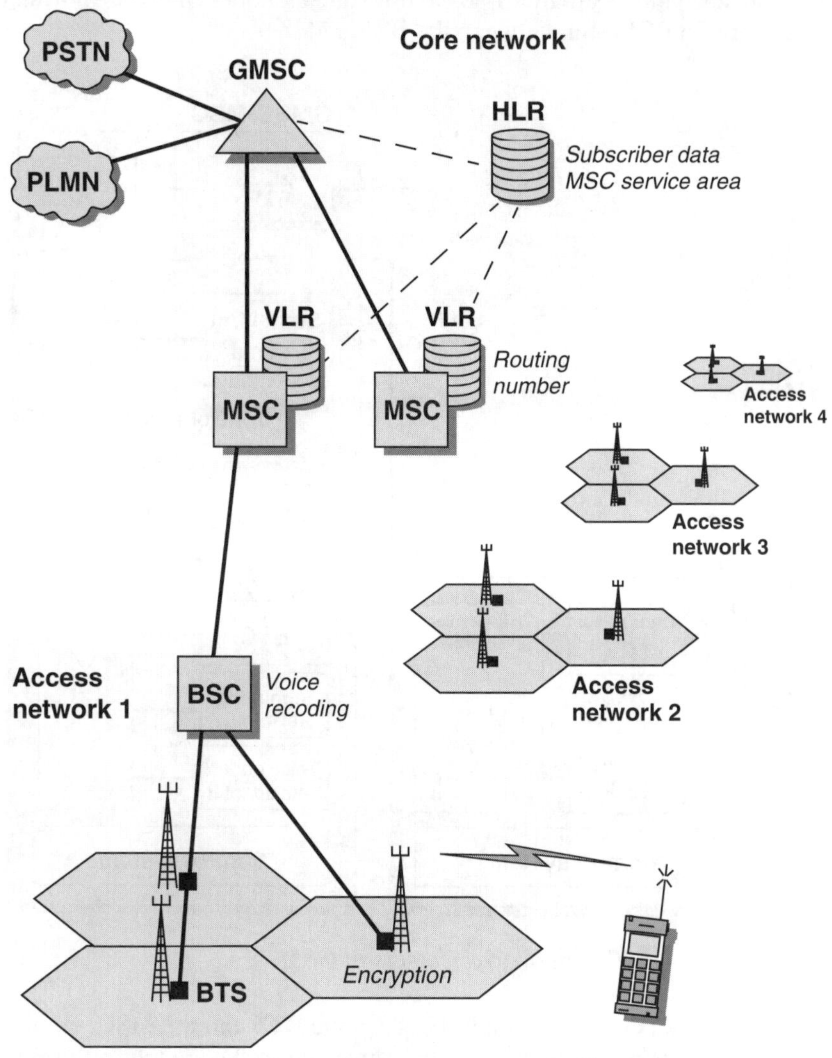

Figure D.3.1 The physical network architecture of a PLMN

Switching is performed at four levels of the structure: in the BTS, BSC, MSC and GMSC, shown in *Figure D.3.1*.

Concentration is performed in the air interface, because the number of traffic channels is limited. This concentration is controlled by the BSC, which assigns idle traffic channels to mobiles. After decryption in the BTS, four 13 kbit/s traffic channels are multiplexed onto one 64 kbit/s channel – normally a time slot of a PCM link between the BTS and the BSC.

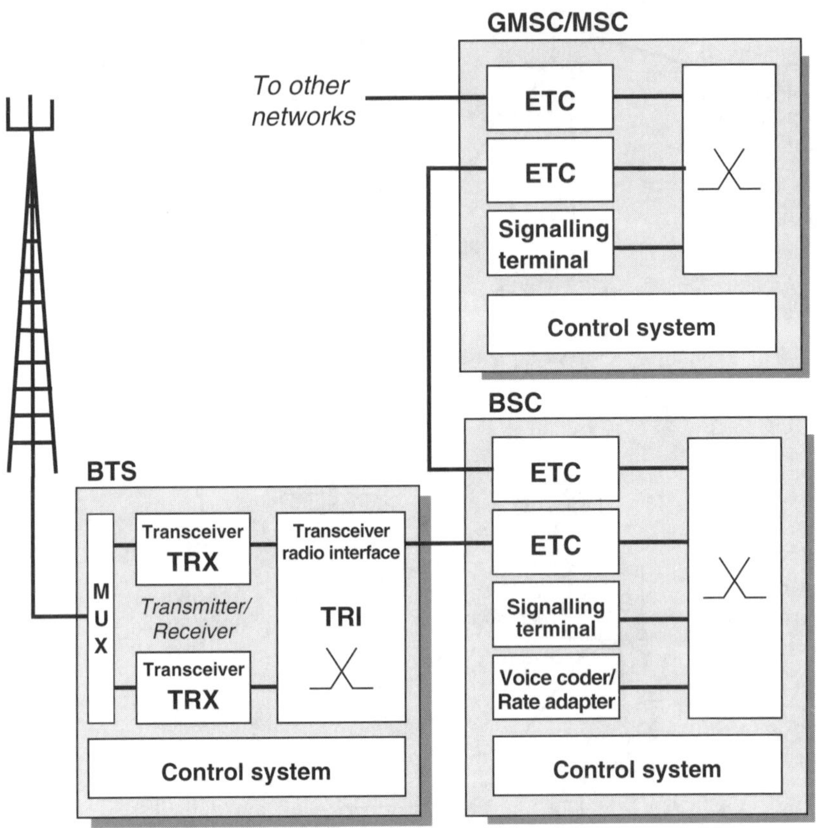

Figure D.3.2 Switching network elements in GSM

The BSC connects traffic channels between the BTS and the MSC, employing a pool of voice coders that can be connected to the switch in the BSC. The BSC also performs the required switching during a call in progress, as the mobile moves from one cell to another within a BSC service area.

Ordinarily, an MSC switches 64 kbit/s traffic channels between the GMSC and one of its BSCs. It must continuously keep track of (or be able to find out) which section of its own service area a called mobile is in. It must also be capable of switching to another MSC whenever a mobile moves to a cell in another MSC's service area during an ongoing call, as described in Subsection 3.3.

A GMSC switches 64 kbit/s traffic channels between external networks and the MSCs of its own PLMN as well as between external fixed networks and interworking PLMNs. As mentioned earlier, GMSCs are connected to external networks at the national or international hierarchical network levels.

When a GMSC receives a call from an external network, it must determine the MSC (or the interworking PLMN) that is currently capable of reaching the called mobile – in other words, which MSC service area or which interworking PLMN it must connect to. This is where network intelligence enters the picture. The HLR informs the GMSC of which MSC to use, and because the calling mobile does not have a fixed extension to that MSC, the HLR will also provide the GMSC with a temporary routing number to be used for signalling. This number was retrieved by the HLR from the VLR involved. The roles of the HLR and VLR are described in more detail in Chapter 6.

3.3 Reswitching during a call (due to handover)

When we have studied other circuit-switched networks, we have come to perceive all switching as occurring when a call is being set up. In fact, call forwarding is part of the same procedure.

Mobile networks must be capable of switching during an ongoing call, too, because the mobile can change base stations and in some instances even MSCs. As mentioned in Section 3.1, handover can lead to reswitching in the base station, in the BSC and possibly in the MSC, as well.

Figure D.3.3 Handover – changing base stations during an ongoing call

This chapter addresses only the switching aspects of handover. Signal quality aspects, which determine whether or not handover will actually be performed, are addressed in Chapter 5, Section 5.4.

Under unfavourable conditions, switching in a mobile network during a call in progress can interfere with the call. Consequently, it is vital to a network operator's success that such switching is performed without any disturbance. Calls that are frequently cut off or disturbed due to badly performed handover can lead to irate subscribers who may choose to subscribe to another operator or simply stop using their mobile telephones.

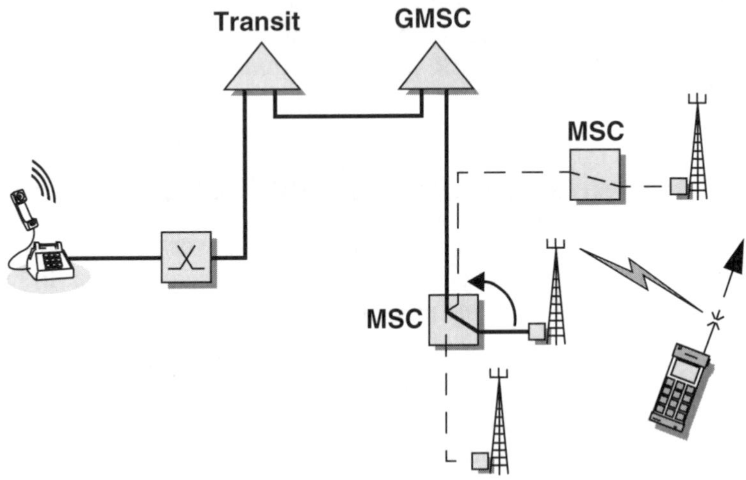

Figure D.3.4 Switching in MSCs during handover

There are five types of handover:

- Intra-cell handover: A new channel is selected in the same cell due to interference or other disturbance on the channel being used by the mobile. In the case of GSM, the resultant reswitching only involves the BSC.
- Intra-BSC handover (in GSM): A new channel is selected in a cell that is managed by the same BSC. The resultant reswitching only involves one BSC.
- Intra-MSC handover: A new channel is selected in a cell that is managed by another BSC but by the same MSC. In the case of GSM, the resultant reswitching involves two BSCs and one MSC.
- Inter-MSC handover: A new channel is selected in a cell that is managed by another MSC in the same mobile network. The resultant reswitching involves several MSCs.

- Inter-system handover: A new channel is selected in a cell that is managed by another mobile network, with which "our" PLMN interworks.

3.4 Architecture of large mobile networks

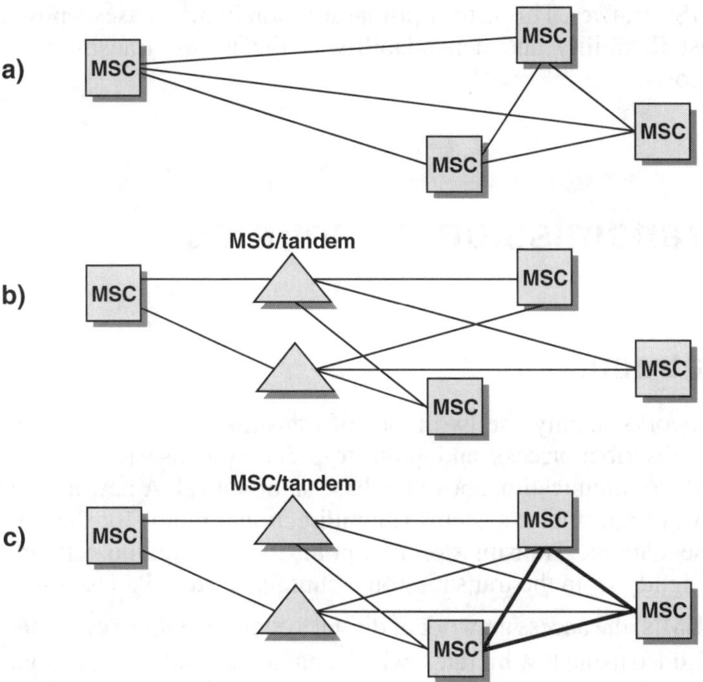

Figure D.3.5 PLMN core networks – three different solutions

The various elements of the core network (the MSC, the GMSC, the HLR and so forth) are interconnected in much the same way as local, transit and network-intelligence nodes in PSTN/ISDN. In the dimensioning process, operators must nevertheless consider a PLMN's special traffic and signalling profiles; for example, the fact that the majority of connections are set up between a mobile and a PSTN user. Registration and handover between MSCs (that is, inter-MSC handover) also cause significant signalling in mobile networks (approximately 4% of all calls make use of inter-MSC handover).

A PLMN core network can be built in accordance with one of the three principles illustrated in *Figure D.3.5*.

Alternative *a* shows a solution in which all MSCs are connected to each other regardless of how their service areas are related geographically. In alternative *b*, tandem exchanges have been introduced, and all direct routes have been removed to achieve greater flexibility. All inter-MSC traffic is routed over the tandem exchanges – a practical solution in cases where traffic demand is uncertain. Alternative *c* has combined the routing principles employed in *a* and *b* and has introduced direct routes between MSCs handling high traffic loads (resulting from frequent handover and great demand for inter-MSC traffic). This is the optimal solution in most cases – providing the greatest flexibility and dependability at the lowest transmission and operating costs.

4 Transmission techniques

4.1 Introduction

Mobile networks mainly use two types of transmission technique: cellular radio for subscriber access and point-to-point systems (including radio links) for all communication above the base station level. A new trend is the use of point-to-multipoint systems (omnidirectional radio) for the connection of base stations. Transmission in a point-to-point mobile network differs only slightly from the transmission technique used in PSTN networks.

- In the PLMN, the access network of digital systems handles voice channels that are coded using low bit rates, which enables several traffic channels to be transmitted over a 64 kbit/s connection (four 13 kbit/s connections in GSM). Conversion between 13 and 64 kbit/s is performed by the BSC.
- The majority of mobile network owners are new operators who have no transmission networks of their own. They often make use of leased lines to interconnect the various elements of the access and core networks. Alternatively, they can build their own radio links for the communication between base stations and BSCs.

What is typical of mobile network transmission (and indeed challenging) is the radio path between the base station and the mobile. This chapter will only deal with that particular transmission path.

4.2 The radio medium

4.2.1 Mobile transmission frequency ranges

The way in which radio waves propagate makes it possible for us to listen to radio stations broadcasting from the other side of the earth, even though no galvanic connection exists between the transmitter and receiver. Radio waves are naturally employed in applications such as television and radio broadcasting but can also be used as an alternative to cable.

Different radio frequencies are suited to different fields of application:

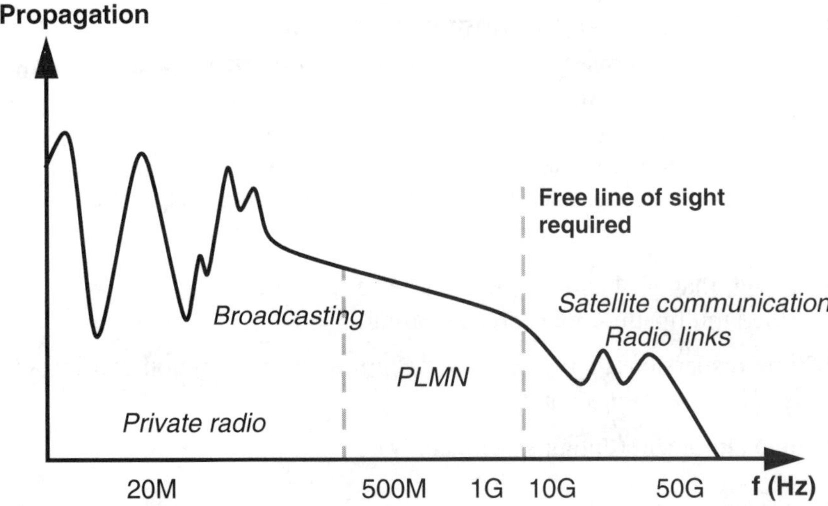

Figure D.4.1 Propagation and utilisation of different frequency ranges

Low frequencies (below 30 MHz) are able to propagate around the earth using the ionosphere as a reflector. This can be utilised for long-distance communication with ships and aircraft. On the other hand, it is difficult to reuse these frequencies – which happens to be a prerequisite for mobile communications. They are therefore unfit for use in cellular architectures and, besides, they would not provide any degree of stable quality comparable with the quality required in the PSTN.

Frequencies between 30 and 300 MHz are especially suitable for nationwide radio broadcasting. They cannot be reflected by the ionosphere, are only slightly affected by attenuation and are relatively insensitive to large obstacles, such as buildings and terrain formations.

Frequencies in the band between 300 and 2000 MHz are more suited to mobile telephony. Attenuation is no problem, thanks to the limited size of cells; the connection between transmitter and receiver can contain smaller obstacles without causing any serious shadowing effects. This ability falls off at higher frequencies, because a base station's coverage radius is reduced with increased frequency (at constant output power).

Shadowing effects increase in the frequency band above 2 GHz. These frequencies are more suitable for use in microcells or in other applications in which free line of sight exists along the radio path. Precipitation attenuation starts to significantly reduce radio-wave propagation at frequencies above 20 GHz.

4.2.2 Cellular system transmission issues

The part of the transmission network which utilises the air interface must take into account a number of factors: the radio medium, the frequency range that has been selected, the topology, the transmission technique used (analog or digital) and the need for frequency reusability. The problems that must be overcome are usually related to the following categories:

- path loss;
- fading, that is, shadowing or long-term fading and Rayleigh fading, also called multipath or interference fading;
- time dispersion arising because of multipath propagation causing intersymbol interference; and
- time alignment (digital systems only).

Path loss

Due to power scattering, the theoretical attenuation of signal strength in free space is proportional to the square of the distance from the transmitting antenna. For mobile systems, the increase of this attenuation is proportional to (nearly) the fourth power of the distance. This is explained by the fact that when signals travel close to ground level, a great deal of their power is absorbed by the earth. The output power and receiver sensitivity of the mobile sets an upper limit to the size of a cell. Above this limit, signal strength starts to fall below receiver sensitivity, both in the base station and in the mobile.

Path loss affects the minimum number of base stations in an area and the necessary output power within the cells.

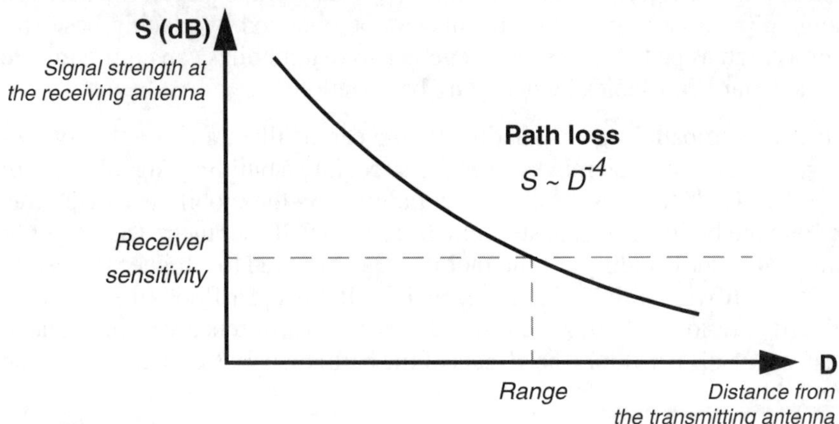

Figure D.4.2 Path loss

Shadow fading

Path loss is a theoretical attenuation which occurs under free-line-of-sight conditions and which increases with the distance between base station and mobile. Fading, on the other hand, refers to attenuation that varies between a maximum and minimum value in an irregular fashion. The mobiles used in a PLMN ordinarily move through areas with obstacles of various sizes, such as mountains, buildings and tunnels. Occasionally, these obstacles will shadow or completely cut off the signal. Although the consequences of such shadowing effects will depend on the size of an obstacle and on the distance to it, the received signal strength will inevitably vary. This type of fading is referred to as *shadow fading*.

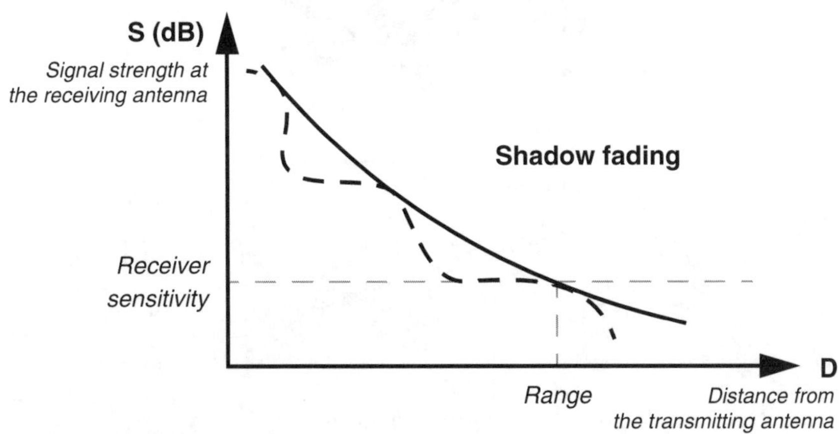

Figure D.4.3 Shadow fading

Minimising the effects of shadow fading in a network is part of the network planning process. Satisfactory results can be obtained by placing base stations as high as possible or closer together so that mobiles can communicate "around" large obstacles by changing base stations.

The effects of path loss and shadow fading can be illustrated by the following values. As a mobile moves from the street into a building, signal strength drops by 10 dB (the result of shadow fading). As the mobile is carried further into the building, signal strength drops by 0.6 dB per metre (the result of increased shadow fading). If the mobile is now carried to a higher floor, signal strength will initially increase by 1.2 dB for each floor (the effect of reduced path loss). Above the thirtieth floor, the difference will be reduced to only 0.05 dB per floor (the effects of the earth on path loss start to become negligible).

Rayleigh fading

Rayleigh, or multipath, fading is a completely different type of fading that can be problematic and difficult to overcome. As illustrated in *Figure D.4.4,* it arises due to the reception of several signals at the receiver – reflected from objects in the vicinity. These signals, arriving from different directions, will necessarily be out of phase with one another when they reach the receiving antenna, because they have travelled over different distances. As the transmitter moves, the phase difference varies and causes the signals sometimes to reinforce and sometimes to counteract one another. This results in fading that at times displays extremely high levels of attenuation (fading dip).

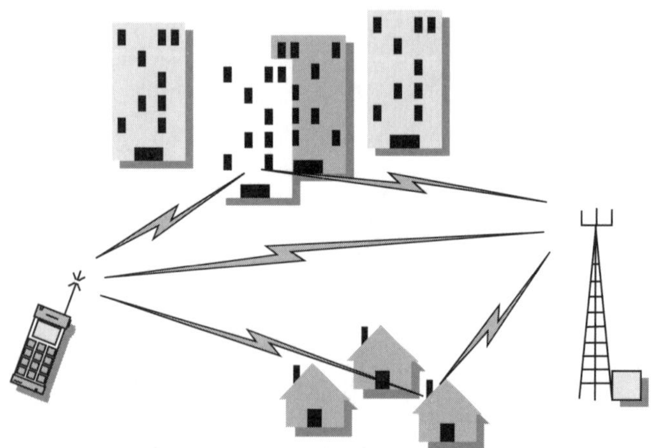

Figure D.4.4 Rayleigh fading (multipath fading)

Rayleigh fading is most perceptible in urban areas. A car mobile in the 900 MHz band, when used at a speed of 50 kilometres per hour in a densely built-up area, will give rise to a fading periodicity of 10.7 ms (that is, one dip for every 0.3 metres). Dips will occur more frequently at higher frequencies and more rapid mobile movement.

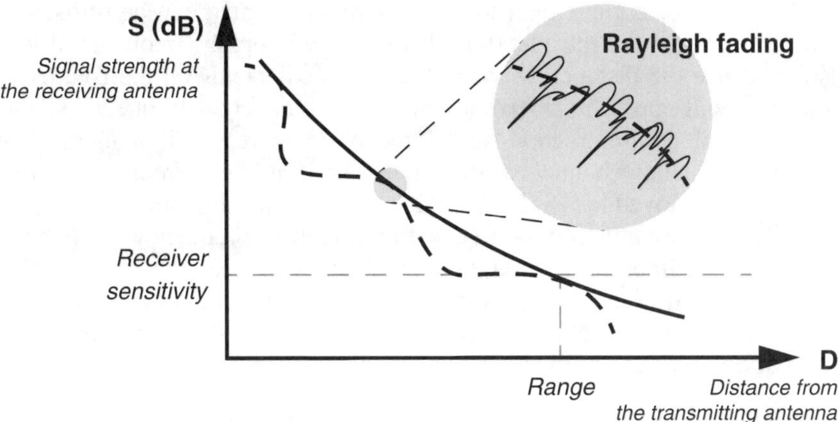

Figure D.4.5 Rayleigh fading

Base stations often have two antennas mounted at a certain distance from one another to counteract the interference that arises as a result of Rayleigh fading. This arrangement is referred to as space diversity. If the distance between the antennas is sufficiently large, their signals will be uncorrelated and the risk of simultaneous fading dips is significantly reduced.

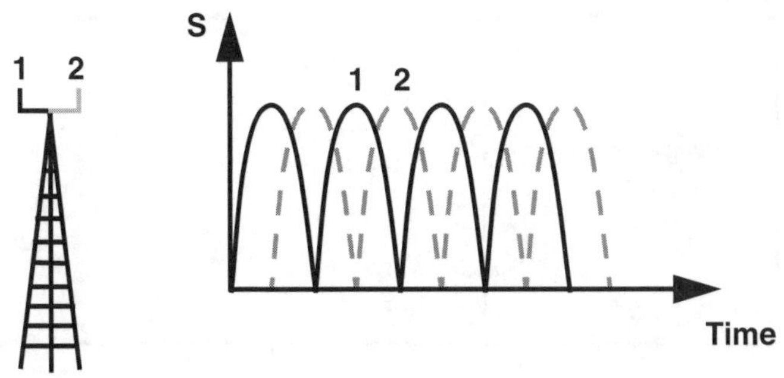

Figure D.4.6 An antenna system for space diversity

The minimum distance required to obtain improved reception depends on the wavelength of the signal. In practice, this distance is a few metres between the antennas. Using space diversity, the improvement at 900 MHz could be approximately 9 dB compared to a single-antenna arrangement. A disadvantage is the increased complexity of the antenna equipment and the resulting increase in cost.

An alternative or complement to space diversity, which can be utilised in digital systems, is the introduction of frequency hopping (frequency diversity). Because the distance between fading dips depends on the frequency used, dips will appear at different distances for different frequencies. The probability of attaining good signal reception increases if a method of changing frequency channels at short intervals is applied. Frequency diversity can be employed in GSM (at the discretion of the network operator), so all GSM mobiles must contain such functionality. Frequency is changed more than 200 times per second, in accordance with a parameter-controlled algorithm stored in the mobile and the base stations. The mobiles are supplied with parameter values for each cell, together with other cell-related information, over one of the control channels.

As is obvious from the figures shown in this subsection, the total attenuation of the received signal is a combination of three attenuation effects: path loss, shadow fading and Rayleigh fading. All of them must be considered in the detailed cell planning as it relates to antenna equipment, transmitter power and receiver sensitivity. *Figure D.4.7* illustrates signal-strength levels at a given distance from a base station.

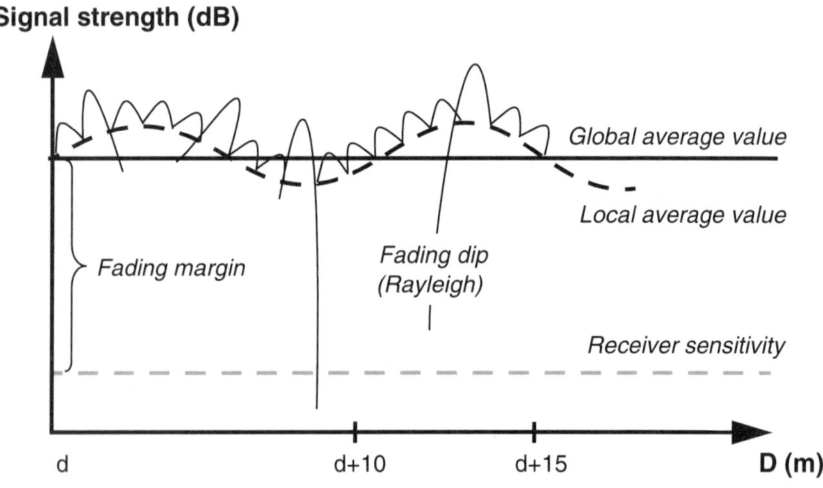

Figure D.4.7 Received signal strength, distance in metres

It is evident from *Figure D.4.7* that cell planning cannot be based only on path loss and shadow fading. One must also consider Rayleigh fading to attain a sufficient fading margin. To achieve error-free communications, the global average value must be as many decibels above receiver sensitivity as the strongest expected fading dip.

Time dispersion

Another problem caused by reflections is time dispersion.

Figure D.4.8 illustrates the transmission and reception of a bit sequence (here, a one followed by two zeros). The mobile will receive two signals; one of them is a reflection that occurred a few kilometres from the mobile. The bit rate of GSM frequency channels is 270 kbit/s, which is equivalent to 3.7 microseconds per bit – a time during which the signal travels 1.1 kilometres. If the difference in distance between the two signals is close on 2 kilometres, the mobile will detect a 0 from the direct signal (the third bit) and a 1 from the reflected signal (the first bit). This phenomenon is referred to as *inter-symbol interference*. If the reflected signal is of sufficiently high power, such interference will cause the mobile difficulties in determining whether it received a 1 or a 0.

While Rayleigh fading is caused by small differences in distance between signals (decimetres or metres), time dispersion is caused by differences on the order of kilometres. Note also that time dispersion is a phenomenon that only arises in digital networks.

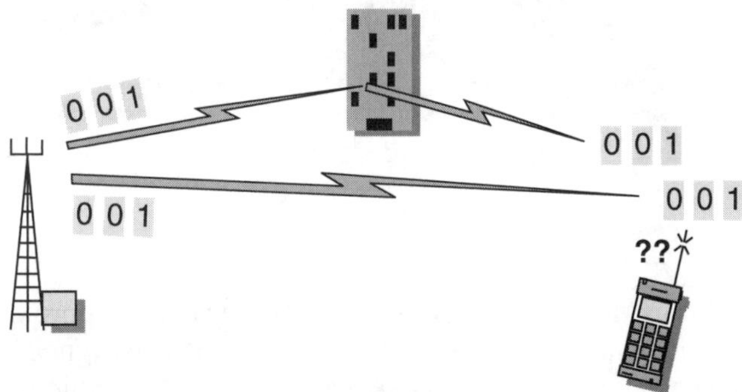

Figure D.4.8 Time dispersion

To neutralise the effects of time dispersion, a technique called *equalising* is used. This technique is described in Subsection 4.3.4.

Time alignment

If mobiles in a digital mobile network share a common frequency channel, they must all send in their assigned time slots so as to avoid overlapping bursts. The instant at which a mobile is allowed to send will also depend on its distance from the base station. Both the network and the mobile must therefore include functionality that continuously regulates the sending instant (time alignment).

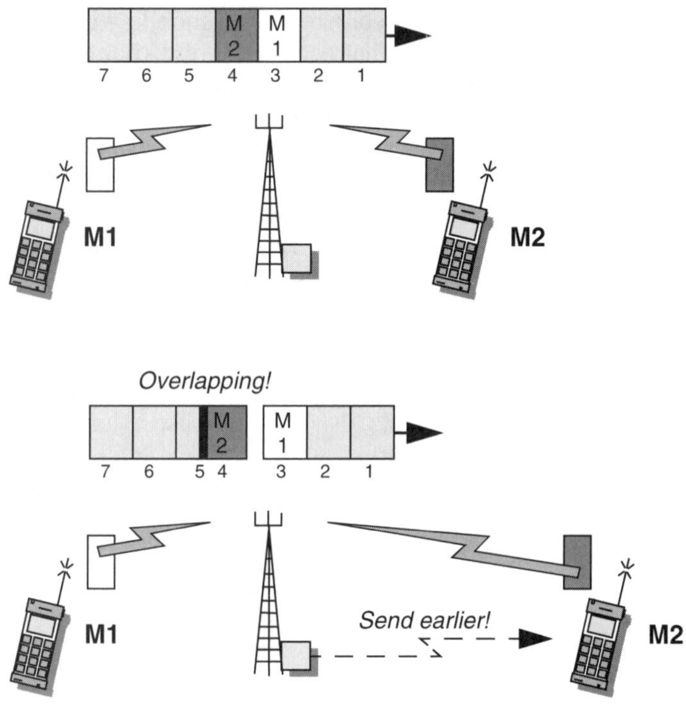

Figure D.4.9 Time alignment

Figure D.4.9 illustrates two mobiles which are located at approximately the same distance from a base station and which have been assigned time slots 3 and 4. This means that the interval between the instants at which they send is approximately 600 microseconds (the length of one time slot). As mobile M2 moves away from the base station, the time slot it uses (time slot 4) will be received by the base station later and later. There is then a risk that time slots 4 and 5 will start overlapping one another (see the bottom illustration in *Figure D.4.9*). Thus, the mobiles' sending instants must be adjusted at regular intervals, which is controlled via signals from the base station.

To avoid a need for frequent adjustment, GSM has been designed to include extra space equivalent to just over an eight-bit sequence (30 microseconds) in its time slots. This space is used by the base station to balance time delays between different mobiles. Repeated adjustment is needed only when the signal delay from a given mobile is close to 30 microseconds (approximately 8 kilometres difference in distance) in relation to the last adjustment.

The base stations of a D-AMPS network can continuously order adjustment of the sending instants up to a distance of 92 kilometres.

See also Subsection 4.3.4, which deals with burst formats in GSM.

4.3 Transmission technique for the radio path

Digital and analog mobile networks both require the following:

- suitable antennas;
- a modulation method;
- frequency and channel multiplexing; and
- some sort of error handling (both digital and analog mobile networks employ error-correction techniques for signalling and control information; digital systems also include functions for error correction on traffic channels).

Additional requirements applicable to digital mobile networks:

- the need for voice coding (see also Chapter 2, Section 2.2) and
- encryption across the air interface.

The "layered" model shown in *Figure D.4.10* schematically illustrates the functions included to support the above requirements. The model is best suited to digital mobile networks.

The following description focuses on transmission technique for the radio path in GSM. A short introduction is provided to facilitate understanding of the functions across the air interface as shown in *Figure D.4.10*.

Voice is analysed in blocks 20 milliseconds long; in other words, 50 times per second.

Including protection bits, voice blocks are represented by a total of 456 bits arranged into eight "payload bit sequences" of 57 bits each.

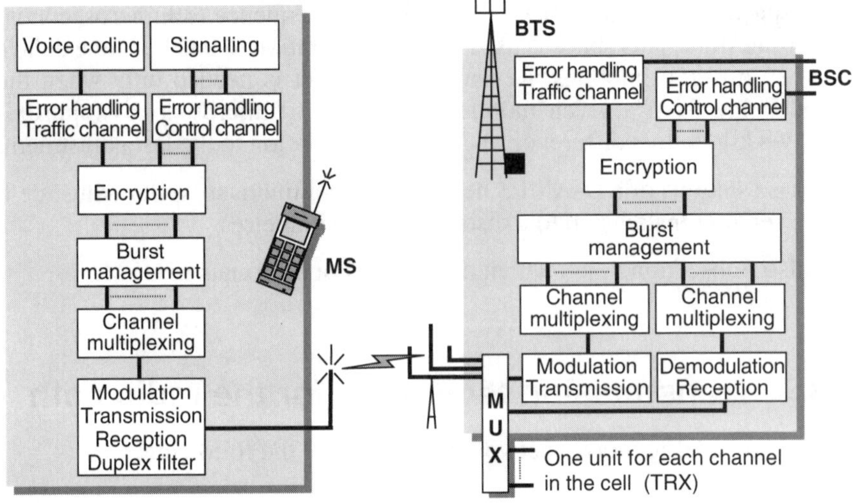

Figure D.4.10 Functions across the air interface

Mobiles send in bursts every fifth millisecond. Between the bursts sent by one mobile, seven other mobiles (at peak load) send over the same frequency employing time-division multiplexing (TDM).

Each burst contains 25% of the number of bits representing a block, that is, 114 "payload bits". The length of a burst corresponds to a time slot.

With TDM, eight time slots in a frame are carried by a single frequency channel. At any particular instant, several mobiles use the same time slot but on different frequency channels. On one of the frequency channels, two time slots in each cell are reserved for signalling. The technique for allocating a time slot to a call is called time division multiple access (TDMA), illustrated in *Figure D.4.11*.

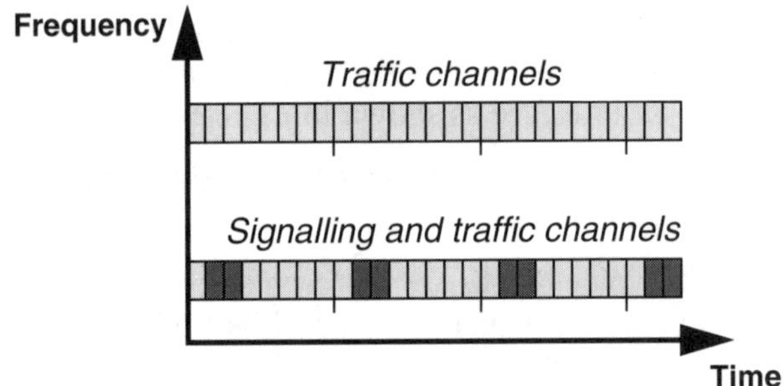

Figure D.4.11 Time division multiplexing of channels in GSM

4.3.1 Voice coding and signalling

In accordance with the structure of our books, we have addressed voice coding in Chapter 2, Section 2.2. What is most interesting when we study it from the transmission aspect is the resultant 13 kbit/s bit stream from the voice coder – corresponding to 260 bits per 20 ms block. This user information is carried by traffic channels.

Air interface signalling is carried by nine types of control channel, described in greater detail in Chapter 7.

Signalling normally accounts for only a small portion of the total transmission capacity of the air interface.

4.3.2 Error handling

The dependability of the radio medium – with regard to radio interference – cannot compare with the dependability of a cable. The radio medium contains no insulation capable of shielding "the line". Consequently, some sort of error handling is required to attain a transmission quality comparable with that of the fixed network.

Error handling in a mobile network includes both traffic and control channels and is usually divided into error detection and error correction. Errors are detected by redundant bits – parity bits, checksums or both – added to the information to be transmitted across the air interface. Errors are corrected either through retransmission or through the use of some type of error correcting code (the latter requires redundant bits over and above those used for error detection). For obvious reasons, it is not suitable to retransmit information over channels that are used for telephony (the delays caused by voice coding are enough of a problem to deal with), whereas retransmission in signalling is fully acceptable. Hence, different error handling methods are used for traffic channels and control channels.

Control-channel error handling

Relatively advanced error handling methods are applied in mobile networks that use digital control channels (time slots for signalling). In GSM, a slimmed-down version of link access procedure on the D-channel (LAPD) is used across the air interface. This link protocol is referred to as LAPDm. The protocol employs a mode of error detection based on the use of checksums. Errors are corrected in two different ways: either through retransmission or by simply discarding faulty signalling messages.

AMPS uses a more simple error handling technique. Twelve parity bits for error detection are added to the end of each message, and messages found to be faulty are discarded. This technique assumes that message reception is acknowledged within a specified time so that incorrectly received messages can be retransmitted.

Digital traffic-channel error handling

The following example is based on the error handling method used by GSM for information transferred on traffic channels. The process includes two phases. In the first phase – called channel coding – redundant bits are added to the information. In the second phase, the bits are distributed over a number of bursts in accordance with a predetermined pattern (interleaving).

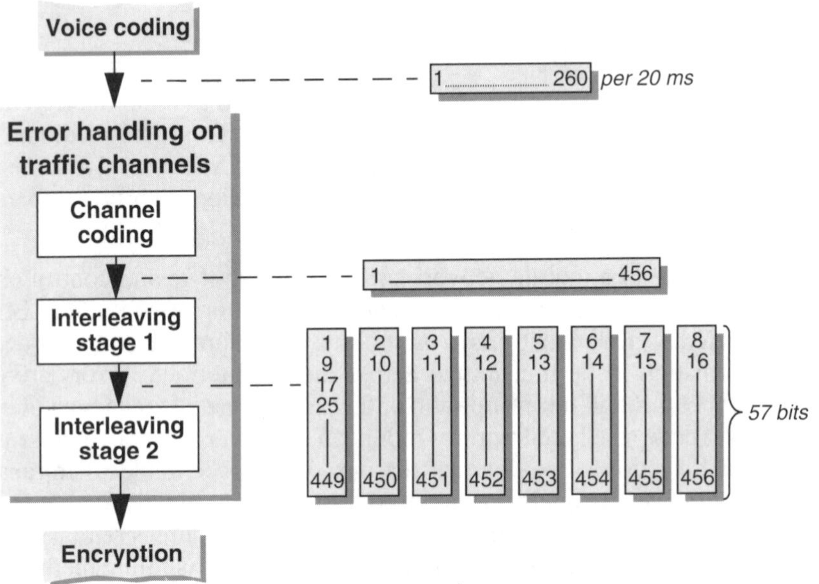

Figure D.4.12 Error handling on GSM traffic channels

The majority of the bits delivered by the voice coder to the channel coder are first block-coded, which means that parity bits are added for error detection. Additional bits are then added (convolution coding) for error correction. The original 260-bit sample has now almost doubled in size (456 bits).

The use of channel coding makes it possible to detect and correct single-bit errors, but one cannot guard against disturbances involving bursts of erroneous bits – a situation that frequently occurs. Interleaving is a technique that may be able to solve this problem. The interleaving process is performed in two stages and does not add any bits. The first stage involves breaking up the 456 bits into groups of 57 bits, as illustrated in *Figure D.4.12*. A burst can only carry two such groups (as described in Subsection 4.3.4), so that if portions of a burst are lost, only stray-bit losses will occur and these losses will be evenly distributed over the voice block. The lost bits can ordinarily be recovered through channel coding.

If a complete burst is lost, 25% of the total number of bits will be missing, and such situations cannot be corrected through channel coding. To guard against this happening, the second stage produces bursts that are a mixture of 57-bit groups belonging to consecutive voice blocks. The maximum loss will then be reduced to 12.5% of the total number of bits, which can be corrected by channel coding. However, this technique increases the delay.

4.3.3 Encryption

Encryption, which is dealt with in Chapter 6 (Subsection 6.2.4). does not contribute any additional bits.

4.3.4 Burst management

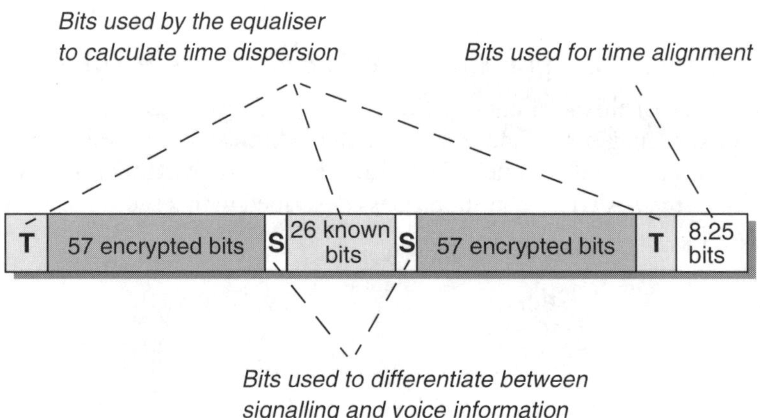

Figure D.4.13 An example of a GSM burst format (normal burst)

The principal purpose of burst management is to minimise the effects of bit error bursts. GSM uses four different burst formats, depending on the type of logical channel. *Figure D.4.13* shows the format used for the majority of logical channels (normal burst).

Every burst of this sort is capable of carrying 2 • 57 = 114 encrypted payload bits. 26 known bits, located between the two blocks of payload bits, are used to cope with any time dispersion and the resultant inter-symbol interference that can have arisen (see Subsection 4.2.2). By comparing the known bits with the received signal sequence, it is possible to draw conclusions about the time dispersion. In GSM, this applies to differences of up to five kilometres between the path travelled by the direct signal and that travelled by the reflected one. The known bit pattern, along with a method referred to as equalising, is used to calculate what was actually transmitted. The tail-bits (T-bits) mark the beginning and end of a burst.

The burst format also takes into account the need for time alignment (described in Subsection 4.2.2). A buffer space 8.25 bits in length (approximately 30 microseconds) is allocated at the end of the bursts, corresponding to about eight kilometres' difference in distance. Thanks to this buffer, there is no longer any need for mobiles to constantly adjust their relative sending instants when approaching or moving away from base stations.

In special cases – primarily for handover control – it may be necessary to utilise individual bursts for signalling rather than for voice. In such situations, the "stealing flags" (S-bits) are changed to indicate this "theft". See also Chapter 7, Subsection 7.3.3, where the subject of fast associated control channel (FACCH) is addressed.

4.3.5 Channel multiplexing: Physical channels in TDMA

The purpose of this section is to describe the GSM subprocess which follows burst management and which results in traffic from the bursts being loaded onto physical channels. We also describe the corresponding system techniques in D-AMPS. The subprocess described in this section is based on TDMA.

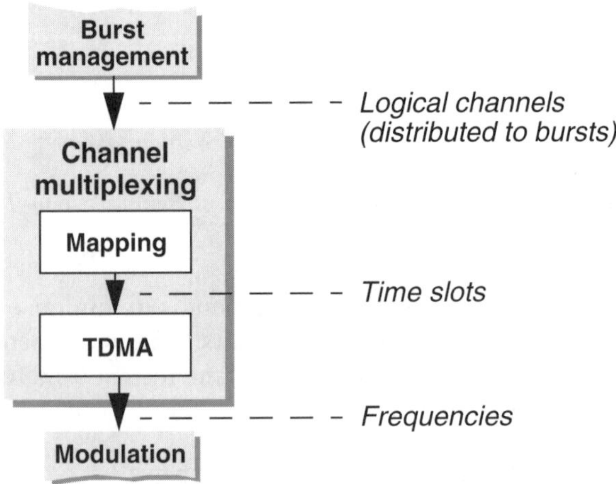

Figure D.4.14 Channel multiplexing

As mentioned in the introduction to Section 4.3, a GSM mobile sends in bursts every fifth millisecond. Every burst contains 25% of the number of bits representing a voice block. The length of a burst corresponds to one time slot which can be regarded as a physical channel in the air interface. We usually differentiate between logical channels, which indicate how a channel is used, and physical channels, which represent a transmission resource.

A physical channel – for example, a time slot on a particular frequency channel in a TDMA system – can be said to be a carrier of a logical channel, such as a traffic channel (sometimes abbreviated TCH), or several logical channels, such as various control channels in a multiframe structure. The latter case is discussed in Chapter 7, Subsection 7.3.9.

In digital systems based on the TDMA principle, such as GSM and D-AMPS, the mapping process means that a time slot and a frequency are allocated to the traffic burst. If frequency hopping is applied, the frequency of a traffic channel also changes – in GSM slightly more than 200 times a second (see Subsection 4.2.2).

The frequency channel separation in GSM is 200 kHz; in D-AMPS 30 kHz. In GSM, each cell is provided with a frequency channel (C_0) for control channels. Normally, time slots 0 and 1 (TS0 and TS1) on C_0 are used for this purpose. The remaining six time slots on C_0 and all eight time slots on other frequencies are used for traffic channels. See *Figure D.4.15.* In D-AMPS, each frequency channel is normally used for three traffic channels.

The traffic channels convey voice or data (such as Internet traffic) between the mobile and base station. The channels are allocated on a per call basis. Ordinarily, a time slot is used for one call only (full rate), but an alternative with two calls per time slot (half rate) has also been specified.

The physical channel in GSM – that is, the time slot – has a length of 0.577 milliseconds. This length is sufficient for one traffic channel burst plus a guard period. For the frequency channels between the mobile and base station (uplink), the frequency range 890–915 MHz is used, while the downlink utilises the range 935–960 MHz.

The total number of duplex frequency channels is 124, resulting in 992 physical channels (compared to 823 in AMPS and D-AMPS).

In contrast to AMPS, GSM does not dictate how the 124 frequency channels may be used. However, each GSM cell must have a C_0 frequency.

All modern mobile systems are based on multiple access, which means that all users have simultaneous access to the medium. This requires a number of rules to prevent situations in which mobiles "all talk at the same time". The medium, which is a common resource, must satisfy the needs of all users.

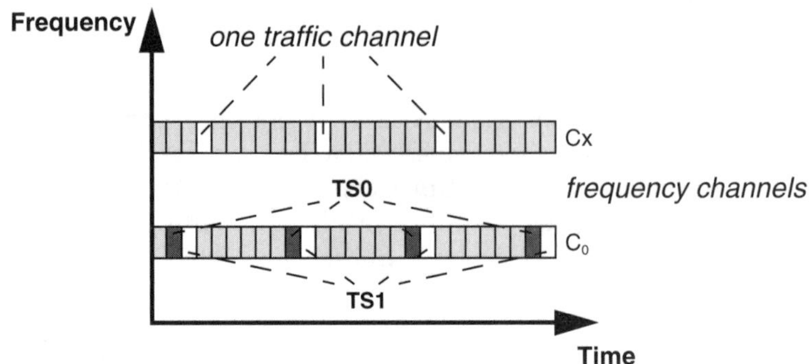

Figure D.4.15 The time division multiple access principle

Traffic channels are assigned through control-channel signalling.

Each cell in a cellular system can be regarded as an individual medium because a mobile leaving the cell loses contact with that cell's base station. However, all mobiles in the cell utilise the same radio resource, namely, that portion of the frequency spectrum which has been assigned to the cell. The following describes two other techniques applicable to channel multiplexing using multiple access: FDMA and CDMA.

4.3.6 Alternative 1: Physical channels in FDMA-based systems

Frequency division multiple access (FDMA) is the technique used by analog mobile telephone systems, such as NMT and AMPS. The access principle is illustrated in *Figure D.4.16.*

The frequency range assigned to the cell consists of one uplink (mobile to base station) and one downlink (base station to mobile). The frequency separation between these links must be sufficiently large – normally 45 MHz (duplex separation) – so that no interference between them will arise at the mobile.

Each link is divided into an equal number of unidirectional channels. One channel should be sufficiently wide (25–30 kHz) to be able to transmit telephone-quality voice (approximately 3 kHz). To be able to make use of duplex telephony, the mobile must have access to one uplink and one downlink channel – two channels combined to form a traffic channel pair.

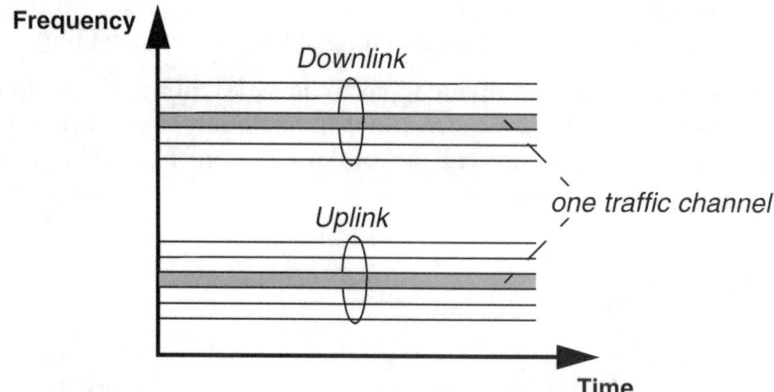

Figure D.4.16 The frequency division multiple access principle

However, a cell consists not only of traffic channels; each cell contains a number of channels that are predefined as control channels. Such channels can use the downlink for the distribution of cell and network information and to transfer call requests arriving from the network and use the uplink frequency for call signalling generated by mobiles. One or more other channels may have been defined as control channels for two-way signalling between the mobile and the network.

The total number of FDMA system channels is standardised and is specified by the government agency that allocates frequencies. The uplink frequency range of the AMPS system is 824–849 MHz and its downlink range is 869–894 MHz. Every link contains a total of 823 unidirectional channels. Only half of the channels are available to any given operator, since the standard stipulates that there is to be room for two competing AMPS operators in every geographical area. AMPS also stipulates which channels are to be used as control channels and which will be used for traffic.

A comparison between TDMA and FDMA

The primary advantages of TDMA over FDMA are its greater capacity and the fact that TDMA is less sensitive to noise, so mobiles can operate with lower power. Another advantage is that the mobile can use a number of time slots freely (since it can only send in its own time slot). For example, the mobile may perform alternative frequency signal measurements – a prerequisite for mobile-assisted handover (MAHO), as in GSM, or mobile-controlled handover (MCHO) as in DECT.

4.3.7 Alternative 2: Physical channels in CDMA-based systems

Code division multiple access (CDMA) is no new technique. It has been utilised in military systems and for satellite communications for many years, but it has also started to be used in mobile network applications.

CDMA systems are not divided into frequencies, nor are they divided into time slots. All mobiles are capable of transmitting and receiving over the entire frequency band. Instead, a "third dimension" is used to separate traffic channels, namely coding.

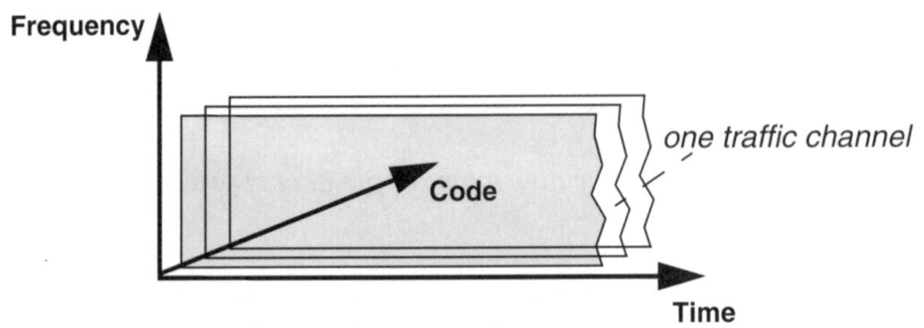

Figure D.4.17 The code division multiple access principle

A typical feature of the CDMA technique is that all mobiles in the network are assigned a unique code: a chip sequence. When a mobile wishes to transmit a bit stream, it replaces every bit with its code (for ones) or with the code's ones complement (for zeros). *Figure D.4.18* illustrates the simultaneous transmission of two bits from each of two mobiles which have different chip sequences. We assume in this example that the network uses eight-bit chip sequences; in reality, they are much longer.

The result is that eight bits (referred to as a "chip") are transmitted for every bit. Provided that the same modulation methods are used as those used in TDMA, the required bandwidth will be correspondingly larger. Instead of using some tens of kHz for a voice channel, the chip will be modulated over approximately 1 MHz. That is why this technique is also referred to as a spread-spectrum technique.

The two mobiles in *Figure D.4.18* transmit at the same time and use the same frequency band. Consequently, the chip streams will be interleaved in the base station. How then can the base station detect and separate the two bit streams: 01 and 11? The mathematical method is somewhat complicated. It is based partly on the fact that each mobile has a unique chip sequence, which is also known to the base station, and partly on the fact that all chip sequences are orthogonally paired. This means that if any two chip sequences are multiplied, the product is always zero. Only when a chip sequence is multiplied by itself will the product be a 1. When the receiver is to extract the chip stream for mobile A, it multiplies this mobile's chip sequence by the received, interleaved chip stream. Thus, all chip streams except those pertaining to mobile A are eliminated. It is then a simple matter to reduce the chip stream to A's bit stream by applying A's chip sequence.

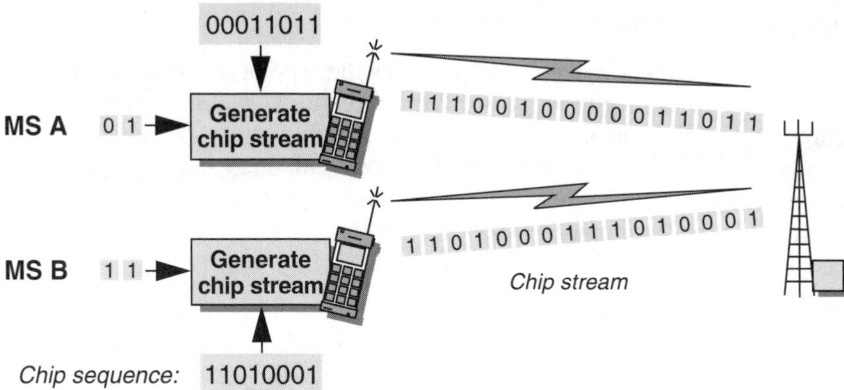

Figure D.4.18 Two mobiles simultaneously transmitting two bits each

4.3.8 Modulation

Modulation, transmission and reception are performed at the bottom of the functional hierarchy, as shown in *Figure D.4.10.* All channels to the transmitting antenna and from the receiving antenna are multiplexed and demultiplexed, respectively, in the base station. Every duplex channel is handled by a separate transceiver (TRX). The mobile contains a controllable oscillator for channel selection and a duplex filter that separates the send and receive frequencies.

Base station transmission power is 1–50 W, depending on the type of system and the desired cell size: a macrocell, a microcell or a picocell. Mobile output power is 0.6–20 W, depending on the type of mobile (hand-held or car-mounted). Mobiles must be capable of adjusting their output power in steps if ordered to do so by the base station (power regulation).

Receiver sensitivity is expressed in dBm.

The modulation methods described in Volume 1, Chapter 4, Subsection 4.4.2, are also used in mobile networks. Analog systems employ frequency modulation whereas, as a rule, phase shift modulation is applied in digital systems.

4.3.9 Antennas

Mobiles are equipped with omnidirectional antennas of the quarter-wave type adapted to the frequency band used (450, 800, 900, 1800 or 1900 MHz). The mobile uses the same antenna for transmission and reception. The antenna must have broadband characteristics, that is, similar radiation characteristics over the entire frequency range in question (for GSM, 70 MHz between the lowest and highest frequencies).

A cell's geographical coverage determines the type of antenna that the base stations are to be equipped with. Omnidirectional antennas are used for omnidirectional cells, and directional antennas – with or without space diversity – are used by sector cells. Different antennas are sometimes used for transmission (high-power) and for reception (low-power) but are usually mounted on the same mast. If the same antenna is used for transmission and reception, it must be fitted with a duplex filter.

The ideal antenna radiates all its power in the horizontal plane; if it were omnidirectional it would do so equally well in all directions. But in reality no antenna is perfect, because the mast, the proximity to the earth and conductive objects affect the radiation pattern.

Figure D.4.19 A base station's actual radiation pattern

Figure D.4.19 illustrates the radiation pattern in the horizontal plane. The inner grey area shows the measured radiation for an omnidirectional antenna mounted a bit up the mast. Note especially the lobed form and the screening effect of the mast on radiation. The outer area (dark grey) represents the radiation of another omnidirectional antenna that is equipped with a quarter-wave reflector, intended to decrease the lobe formation.

The choice of antenna type, antenna placement on the mast and the resulting radiation pattern are important factors that operators must consider in their cell planning.

5 Trunk and access networks

5.1 Introduction

In Chapter 4 we stated that the main difference between transmission in a mobile network and transmission in a fixed network lies in the methods of access. Key differentiating factors are the PLMN's multiple access and the way in which contact is maintained between mobiles and the network. In this chapter, we will discuss the access network seen as an infrastructure for the transport of user information and signalling. (See *Figure D.5.1.*) Other functions needed in mobile telephony (registration, set-up, authentication, and so forth) require considerably more network intelligence and are therefore discussed in Chapter 6.

The trunk network is viewed as the transport section of the core network. Since it is technically similar to the trunk part of other networks (such as the PSTN and ISDN), it will not be treated here.

The access network's resources in the form of traffic channels are shown in *Figure D.5.2.*

Figure D.5.1 and *Figure D.5.2,* together with *Figure D.7.1* in Chapter 7, illustrate two aspects of the access network:

- A rough, geographical division of the PLMN into an access network and a core network. Here, all MSC functions belong to the core network, while the BSC is part of the access network.
- A more detailed, function-dependent division (see the introduction to this chapter) where the access network is regarded as a resource for transporting user information and signalling between mobiles and the MSC.

The latter alternative is used only when the functionality of the access network must be divided into layers. This applies to Chapter 7 in particular, but also to the description given in this chapter.

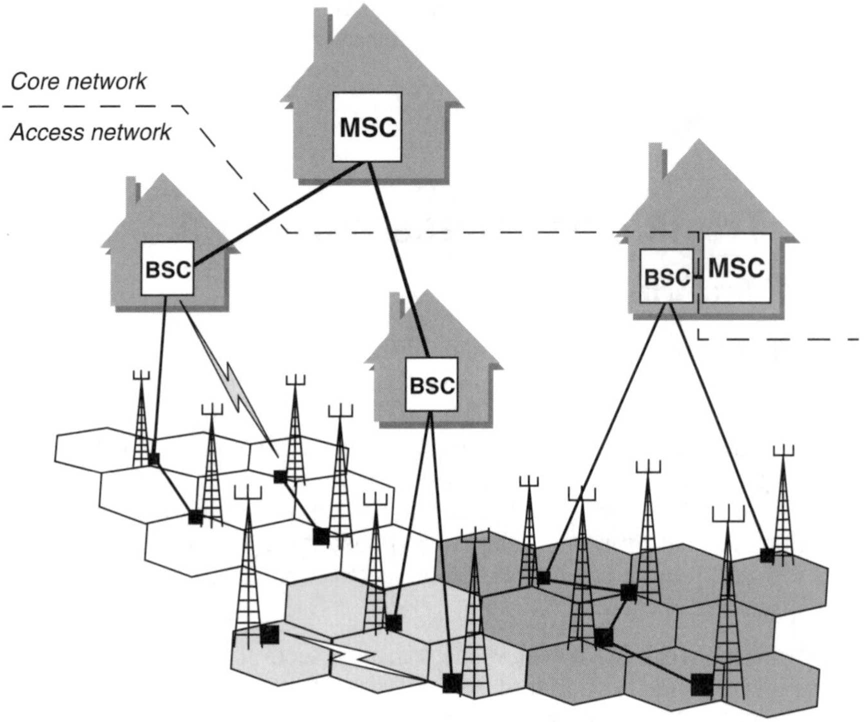

Core network

Access network

MSC

BSC

BSC

BSC

MSC

Figure D.5.1 GSM access network

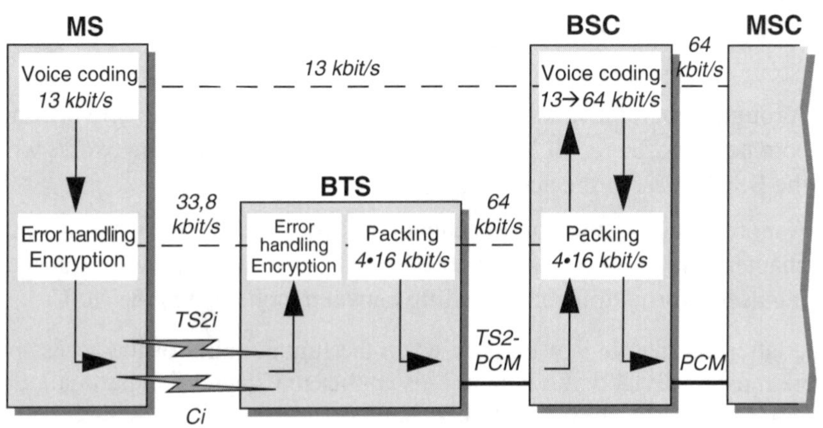

Figure D.5.2 Access network resources for traffic channels in GSM

The access network consists of two main parts: the air interface and the fixed part.

Time slots TS2–TS7 on frequency channel C_0 plus all eight time slots on the other available frequencies are used as traffic channels across the air interface of a cell. Those PCM time slots which are not dedicated for synchronisation and signalling are used between the base station and the BSC, and between the BSC and the MSC.

Logical traffic channels are available at two levels: 13 kbit/s full-rate channels (at the top level), which interconnect the voice coders of the mobile and the MSC, and 64 kbit/s channels between the BSC and the MSC.

If the network offers half-rate coding as well, the model will include 6.5 kbit/s channels and coders in addition to the 13 kbit/s channels and coders. Pooling the voice coders in the BSC makes it easier (and cheaper) to offer different types of voice channel than it would be if they were installed in the base station.

To obtain channels having a useful bandwidth of 13 kbit/s and acceptable quality across the air interface we need functions for error handling, encryption/decryption, burst management, and the like. (See Chapter 4, Section 4.3.) A 33.8 kbit/s traffic channel across the air interface is used to accommodate these functions, together with the useful bandwidth. A 64 kbit/s channel is used for transporting four full-rate traffic channels between the base station and the BSC. This section requires no special protection bits.

Access network signalling is dealt with in Chapter 7.

5.2 The air interface

The air interface is the shared boundary between a mobile and the base station. Physically, it is delimited by the cell structure. The characteristics of individual cells are determined by the structure of the base stations and by the resources allocated to these stations.

5.2.1 Cell pattern

The features of a cell are determined by two basic factors: its geographic reach (in practice, its coverage) and the frequencies that have been allocated to it. The geographic reach of a cell is dimensioned by the choice of type of antenna, the position of the antenna, and its output power. Theoretically, a cell can be described as a hexagon, but its actual geographical coverage must be determined through different types of measurement.

Each cell is allocated a number of frequencies for control and traffic channels. The number of traffic channels is determined by the expected traffic intensity and the congestion threshold, that is, the GoS. Traffic intensity (measured in Erlangs) is calculated as the average number of simultaneous calls per unit of time. Using Erlang's first formula, we can calculate the number of channels that the cell will need for a given probability of congestion.

Let us look at a simple case. If the average number of mobiles in the cell is 80 and each mobile is assumed to generate a traffic flow of 0.025 Erlang (corresponding to a 90-second call every three hours), and if we accept a probability of congestion of 2%, then the cell will need six traffic channels.

If the system is of the AMPS type, we will need six frequency channels for traffic – in addition to the control channels. If the system is of the GSM type, only one frequency channel (the one for frequency C_0) will be needed. Time slots 0 and 1 on C_0 are available for use as traffic channels.

To cover a large area that is visited by many mobiles, we need a large number of cells, and the available frequencies will also have to be reused. Since two adjacent cells cannot use the same frequencies because of the risk of interference, we must set a minimum reuse distance to prevent a given frequency in one of the cells from interfering with the same frequency in another cell (co-channel interference). We must also take a closely related phenomenon into account: adjacent channel interference (C/A).

The reuse distance for frequencies is defined as the relationship between the desired signal strength (in the cell) and an undesired signal strength (in the nearest cell allowed to use the same frequency). This relationship is called carrier-to-interference ratio (C/I).

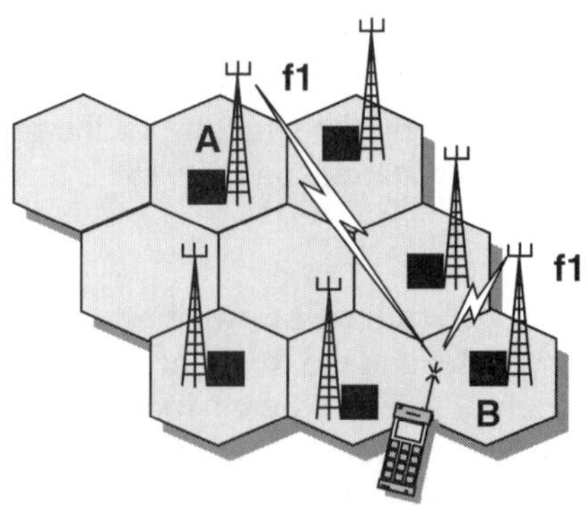

Figure D.5.3 Co-channel interference

In *Figure D.5.3*, cell A and cell B use the same frequency f1. This is acceptable as long as the C/I between the signal strength from B (S(B,f1) = the signal strength in B of the frequency f1) and the signal strength from A – that is, S(A,f1) – recorded in all parts of cell B, exceeds the minimum value that the system can accept. See *Figure D.5.4*. Minimum values are 18 dB in analog and 7 dB in digital systems.

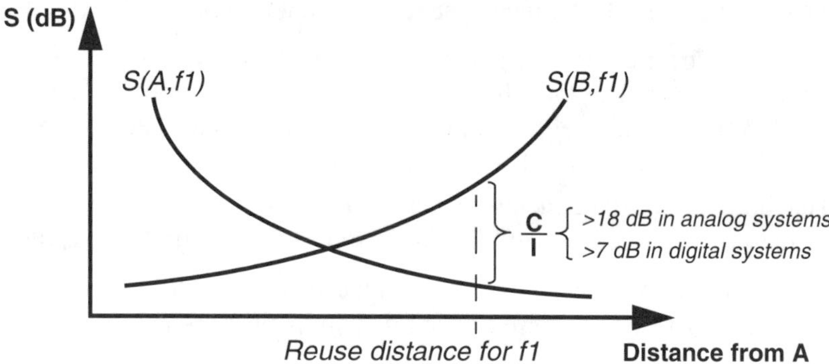

Figure D.5.4 Reuse distance and carrier-to-interference ratio

A similar definition applies to interference between adjacent channels. In GSM, the term "adjacent channel" denotes a frequency that is 200 kHz from the desired frequency. In AMPS, the corresponding figure is 30 kHz.

By arranging the cells in clusters we can easily ensure a sufficient reuse distance between two cells that use the same frequencies, see *Figure D.5.5*.

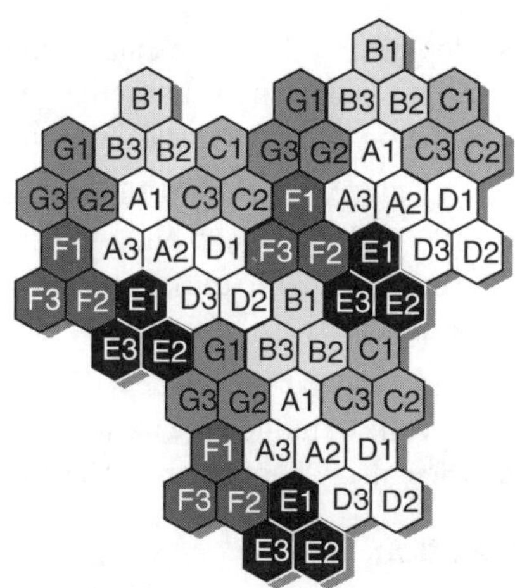

Figure D.5.5 A "7/21" cell pattern for reuse of frequencies

Figure D.5.5 illustrates a 7/21 cell pattern, a common method for reusing frequencies. In 7/21, the available number of frequencies is divided into seven groups, A to G. A group consists of three cells, and the frequencies are distributed among the three cells of each group. The seven groups can be arranged in a cluster consisting of 21 cells. A larger network is then created by adding more clusters (in the figure there is three clusters). The cells are dimensioned so that the distance between a group in a cluster and the corresponding group in the neighbouring cluster meets the requirement for C/I.

However, the traffic intensity in the geographical area covered by the cell is not homogeneous. The fact that it increases with time must be taken into account in the original cell planning. Many methods have been designed to adapt cell planning to the actual traffic situation:

- The number of frequencies in cells with large traffic volume can be increased. The requirement for reuse distance is a limiting factor, though.
- The reuse of frequencies can be increased through the introduction of smaller cells in areas where traffic intensity is high (cell split).

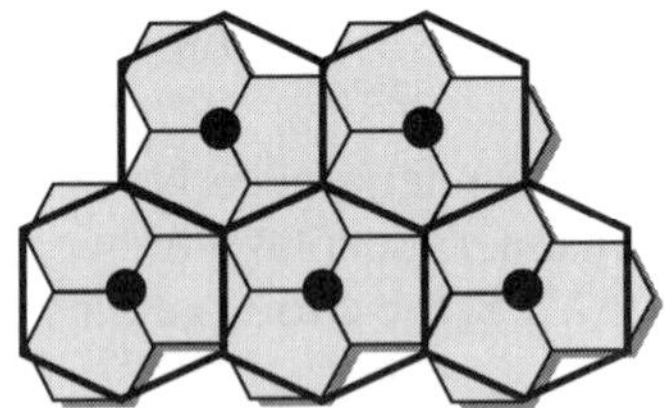

Figure D.5.6 Cell split

- In networks with analog air interface, we can increase capacity by introducing digital cells. This solution is attractive on condition that the mobiles can use both analog and digital traffic channels (dual mode).
- A network consisting of 800 MHz or 900 MHz cells can be extended to include 1800 MHz or 1900 MHz cells as well. A transition from GSM 900 to GSM 1800 means an additional 2992 traffic channels. The mobiles should be able to operate on both 800/900 MHz and 1800/1900 MHz (dual band).
- Hierarchical cell patterns can be introduced. Fast-moving mobile units can be referred to large cells to reduce the network load caused by handover and registration. (See also Chapter 10, Subsection 10.4.4.)

5.2.2 Channel allocation

Channels can be allocated according to two different principles: fixed and dynamic allocation.

Fixed allocation is the traditional method. This means that the frequency spectrum is divided into a number of groups corresponding to the number of cells in a cluster. The cells in the core of a city and other areas with high traffic density are small, while larger cells are used to cover backstreets with relatively sparse traffic. However, forecasting traffic intensity with sufficient accuracy is no easy task. We will either have to make extensive measurements or allow wide margins.

Dynamic channel allocation means that the cell is given access to a channel only when the need arises. This method takes interference into account: The cell is allocated a channel that will neither disturb nor be disturbed by adjacent cells. But then, all cells must be capable of handling all channels of the frequency spectrum, which requires more advanced antenna equipment and, hence, results in higher costs.

We also distinguish between two types of dynamic allocation of channels, as described below.

Channel allocation based on traffic demand

The planned reuse distance is maintained (which means limited flexibility), but the channels can be reallocated to suit the current traffic demand.

Channel allocation based on traffic demand and interference

The main difference between this method and the previous one is the introduction of the interference factor, making the reuse distance less important. When the channels are reallocated, the interference level is assessed by estimating the resultant bit error ratio. In this way, a channel can be used in any of the cells, provided it does not cause interference.

The latter method means considerably less planning work, which is of great significance in the case of microcells and picocells. Besides, there will be a certain increase in capacity because the margins set when planning fixed reuse distances are usually quite generous.

5.3 The fixed part of the access network

5.3.1 Base transceiver stations and base station controllers

A base station handles the air interface for one or more cells, its primary task being to relay traffic between mobiles and the rest of the network (BSCs and MSCs). A base station also provides the infrastructure for the resources allocated to one or more cells.

In *Figure D.5.7,* which gives a basic overview of a GSM access network, all base stations except BTS112 serve a single cell, while BTS112 serves three cells. All base stations are physically connected to a drop-and-insert transmission system (the model on the left), but in logical terms each cell must have its own channels in this transmission system (the model on the right).

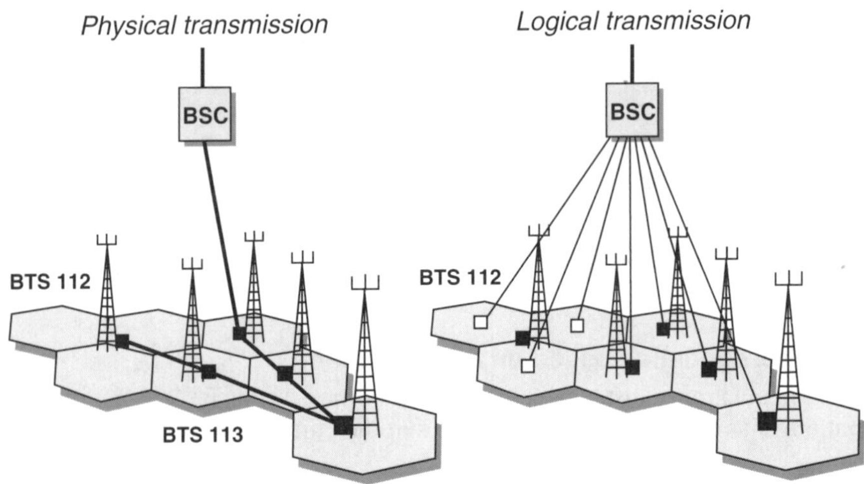

Figure D.5.7 Physical and logical structures in the access network

The dimensioning of the access network between the BTS and the BSC is based on the number of channels required by each cell. To be able to determine this figure, we must be somewhat familiar with the design of a base station. (See *Figure D.5.8.*)

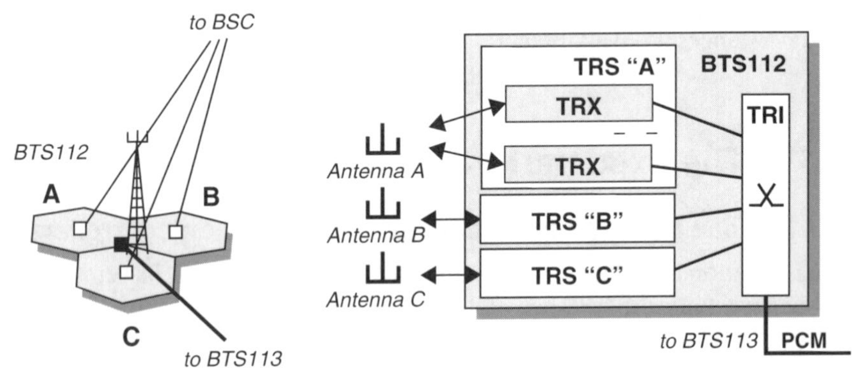

Figure D.5.8 A base station in GSM

The base station in *Figure D.5.8* handles three cells: A, B and C. Each cell has a separate antenna, but all three antennas are mounted on the same mast. Each cell is allocated a number of channel units, or transceivers (TRX), one for each frequency channel used in the cell. The group of TRXs that belongs to a cell is called a transceiver subsystem (TRS).

Traffic to and from base stations is coordinated by a unit called the transceiver radio interface (TRI). The TRI contains a selector since its primary functions are to distribute channels between the BSC and the appropriate channel unit and to relay channels between the BSC and neighbouring base stations. The TRI can also communicate with the BSC over a separate 64 kbit/s channel on the PCM link. This channel can be used by the TRI and its BSC to transfer control channel information and to communicate in matters related to operation and maintenance in the base station. The BSC uses the same channel for a number of tasks, such as adjusting the frequency and power of the channel units (TRXs); determining in which cells these units should be employed; disconnecting defective channel units; and receiving alarms.

PCM links are used to interconnect base stations and to connect them to the BSC. A TRX in GSM is used for six or eight 13 kbit/s traffic channels, depending on whether the cell's C_0 channel or some other frequency channel is used. A 64 kbit/s PCM channel can transport four such traffic channels to and from the BSC. As we just said, each TRI (hence, each base station) requires a separate 64 kbit/s channel. We can use this information, and the number of frequencies allocated to each cell, to dimension the transmission network between the BSC and its base stations. *Figure D.5.9* exemplifies drop-and-insert transmission between the BSC and three base stations.

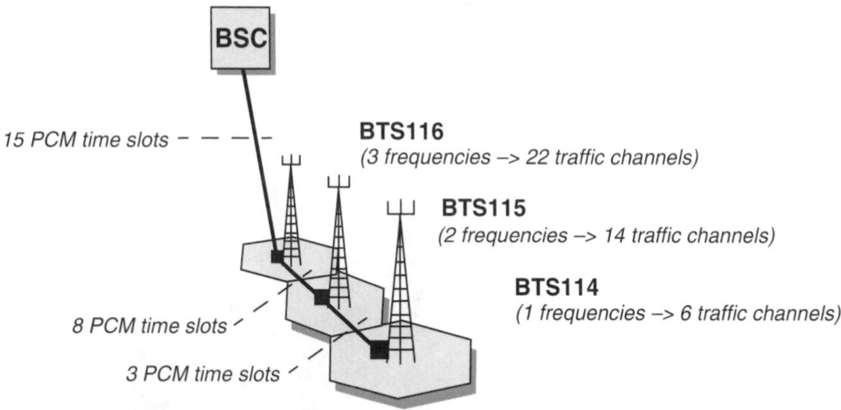

Figure D.5.9 Dimensioning access using drop-and-insert transmission in GSM

In the example, only one frequency is used in the BTS114 cell, which means six traffic channels. This requires two PCM time slots plus one PCM time slot for the TRI in BTS114. In other words, BTS114 will have access to three PCM time slots on the link to BTS115. The link between BTS115 and BTS116 will carry time slots to both BTS114 and BTS115. Between BTS116 and the BSC we need three time slots for traffic between the TRI and the BSC, or a total of 12 time slots for the 42 traffic channels. This means that a single PCM link will suffice in this example. There are plenty of free time slots on the PCM links, plus spare space in the PCM time slots used, unless all traffic channels on the available frequencies are occupied.

5.3.2 Base station controllers and mobile switching centres

The purpose of the BSC concept in GSM is to relieve the MSC of the handling of functions and resources that relate to the radio medium and to terminal mobility. All traffic channels in the interface to the MSC are 64 kbit/s channels and use SS7 for signalling. Under these circumstances, the MSC will have the same basic structure as an exchange in the PSTN.

When dimensioning the access network in GSM, the operator must determine how each BSC should be deployed in relation to its MSC. An important consideration in this deployment is the fact that a BSC will be most cost-effective if it can serve a whole MSC service area.

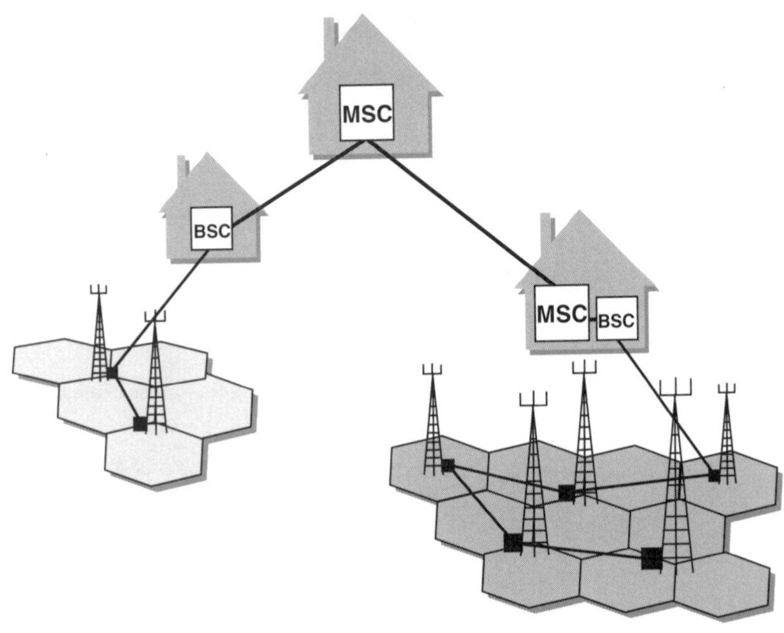

Figure D.5.10 Deployment of BSCs

A BSC can either be located on the same site as the MSC or it can be a stand-alone unit deployed as close as possible to the base stations it serves. For several reasons, co-location can be the most economical solution, but transmission costs must also be taken into account. *Figure D.5.10* shows a possible scenario.

The illustration to the left shows a network section in which the traffic volume is moderate but expected to increase. Consequently, a BSC has been located centrally in the area. When the number of subscribers increases to a level that justifies the use of a separate MSC, this node can be installed at a relatively low cost in the same building as the BSC (as shown on the right).

5.4 Handover

5.4.1 Introduction

Reswitching due to handover is described in Chapter 3, Section 3.3. We will now describe the process leading up to handover.

Since a mobile often moves while communicating, the signal via radio access can deteriorate, especially near cell boundaries. To cope with this problem, the system must check whether a free traffic channel in a neighbouring cell would improve signal quality, and – if this is the case – switch the call to that channel. This process includes three phases:

- continuous recording of signal strength and signal-to-noise ratio between mobile and base station;
- analysis resulting in the selection of a suitable cell and radio channel; and
- switch-over to the new cell and radio channel.

Locating is the collective term for the first two phases.

5.4.2 Locating

Quality supervision

In digital systems, the signal quality is supervised through separate measurements on every traffic channel. For a change, we will now exemplify the locating function by means of an application in analog systems. In this application, every frequency is supervised by a special tone, called the supervisory audio tone (SAT), which is applied to the traffic channel. The tone is above the upper limit of the speech band and cannot be perceived by the users.

The base station sends the SAT with voice to the mobile, which receives the tone and returns it to the base station, where signal strength and signal-to-noise ratio are measured. However, there is a certain risk of the process going adrift. A channel in a base station can receive an SAT not only from a mobile in its own cell but also from a mobile in another cell that uses the same frequency. If so, the base station might check the wrong channel and obtain a misleading indication. To avoid this, several SAT frequencies (mostly 5970, 6000 and 6030 Hz) are used. Cells using the same channels where interference problems are liable to occur have different SATs.

Two alarm levels are used when measuring signal-to-noise ratio:

- signal-to-noise ratio for handover request (SNH) and
- signal-to-noise ratio for release (SNR).

If the result of the measurement is less than the SNH value, handover is requested. If the handover attempt fails (for example, because of congestion in neighbouring cells) and the signal-to-noise ratio keeps falling to the SNR value, then the call is disconnected.

The recorded signal strength is compared with the following levels:

- signal strength decrease (SSD) initiates a request for power reduction;
- signal strength increase (SSI) initiates a request for power increase;
- signal strength handoff (SSH) initiates a request for handover; and
- signal strength blocking (SSB) initiates a request to block a voice channel.

If the measured signal strength exceeds the SSD value, the mobile is ordered to reduce its output power. (Excessive output power can cause interference in other cells.) An increase in output power is ordered when the recorded signal strength is below the SSI value. If the signal strength is decreased further, the network will order the output power to be increased to the maximum value specified for the type of mobile involved. If the signal strength is not increased, the sound quality will deteriorate, and when the signal strength has reached the SSH value, the network will make a handover attempt.

The SSB value is used when measuring idle voice channels. A signal strength value exceeding SSB is an indication of interference from another cell and will cause blocking of the channel in question.

Handover methods

Several standardised handover methods are available. (See *Figure D.5.11.*) In GSM, the network (that is, the BSC) decides when handover is necessary, whereas in DECT systems the mobile itself measures signal strength and makes handover decisions. Of course, delegating the decision-making process to the mobile reduces network load.

Method	Measurement	Decision
Network-controlled handover (NCHO) – NMT, AMPS	Network	Network
Mobile-assisted handover (MAHO) – GSM, D-AMPS, PDC	Network and mobile	Network
Mobile-controlled handover (MCHO) – DECT, CT3	Network and mobile	Mobile

Figure D.5.11 Different handover methods

Network-controlled handover (NCHO) is common in analog systems. The network measures the transmission quality via the base stations and decides when handover should be executed. The mobile makes no measurements. This method results in intense signalling between the base station and the node that decides on handover, but, on the other hand, signalling on the air interface is minimised because there are no recorded values to be transferred.

MAHO means that the mobile continuously measures the signal strength from neighbouring base stations and sends the recorded values to the base station to which it is currently connected. At the same time, both the mobile and the base station test the quality of the established connection. On the basis of these test values, the network decides when handover should take place. An advantage of this method is the fact that the mobile's situation is taken into account, since the mobile itself does the measuring. Also, the need for measurements in neighbouring base stations will decrease drastically. A disadvantage (as compared to the NCHO method) is considerably increased signalling across the air interface. However, despite this increase, the transfer of recorded values will only represent a few percent of the total traffic and thus pose no major problem.

MCHO resembles the MAHO method except in one respect: the handover decision has been delegated to the mobile. The result is a system which reacts quickly to changes in the radio environment. On the other hand, it can be more difficult to change the conditions for handover in a decentralised system.

In certain situations, handover cannot be executed. All traffic channels in the new cell may be busy, especially in those parts of the network where traffic volume is increasing rapidly. Also, all idle channels can be blocked by radio interference, in which case the mobile must stay connected to the original channel although the voice quality decreases. At best, the mobile is approaching a third cell with idle traffic channels; at worst, the voice quality falls to a level that causes disconnection of the call.

In countries where different operators compete in the same geographical area, they sometimes enter into agreements that allow them to use one another's systems. This means that handover can take place between neighbouring cells that belong to different mobile networks.

5.4.3 Handover – An example

Figure D.5.12 illustrates a complex case of inter-MSC handover in GSM.

The mobile is in cell BTS112 and moving towards cell BTS211. Cell BTS112 is handled by BSC11 under MSC1, while cell BTS211 is handled by BSC21 under MSC2. The original connection is assumed to have been established between a subscriber in the fixed network – via GMSC, MSC1, BSC11 and BTS112 – and the mobile.

The locating function in BSC11 has identified the mobile's need for handover, based on the quality of its signals reported by BSC11's base stations. The mobile itself has also reported the quality of signals generated by a number of base stations around cell BTS112, including base stations in cells handled by other MSCs and BSCs. By analysing all this data, BSC11 has been able to identify a number of cells (usually the best six) that provide acceptable signal quality, including BTS211. BSC11 has also found that it is not responsible for any of the cells.

1. BSC11 informs its MSC that the mobile needs handover. It also indicates the cells that are suited for handover and gives priority to BTS211.

2. After analysing the situation, MSC1 sends a signal to MSC2, requesting handover to cell BTS211. MSC1 also sends the mobile's subscriber data which is stored in its VLR.

3. MSC2 orders BSC21 to allocate an idle traffic channel to the mobile.

4. BSC21 allocates an idle channel (provided such a channel is available).

5. MSC2 indicates the channel in BTS211 to which the mobile should be connected. Then MSC1 and MSC2 reserve new paths for the connection through their switches.

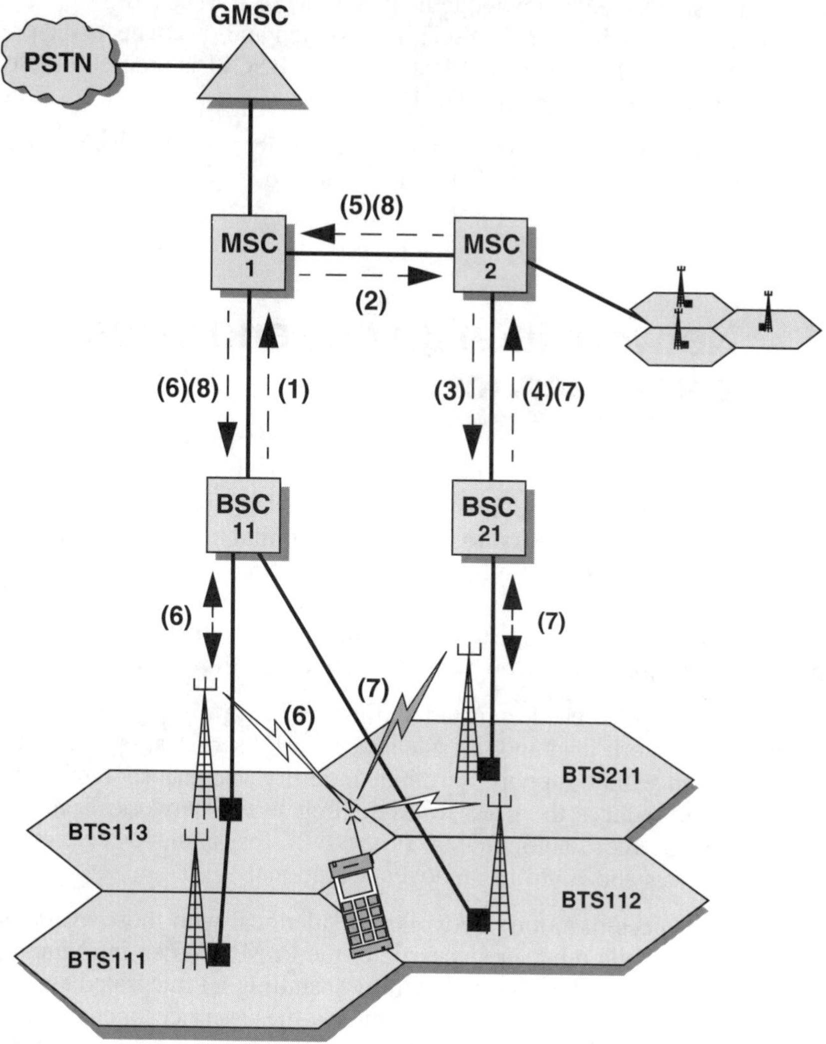

Figure D.5.12 Inter-MSC handover

6. MSC1 orders BSC11 to check that the mobile is connected to the new traffic channel in BTS211, and BSC11 orders the mobile to change channels.

7. After the mobile has changed channels, it must acknowledge this order. The acknowledgement is received by BSC21 and sent on to MSC2. If no acknowledgement appears within a preset time, the connection is cleared.

8. MSC2 now makes a through-connection from MSC1 to BSC21 in its own switch and sends the acknowledgement on to MSC1. MSC1 sets up the new path between the GMSC and MSC2 in its switch and disconnects the previous one between the GMSC and BSC11. Then BSC11 is ordered to release the original traffic channel in BTS112.

The handover process is now finished. If the selected cell does not accept handover, the next cell on the list will be selected.

6 Network intelligence and value-added services

6.1 Introduction

Two aspects of network intelligence are addressed in this chapter: the increase in intelligence required by radio access and terminal mobility functions, and the significant role that intelligent network services (IN services) play in mobile networks. Most basic services in mobile systems are more or less identical, regardless of operator. But by introducing and marketing IN services, an operator can make his network more attractive than those of his competitors.

In mobile networks recently installed, the trend is towards decentralisation. To reduce network load and provide space for IN services, operators move the intelligence that supports terminal mobility and incorporate it in the mobile. This reduces the need for signalling in the network, because the mobile will be more autonomous. In the DECT system, for example, the mobile initiates and controls handover operations.

Some IN services in mobile networks are identical with those available in PSTN/ISDN, while others are specific to the PLMN. When introducing IN services it is often advisable to begin by installing an integrated switching and service node (SSCP). As the demand for these services increases, separate SSP nodes and a common SCP can be introduced. In a growing network, it can also be advisable to deploy the SSPs (which are call-switching units) as close to the subscribers as possible in order to shorten transmission paths. Integration of the SSP and MSC in one and the same network element can be a viable alternative. *Figure D.6.1* illustrates this scenario.

An integrated MSC/SSP must have extremely great processing power, because the network element must be capable of handling call set-up, registration, paging, handover and SSP functions. To ensure high availability performance (and satisfied customers), the operator usually duplicates the network intelligence nodes.

IN is used not only in one or more mobile networks. In combination with universal personal telecommunication (UPT), for example, IN is also an excellent tool for integrating different types of bearer network, such as the PSTN, ISDN, PLMN and satellite-based networks for mobile communications. Number portability is an important service when mobiles move from one operator to another within the same type of network or between different networks.

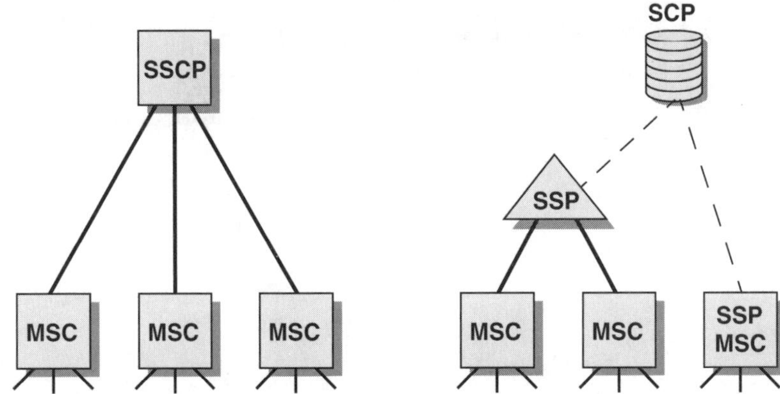

Figure D.6.1 Scenario for IN services in the PLMN

6.2 Registration and paging

The three concepts *registration*, *paging* and *location area* are explained in Chapter 1, Subsection 1.1.4. An example of how some of these functions and features are utilised is given below.

Figure D.6.2 exemplifies registration and paging in a GSM mobile network. The network is logically divided into four location areas, LA1-LA4, each corresponding to a BSC service area:

1. When the mobile is turned on, it is activated in LA1. (At this stage the network does not know that the mobile is active.) The mobile locks onto the cell in which it is currently located and is given the local area identity (LAI) through the cell's control channel. The LAI consists of three parts – a mobile country code (MCC), a mobile network code (MNC) and a location area code (LAC) – which together make up the global identity of the area. Since the mobile is not registered as active in the network, it must contact the MSC

and report its position, that is, LA1. MSC1 enters the mobile's position in its VLR and then sends a signal to the HLR reporting the mobile active in its service area. The mobile receives an acknowledgement, which concludes the registration process.

2. The mobile enters an LA2 cell, reads a new LAI on the control channel and makes a new registration. This information, too, is received by MSC1, which changes the LAI in its VLR. Note that the change need not be reported to the HLR, because the mobile is still in the same MSC service area.

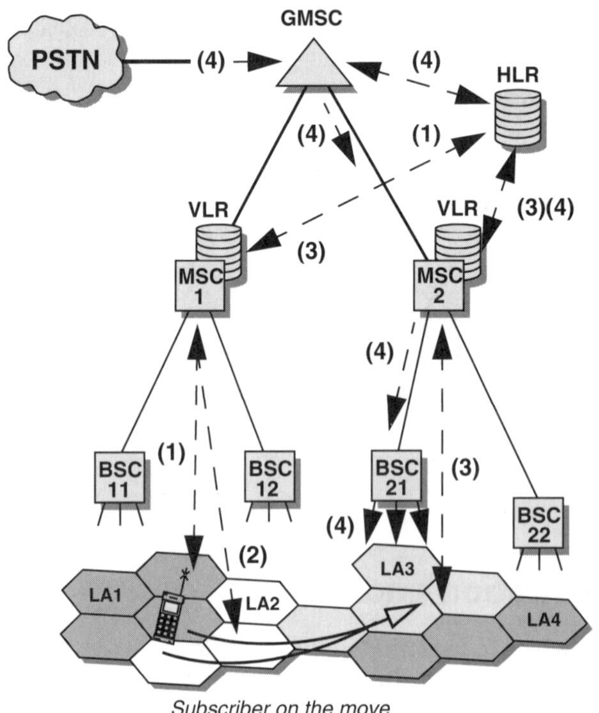

Figure D.6.2 Registration and paging

3. The mobile enters an LA3 cell, and now the registration is received by MSC2. Since the mobile is "new" in MSC2's service area, it is reported to the HLR, which informs MSC1 that the mobile has entered another MSC service area. Consequently, MSC1 deletes it from its VLR.

4. This is the paging sequence. Now, assume that the GMSC receives a call addressed to the mobile after it has been registered in LA3. In answer to a question to the HLR, the GMSC is informed (indirectly through a routing

number) that the mobile is in MSC2's service area. From its VLR, MSC2 finds out that the mobile was last registered in LA3. Provided LA3 only consists of cells within BSC21's service area, MSC2 requests paging from BSC21, which responds by sending a paging call to all base stations in LA3. If the mobile is still in an LA3 cell, it will answer the call.

The example illustrates the importance of the mobile being able not only to *register* when it is turned on and when it enters a new location area, but also to report when it is turned off. This procedure is called *detachment* in GSM. Information showing that the mobile is turned off is stored in the MSC that receives the information and in the HLR. Thus, if a mobile that is currently off is called from another network, the call will stop at the GMSC level.

Instead of automatic registration, a manual procedure can be initiated (by means of a smart card in GSM). The user gains access by inserting the smart card into his mobile, and registration then proceeds as in step 1 above.

6.3 Setting up and releasing a mobile call

Figure D.6.3 shows how a connection is set up between a telephone in the fixed network (PSTN) and a mobile in a mobile network.

1. The subscriber in the fixed network dials the B-subscriber's mobile number. The PSTN identifies the number and sets up a connection to the called network (GMSC).

2. The GMSC does not know through which MSC (or in which interworking mobile network) the mobile can be reached; nor does it know whether the mobile is free, busy, turned on or turned off. To be able to continue, the GMSC must therefore request a routing number from the HLR.

3. The registration function continuously updates the HLR on the location of the mobile (that is, in which MSC service area it is to be found). Provided the mobile is turned on and free, the HLR will call that service area's VLR and request a free routing number. The mobile's subscriber data is sent along with this request.

4. The GMSC receives the routing number and uses it to select a route in the PLMN. In our example, the GMSC forwards the call to MSC1.

5. MSC1 consults its VLR to find out in which group of cells (location area) the mobile is at the moment. (Keeping the VLR informed of the mobile's location is also part of the registration function.) MSC1 then orders BSC11 to find the mobile.

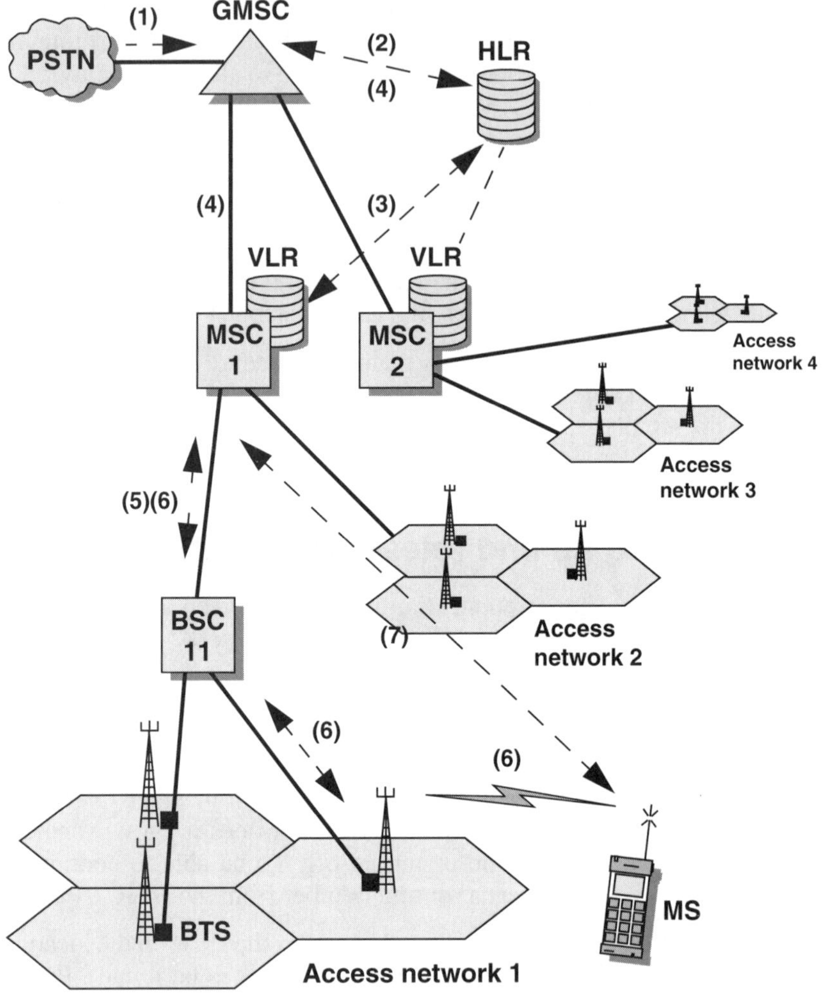

Figure D.6.3 Setting up a connection from the PSTN to a mobile

6. BSC11 sends a paging call to all cells in its service area that can be visited by the mobile at the moment. When the call is answered, BSC11 allocates the mobile a control channel for signalling with MSC1. A traffic channel over radio access and between MSC1 and BSC11 is also reserved for the call.

7. Signalling between MSC1 and the mobile concludes with the set-up of a traffic channel through the switches in BSC11 and MSC1. A connection has

now been established between the telephone in the fixed network and the mobile.

In all essentials, the procedure for clearing the connection is the same as in fixed networks.

The procedure for setting up calls initiated by a mobile is simpler as far as routing is concerned; either the GMSC is not involved at all (a call between two mobiles in the same network) or only has to make a connection to another mobile or fixed network. A special situation arises if a mobile cannot be allocated any traffic channel across the air interface because there is no idle channel in the cell it is visiting. The network will then prompt the mobile to make a new attempt in a neighbouring cell (directed retry).

6.4 Security functions

Functions handling security mechanisms are an important part of the intelligence of a mobile network. For obvious reasons, the need for such functions is considerably greater in mobile networks than in fixed networks; mobile equipment is especially liable to be lost or stolen, and radio access invites eavesdropping. Security in the PLMN encompasses four areas: authentication, encryption, equipment identification and subscriber identity confidentiality.

6.4.1 Authentication

When a new subscription is registered in GSM, the mobile is given a subscriber authentication key (Ki) and a telephone number, or international mobile subscriber identity (IMSI), which are used in the network to identify the mobile. The Ki and IMSI are stored both in the mobile and in a special network element called AUC. The AUC uses the Ki and IMSI to calculate an identification parameter called signal response (SRES). SRES is calculated as a function of Ki and a random number (RAND) generated by the AUC. RAND and SRES are then stored in the HLR for use in set-up procedures.

Set-up or registration will not be accepted until authentication has been performed. Using the mobile's IMSI, the MSC fetches the corresponding RAND and SRES from the HLR. RAND is sent to the mobile, which uses its stored Ki value to calculate SRES. It then returns the calculated SRES to the MSC, where it is compared with the SRES value received from the HLR. If the values tally, the set-up is accepted; if not, set-up is rejected.

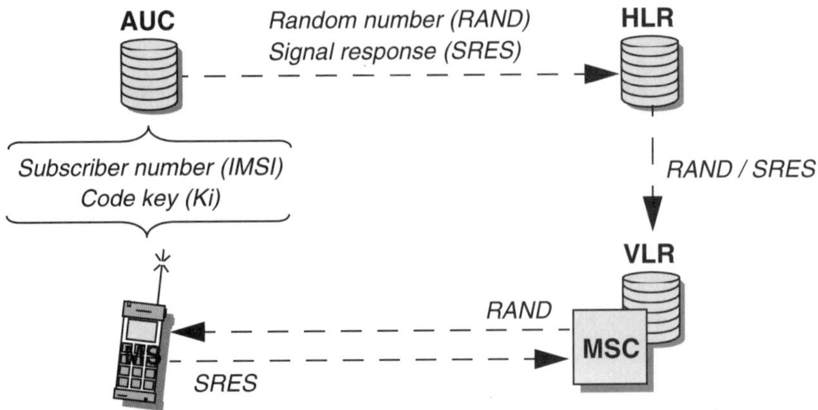

Figure D.6.4 Authentication in GSM

6.4.2 Encryption

Since radio communications can be intercepted by practically anyone in the immediate surroundings, protection against eavesdropping is an important service in a mobile network.

The best solution is an encrypted air interface, for both traffic and control channels. Since encryption of voice requires digital coding, it cannot be used in analog mobile networks. Control channels can, in principle, be encrypted in both analog and digital systems, but encryption is more common in mobile networks that use digital control channels, such as GSM and D-AMPS.

In GSM, voice is encrypted as follows:

In addition to SRES, the AUC calculates an encryption key (Kc) based on Ki and RAND. This key is stored in the HLR together with RAND and SRES. In connection with authentication, the mobile calculates a Kc value based on the RAND value received from the MSC and on the Ki value stored in the mobile. If the result of the authentication is approved, the MSC will store the encryption key in the base station (via the BSC) for use in encryption/decryption operations. The BSC then sends a "test signal" (encryption mode command) to the mobile. In response, the mobile should generate an encrypted signal (encryption mode complete) which – if the BSC can interpret it – permits continued signalling and communication. All signals, including voice signals, are encrypted.

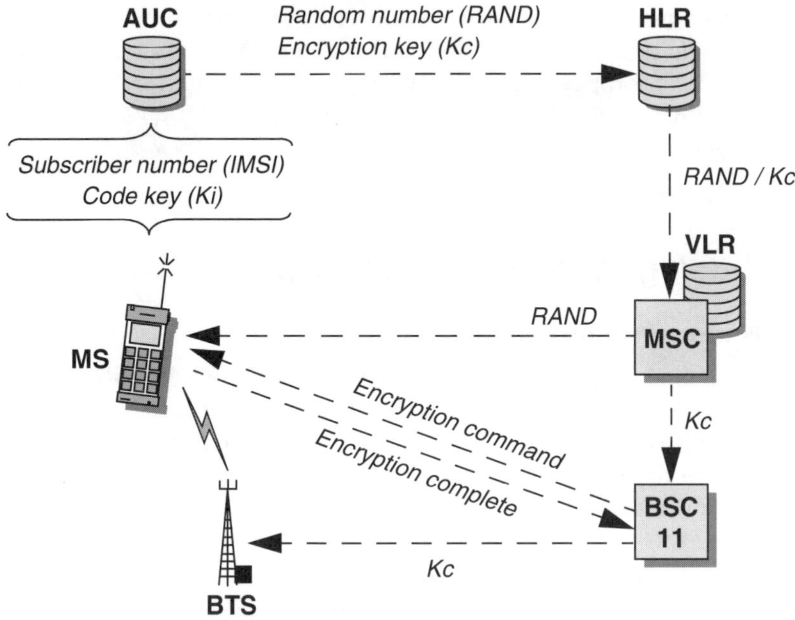

Figure D.6.5 Encryption in GSM

6.4.3 Equipment identification

The purpose of equipment identification is to ensure that no stolen or otherwise unauthorised mobiles are used in the network. To this end, every mobile is provided with a tamper-proof equipment number in the manufacturing process, in GSM an international mobile equipment identity (IMEI). During the set-up phase, the MSC can request this number from the mobile and then send it on for checking in the network element called EIR (in GSM). If the number is barred or unknown, the set-up attempt is rejected.

6.4.4 Subscriber identity confidentiality

Subscriber identity confidentiality means that the operator tries to protect the user's telephone number (the IMSI) from unauthorised tapping. A temporary mobile subscriber number (TMSI in GSM) is used in the dialogue between the mobile and the network, except for the first contact attempt in a set-up phase. The MSC gives the mobile a random TMSI for each set-up.

6.5 Distributed supplementary services

Mobile calls are usually more expensive than calls in fixed networks. Besides, many users (at least business subscribers) subscribe to services in one or more additional networks, for example, the PSTN. As a result, supplementary services for call control, such as call barring and call forwarding (see Volume 1, Chapter 6, Section 6.2), are especially important to subscribers in a mobile network.

6.6 Intelligent network services

6.6.1 Personal number

The personal number service can be useful for people who subscribe to services in more than one network. Callers can always dial the same number: the subscriber's personal number. Network intelligence connects the call to the terminal where the subscriber can be reached at that moment (perhaps in another network). The network selected can depend on the time of day, on the terminal that is turned on when the call is made or on the temporary terminal number that the subscriber has registered. *Figure D.6.6* shows an example of the use of this service, which can also include voice mail for storing messages left by the caller if the subscriber is not accessible.

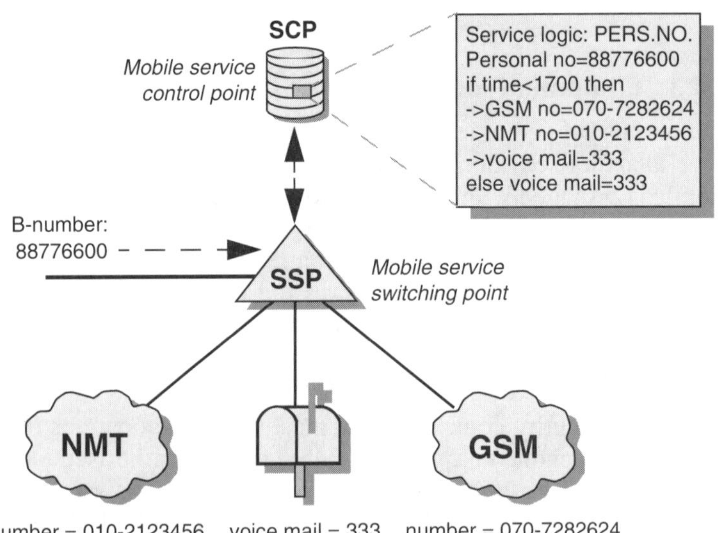

Figure D.6.6 A single personal number for two PLMN subscriptions

An operator can offer his subscribers the personal number service to retain them; for example, if they already have a subscription in the analog mobile network when they buy a digital mobile telephone. Of course, the service can also be connected to networks other than mobile networks.

6.6.2 Cellular VPN

Virtual private networks in the PLMN are called cellular virtual private networks (CVPN). This service enables a group of users (usually employed by the same company) to specify a common numbering plan of abbreviated numbers, which can be identical to their office extension numbers. Only the abbreviated number is dialled for calls within the group, while calls to subscribers outside the group require an external prefix to the regular number.

In a CVPN, the operator of the mobile network connects a company's PBXs directly to an MSC in the network.

6.6.3 Prepaid calls

Prepaid calls can be an attractive solution when subscribers have no permanent address or no credit references. Decentralised prepayment systems have been used by operators in low-income countries for many years. IN technology makes it possible to centralise this service and make it more flexible. In GSM, users can access the service through the SIM card, which they replenish with the desired amount from a cash dispenser.

The prepaid calls service can be implemented in two ways. Information showing the available balance is stored either on the subscriber's card or in the network. In the latter case, a database in the network is updated each time the card is used for calls or replenished, and the card number is only a reference to a field in the database. Many operators prefer the network-based solution because it makes improper use more difficult.

One way of making the prepaid calls service attractive is to offer users reduced tariffs. This is financed by the subscriber paying for his calls in advance, thus reducing the operator's interest expense.

6.6.4 Position-related services

The mobile network is continuously updated on each user's location by the registration functions, and this information can be used as input data for IN-based services.

- A common number for nationwide local traffic information or weather reports. The information given by the announcing machine or database depends on the caller's current location.

- Calls to a company with universal subscriber number. The caller is connected to the company's nearest office.
- Charging based on the subscriber's position. In predefined areas with special tariffs, the operator of the mobile network can offer "discount calls" (see *Figure D.6.7*) in the subscriber's immediate surroundings. In this way, the mobile-network operator can compete with PSTN operators.

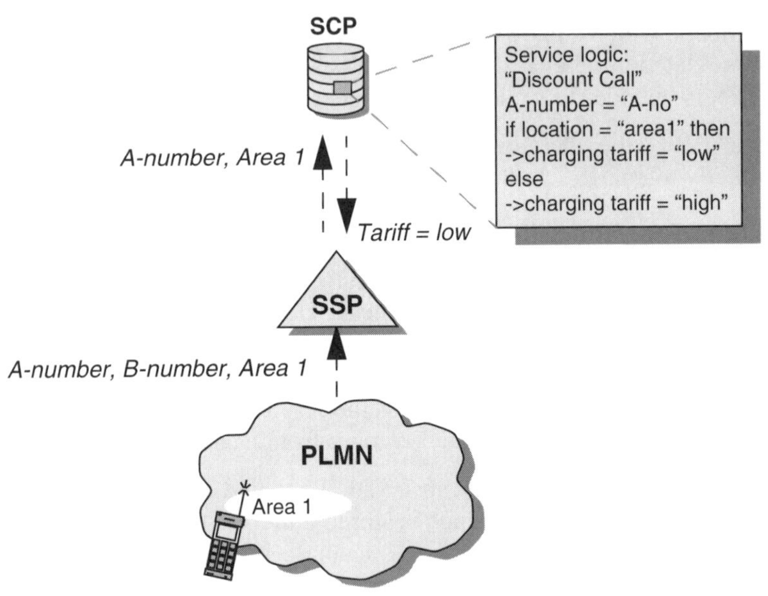

Figure D.6.7 Economy call from the A-subscriber's "home zone"

6.7 Value-added services

In networks with mobile terminals, the need for "mailboxes" for voice or fax messages is greater than in the PSTN, where the telephones are often combined with answerphones. Mobile terminals are sometimes turned off and can occasionally pass through areas where buildings and hills create radio shadows.

Of course, the PLMN can also offer other value-added services, such as information services and telephonist services.

7 Signalling

7.1 Introduction

The need for signalling in mobile networks has increased gradually as message services, international roaming and IN services (see Chapter 6) have been introduced.

The signalling structure can be divided into two functional parts:

- The base consists of signalling bearers, that is, functions for the transport of signalling information between network elements. These bearers can be either standardised or proprietary.

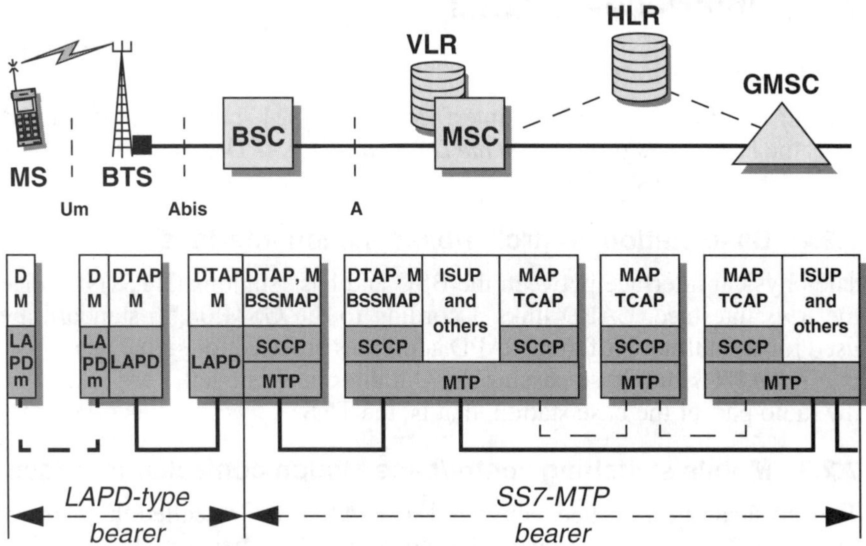

Figure D.7.1 Signalling bearers (grey), signalling protocols and interfaces in GSM. (D = DTAP = direct transfer application part; M = initial mobile station message; TCAP = transaction capabilities application part.)

- The signalling bearers transport signalling protocols that define how functions in network elements cooperate in the creation of network services, including operation and maintenance aspects. The signalling protocols are standardised in those interfaces between network elements which require interworking between equipment from different suppliers. In GSM, the mobile application part (MAP) and the ISDN user part (ISUP) are used as protocols between MSCs, while the ISUP is used between MSCs and the GMSC. GSM signalling protocols are dealt with in Subsection 7.4.

In AMPS, the EIA/TIA-553 protocol is used in the air interface. This protocol also defines signalling across the air interface.

Each type of PLMN has its own signalling scheme, especially in the access networks and across the air interface. This chapter gives a brief description of signalling and the associated interfaces in GSM. *Figure D.7.1* gives a schematic picture of the signalling bearers, signalling protocols and interfaces of the system.

7.2 Interfaces in GSM

7.2.1 Air interface

The air interface is called *Um* interface in the GSM standard. In this interface, the *link access protocol on the Dm-channel*, *LAPDm*, is used according to the GSM:04.06 standard.

7.2.2 Base station controller/base station interface

The physical interface between the BSC and base stations (BTSs) is called the *Abis* interface. LAPD links according to the GSM:08.56 standard are used for signalling. Different LAPD addresses are used for signals terminating in the BTS and those passing the Um interface. The latter are relayed in the radio part of the base station, that is, the TRS.

7.2.3 Mobile switching centre/base station controller interface

The physical interface between the MSC and the BSC is called the *A-interface*. Two MTP/SCCP variants are used as signalling bearers. (See *Part E – The signalling network*, Chapter 2, Section 2.1, for an explanation of MTP and SCCP.) The signals involved in a specific connection are carried by SCCP's connection-oriented service, while other signals are carried by its connectionless service. In addition, all signalling using SCCP is marked by a discrimination parameter which decides whether the signals should be relayed by or terminated in the BSC. This function is part of the standard for the base station system application part (BSSAP). The BSSAP also defines the signalling protocol between the MSC and the BSC. The discriminating function in the BSSAP is called "BSSAP discrimination", to distinguish it from the signalling protocol part.

7.3 Signalling resources of the access network

7.3.1 Survey

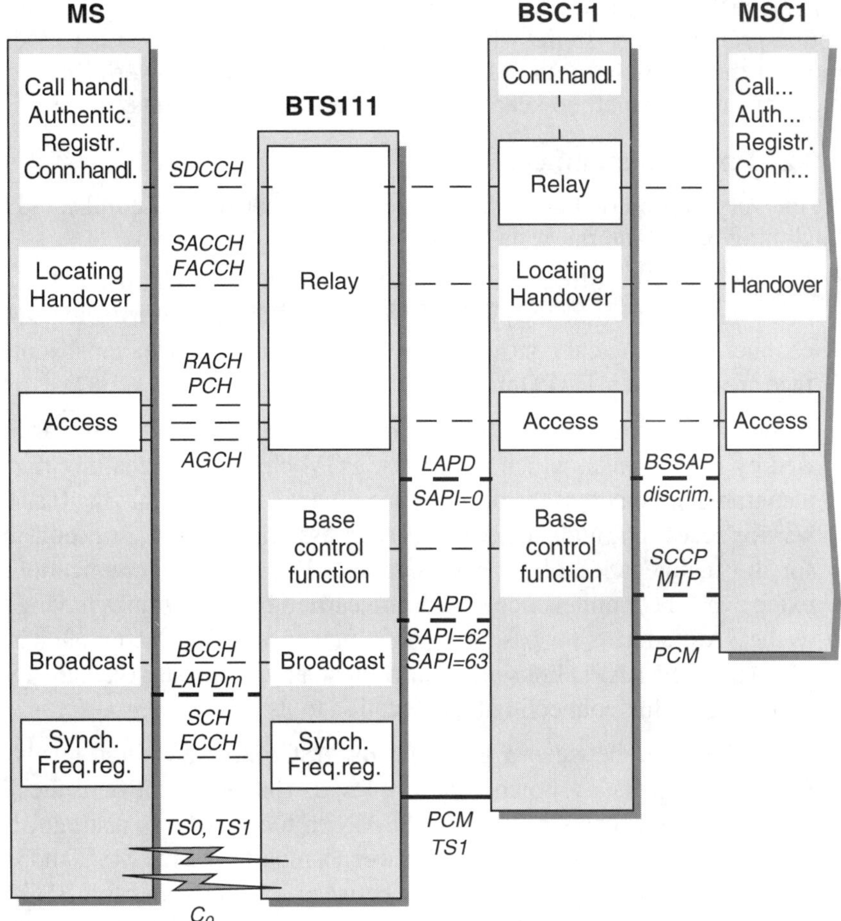

Figure D.7.2 Signalling resources of the access network

The task of the access network is to provide the network with resources for transport of user information and signalling. These resources are designed in different ways, depending on their location in the access network. In the air interface, they consist of control and traffic channels. *Figure D.7.2* shows the complex configuration of signalling resources in a GSM access network: logical and physical channels – different in different network interfaces – and relay functions in the BTS and the BSC.

Figure D.7.2 shows how the GSM network elements in the access network are utilised to provide functions for call handling, authentication, registration (location updating), connection handling, locating, handover, base station control and distribution of network and cell information (broadcast).

Each type of mobile network has its own way of solving this function allocation problem. In systems with no BSC, the obvious solution is to locate most of the functions in the MSC, because they require powerful network elements and this method keeps down the cost of base stations.

7.3.2 Physical channels

At the very bottom of *Figure D.7.2*, the physical channels are indicated by "lightning bolts" and thick, dashed lines:

- In the air interface, frequency channel C_0 and time slots TS0 and TS1 on that channel constitute the physical channels. Each cell has a dedicated C_0 channel. Most logical control channels for signalling across the air interface are carried by LAPDm.
- In the interface between the base station and the BSC, all signalling is carried by LAPD links, which in turn use PCM channels. Signalling that is also transported across the air interface is carried by links having 0 as the service access point identifier (SAPI) address. Since a BSC is responsible for the maintenance of its base stations, BSC–BTS communication is extensive. The maintenance signals are carried by LAPD links having 62 as the SAPI address for base station maintenance and 63 for maintenance of LAPD. The LAPD links are in turn carried by a time slot (usually TS1) on the PCM link connecting a base station to its BSC.
- In the interface between a BSC and its MSC, there are three levels of physical channels, as shown in *Figure D.7.2.* The topmost level is the discrimination mechanism of the BSSAP protocol, which distinguishes between signals to be transported between a mobile and the MSC and signals that are to be transported only between the MSC and the BSC. In both cases, BSSAP signals are carried by the SCCP in SS7. As we mentioned in Subsection 7.2.3, all call-related signalling uses SCCP's connection-oriented service, while the connectionless service is used in all other cases. SS7 normally uses one or more time slots in a PCM system.

The physical channels – together with the relay functions – are used to create logical channels through all or part of the access network. In the air interface, these logical channels are divided into nine types of control channel and two types of traffic channel, all of which are mapped onto the time slots of the physical channels. (For the mapping of traffic channels, see Chapter 4, Subsection 4.3.5.)

7.3.3 Control channels

Control channels are divided into three classes, based on how and when they are used: broadcast channels (BCH); common control channels (CCCH); and dedicated control channels (DCCH).

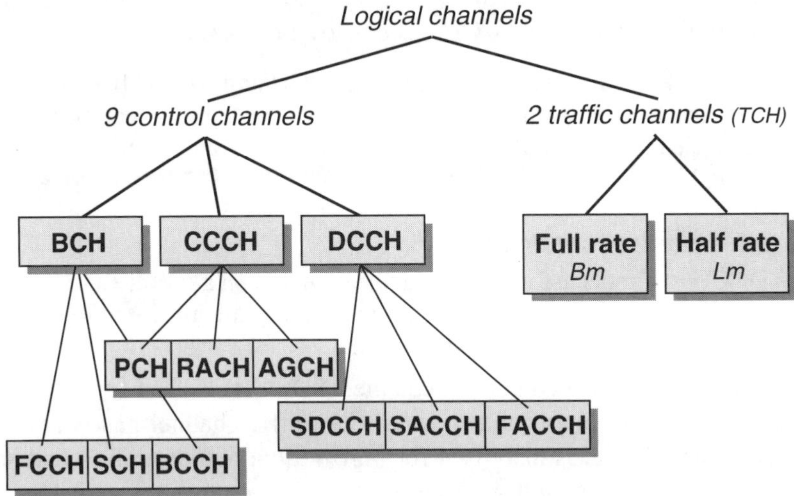

Figure D.7.3 The GSM system has 11 logical channels

Broadcast channels

Class BCH channels continuously send information about cell and network parameters to the mobiles. They are unidirectional (from base station to mobile) and used jointly by all mobiles.

There are three types of broadcast channel:

- A frequency correction channel (FCCH) carries frequency correction information.
- A synchronisation channel (SCH) carries frame synchronisation information and information for identifying the base station.
- A broadcast control channel (BCCH) carries cell-specific information.

These channels are shown at the bottom of *Figure D.7.2*.

Common control channels

Class CCCH channels are used for access to the network. These three channels, too, are common to all mobiles.

- A paging channel (PCH) is used by the network to call terminals.
- A random access channel (RACH) is used by a mobile to answer paging calls and call the network when the mobile initiates set-up.
- An access granted channel (AGCH) is used by the network to allocate a dedicated control channel (SDCCH – see below) for continued signalling or some other channel (FACCH – see below) for handover.

All these logical channels are unidirectional: PCH and AGCH from network to mobile, and RACH from mobile to network. The signals sent on RACH, AGCH and PCH are relayed via the base station and transferred to and from the BSC on LAPD links. (See *Figure D.7.2.*)

Dedicated control channels

Class DCCH channels are used for signalling between a mobile and the network before and during a call. These three channels are allocated to individual connections and are always bidirectional.

- A stand-alone dedicated control channel (SDCCH) is used for signalling during the set-up phase; that is, before a traffic channel has been allocated. This channel is also used for registration, authentication and signalling in connection with clearing.
- A slow associated control channel (SACCH) is a locating channel that the mobile to continuously report received signal strength in the visited cell and from surrounding cells. The channel can also be used for controlling the output power of the mobile. Note, however, that SACCH does not have the signalling capacity required to control handover.
- A fast associated control channel (FACCH) – only available in conversation state – is used for handover operations. FACCH is allocated 20 ms of the traffic channel when rapid signalling is required. The listening party does not notice the loss of 20 ms conversation because the receiving unit repeats the last 20 ms. There is one FACCH for each traffic channel.

Signals on SACCH, FACCH and SDCCH are relayed to the BSC via the base station. As shown in *Figure D.7.2,* signals related to call handling, authentication and registration are relayed via SDCCH and then sent to the MSC. Connection handling is performed in both the BSC and the MSC.

All control channels except SCH and FCCH use LAPDm.

The following comments complete the information given in *Figure D.7.2*:

- Between the BSC and base stations, LAPD links are used for maintenance of base stations (base control function, BCF, in GSM).
- Between the BSC and the MSC, BSSAP (discrim.) signalling is used for paging (in the case of a call to a mobile) and for handover, if the MSC is involved in this handover.

7.3.4 Mapping of control channels onto physical channels

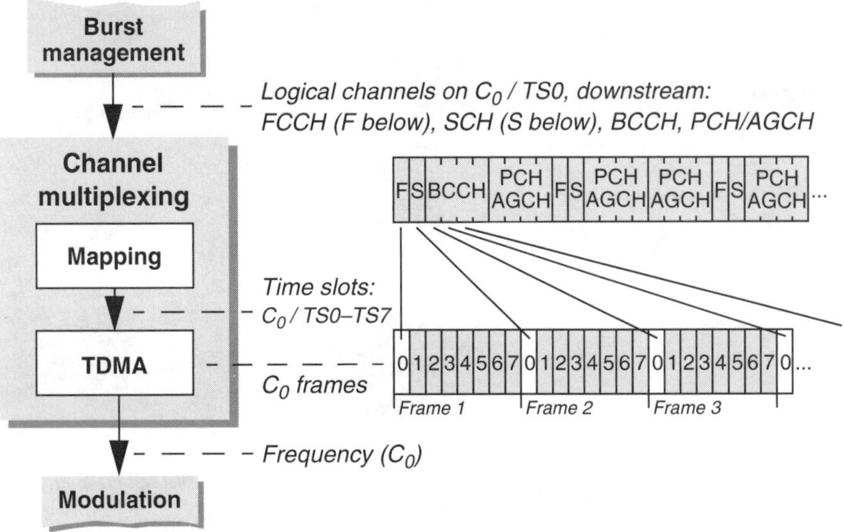

Figure D.7.4 Example of the mapping of logical channels onto time slot 0, frequency channel C_0

A multiframe structure is used for several of the "downstream" control channels. Here we will focus on time slot 0 on frequency channel C_0. "Downstream", the time slot is used for control channels FCCH, SCH and BCCH (all of which are of the broadcast type), and for PCH and AGCH. "Upstream", the time slot is only used for the random access channel, RACH, so no multiframe is necessary from mobile to base station.

The multiframe covers 51 TDMA frames; see *Figure D.7.4*. During the time it takes to receive the frames (about 0.25 s), BCCH occupies four time slots, SCH and FCCH five each, and PCH and AGCH together thirty-six time slots.

Time slot 1 on frequency channel C_0 is used for control channels SDCCH and SACCH.

As we have seen, the only remaining control channel in the air interface – FACCH – uses traffic channels (see Subsection 7.3.3).

7.4 Signalling protocols in GSM

Figure D.7.5 shows the signalling protocols used in GSM. All of them, except ISUP, are specified for GSM. The ISUP protocol is described in *Part C – N-ISDN*, Subsection 7.3.

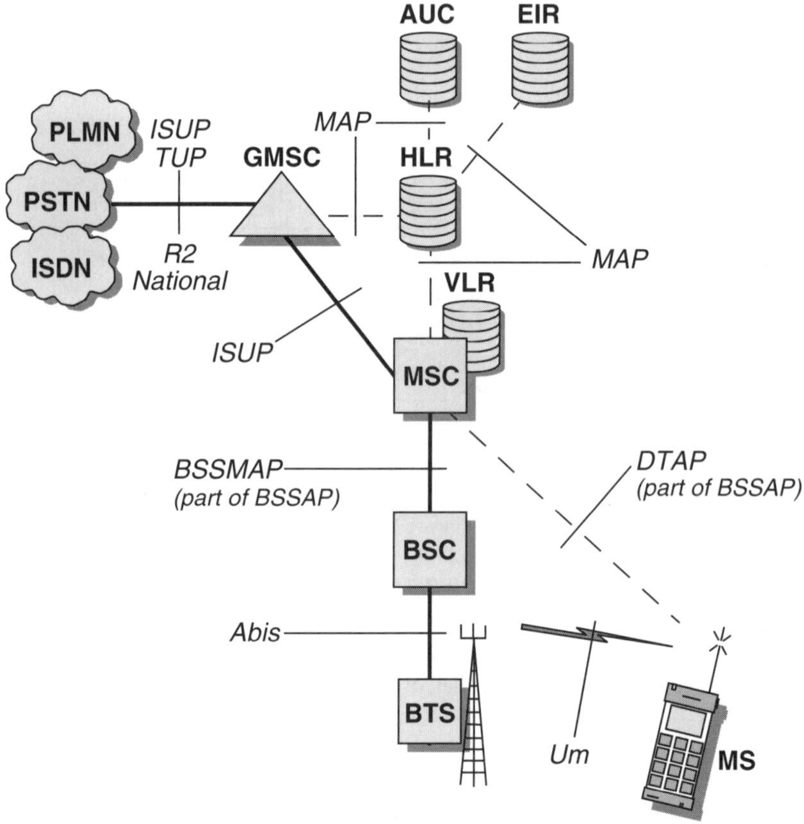

Figure D.7.5 Signalling protocols in GSM

Protocols used on the BSC–BTS–MS section

The protocols in the Um and A*bis* interfaces (see *Figure D.7.5*) conform to the ETSI standard. The following BSC and BTS functions are supported by these protocols:

- Sending of network and cell information. The information is updated from the BSC but stored in and continuously sent from the BTS.
- Paging. This activity is initiated by the MSC, which orders the BSC (over BSSMAP) to take the necessary action. The BSC in turn orders the base stations in the location area to take action. The BTSs concerned send continuous paging calls, detect answer signals and send reports to the BSC. They also receive calls initiated by the mobiles and send them on to the BSC for action.
- Allocation and release of a control channel (SDCCH). The BSC initiates these activities, and the base station handles the exchange of information to and from the mobiles.
- Allocation and release of a traffic channel (TCH) in connection with set-up, clearing and handover. The BSC initiates these activities, and the base station handles the channel units involved.
- Identification of completed handover. The base station reports to the BSC when it has detected the mobile's signals on the new traffic channel.
- Control of encryption/decryption. The base station controls the activation and deactivation of its own encryption function by order of the BSC.
- Control of voice coders and rate adaptation of information channels. The equipment involved (the transcoder rate adaptation unit) is usually located in the BSC but controlled by the base station, since it is dedicated to individual traffic channels.
- Measurement of transmission quality and signal strength on busy and idle channels on the uplink. Measurements are made in the base station, and the results are reported to the BSC.
- Measurement of sending instants for mobiles (time alignment). The base station measures these parameters on traffic channels. The recorded values are reported to the BSC.

The air interface protocol also includes functions that are autonomously handled by the base station:

- Synchronisation information and BTS identity are sent continuously from the BTS.
- The frequency control function is handled by the BTS. Frequency control signals are continuously sent from BTS.

In addition, the air interface protocol includes functions for:

- channel coding;

- channel multiplexing;
- burst management (see Chapter 4, Subsection 4.3.4);
- TDMA; and
- modulation.

Protocols used on the MSC–BSC and MSC–MS sections

The BSSAP *signalling* protocol contains the following components: BSSMAP, DTAP and INITIAL MS messages. The BSSAP discrimination mentioned in Subsections 7.2.3 and 7.3.2 is a low-layer function and thus not discussed here.

- DTAP messages are exchanged between the MSC and the mobile in connection with registration and authentication and when the mobile is turned off. DTAP messages are relayed via the BSC and the base station.
- Initial mobile station messages (IMSMs) are exchanged between the MSC and the mobile in connection with location updating and paging.
- BSSMAP is the protocol used between the MSC and the BSC in connection with paging, calling, handover, allocation and maintenance of traffic channels and to initiate encryption in the base station and in the mobile. This protocol is also used for maintaining time slots on the PCM link between the MSC and the BSC.

Protocols between mobile switching centres

When handover between MSCs is executed, MAP is used for handover signalling, while ISUP is used for setting up and clearing connections.

Protocol between gateway mobile switching centres and mobile switching centres

ISUP is used here in the same way as in PSTN/ISDN.

Protocols between mobile switching centres and the HLR, VLR, AUC and EIR

MAP is used for all signalling. It primarily supports registration, signalling for roaming numbers, authentication and equipment identification.

Protocols for communication with other networks

The telephony user part (TUP), ISUP and – where applicable – channel-associated protocols and national variants are used for communication between the GSM network and other networks.

7.5 A traffic case in GSM

To illustrate how different signalling protocols and signalling bearers interact during the set-up phase, we have chosen the traffic case that we discussed in Chapter 6, Section 6.3. The case, shown in *Figure D.7.6,* involves all interfaces and protocols in the GSM network.

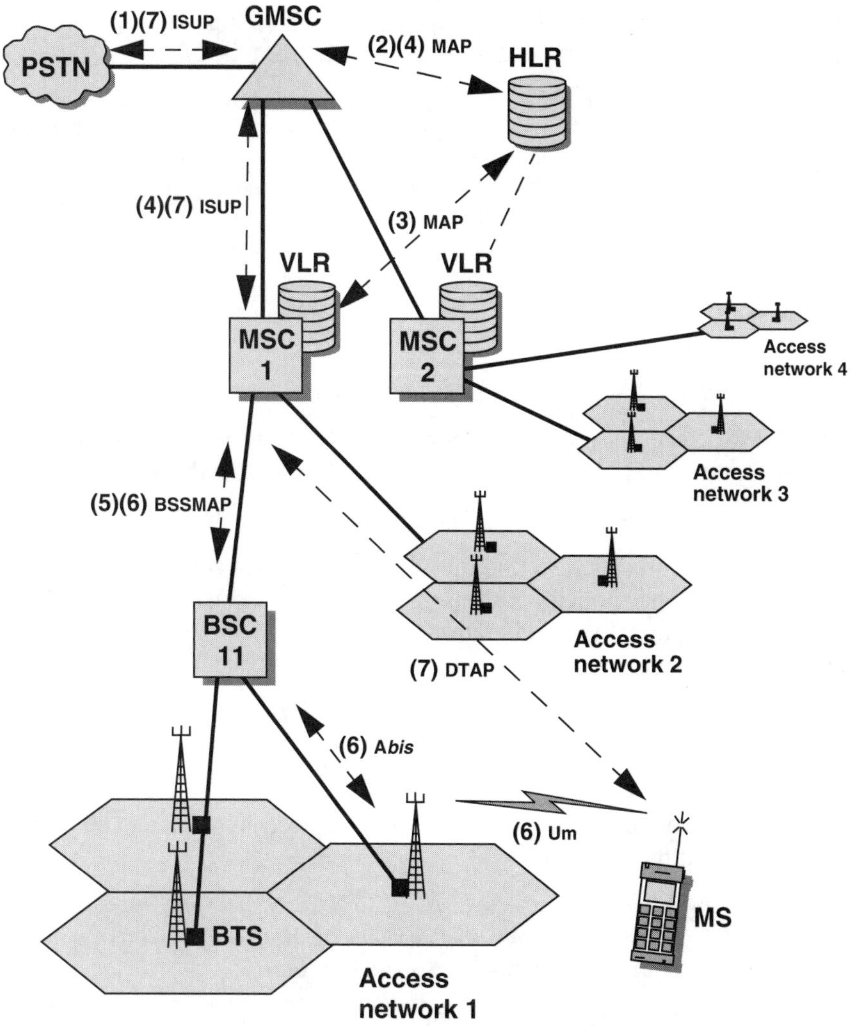

Figure D.7.6 Setting up a connection from the PSTN to a mobile

1. The subscriber in the fixed network dials the B-subscriber's mobile number. The PSTN identifies the number and sets up a connection to the called network (GMSC).

In Figure D.7.6, we assume that ISUP is the signalling protocol between the GMSC and the PSTN, but TUP or a channel-associated protocol could also be used. ISUP and TUP use MTP as a signalling bearer.

2. The GMSC does not know through which MSC (or in what interworking mobile network) the mobile can be reached; nor does it know whether the mobile is free, busy, turned on or turned off. To be able to continue, the GMSC must therefore request a routing number from the HLR.

The GMSC uses the MAP protocol for this request. MAP uses the transaction capabilities application part (TCAP), which in turn uses the SCCP as a bearer.

3. The registration function continuously updates the HLR on the location of the mobile (that is, in which MSC service area it is to be found). Provided the mobile is turned on and free, the HLR will call that service area's VLR to request a free routing number. The mobile's subscriber data is sent along with this request.

The MAP protocol is used for this communication, too.

4. The GMSC receives the routing number and uses it to select a route in the PLMN. In our example, the GMSC forwards the call to MSC1.

ISUP is used for signalling between the GMSC and the MSC.

5. MSC1 consults its VLR to find out in which group of cells (location area) the mobile is at the moment. (Keeping the VLR informed of the mobile's location is also part of the registration function.) MSC1 then orders BSC11 to find the mobile.

Communication at this stage is in the form of BSSMAP signals in the BSSAP protocol. These signals are carried between the MSC and the BSC by the connectionless SCCP service.

6. BSC11 sends a paging call to all cells in its service area that can be visited by the mobile at the moment.

The paging procedure is described in the GSM standard. The paging call is carried by LAPD (SAPI address 0) between the BSC and the base station, and on control channel PCH across the air interface.

Next, the call is answered by the mobile.

The answering procedure is described in the GSM standard. The answer is carried by control channel RACH across the air interface and then sent on to the BSC on LAPD.

BSC11 allocates the mobile a control channel (SDCCH) for signalling with MSC1.

This information is carried by LAPD (SAPI address 0) between the BSC and the base station, and by control channel AGCH across the air interface.

A traffic channel over radio access and between MSC1 and BSC11 is also reserved for the call.

7. Now the mobile communicates directly with the MSC.

This communication is in accordance with the DTAP protocol. The signals are carried by BSSAP/SCCP/MTP between the MSC and the BSC, relayed through the BSC, and carried by LAPD (SAPI address 0) between the BSC and the base station, and on SDCCH across the air interface.

The DTAP signalling concludes with the set-up of a traffic channel through the switches in BSC11 and MSC1. An acknowledgement of this through-connection is sent backwards to the PSTN.

8 Network management

Time to market is becoming an increasingly important factor for the ever-growing number of mobile-network operators. Operators must get started quickly to be able to create a sufficiently large circle of satisfied, revenue-generating customers. To this end, a powerful and flexible network management system is a must.

8.1 Traffic measurements

The rapid increase in the number of mobile subscribers requires regular measurements of the traffic generated. The results of these measurements, which are used as basic data when deciding on modifications and extensions to the network, indicate:

- *Telephone traffic per cell.* The recorded data are compiled in statistical form by the support system for operation and maintenance. These statistics show the number of call set-ups, the number of prematurely released calls, signal strength, information on handover, the percentage of imperfect handovers, and so forth.

- *Signalling per cell.* Statistics on signalling in the cells show the number of registrations, the number of calls to each mobile (paging), the number of calls from each mobile, the number of directed retries, the identities of voice channels allocated to calls and how often these channels have been used, the number of handovers and the number of cleared calls.
- *Air interference.* The number of blocked voice channels, the percentage of blocked time per voice channel and interference that affects the SAT are reported.
- *Performance.* Examples of performance values include: voice quality, the number of prematurely released calls and the system's access capacity.

8.2 Operations support

An operations support system should have functions for:

- statistical processing of traffic-measurement results;
- network configuration;
- graphic representation of cell planning; and
- support for radio-channel testing.

The system must also have a database containing network and system parameters:

- number of subscribers;
- number of cells;
- mast sites;
- reuse factor for voice channels; and
- reuse factor for control channels.

By adjusting the output power of a base station the operator can change cell boundaries to meet a local, temporary increase in traffic volume. Such adjustment is called *cell shaping*.

To cope with the increase in the number of subscribers, new channel units (more frequencies) and base stations must be introduced to keep radio congestion at an acceptable level. This will require frequency replanning at regular intervals.

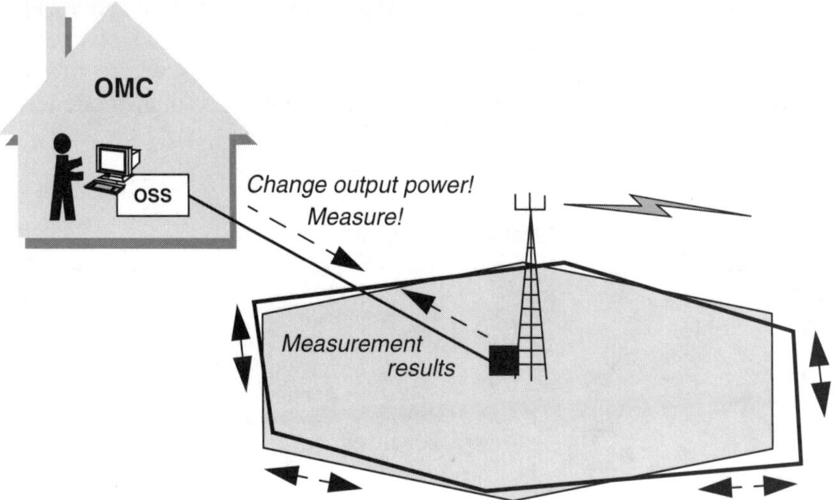

Figure D.8.1 Cell shaping

9 Interworking between networks

9.1 Interworking between operators

Agreements that allow operators to connect their equipment to one another's networks are nothing new. However, earlier agreements of this kind only concerned traffic capacity, signalling and the settlements of accounts in international dealings between national monopoly operators.

With the advent of mobile networks, competition entered the world of telecommunications. Mobile systems also introduced the concept of international roaming in the cooperation between operators in different countries.

National competition requires cooperation in the use of frequencies, numbering plans and other resources. Operators also sign agreements to lease transmission capacity (both trunk and access lines). In many cases, lines are leased from fixed-network operators. Of course, negotiations on price and quality can be rather difficult, and experience from several countries shows that national authorities must often act as mediators.

International roaming requires roaming agreements between operators. So far, this has applied to operators that have the same type of mobile system, such as GSM. Today international roaming between systems based on different standards can also be effected by connecting an interworking location register between the operators' HLRs (or their equivalent). However, for subscribers to use the same mobile telephone in areas where different mobile technologies have been deployed, they must have dual-mode terminals.

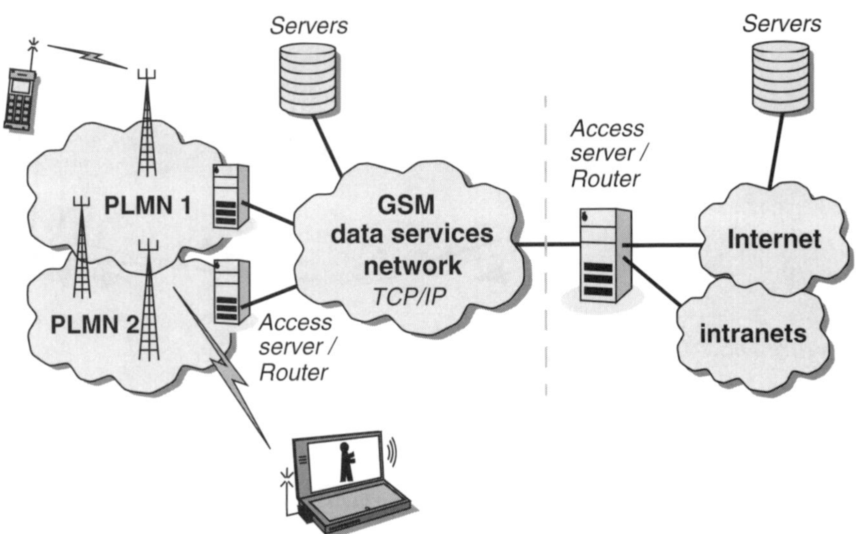

Figure D.9.1 Interworking between PLMNs and the Internet

Another type of interworking between operators occurs between mobile operators and Internet service providers (ISPs) when the Internet is connected to the PLMN, as shown in *Figure D.9.1*.

"GSM data services network" corresponds to the intermediate access network dealt with in *Part H – The Internet*, Chapter 5, Subsection 5.4.4.

9.2 Interworking between bearer networks

Figure D.9.2 shows the most important interfaces to other networks. Interworking with the PSTN is the predominant configuration as far as traffic volume and number of circuits are concerned. A mobile network is usually connected to the PSTN at the transit level.

Mobile networks can also establish interworking with public data networks, which as a rule have been reached through the PSTN and ISDN. Finally, two mobile networks can be directly interconnected.

The interface between the PLMN and other networks is handled by a GMSC.

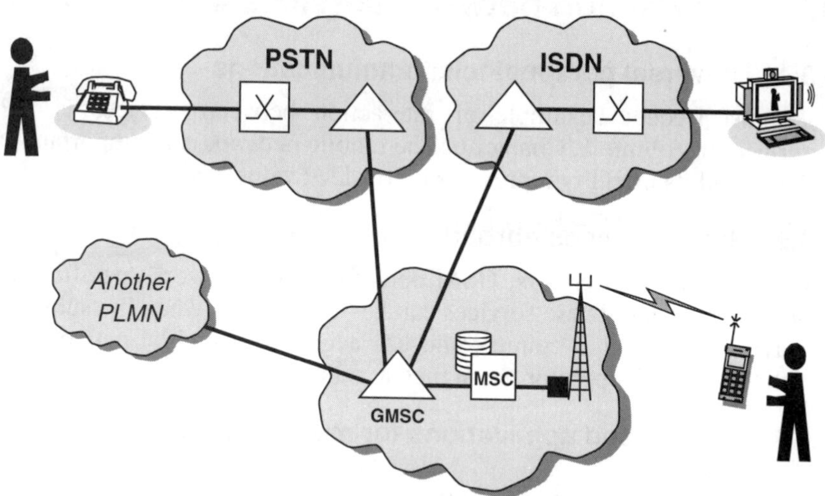

Figure D.9.2 Interworking between the PLMN and PSTN and between the PLMN and ISDN

9.2.1 Fixed cellular systems

Installing traditional telecom cable in rough country (mountainous regions or dense forests, for example) can be extremely labour-intensive and costly. Also, updating and expanding the PSTN in a city with an out-of-date, worn-down cable network can take a long time. In such cases, radio-based solutions are often attractive. They can be based on radio in the local loop or on "fixed cellular" systems. For example, isolated villages in rain-forest regions have been equipped with payphones connected to the fixed telecommunications network through a PLMN. Fixed cellular systems can be profitable and effective, provided that a mobile network is available and that legislation permits fixed subscribers to use it.

Fixed cellular operation entails a lighter load on the processor in the MSC, compared to regular mobile telephony. One disadvantage is increased transmission costs; for instance, when a fixed cellular subscriber makes a call to a neighbour who is connected to the PSTN in the usual manner. Such calls must be connected through the PLMN and the MSC as well as through the local PSTN exchange. Fixed cellular subscribers pay the same tariffs as regular PSTN subscribers.

9.3 Interaction between services

9.3.1 Universal personal telecommunications

The most frequent example of interaction between services is UPT, described in Volume 1, Chapter 6. The mobile network is an important part of UPT, and its mobility represents high added value.

9.3.2 Home services abroad

To compete for subscribers, GSM operators offer network-specific, often IN-based, services. These services can be "forwarded" when the subscriber is staying in a foreign country and has access to a mobile network with which the "home" operator has signed a roaming agreement.

9.3.3 Customised applications for mobile network enhanced logic

Customised applications for mobile network enhanced logic (CAMEL) is a GSM recommendation covering functions and procedures that make operator-specific (not standardised) services available to subscribers who are outside their own network.

CAMEL is based on detectable, well-defined events, such as call set-up, clearing, service activation, and registration. When one of these events occurs, the visited network can temporarily interrupt the set-up process and contact an SCP in the home network. In CAMEL terminology, the SCP is called *CAMEL service environment* (CSE). The CSE provides instructions for how the process should continue. Examples of modification to a set-up procedure are changed B-no., changed tariff and set-up process interruption.

Figure D.9.3 shows an example of a VPN. (See Volume 1, Chapter 6, Subsection 6.2.3.) A subscriber who has a VPN service in his home network is "roaming" in a network abroad. To call a colleague at the home office, all he has to do is dial the colleague's four-digit extension number. The exchange (SSP/MSC) in the visited network classifies the call as a "CSE event", the set-up process is temporarily interrupted and the CSE in the home network is contacted over the signalling network. The CSE translates the extension number into a B-number for international routing and transfers the information to the MSC in the visited network, which resumes the set-up process.

In addition to event-triggered service execution, CAMEL can also request information at any time from the visited network about the subscriber's terminal; for example, in which location area it is at the moment, if a call is in progress or if the terminal is turned off. This function is called *any time interrogation*. Information given in response to such a request can be used for other services in the home network, such as position-related services (see Subsection 6.6.4). A shipping and forwarding agency can be continuously updated on the whereabouts of its vehicles, thus improving security, planning and information to customers.

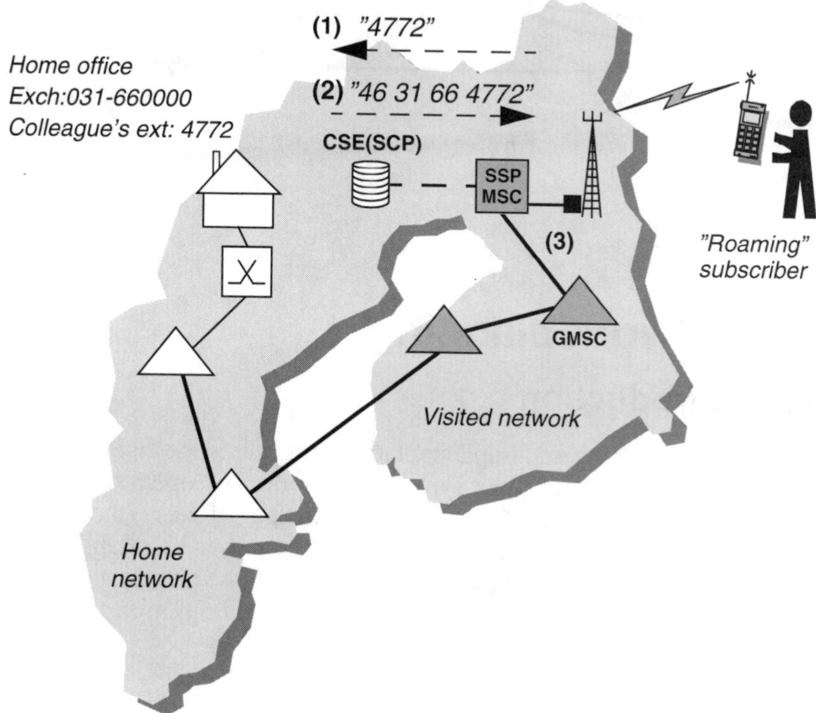

Figure D.9.3 A VPN in a visited network using CAMEL

9.3.4 Dual mode

In areas with extremely high subscriber density, DECT-type systems (see *Part B – PSTN*) might be more economical than a PLMN, as exemplified in *Figure D.9.4*. For cars, however, the speed of the terminals would favour the PLMN, so an optimal solution might be a system combining the PLMN and DECT (PSTN). With seamless handover and dual-mode mobiles capable of handling both systems, such a combination would be an attractive solution, especially if it resulted in lower tariffs than exclusive PLMN switching.

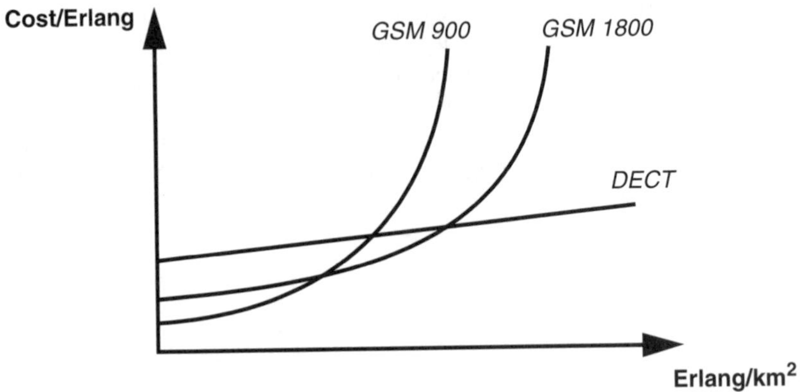

Figure D.9.4 Graphs showing examples of cost differences among radio technologies

10 Network planning

10.1 Introduction

Basically, the planning and implementation procedures for mobile networks are the same as those for other types of network. The operator sketches a network structure based on forecasts of the number of users, their need for services and his own estimated financial situation. Then he establishes suitable quality of service (QoS) and grade of service (GoS) levels, to be able to make more accurate forecasts of traffic volumes and optimise the network technically and economically.

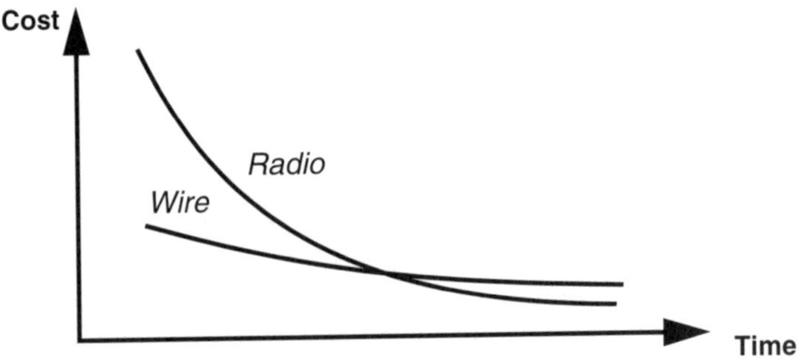

Figure D.10.1 Example of total investment cost evolution (access+terminal)

At all these stages, mobile networks are characterised by the special conditions and properties discussed in this chapter. The operator must take into account the fact that mobility is appreciated by more and more users and that the cost trend for radio solutions is favourable when compared to wire-based solutions. See *Figure D.10.1*.

10.2 Cost aspects

A prerequisite for effective network planning is that the operator can make a reasonably correct estimate of the costs involved (operation and maintenance, licence, hardware, software, personnel, rent, installation and transmission).

Base stations require heavy investment. The number of base stations is mainly determined by the need for coverage and capacity, but several factors can reduce costs: short installation time, small sites and easy-to-manage operation and maintenance. Needless to say, short installation time also means that the system will start generating revenues more quickly.

The cost of transmission between network nodes is another heavy item on the investment list. In the normal case, the mobile operator uses leased lines or a radio-link network of his own. The cost of leased lines varies considerably. If the owner, besides being in a fixed-network monopoly position, owns a competing mobile network, the price is likely to be higher than it would be if transmission capacity were leased from a railway company or municipal authorities.

10.3 Fundamental technical plans

In some respects, the fundamental technical plans for a mobile network differ strikingly from the corresponding plans for other networks; see Chapter 10 of Volume 1 (Subsection 10.8.5).

10.3.1 Frequency plan

The frequency plan is much more important to mobile operators than to other categories of operators. The mobile operator must try to obtain as wide a frequency band as possible and use the allocated frequencies in the most economical way. The means available for optimising operations is frequency reuse and detailed planning that takes into account co-channel interference and adjacent-channel interference in the network.

In countries where different mobile systems use the same frequency bands (NMT 900, TACS, AMPS and GSM), operators must have a plan that shows which frequencies the different systems use and a plan for future modifications. Frequency hopping (frequency diversity), as a method for counteracting multipath fading in digital systems, should also follow a plan.

10.3.2 Numbering plan

The numbering plan for a mobile network can be fully integrated with the plan for PSTN/ISDN (E.164), but in most cases the PSTN subscriber dials a special access code when addressing a mobile subscriber. ITU-T Recommendation E.213 includes a special international numbering plan for the PLMN. If a country has several mobile-network operators, they can have the same access code and must therefore coordinate their numbering plans.

10.3.3 Routing plan

The routing plan must be supplemented with a plan showing the routing procedure to be used in connection with inter-MSC handover, taking into account the existing network structure. (See also Chapter 3, Section 3.3.)

10.3.4 Charging plan

A domestic mobile call is usually charged on the basis of call duration and not distance. In connection with international roaming, however, distance is a factor to be considered, and this can create complicated situations. It would not be reasonable to charge the A-subscriber with the extra cost incurred by the B-subscriber "roaming" to a mobile network in another country; instead, it should be charged to the B-subscriber. In modern mobile networks, toll-ticketing is used to deal with this kind of situation.

10.3.5 Synchronisation plan

Many mobile-network operators extract synchronisation signals from a transport network run by another operator. For this purpose, it is important to have a detailed synchronisation plan that prevents errors from occurring in the cooperation between operators, such as loops in the synchronisation network. Two strict synchronisation requirements must be met by base stations in a digital system: absolute time ("When should I send?") and sufficient frequency accuracy to avoid slip.

Other operators prefer to synchronise their networks through a satellite, for example, the global positioning system (GPS).

10.3.6 Grade-of-service plan

A number of factors affect the GoS in a mobile network. Underdimensioning can cause congestion in the fixed part of the network, and to this must be added any radio congestion that can occur in temporarily overloaded cells.

In a mobile network, available set-up facilities are not the only factor that determines the GoS; another factor is the risk of unsuccessful handover attempts. This type of fault can result in disconnection of the call, and most subscribers find this more irritating than an unsuccessful set-up attempt. A standard rule is that the risk of an ongoing call being disconnected should be 10 to 100 times smaller than the risk of an unsuccessful set-up attempt.

The following are suggested maximum permissible congestion percentages:

- MSC – PSTN: 1%
- MSC – MSC: 1%
- MSC – BSC: 0.5%
- air interface: 2%

10.4 Cell planning

The cell planning phase, which also includes planning the network of base stations, should give the following results:

- full coverage of the service area;
- compliance with current and future traffic requirements; and
- capability to provide the desired GoS and QoS

while at the same time minimising the operator's total system cost.

The traffic demand – that is, the number of subscribers who will be connected to the system and the amount of traffic they will generate – forms the basis of cell planning. The volume and the geographical distribution of the traffic demand can be forecast by using demographic data, such as structure of the population, motor-vehicle density, distribution of income, telephone density and data on land utilisation. The result of this forecast is the starting point for the initial cell planning work in areas that have no previous experience from mobile systems.

Figure D.10.1 shows the basic components of the cell planning process.

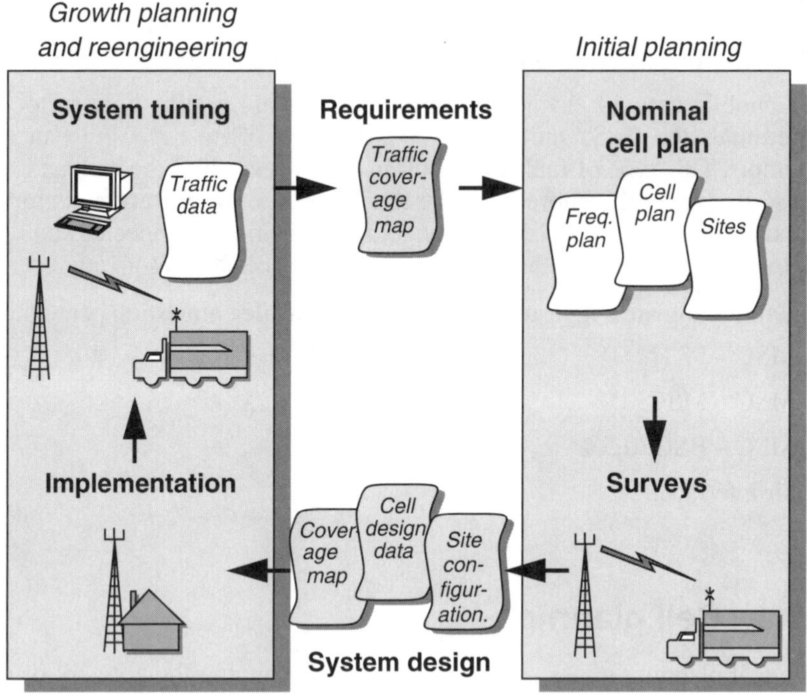

Figure D.10.2 The cell planning process

10.4.1 Nominal cell plan

A nominal cell plan shows the mast sites of the base stations, the coverage of each antenna and the distribution of frequencies among the cells. These factors and others are based on the traffic demand forecast. The nominal cell plan often takes the form of a hexagonal pattern.

When preparing the nominal cell plan, the operator must take into account not only current traffic demand but also the possibility of future cell splitting. Hence, mast sites should be planned to permit use in future network configurations.

The propagation of radio waves is primarily affected by the topography of the area but is also affected by the type of vegetation, rivers and lakes, buildings and so forth. For this purpose, different digitised maps and other land-use data can be used in preparing the nominal cell plan.

The operator should try to calculate the received signal strength in the different parts of each cell in the system. Since the operation of cellular systems is limited by interference rather than by noise, the calculation of co-channel and adjacent-channel interference is a very important part of cell planning work.

10.4.2 Radio survey

The purpose of a radio survey is to test the nominal cell plan and the calculated signal strength and interference values. Movable test transmitters are installed at the proposed antenna sites, and a specially equipped vehicle is used to measure received signal levels in all parts of the service area.

The radio survey is followed by calculations aimed at giving a rough description of how the system will operate. After any required modifications have been made to the cell plan, the system is installed.

10.4.3 Tuning

After the system has been in commercial use for a couple of months, it must be tuned. The operator uses the traffic data collected to decide on any measures required to adjust system operation to the actual traffic demand. The following are examples of such measures:

- changing the parameters for handover in individual cells to transfer traffic from a frequently congested cell to an adjacent cell;
- changing the routing parameters to optimise traffic handling capacity in the core network; and
- adding cells and frequencies in overloaded cells and reducing the number of frequencies in cells that carry less traffic than expected.

To cope with the rapidly increasing number of mobile subscribers, there must be margins for growth during the period immediately after the planning phase. However, it can be advisable to start a new cell planning process shortly after the system has been tuned.

10.4.4 Cell hierarchies

A number of hierarchical cell concepts have been developed to ensure better utilisation of the limited number of frequencies.

"Superimposed" cells

In areas with high traffic intensity, capacity can be increased if one cell is "superimposed" on another one. The two cells use the same base station infrastructure and the same control channel, but the coverage of the "superimposed" cell is limited. This can be a practical solution to capacity problems in cases where the traffic demand near the base station is decidedly higher than near the cell boundary.

Umbrella cells

An umbrella cell, which covers several smaller cells, can be used to eliminate coverage gaps and to serve as backup in case of radio congestion. Since it is difficult to fit the frequency (or frequencies) of the umbrella cell into a reuse pattern, this solution is only used for systems with spare frequencies.

Hierarchical cell structure

The next developmental stage after umbrella cells is a hierarchical cell structure (HCS), which means that the cell plan has three levels: microcells, macrocells and umbrella cells. Mobiles will always try to establish contact within a microcell first, and fast-moving mobiles will then be directed to the highest possible level to minimise the number of handovers.

10.5 Network architecture

Of course, it is important to fix the boundaries between different exchange areas to make optimum use of the network. Networks without mobility apply proven methods for this purpose. The best pattern of boundaries is achieved by determining the subscribers' geographical positions and mapping their traffic interest.

A mobile network requires much more advanced methods. Knowing how the subscribers use their telephones is not enough; the operator must also know their travelling habits to be able to minimise registration activities and inter-MSC handover in the network.

10.5.1 The access network

Transmission alternatives

Cell planning and frequency planning undergo frequent changes due to the rapid increase in the number of mobile subscribers. Hence, the access part of the network demands great flexibility. In principle, two basic methods can be used to achieve this flexibility:

- Base stations can use over-capacity in an existing transport network. This alternative is often realistic for use in metropolitan areas.
- Radio-link systems can be used – either the point-to-point or the point-to-multipoint variant.

Both methods are usually employed in the access network. National rules and regulations can decide the choice in each case.

Positioning of base station controllers

Wherever possible, a BSC's coverage should be chosen such that the boundaries run across areas with low handover intensity. This is because high handover frequency put an extra load on MSCs and BSCs. Consequently, boundaries should not run through town centres or near through-routes and motorways.

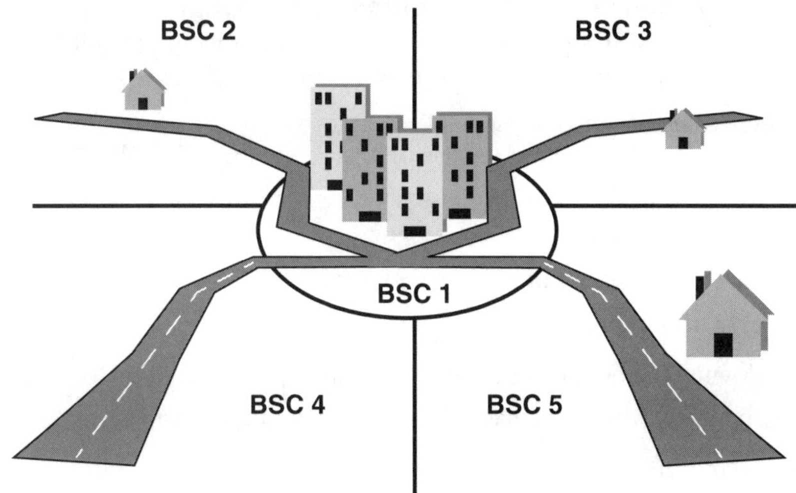

Figure D.10.3 BSC boundaries in town centres or near motorways

Location of voice coders

In digital mobile telephony systems, voice is coded to bit rates lower than the 64 kbit/s of the fixed network. This means that the location of the voice coder in the network hierarchy is an important consideration in mobile-network planning.

Note that, in theory, the rate of expansion in a cell of an analog system could be one channel at a time, whereas in a digital system this rate – expressed as the number of channels – cannot be lower than the number of time slots in a frame.

Bit rate per voice channel

Naturally, introducing a half bit rate in digital systems will affect network planning. Channels with half bit rate will have twice the capacity of today's full-rate channels.

Today's full-rate mobiles must still be served by the system. This means that two rates in a system will result in three different grades of service: full rate, half rate and dual rate. A dual-rate mobile will first try to seize a half-rate channel then, if no such channel is available, will try to seize a full-rate channel. Since the mobiles and the network can handle both full rate and half rate at the same time, the capacity of a cell will vary depending on the types of mobiles that are within the cell boundaries at the moment.

10.5.2 The core network

Location of mobile switching centres

The location of MSCs depends on users' expected travelling habits and on the solution chosen for transmission between the base stations and the MSC.

Operators often have to choose between many small and a few large MSCs. The following factors favour the use of a large number of small MSCs:

- high cost of available transmission or high cost of installation of new transmission facilities;
- high cost of relaying through the PSTN; and
- low cost of buildings.

The following factors favour the use of a small number of large MSCs:

- the operator owns or can easily build his own radio-link network;
- the operator pays a flat rate for calls to the PSTN; and
- lower cost of operation and maintenance.

Location of gateway mobile switching centres

The geographical distribution of the traffic demand between the PSTN and the PLMN plays a decisive role in the location of GMSCs. Optimum utilisation of the different networks is always the goal. Using the PSTN for internal mobile network traffic over long distances can be advantageous in some – but far from all – configurations. If the different networks are administrated by different operators, optimisation also depends on their pricing.

Location of operation and maintenance centres

The location of OMCs in the network requires a delicate balance between the factors listed below.

Arguments that favour dispersed units:

- low travelling cost (personnel) and
- minimum signal load in the network.

Arguments that favour a few, centralised units:

- efficiency gains;
- reduced number of staff; and
- low investment cost.

The operation and maintenance plan defines basic rules for operations support, organisation and the distribution of responsibilities among national and regional OMCs.

Location of Internet access points

Internet traffic is gradually increasing the load on PLMN systems. This traffic should preferably be extracted at the MSC trunk side. At that location, the operator can connect an intermediate access network with servers containing local information. (See *Figure D.9.1.*) Other solutions are described in *Part H – The Internet.*

Dimensioning of the traffic-handling network

A connection in the PSTN seizes some devices for a certain time, which makes calculation of traffic load relatively easy. The calculating process in a mobile network is more complicated, because new devices can be seized during a call in progress. For example, handover between two MSCs will involve another exchange and additional links.

The signalling network

The mobile network is the most signal-intensive of all public networks.

On the whole, the introduction of new, sophisticated IN functions will increase the signal load in telecom networks. These functions are used for call handling. In mobile networks, there is the additional load caused by registration, locating, handover, paging and authentication. The handover frequency will depend on the size of the cells (the present trend towards smaller cells will result in more handovers), the average call duration (which will probably increase with lower tariffs) and the average speed of the mobiles. The net effect will certainly be more signalling per call.

Any measures taken with a view to improving network security will also increase the signalling volume.

In addition, signalling will be used for user data sent as short messages. This type of traffic can have a considerable effect on future signalling, because it is likely that the short-message service will be very attractive (such as for notification of stored voice messages).

The connection between the MSC and the HLR must be of high quality. If the HLR is a stand-alone, centralised database, it will need links of its own.

Given the heavy signalling load that mobile networks can be expected to carry in the near future, it may be necessary to design a dedicated signalling network for the PLMN.

10.6 Network planning tools

Computerised planning tools facilitate the dimensioning, optimisation and costing of large mobile networks. The following are examples of tasks that can be supported by such tools:

- calculation of radio propagation;
- calculation of C/I;
- optimisation of transmission in the core network;
- optimisation of transmission in the access network;
- calculation of signalling volumes;
- planning of radio links; and
- costing.

Part E – The signalling network

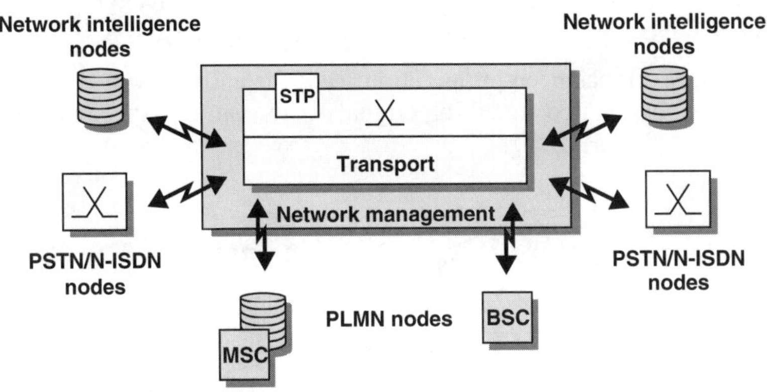

Figure E.0.1 Reference model

A general introduction to signalling is given in Chapter 7 of Volume 1.

1 User services

In this part we will be dealing with a very important bearer network: the signalling network. Basically, its task is to support other networks, but it can also carry traffic transparently in the form of short messages between subscribers or signalling between PBXs. We have chosen to call it the *SS7* network, which is an abbreviated form for the complete terms "ITU-T Signalling System No. 7" and "common channel signalling system No. 7".

The SS7 network has been in operation since the early 1980s. Before then, only channel-associated signalling (signals sent along the speech path) was available. See *Figure E.1.1.*

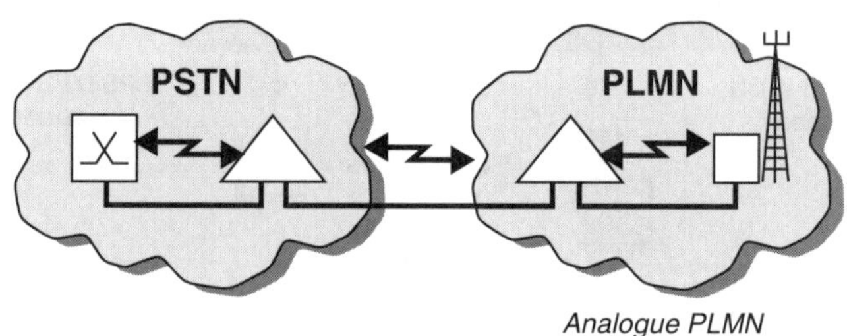

Figure E.1.1 Channel-associated signalling

There are certain similarities between the bearer service of the SS7 and that of the X.25 network described in *Part F1 – X.25*. Both networks are packet-switched and have a three-layer protocol structure, which essentially corresponds to open systems interconnection (OSI) layers 1–3.

One difference is that X.25 is connection-oriented – "the first packet marks the path" – whereas the SS7 network is usually connectionless, which means that all packets (datagrams) are individual in the sense that they are independent of other packets. Another difference has to do with user services. The SS7 network carries signalling message packets, or message signal units (MSU), between processors in the telecommunications network. The protocols for processor communication (that is, data messages or user information) reside above OSI layer 3 and are called user parts (UPs) and application parts (APs). The X.25 network, on the other hand, handles the exchange of data messages between subscriber terminals or other network connection elements but is also used as a support network for transmission of management information (see Volume 1, Chapter 8).

Figure E.1.2 illustrates the function of the SS7 network. A switching node in the network is called a signal transfer point (STP). It handles packet traffic between nodes in the PSTN, narrowband integrated service digital network

(N-ISDN), PLMN and virtual private networks (VPNs) as well as traffic to and from intelligent network (IN) nodes, notably service control points (SCPs). Nodes connected to the signalling network are called signalling points (SP).

The SS7 network will also support broadband ISDN (B-ISDN).

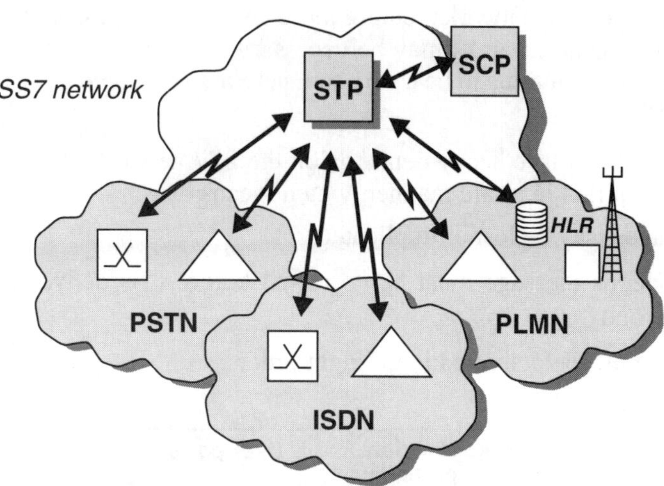

Figure E.1.2 SS7 applications with associated signalling points

The user services – user parts and application parts – of the SS7 network play an important role as functional building blocks in other networks:

User part/Application part	Application	Described in Part
Telephony user part (TUP)	Signalling in PSTN	B, Chapter 7
ISDN user part (ISUP)	Signalling in N-ISDN and PSTN	C, Chapter 7
Mobile application part (MAP)	Signalling and database communication in PLMN	D, Chapter 7
Transaction capabilities application part (TCAP)	Support for communication with IN databases and for signalling in PLMN	A, Chapter 6
Intelligent network application part (INAP)	Communication with IN databases	
Operation and maintenance application part (OMAP)	Communication in management networks	A, Chapter 8

Figure E.1.3 The user services of the SS7 network

The user parts and application parts handle user information, such as control information for setting up and clearing voice or data connections, and information for centralised supplementary services (IN services). They communicate with other UPs and APs of the same type and at the same level in the signalling network. The relationship with OSI is shown in *Figure E.1.4*.

The SS7 network normally uses 64 kbit/s links in the transport network. Since traffic-carrying networks require more and more processor communication, faster signalling links may be necessary in the future. Even so, the SS7 network will continue to be a very thin network compared to the PSTN/ ISDN and PLMN.

The UPs and APs place heavy demands on the SS7 network. All messages must be transmitted in a safe manner, which means that

- no messages may be lost or duplicated;
- any erroneous message must be corrected before it is delivered to the recipient; and
- messages must be delivered in the right order.

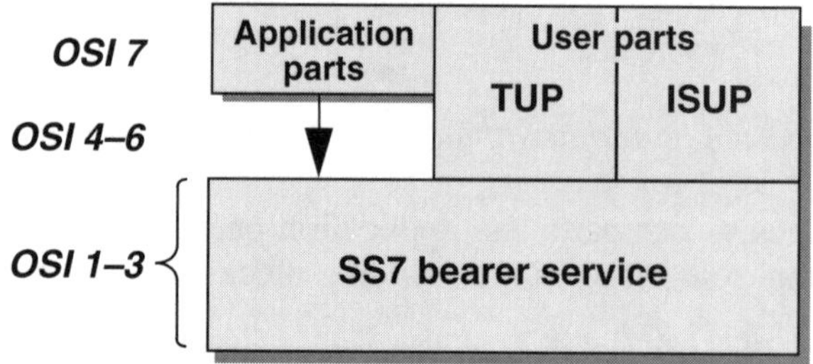

Figure E.1.4 SS7 and OSI

2 Standardisation

2.1 General

SS7 was first specified in 1979–80 in the *Yellow Book* of the Consultative Committee on International Telegraphy and Telephony (CCITT), now known as the International Telecommunication Union-Telecommunications Standardization Sector (ITU-T). The number of teleservices increased dramatically in the 1980s and 1990s, and SS7 has been developed gradually to meet the signalling requirements of the new services.

In the ITU-T's red, blue and white recommendations of 1984, 1988 and 1992, respectively, more functions have been added to the signalling system. SS7 is described in the recommendations of the Q.700 series.

The standardisation of the signalling network is primarily concerned with OSI layers 1–3, where the message transfer part (MTP) and the signalling connection control part (SCCP) are found. The SCCP may be regarded as a supplement to the MTP; together they form the network service part (NSP).

The MTP forwards MSUs between user parts of the same type, for example, between telephony user parts (TUPs). TUP messages for the set-up and clearing of a telephony connection pass all the exchanges along the traffic path, and instructions for switch control are given in every exchange. This relationship between the traffic path and that of the signalling messages was the cornerstone of the original SS7 specification. The "physical bond" with a traffic path enables SS7 messages to be routed by means of traffic destinations and the applicable routing table, thus simplifying the design of the MTP.

Today's networks also contain intelligent nodes (the SCPs and home location registers, for example) which are usually located outside the traffic-handling machine but which must be accessible from that machine. The MTP protocol has therefore been supplemented with the SCCP protocol, which was first specified in 1984 (Recommendations Q.711–Q.714). The SCCP belongs to OSI layer 3.

The SCCP also supports the use of the SS7 network as an advanced packet-switched network for direct communication between two processors or databases, without physical ties to traffic circuits. Both connection-oriented and connectionless communication are possible.

Figure E.2.1 shows how the SS7 network supports the modern network structure with centralised intelligence. (See Volume 1, Chapter 7, Subsection 7.4.3, for further details.)

The PLMN in particular will benefit from these new possibilities. Registration (location updating) requires updating the home location register (HLR) with information showing the location of mobile terminals. The HLR must be able to exchange data messages with different visitor location registers (VLRs), and this is done through the SS7 network.

Another example is the execution of IN services. The service logic is implemented in a database called service control point (SCP). To be able to execute a centralised supplementary service, the exchanges operating as service switching points (SSPs) must establish a separate dialogue with an SCP through the SS7 network to receive the necessary service data. The transaction capabilities application part (TCAP) is one of the protocols used in this dialogue.

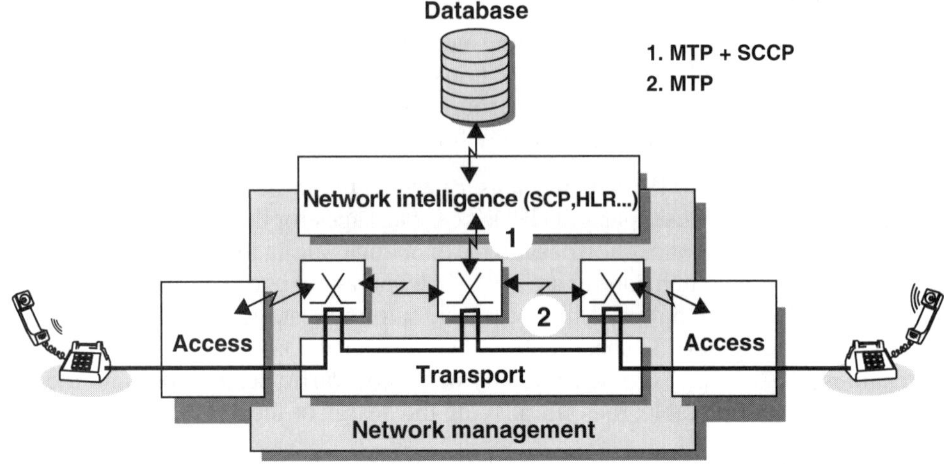

Figure E.2.1 SS7 network functions in a modern network structure

2.2 Layers and levels in SS7

For SS7 protocols we use the term "level" to denote what is meant by "layer" in OSI terminology. Broadly speaking, OSI layers 1–3 correspond to MTP levels 1–3, including the SCCP. OSI layers 4–7 correspond to user parts and application parts. To avoid confusion, we will use the OSI term "layer" in the following.

Layer 1: *Signalling data link level*

This level defines the requirements to be met by the physical circuit, normally a PCM channel.

Layer 2: *Signalling link functions*

The signalling link level has functions for reliable transfer of messages over a physical circuit (signalling data link), that is, separation of messages, error detection and error correction.

Layer 3: *MTP, signalling network functions*

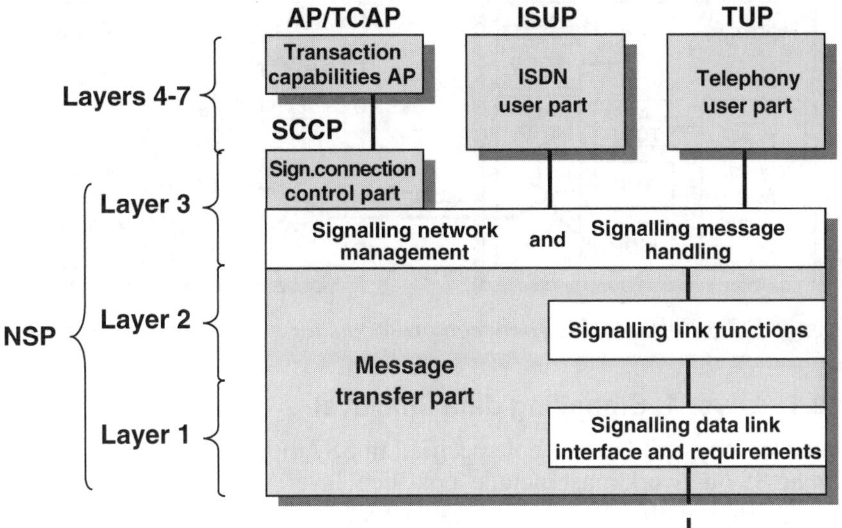

Figure E.2.2 The main functions of each layer (NSP = network service part)

This layer has functions for signalling message handling: separation, distribution and routing. Functions for signalling network management are also included, for example, supervision of the signalling network with respect to capacity, transmission quality and the need for rerouting.

Layer 3: *Signalling connection control part*

Main functions include SCCP-specific, connection-oriented and connectionless control, routing and network management.

Layers 4–7: *User parts and application parts*

SS7 allows several users to send signals in the same signalling network. Functions in layers 4–7 handle the connected user's communication protocol.

In a point-to-point connection between with two nodes – both incorporating ISDN, PSTN and IN functions – the relationships between protocols will be as shown in *Figure E.2.3*.

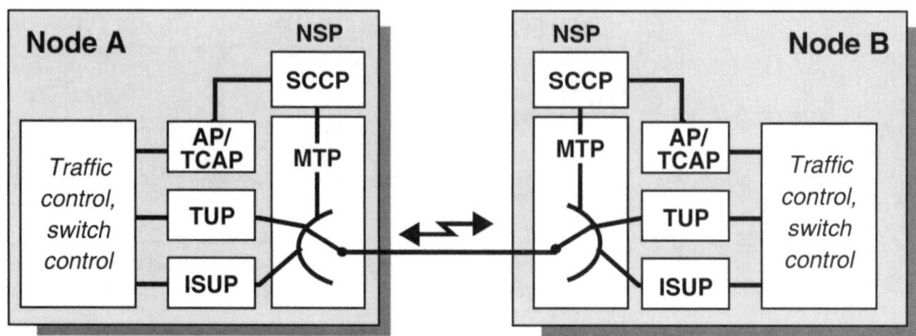

Figure E.2.3 Relationships between protocols for two communicating nodes

2.2.1 Layer 1. Signalling data link level

Since the physical layer is not specified in SS7, no MTP layer 1 is defined. But an SS7 network must include a physical layer, of course. Recommendation Q.702 specifies the characteristics that this layer should have to meet the MTP's requirements.

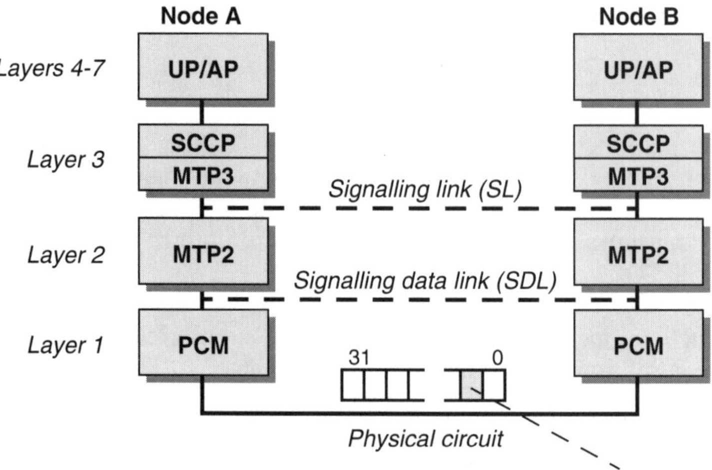

Figure E.2.4 Signalling data link and signalling link – OSI relationships

The signalling terminals in the traffic switching or network intelligence nodes are interconnected by physical circuits to form a signalling data link.

In digital systems, this circuit is a channel in a PCM system with a bit rate of 64 kbit/s. (SS7 "leases" the channel from the transport network.) Any PCM channel can be used as a signalling data link except channel 0, which must always be used for synchronising the PCM system. In Sweden, channel 1 is used as a signalling data link. See *Figure E.2.4*.

The rest of the channels are used for traffic circuits carrying voice or data, for example.

2.2.2 Layer 2. Signalling link functions

The signalling link (SL) consists of the signalling terminals in either node (or signalling point), the intermediate signalling data link (SDL; that is, the PCM channel) and the equipment that links terminals and the PCM channel together.

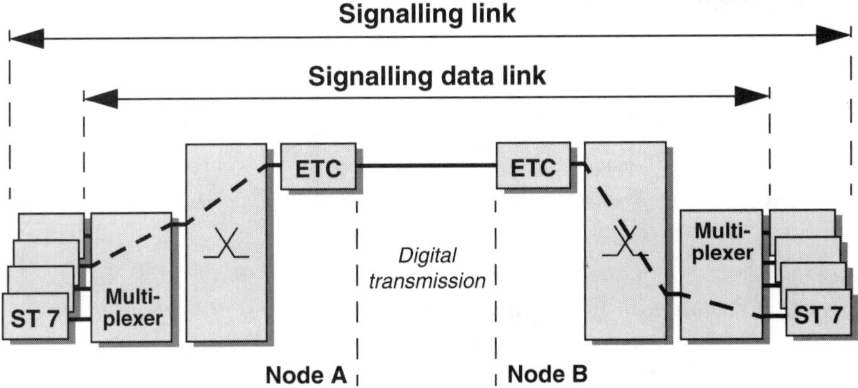

Figure E.2.5 Signalling data link and signalling link – Physical implementation (ETC = exchange terminal circuit)

The signalling link functions handle traffic on the signalling link and ensure reliable transfer of MSUs on the link. For this purpose, the signalling link functions in the signalling terminal (see *Figure E.2.6*) include:

- separation of messages;
- error detection;
- error correction; and
- supervision.

The messages are temporarily stored in the *transmit* and *receive* buffers. A copy of every transmitted MSU is stored in the *retransmit* buffer, from where it will be retransmitted if necessary. The other functions shown in *Figure E.2.6* are dealt with below.

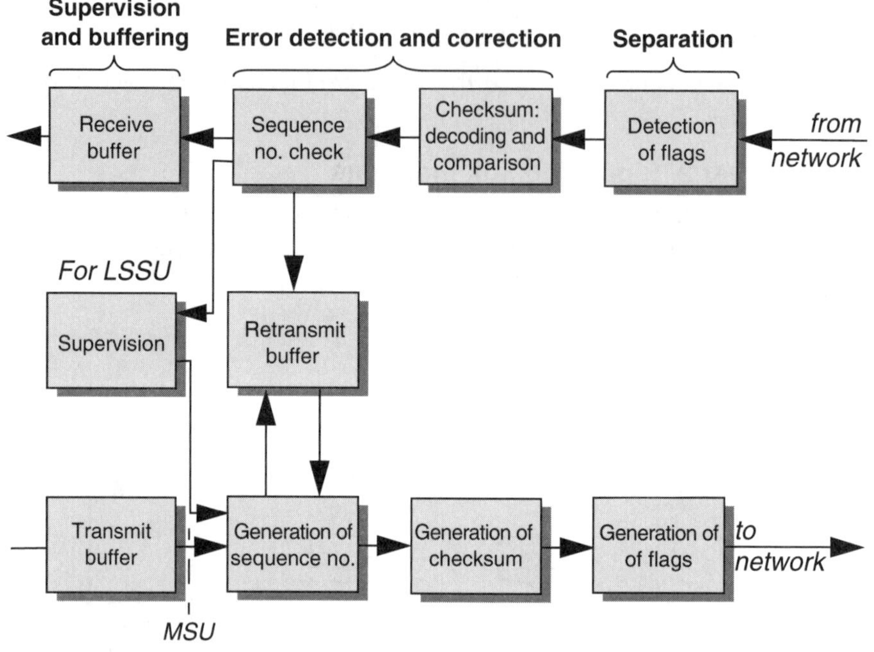

Figure E.2.6 Signalling link functions (LSSU = link status signal unit)

Message types

Not just "useful" signalling messages of the MSU type are exchanged on the signalling link. In fact, fill-in signal units (FISU) are more common, since the load on signalling links is usually low. A third type of message is used for exchanging information between signalling points; for example, when a link is put into operation after a fault or for the transmission of flow control information. This type of message is called link status signal unit (LSSU). See *Figure E.2.6.*

Message format

A message is divided into fields, as shown in *Figure E.2.7.* (The number below each field indicates the number of bits.) Several of the message fields serve as "packing" to facilitate error-free transmission. Of particular interest to a user (TUP, for example) is the information in the signalling information field (SIF).

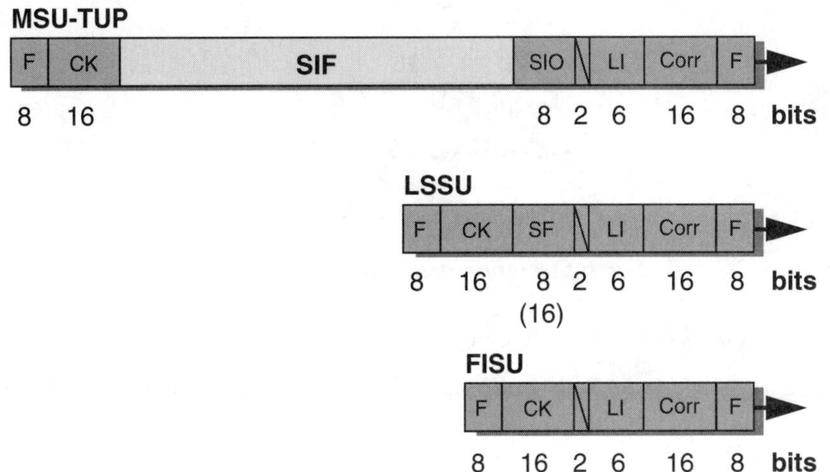

Figure E.2.7 Message format (MSU/TUP)

The dark fields in *Figure E.2.7* represent signalling link functions, that is, layer-2 functions. The main functions of the layer-2 fields are:

F: *flag* indicates the beginning and end of the message. The opening flag usually serves as the closing flag of the previous message. (Flag bit pattern = 01111110)

Corr: *error correction* initiates retransmission on the send side when a transmission error has been detected by the receive side.

LI: *length indicator* indicates the number of octets (8-bit groups) that follow LI up to the CK field, thus indicating which of the three basic messages applies. (The length indicator consists of a binary value between 0 and 63; 63 means 63 octets or more.)

LI = 0: FISU

LI = 1 or 2: LSSU

LI > 2: MSU

SIO: the *service information octet*, which is found in MSUs only, is divided into two parts: the service indicator (SI) and the subservice field (SSF). The SI consists of four bits, the two most significant of which are called network indicators (NI). The SI indicates the network involved, showing whether a TUP belongs to the national or international network, for example. If an MSU carries the SCCP protocol, the SI is set to 0011. Example:

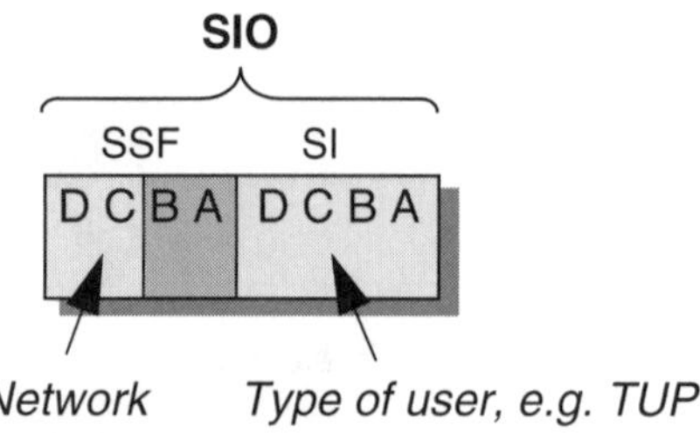

Figure E.2.8 Service information octet, SIO

CK: the *checksum* is used to detect bit errors during transmission.

SF: *status field* in an LSSU message which indicates the state assumed by a signalling link side after a change of state. An SF consists of 8 or 16 bits (1 or 2 octets).

2.2.3 Layer 3 (MTP). Signalling network functions in the MTP

Signalling network functions are the functions required to route messages to the right signalling point and to the right user in the network.

Signalling network functions fall into two categories:

- signalling message handling, and
- signalling network management.

Signalling message handling

Signalling message handling means ensuring that the user data of the received MSUs reach the right user (UP, or AP via the SCCP) in a terminating signalling point or that it is sent onwards to the next signalling point. If an MSU is addressed to another signalling point in the network, then it is routed to a suitable signalling link according to instructions from the signalling network management.

Signalling message handling means that an MSU is

- distributed;
- discriminated; and
- routed.

An MSU that is to be sent from a signalling point is routed to the signalling link – in a signalling link set – selected for the transport of this MSU. The selection of a signalling link set will be based on the MSU's destination point code (DPC).

Incoming MSUs are separated. If an MSU addressed to another signalling point is received, it will be rerouted after a new signalling link has been selected. A terminating MSU is sent onwards to the right user part, based on the contents of the SIO.

Signalling network management

The signalling network management functions perform continuous supervision of the signalling network to detect errors and abnormal situations. Both autonomous and manual network control functions are employed to ensure optimal use of available signalling resources.

Depending on the state of the network – such as performance affected by defective signalling links or signalling points – signalling traffic may have to be rerouted over alternative routes to reach its destination. In situations where rerouting is not possible or practical, the traffic must be stopped or restricted at the source.

MSU types

There are three types of MSU, each having its specific contents:

- MSUs with signalling information to and from users, such as the telephone user part (TUP);
- MSUs containing signalling information for signalling network management (SNM); and
- MSUs containing signalling information for signalling network testing and maintenance (SNT).

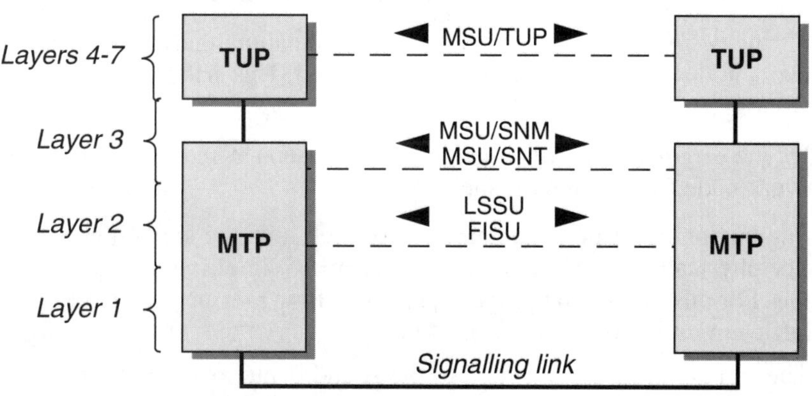

Figure E.2.9 Message types

Figure E.2.10 and the subsequent text describe in particular those parts of the signalling information field that are used by MTP layer-3 functions.

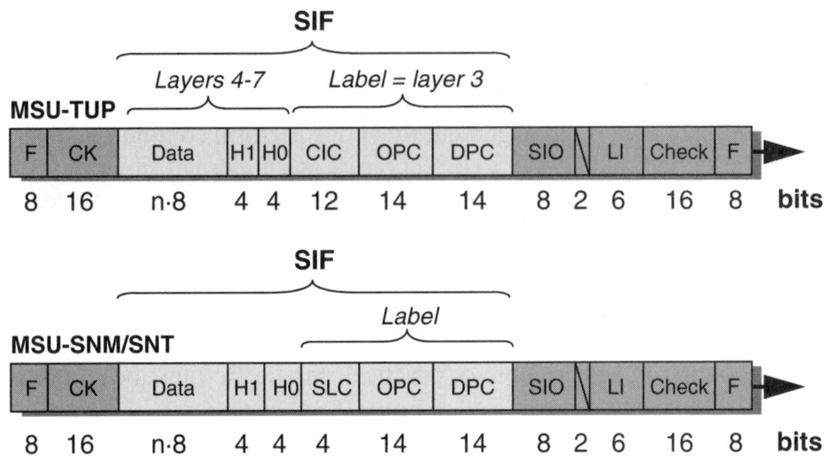

Figure E.2.10 MSU formats

SIF: the *signalling information field* contains a label, a heading (UP or AP) and data. The SIF, which is found in MSUs only, is transmitted to the user (UP or AP) in layers 4–7. The SIF in MSU-SNM and MSU-SNT is sent to signal network management in layer 3.

As far as the signalling network is concerned, the label is the most interesting part because it contains the information that corresponds to A and B-numbers in traffic-carrying networks, namely DPC and OPC:

DPC: the *destination point code* identifies destination; that is, the signalling network node to which the message is addressed. This is the key information for routing.

OPC: the *originating point code* identifies the sender; that is, the signalling network node from which the message is sent.

At the beginning of this chapter we described how the signalling network can be physically related to the traffic network to simplify the design of protocols. For this to function properly, the signalling message can be related to a traffic circuit in different ways:

- The signalling message is tied to the A and B-numbers of the traffic circuit by means of the contents of SIF's data field (TUP, ISUP and so forth).

- The signalling message is tied to the number of that traffic circuit which is controlled by MSU-TUP, MSU-ISUP and so on. This number is called CIC:

CIC: the *circuit identification code* includes signalling link selection (SLS). The corresponding field in MSU-SNM and MSU-SNT is called SLC:

SLC: the *signalling link code* is the number of the signalling link to which MSU-SNM or MSU-SNT is related.

Finally, there is a part that corresponds to user information (OSI layers 4–7):

H0, H1: these two *headings* together form the code that indicates the type of information in the SIF, such as initial address message (IAM).

Data: the *information carried in the SIF* can be up to 256 octets. (FISU and LSSU messages contain no data.) This information is intended for users, network management or testing. ISUP has a different SIF structure. (See *Part C – N-ISDN,* Chapter 7, Section 7.3.)

2.2.4 Layer 3 (SCCP). Signalling connection control part

As mentioned earlier, the SCCP function performs the following main tasks:

- SCCP connection-oriented control;
- SCCP connectionless control;
- SCCP routing; and
- SCCP network management.

When added to the MTP functionality, the first three functions provide powerful signalling message handling in the SS7 network. Signalling message handling can be made independent of the traffic part, and it will also be possible to make connection-oriented transfers. Connection-orientation is used when many messages or long messages are to be sent to the same address.

Location updating of mobile subscribers and generation of alarm messages are examples of connectionless communication (where every MSU contains an address).

Separating the signalling routing function from the traffic path requires a great deal of functionality. The aim is to make it possible to set up autonomous SS7 connections over long distances, basically in the way X.25 connections are established. What lies at the bottom is the most demanding application: the constant supervision of all subscribers in a mobile network and the storing of the recorded information in a central point: an HLR. Ideally, this supervision should be performed worldwide.

Other applications using the SCCP are more restricted in the geographical sense. Local applications include – or will include – the number portability service, which means that we can move without having to change our phone number; for example, when served by another local exchange. National applications include many IN services, all of which require contact with centrally located SCPs.

SCCP routing functions

An important objective of the SCCP's routing function is to determine the DPC. In SCCP applications, the DPC values also comprise all types of network intelligence nodes: SCP, HLR, equipment identity register (EIR) and authentication centre (AUC). (In some types of PLMN, an EIR and an AUC are used to increase security.)

Volume 1, Chapter 10, Subsection 10.8.4, describes how different network applications can use the same platform. For instance, we can combine PLMN and IN applications. The whole destination will then consist of a specific platform (DPC) and a specific network application. For the network application, the SCCP has a subsystem number (SSN, which for the HLR is "6" or the octet "00000110"). The network application can be represented by a user part or an application part (MAP, OMAP, TUP, ISUP) or by a function (HLR, VLR, MSC, EIR, AUC). An SSN is also used in SCCP management.

To determine a DPC, the SCCP uses a *global title* (GT) as input information. This could be a number dialled in the PSTN, ISDN or PLMN or the number of a roaming mobile subscriber.

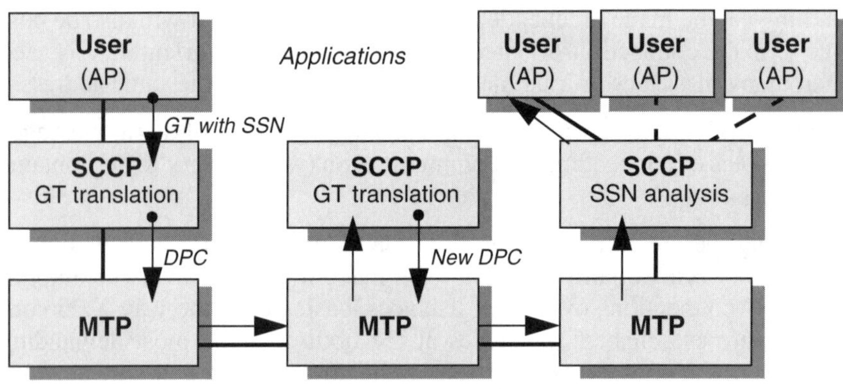

Figure E.2.11 SS7 connection set-up using SCCP

The SCCP contains all the network and routing information required to analyse a global title and translate it into a "compass point" which gives a DPC value for all or part of the signalling connection to be established.

Figure E.2.12 shows how MSU/SCCP is composed. The SCCP field in the frame also contains the TCAP and other application parts in OSI layer 7.

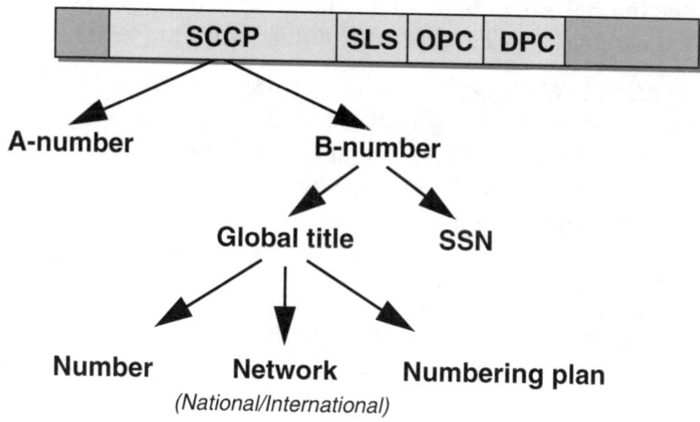

Figure E.2.12 MSU/SCCP structure

3 Switching and switch control

3.1 Introduction

As we have seen, SS7 is a packet-switched data network. In contrast to X.25, but in conformity with the Internet's TCP/IP, connectionless packet mode is the normal set-up procedure.

Switching of signalling messages is performed by the STP. The "subscribers" are exchanges and network intelligence nodes – in this context called signalling points (SP).

The following describes the network functions in more detail.

3.2 Terms and definitions

It is important to distinguish between *traffic-carrying functions* and *signalling functions*. When we describe traffic handling, we use expressions such as "two exchanges are interconnected by a direct traffic route". If no such route is available, the traffic must pass one or more transit exchanges; for example, a local tandem exchange or a transit exchange for long-distance traffic.

In the SS7 network, two exchanges have a signalling relationship if their user parts can communicate with one another. The relationship can be either associated or quasi-associated. In the latter case, the signals are sent through a third exchange (an STP). (For an example, refer to *Figure E.1.2.*)

Every signalling relationship requires one or more signalling links to transfer messages between two SPs, either direct or via an STP. The signalling links usually have signalling terminals at each end, a time slot for 64 kbit/s transmission between the SPs and switching and multiplexing equipment. (See Chapter 2, Subsection 2.2.2.)

Several parallel signalling links form a link set. If the signalling relationship uses one or more STPs, several signalling links in a tandem arrangement will be required. In these cases, the signalling does not follow the same path as the traffic.

A signalling point for the generation of MSUs is called the originating point (OP), while the receiving point is called the destination point (DP). Since an STP is just a switching point in the network, it cannot be a destination point; all it does is read the address of the message and send it onward through the signalling network, or to a co-located DP.

The predefined path that a message seizes between the OP and DP is called the *signalling route,* or signalling route set if several routes are required to reach the DP. Consequently, if the message passes one or more STPs, a set of routes will be required. As a rule, several alternative paths are defined between two SPs for reliability reasons. (For more details, see Chapter 10, Section 10.2.)

There are two variants of STPs:

- integrated STP, and
- stand-alone STP.

An integrated STP is a node – often in the form of a tandem or transit exchange – which handles both signalling messages and user traffic in the PSTN/ISDN or PLMN.

A stand-alone STP is a node that conveys signalling traffic only.

To permit identification of the network nodes during signalling, all SPs are numbered according to a predetermined system: the numbering plan of the

SS7 network. The SP number is called the signalling point code (SPC). (For more details on SS7's numbering plan, see Chapter 10, Subsection 10.3.1.)

3.2.1 Relationships between switching and traffic cases

Considering SS7's function in the network, we can distinguish between three basic traffic cases:

- set-up of connections in the PSTN/ISDN without support from network intelligence nodes;
- set-up of connections supported by network intelligence nodes of the SCP type; and
- administration of mobile calls with the aid of the HLR.

As we can see from the examples below, the switching procedure in the SS7 network will vary with the traffic cases.

Traffic case 1: Without support from network intelligence nodes

Example: Set-up of a telephone connection with possibilities of alternative routing of the telephone traffic. One signalling path is assumed, and the STP is also assumed to be co-located with tandem/transit exchange B. The SPCs of the nodes appear as in *Figure E.3.1*.

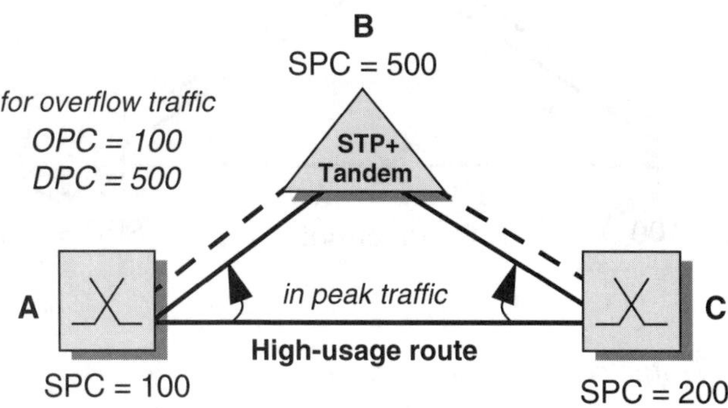

Figure E.3.1 Traffic case 1 (SPC = signalling point code)

Two different situations arise:

Low traffic: All telephone traffic is carried by the high-usage route A -> C
Peak traffic: Overflow occurs on the high-usage route A -> C, and the overflow traffic is routed over B.

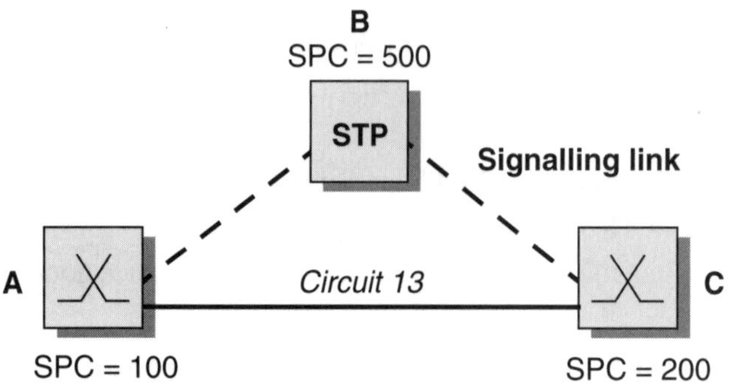

Figure E.3.2 Traffic case 1a – low traffic

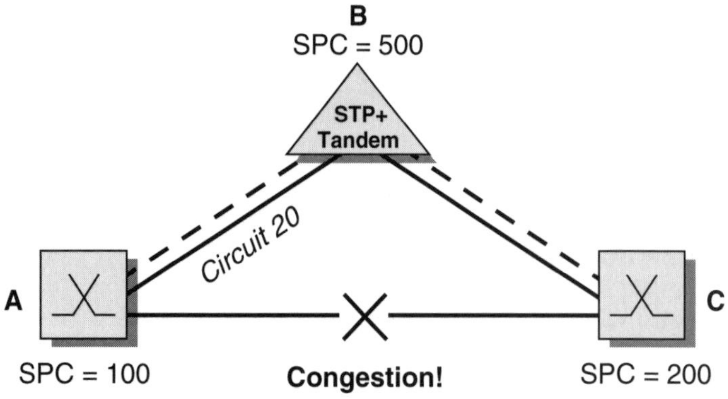

Figure E.3.3 Traffic case 1b – peak traffic

As far as activities in the signalling network are concerned, the most interesting operations are performed in the STP, and this applies in particular to the process in layer 3.

In case 1a, no traffic passes through the tandem exchange, which means that SS7 need not give any switching instructions in B. The message discriminator should therefore send the message on to C. For this to function properly, the destination must be set to DPC = 200, which is the code for exchange C.

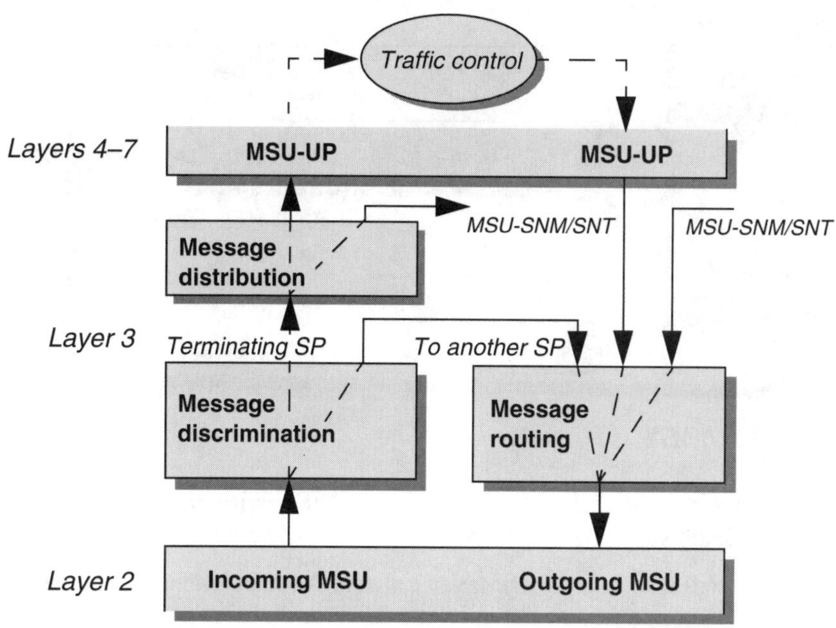

Figure E.3.4 Handling of MSUs in layer 3

An MSU from A to C – via B – will then have the label shown in *Figure E.3.5.*

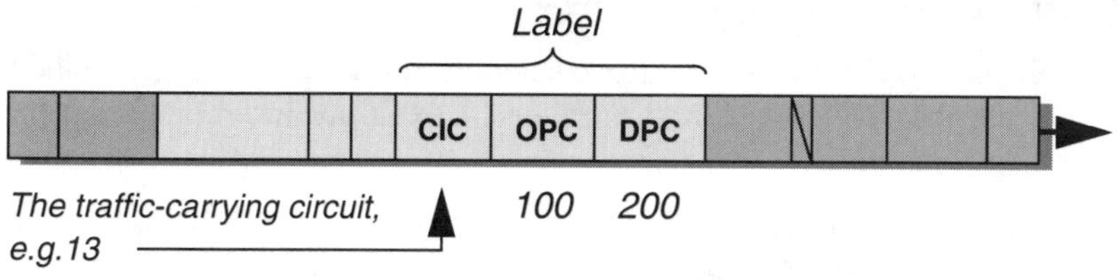

Figure E.3.5 An MSU from A to B

In case 1b, some of the traffic over the high-usage route A–C is barred. This overflow traffic must be handled in a different manner by the signalling system because it is switched in (that is, the line is terminated in) exchange B. Now the label must be as shown in *Figure E.3.6*. To ensure correct connection, the contents of the SIF are sent on to the TUP in the exchange.

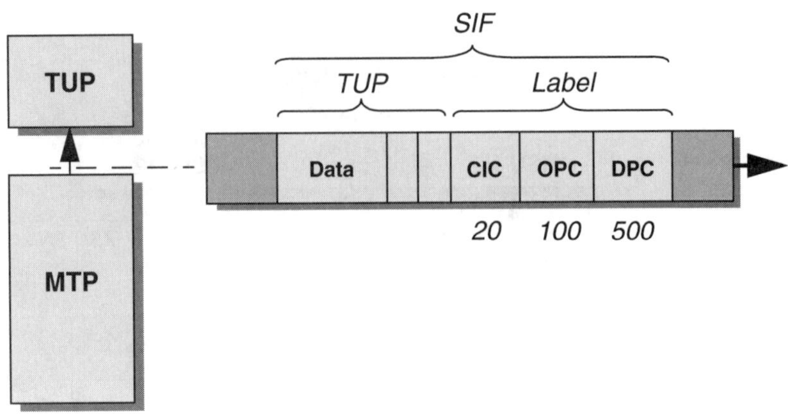

Figure E.3.6 MTP is terminated in B

Here a new need arises; that is, to create an MSU with partly new contents between B and C for connections that are tandem-switched in exchange B.

The MTP will now ask the UP layer for assistance in extending the switching path. Such interaction between the MTP and a user part takes place in every transfer point along the path.

The sequence of events is as follows:

After the number has been analysed in exchange B, an outgoing traffic route is selected. The user part, TUP, is then called once more, and when it receives information showing the selected route, the DPC can be set. DPC = 200 is associated with the B–C route.

A circuit (no. 14) in the B–C route is selected for telephony traffic. The two circuits, number 20 from A and number 14 to C, are interconnected in the switch of exchange B.

A new SIF is compiled and sent to the MTP. This new SIF is identical with the SIF received from exchange A, except that the label has been changed.

The MTP compiles an MSU, in which our SIF is included, and sends it to the destination indicated by the DPC, that is, exchange C (SPC = 200).

As the last example shows, the MSU can be compared to an envelope whose address and sender can be changed without affecting the contents.

Note that OPC will also change value as a result of the switching in exchange B. Signalling point B – not A – is treated as the sender of the MSU, although its contents (SIF) were originally generated by exchange A.

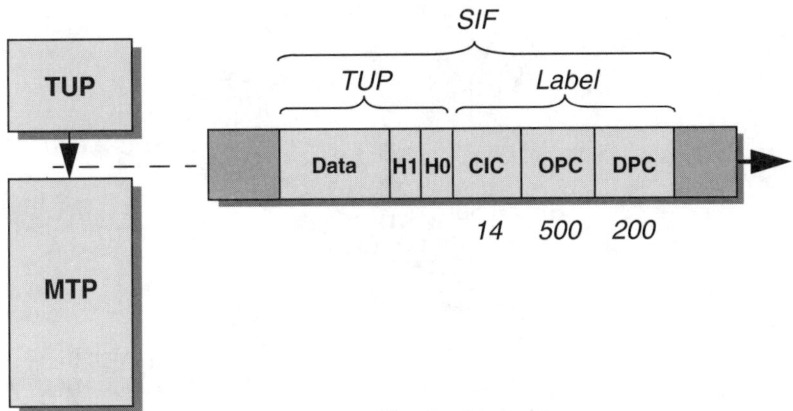

Figure E.3.7. A new MSU is generated in exchange B

If OPC = 100 remains unchanged, then exchange C will not recognise the call on circuit 14 from exchange B but interpret it as a call to circuit 14 on a direct route from exchange A.

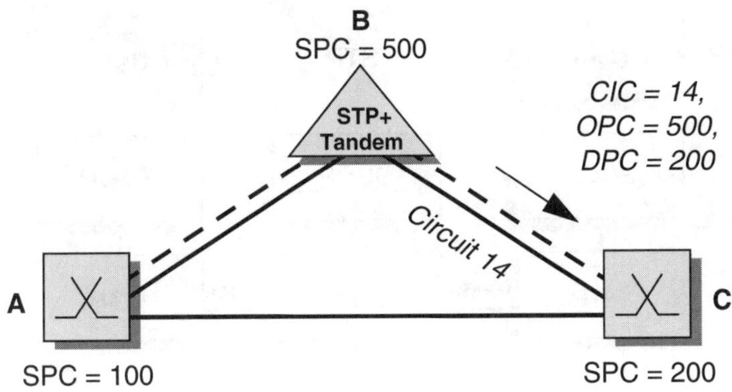

Figure E.3.8. Label parameters between B and C

Traffic case 2: With SCP and SCCP

Example: Setting up a telephone call of the 800 type (reverse-charge call) or other IN-based services.

In this case there is no traffic circuit to D, which means that the SCCP protocol must be used.

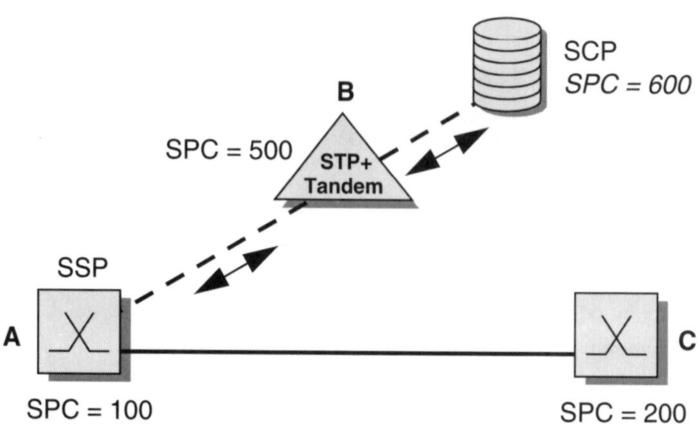

Figure E.3.9 Signalling between SSP and SCP

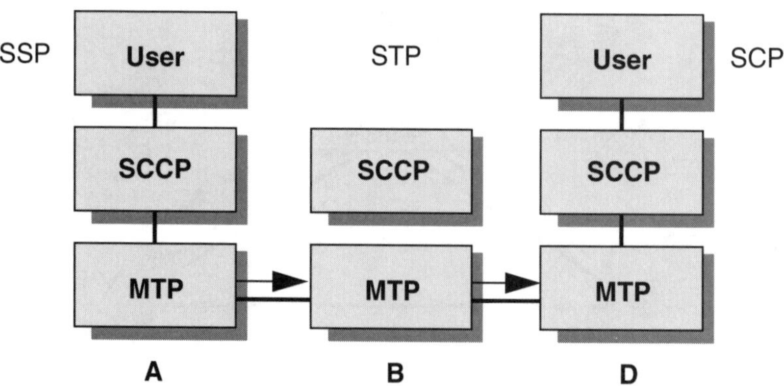

Figure E.3.10 Signalling by means of SCCP

What is the situation at point A in this case? A is an SSP that creates a message in OSI layer 7. The message is sent on to the SCCP, which makes a global-title translation to be able to select a suitable SCP. The result of the analysis is SPC = 600. The SCCP now hands the message over to the MTP, and the complete MSU will then be sent onwards by the STP without any of its values being changed. When the message reaches the SCP, it is analysed as a terminating message. An analysis of the SSN will give the type of SCCP user. See *Figure E.3.11*.

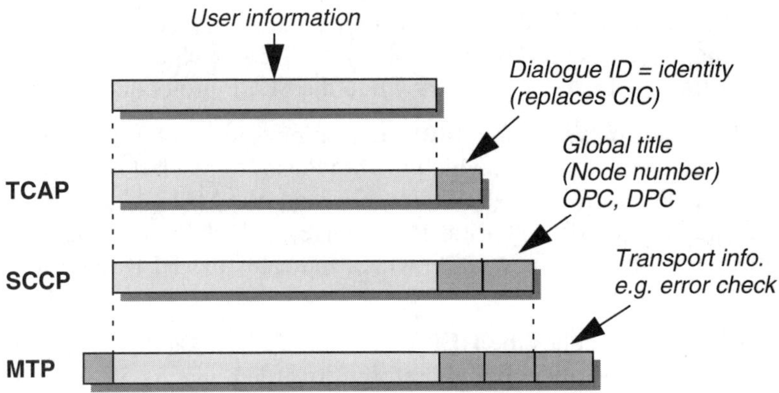

Figure E.3.11. TCAP, SCCP and MTP relationships

Since there is no physical relationship with a traffic circuit in this case, there is no CIC either. (Instead, there is a dialogue identity in the TCAP protocol.)

Traffic case 3: With HLR and SCCP

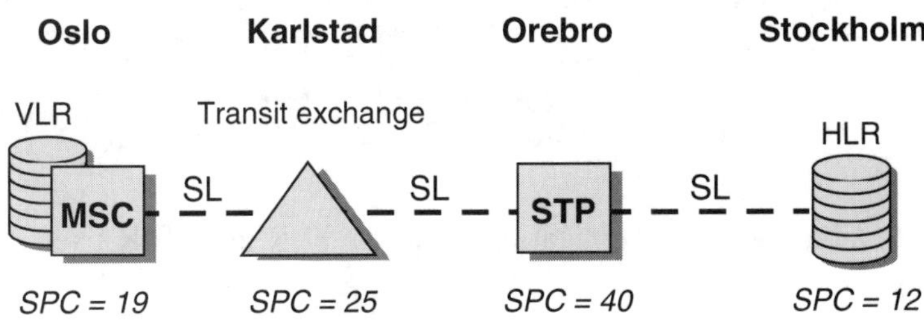

Figure E.3.12. Registration (location updating)

Example: Registration of a mobile subscriber's new location (in roaming).

Let's assume that a GSM mobile terminal (MS) has its HLR in Stockholm. At present, this MS is travelling in Norway – right now entering a new location area (LA) near Oslo, which means that the HLR is to be informed about the change. See *Figure E.3.12* and *Figure E.3.13*.

The VLR (SPC = 19) in the new LA uses the VLR-MAP protocol to create the first message of the dialogue: "MS = X in LAI = 5". The message is taken over by the dialogue handling protocol TCAP (transaction capabilities application part, OSI layer 7), which can be regarded as a gateway to the SS7 network. The VLR-MAP message is given a dialogue identity and packed – according to existing protocol rules – by the TCAP, which sends it onwards in the form of a TCAP message down to the SCCP protocol.

The SCCP then makes a global-title translation. The result is routing instructions in the form of a DPC, which the MTP uses to reach the SCCP node in Karlstad (SPC = 25) over the SL. In Karlstad, the MSU is delivered to the SCCP node (the SP and transit exchange), which in turn analyses the address, resulting in a new DPC which indicates the HLR node in Stockholm (SPC = 12).

When the MSU reaches the HLR node, the SCCP finds that the message is to terminate at this node. It is therefore forwarded, via the TCAP, up to the node's HLR-MAP application.

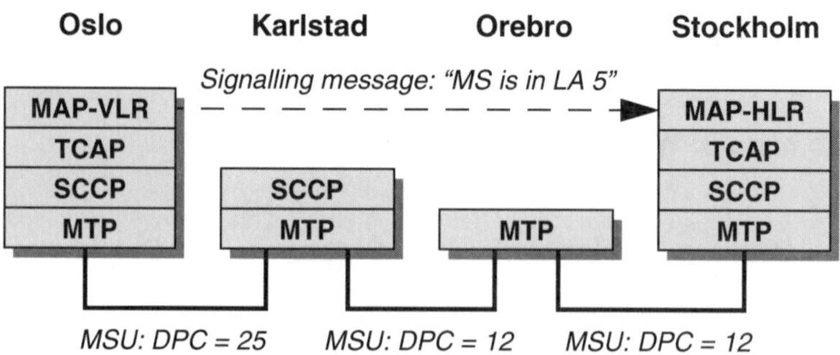

Figure E.3.13. Data communication between VLR and HLR over the SS7 network

In this way, the MSU has been transported through the SS7 network – and in transparent form all the way from the VLR to the HLR – only by means of the NSP.

As the figures show, the MSU also passes a signal transfer point in Orebro (SPC = 40) which only involves the MTP.

What, then, is the situation in Karlstad? This point has an advanced STP function, including both the MTP and the SCCP. From here, the message may be sent onwards because a routing analysis can be made using a global title as input value. See *Figure E.3.14*.

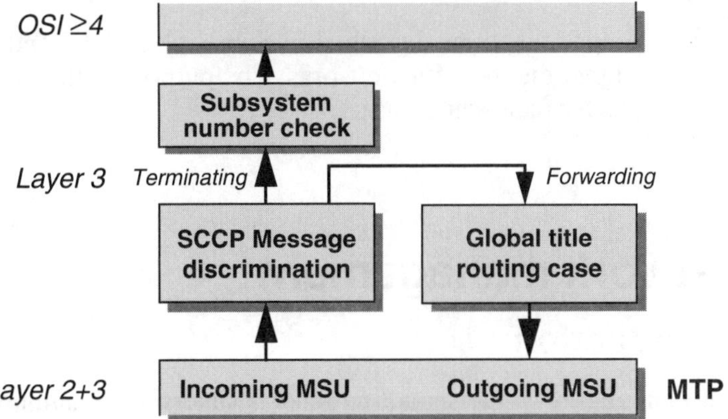

Figure E.3.14. Forwarding by means of the SCCP global title translation

4 Transmission techniques

The SS7 network is normally integrated with ordinary PCM systems for traffic-carrying networks. No special transmission technique is required.

5 Trunk and access networks

Figure E.2.5 shows the connection of SS7 terminals to the transport network. SS7 is just one of many users of the trunk transport network described in Volume 1, Chapter 5.

6 Network intelligence and value-added services

The SS7 signalling network has no centralised functions of the IN type but, as we have seen, it does carry IN traffic between different SSPs and SCPs without using these functions itself.

7 Signalling

The signalling network functions described in Subsections 2.2.3 and 2.2.4 are equivalent to signalling in traffic networks. The purpose is the same: to provide connections for data sent by users.

8 Network management

8.1 Introduction

The transmission quality of the signalling links is supervised continuously. If the quality of a link reaches an unacceptably low level or if the link is unserviceable, signalling traffic is transferred to another link.

The status of the link sets is also supervised. If a link set is no longer able to convey signalling traffic, the traffic on the signalling paths to which the link set belongs will be rerouted to alternative paths, via other link sets. Destinations are also supervised: an alarm is actuated if a destination cannot be reached.

Events recorded by the supervisory functions in a node are reported to the other network nodes, which automatically take the action required to maintain signalling traffic.

Events in the signalling network are reported – through alarms – to the operations staff, thus enabling them to keep a check on the network and to take manual action, should automatic functions prove inadequate in a specific situation. Manual intervention is rare because of the rather small hardware content of an MTP. Besides, such situations need not necessarily be so critical as to require immediate action. Signalling traffic is not affected by isolated hardware faults in the signalling network.

The operating staff are assisted by a number of functions implemented in the MTP, such as signalling terminal test, signalling network monitor and management inhibiting. In normal operation, manual intervention is required only in cases where the configuration of the signalling network is modified on a permanent basis. The staff use commands to change, add or erase data in the network.

Sections 8.2, 8.3 and 8.4 describe examples of supervisory, fault-handling and maintenance facilities provided in SS7 networks.

8.2 Supervision

The SL is a two-way transmission path for signalling between two SPs. Testing and maintenance can be initiated in either of these points.

Since disturbances on an SL may eventually have serious consequences – and even cause an SL to collapse – the SPs have been equipped with automatic supervisory functions. Continuous supervision and routine testing will make it possible to detect any sign of deterioration.

Signalling link functions, such as automatic fault elimination, fault localisation, blocking, alarm generation and recovery, facilitate the work of the operating staff.

8.2.1 Counters

All SLs and signalling terminals are supervised continuously with the aid of disturbance counters:

- signal unit error rate monitor (SUERM), and
- alignment error rate monitor (AERM).

The SUERM is used while an SL is in operation. The AERM is only used during the phase-in procedure; that is, when a link is activated and handshaking takes place. SUERM is incremented each time a signal unit (SU) is rejected by the signalling terminal and decremented after a predetermined number (256) of correct or incorrect SUs have been received. When the counter reaches a threshold value (64), "high error rate" is indicated and the affected SL is taken out of service.

8.2.2 Testing signalling links

To ensure high transmission quality, every SL is tested before it is put into service and at regular intervals while in service.

Test messages are sent on a signalling link every 30 seconds. The signalling terminal in the opposite SP should acknowledge receipt of these messages within 100 ms.

A test message includes a bit pattern that is returned in the acknowledgement message. The bit pattern received must agree with that which was sent. This test method can directly indicate whether functions for access to a link – and signalling on it – are working properly but it cannot trace a fault to a specific part of the signalling path.

The signalling link is indicated as faulty if two consecutive tests give a negative result.

8.2.3 Link status signal

Since the supervisory functions described so far are also performed at the other end of the link, abnormal SL states may be indicated by the opposite SP as well. If the status of an SL changes in an SP, that point can use an LSSU to inform the opposite end of the new status.

8.3 Fault handling

8.3.1 Fault elimination

Once the presence of a fault on an SL has been found to be permanent; that is, when a fault has been indicated by:

- counters in the SP;
- an SL test in the SP;
- other switching equipment in the SP; or
- negative link status signals sent from the opposite SP

then the fault will be eliminated by blocking the link.

8.3.2 Alarms

Before an alarm is actuated, the system tries to activate the blocked SL automatically. If this attempt fails, an alarm is indicated. The table below shows different types of alarm and the appropriate action to be taken in each case.

Type of alarm	Probable cause	Action
SS7 *signalling link failure*	Too many disturbances recorded by the disturbance counter	Check all equipment in the signalling link.
SS7 *link set supervision*	Too few functioning links in the link set	Repair faulty signalling links. Activate functioning signalling links that are not connected.
SS7 *destination inaccessible*	All possible signalling link sets to the destination are faulty. Fault in the signalling point.	

Figure E.8.1 Different types of alarm, causes and actions

8.4 Maintenance facilities

As we have already mentioned, the MTP includes a number of functions for maintenance of the signalling network. Three of these functions are described in the following.

8.4.1 Signalling network monitor

An MTP monitor can be used for recording sent and received MSUs of the MSU-SNM type and for recording the state of the signalling network. The monitor can be used in connection with installation testing and maintenance and for monitoring interworking with other signalling networks.

This monitor should be able to operate in three modes: link set mode, destination mode and combined mode.

Link set mode

All signalling messages of the MSU-SNM type that are related to a specified link set are recorded in this mode.

Destination mode

All MSU-SNMs that are related to the specified destination are recorded in this mode.

Combined mode

Link sets and destinations can be recorded simultaneously; hence the term "combined mode".

The recorded events are printed out on an alphanumeric I/O device after a predetermined number of recordings, when the preset recording period expires or when the monitor is stopped by a command.

8.4.2 Management inhibiting

The management inhibiting function is included in signalling resource management in layer 3, which supervises and controls the signalling resources, that is, the signalling links of the exchange.

To give a user exclusive right to seize an SL in the test phase, traffic from the UP/AP on that link can be inhibited. Inhibition can be ordered by a command and must be accepted by the SPs at both ends.

Note that the SL is taken out of service by transferring the UP/AP traffic to another SL in the link set. This procedure is referred to as *change-over*.

8.4.3 Testing signalling terminals

The purpose of the test function called *signalling terminal test* is to verify the SL's capacity for message transfer and to check the internal maintenance functions of the signalling terminal. The diagnostic test is used in connection with manual intervention by maintenance personnel and is initiated by a command.

The result of the test is a printout – ITU-T NO. 7 SIGNALLING TERMINAL DIAGNOSTIC – which indicates whether the test was passed or not. In the latter case, the fault codes will be the same as in the alarm printout: ITU-T NO. 7 SIGNALLING LINK FAILURE.

8.5 Centralised operation and maintenance

Making changes to a signalling network is a task of great responsibility, considering the large increase in traffic volume and the fact that traffic-carrying networks rely heavily on smooth signalling. Changes that are not correctly made may even cause these networks to go out of service.

The need for changes is created by a number of trends: digitisation of exchanges, reconfiguration of connections, the introduction of new nodes for IN or messaging services and the rapid growth of mobile networks – to mention a few examples. The number of signalling points in the networks is increasing, thus increasing network complexity and the risk of introducing faults.

Faults in a signalling network must be eliminated as soon as possible. (Loss of signalling capacity may have a dramatic effect on the traffic-carrying network's ability to convey traffic and, hence, on the owner's revenues.) A fault in a signalling link generates a number of alarm messages, as each exchange in the traffic-carrying network finds that it cannot communicate over the faulty link. These messages must be analysed quickly to enable detection and elimination of the primary fault that caused the problems.

The network operator must have a powerful management system to be able to handle the signalling network efficiently.

8.5.1 Configuration management

Plans for changes to a signalling network must be based on a correct picture of the present situation. A management system maintains an up-to-date network model, generated on-line from the SPs and updated by alarm and event logs.

When planning the introduction of changes in the configuration of a signalling network, the operator makes a copy (model) of the existing network and modifies it off-line to be able to make simulations. The management system should contain a graphic tool which clearly illustrates the effect of proposed changes.

8.5.2 Fault handling

Fault handling operations are best organised at the network management level, where the operator can "see" the entire network. At this level, the management system filters out the continuous flow of messages from the network and presents them on a multi-window monitor.

Alarms from network elements are received at the element management level in the management system. Loss of SLs, link sets or SPs are reported to this level.

All alarm information is stored in a database, and alarm lists and logs can be studied by maintenance personnel at any time. Alarms and events reported by the network elements are recorded as status changes, which are sent on to the network management level to enable updating of the network configuration.

8.5.3 Load control

The ever-increasing use of the signalling network calls for functions to limit the effect of overload. Two forms of regulation are provided for this purpose. The first concerns each individual SL and means that the receiving end can order the sending end to buffer signalling messages until receiving capacity has been restored. The second concerns the signalling network as a whole and involves checking that signalling traffic can be transported through the network or – if this is not the case – that the traffic can be reduced at the source.

9 Interworking between networks

An increasingly open and deregulated market requires that the network operator should be able to establish interworking with other operators' signalling networks. Situations may also arise where special signalling network operators can sell signalling transport services to operators of the PSTN, ISDN, PLMN and IN – in particular, universal personal telecommunication (UPT) and VPN – for transport of TUP, ISUP, TCAP and so forth.

When we interconnect different logical signalling networks that have separate numbering plans, the SCCP must be included in the interface.

When SS7 networks interwork with channel-associated signalling systems, the exchanges involved operate as gateways. Such transition from old to new technology is quite common, especially in the PSTN. As far as signalling is concerned, this can be described as a stage where rapid and effective packet-switching must interact with slower and more resource-consuming circuit switching, which also has functional limitations.

10 Network planning

10.1 Requirements

The key parameters used when planning a signalling network are

- dependability;
- simple network structure to facilitate network management;
- short delay; and
- reasonable cost.

Dependability is the most important requirement when planning a signalling network. Since the signalling links have large capacity and the signalling traffic is very concentrated, a link fault may have dramatic consequences. High reliability can be achieved in different ways; for example, by adding redundancy to the network in the form of alternative signalling paths.

A simple and manageable network structure is achieved by organising the network in a few hierarchical levels. Besides, a hierarchical structure can easily be extended to meet future demands.

The short delay in setting up a connection is a major advantage of SS7 signalling. A simple network structure and carefully dimensioned signalling links and nodes enable the operator to reduce the delay to less than one second.

Optimal dimensioning also reduces operating costs. On the other hand, the cost factor is not as critical for signalling networks as for traffic-carrying networks.

10.2 Dependability

Because the function of the SS7 network is critical to the operation of traffic-carrying networks, the network is structured so that there will always be at least two separate paths for all signal relationships in the network. In this way, the network will be able to handle traffic even if a fault has occurred.

Prioritisation is a prerequisite for a configuration with alternative signalling paths. *Figure E.10.1* and *Figure E.10.2* illustrate two cases:

- a direct signalling link with alternative routing, and
- load sharing between two STPs (an STP pair).

A link set is used as a resource on the signalling path. The signalling path that has the highest priority is used as long as it is available.

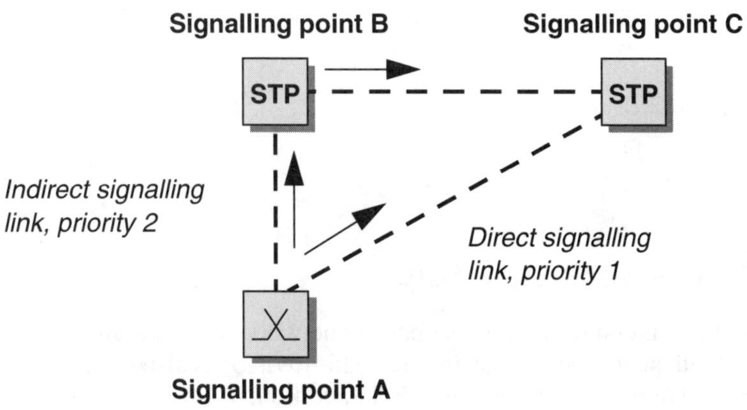

Figure E.10.1. Direct signalling with alternative routing

If two signalling paths have the same priority, signalling traffic is distributed evenly between them (load sharing). In a link set, the traffic is distributed evenly among the signalling links. To ensure smooth signalling even after a fault has occurred, the load on the signalling links must not be too heavy. A recommended standard value is 0.2–0.3 erlangs per link. With this load, the link can take over traffic from another link without becoming overloaded.

The STPs are dimensioned with a redundancy that ensures proper traffic handling even if one of the STPs in a pair goes out of service.

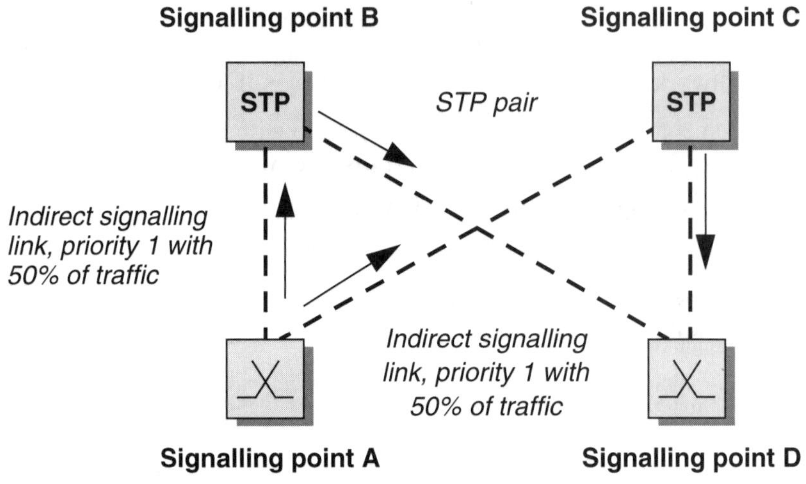

Figure E.10.2 Load sharing

10.3 Network structure

The national and international signalling networks are separated and can be planned independently of one another. This division is also used in the numbering plan of the signalling network. In addition, the numbering plan can be segmented, considering the growing number of operators. See *Figure E.10.3.*

10.3.1 The numbering plan

Every signalling point in a signalling network has a unique number, but the same numbering scheme may be used in other networks, too.

The numbering of signalling points in the international signalling network is completely different from the numbering used in the national signalling networks. If a signalling point belongs to both types of network (an international exchange, for example), a network indicator (NI) will make evident which signalling network the numbering scheme refers to. NIs are used for all signalling points in the networks.

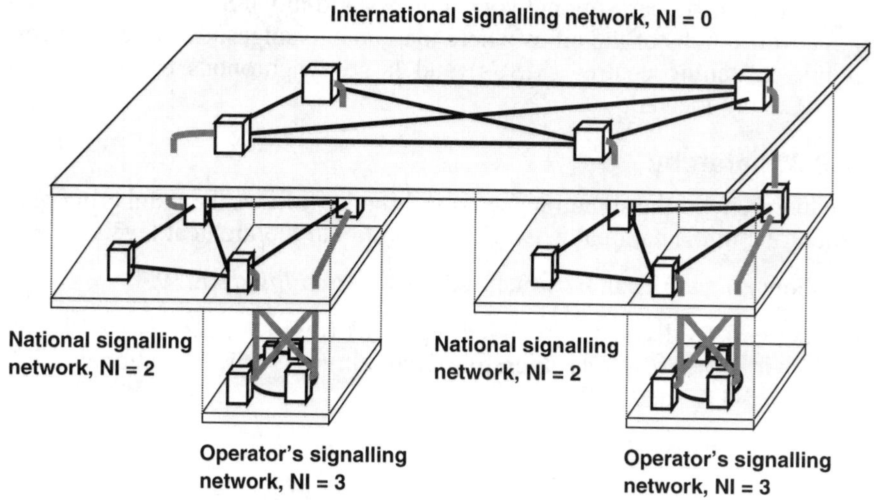

Figure E.10.3. Example of relationship between numbering and network structure

10.3.2 Physical location of STP nodes

As we mentioned in Subsection 3.2.1, two types of STP can be installed in a signalling network:

- an integrated STP, and
- a stand-alone STP.

An integrated STP is usually a tandem or transit exchange equipped with STP functions. This means that only part of the processor capacity (5–10%) can be used for STP functions. The advantage of integrated STPs is their cost-effectiveness and ease of implementation.

Stand-alone STP pairs are used mainly in big cities. Such a pair of nodes can handle the switching of several million PSTN/ISDN subscribers, provided the percentage of IN traffic is normal. If an IN-based number portability service is introduced, IN traffic will be abnormal because even regular calls will need IN support for number translation. This may require a capacity of thousands of translations per second for each city. To handle these situations, the present percentage of stand-alone STPs must be considerably increased.

Even if the number of stand-alone STPs increases, the structure of the SS7 network and the deployment of nodes will agree closely with the configuration of the traffic-carrying network. Large stand-alone STPs will be placed in the traffic hubs of the cities where tandem exchanges, transit exchanges, mobile switching centres (MSCs) and large synchronous cross-connects (SDXCs) are located.

10.3.3 Hierarchy

The hierarchy of the signalling network broadly follows the numbering plan structure, but the national network has additional hierarchical levels.

A national network can be structured as shown in *Figure E.10.4.*

The network is divided into signalling areas (regions), each served by an STP pair. The resulting hierarchy has three levels: 1. national STP; 2. regional STP; and 3. SP.

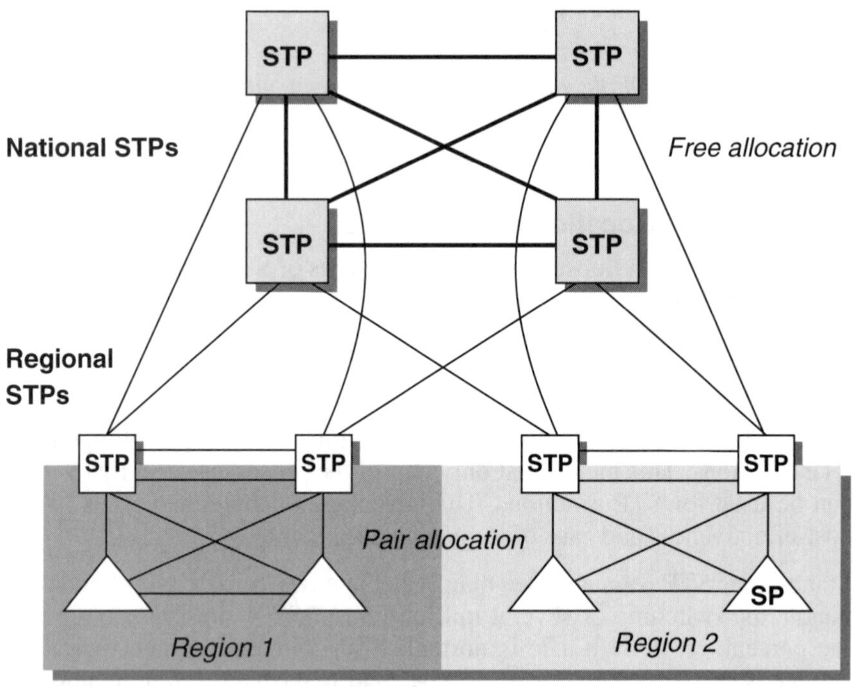

Figure E.10.4. National STP structure

By having STP exchanges at two levels, we can reduce the load on each exchange. In addition, the signalling network will be more robust because a fault in one region will only insignificantly affect the rest of the network.

Each region can be divided into local signalling areas. The connection between two levels – SP to regional STP, or regional STP to national STP – is described in detail in Subsections 10.3.4 and 10.3.5.

Most exchanges would be able to manage with one signalling link, but for security reasons there are always at least two separate links.

10.3.4 Single mate (pair allocation)

In the single-mate structure, all SLs and all STPs are paired. From an SP, two SLs are connected to the STP pair. If an SL is out of service, the other link must be able to handle all traffic. The same principle applies when dimensioning the capacity of STP pairs. Each STP must have the capacity necessary to handle a traffic volume twice the normal value. See *Figure E.10.4* (lower half).

10.3.5 Multiple mate (free allocation)

In the multiple-mate structure, the STPs are arranged in groups of four, for instance. Each STP switches traffic from several regions (or clusters of SPs). Should a fault occur in an STP, the redundancy built into this configuration will distribute to two nodes the traffic that would have been carried by the faulty node alone.

The redundancy required in an STP to cover the loss of another node is the capacity to carry 50% of the maximum signalling traffic in any node. See *Figure E.10.4* (upper half).

10.4 Dimensioning

Traffic in a signalling network consists of the transfer of messages generated by the services that use the network. As we have pointed out, traffic load on the SLs should normally be low.

Dimensioning requires the following information:

- traffic mix PSTN – ISDN, PLMN;
- percentage IN traffic;
- number of MSUs and their length in PSTN, ISDN, PLMN and IN connections;

- call intensity on traffic routes served; and
- degree of utilisation of SLs (maximum value).

10.5 Result of network planning

The network planning should produce the following information:

- location of STPs;
- integrated or stand-alone STPs;
- link set allocation;
- number of SLs in each link set;
- expected traffic in each STP;
- expected traffic on each SL;
- routing tables; and
- expected delay values and bit error ratio.

Part F1 – X.25

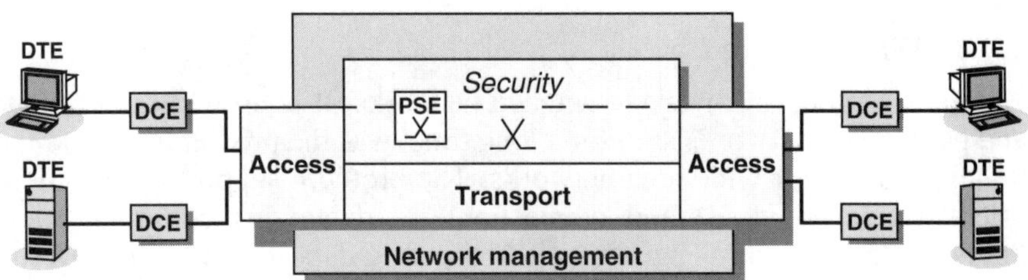

Figure F1.0.1 Reference model

1 User services and terminals

1.1 Introduction

1.1.1 What is X.25?

X.25 is a protocol for packet-switched networks. It is used in both private and public data networks and, for a long time, was the predominant international standard for wide area networks. The protocol supports connection-oriented (conventional) and connectionless (datagram) communication. Public X.25 networks – packet switched public data networks (PSPDN) – have been installed all over the world. Telia's X.25 service in Sweden is called Datapak.

1.1.2 What is packet switching?

In packet switching, user data is divided into packets of varying length, and each packet is assigned an address and the necessary control information.

To achieve high transfer quality, the packets are placed in *frames*. Each frame that is sent over a particular link is saved in a buffer until its information has been checked and the frame has been approved by the receiving node or subscriber. The fact that each node stores the packets in a buffer leads to delays, but information arrives at its user uncorrupted (no bit errors).

The method is referred to as *store and forward,* because each node first stores the packets then sends them forward. The packet handling performed by the nodes consists primarily of checking the packet format, selecting an outgoing path, checking for errors, and waiting for available outgoing path capacity.

See also Volume 1, Chapter 2, Subsection 2.10.8.

1.1.3 Network structure

Figure F1.1.1 shows the basic structure of a packet-switched network.

The user's data terminal equipment (DTE) is connected to the data circuit terminating equipment (DCE), which serves as an adapter to the line. The network includes a number of packet switching exchanges (PSEs). In many cases, these exchanges are interconnected by direct links, thus forming an "all-to-all" configuration. The network's overall control functions are performed by a network management centre (NMC).

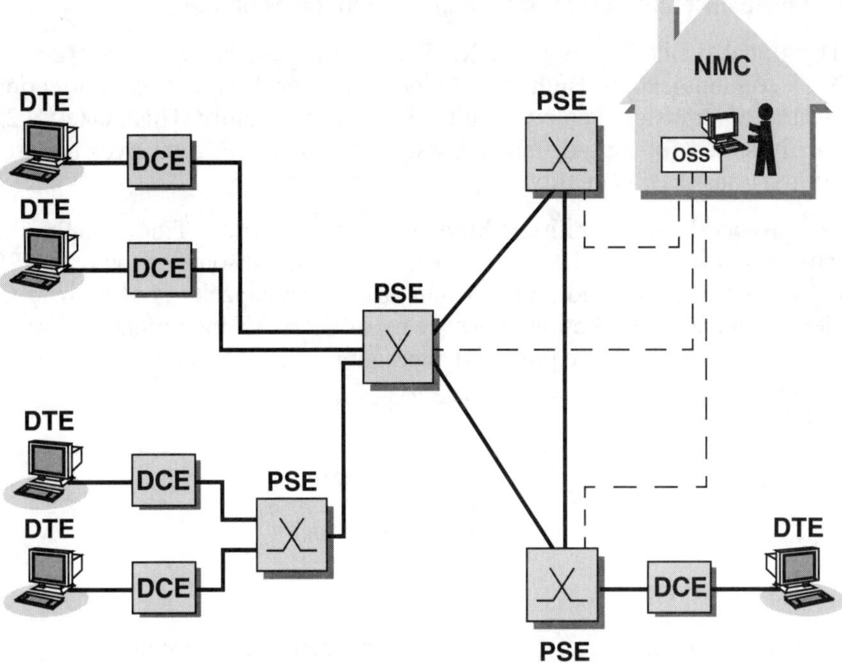

Figure F1.1.1 Basic structure of a packet-switched network

1.2 Features and performance

Packet switching was developed during the 1960s and 1970s as a complement to the telephony-oriented, circuit-switched PSTN. The virtual circuit established (in the case of connection-oriented communication) between users in a packet-switched network only makes use of transmission resources (bandwidth) when information is actually being transferred. On the other hand, a circuit-switched connection reserves a fixed bandwidth for the entire duration of the connection, regardless of whether or not information is being transferred.

As a result, packet-switched networks make more efficient use of available capacity simply because several users are able to share the total available bandwidth.

An advantage of X.25 – as compared to data communication in circuit-switched networks – is that data can be sent to more than one receiver at the same time. Packet switching also enables communication between terminals that have different transfer rates and different types of interface.

The global availability of public X.25 networks is another factor that favours X.25 communication. Built-in functions for error detection and correction ensure safe transfer even on circuits of rather low quality. This makes X.25 ideally suited for long-distance, bursty data communication over links of limited transmission quality.

The protocol's applicability is limited by the bandwidth. Traditionally, the maximum bandwidth of X.25 has been 64 kbit/s, but some of today's X.25 networks use a bandwidth of 2 Mbit/s. Even that capacity is often insufficient for the interconnection of private networks (LAN interconnect). Frame relay and ATM are more powerful alternatives for such interconnection.

1.2.1 X.25 in brief

Transfer mode:	Packet mode
Maximum switched bandwidth:	~2 Mbit/s
Type of service:	Data
Type of circuit:	Permanent virtual circuit Switched virtual circuit
UNI signalling:	X.25
NNI signalling:	Internal network protocol; X.75 between X.25 networks
Mobility:	X.25 in mobile networks
Support for Internet:	Yes

Figure F1.1.2 Brief description of X.25

1.3 User services

X.25 can be used for setting up two types of virtual connection: switched virtual circuit (SVC) – often called virtual circuit (VC) – and permanent virtual circuit (PVC). An SVC connection is set up using the B-number dialled by the calling subscriber, while the set-up information necessary for a PVC is permanently stored in the nodes. A third variant is *datagram*, which is a connectionless service.

X.25 networks are used in a large number of applications, such as:

- information retrieval in national and international databases;
- traffic from terminals to a mainframe (transaction processing);
- file transfer;
- electronic mail; and
- automatic teller machines and card-operated petrol pumps.

X.25 is used primarily by companies and institutions.

1.4 Terminals and network connection elements

A number of more or less complex types of terminal can be connected to an X.25 network. Each connection is represented by an addressable port in the data network. Examples of terminals or network connection elements include:

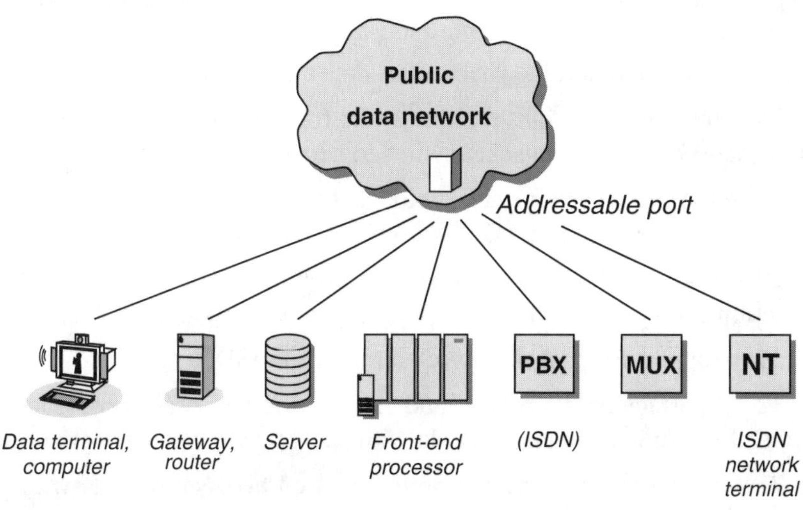

Figure F1.1.3 Examples of X.25 data terminal equipment (DTE) points

- computer;
- server;
- front-end processor;
- PBX;
- gateway to another network;
- subscriber multiplexer;
- cluster with dumb terminals; and
- protocol converter, for example, packet assembler/disassembler (PAD) or black boxes.

2 Standards

2.1 Introduction

2.1.1 Standards for packet-switched networks

The CCITT (currently the ITU-T) started work on the standardisation of packet-switching technology in the early 1970s and published its first X.25 recommendation in 1976. X.25 is one of many recommendations that deal with packet traffic for both asynchronous and synchronous access:

- X.3 – PAD function for asynchronous data equipment
- X.25 – Interface functions and protocols for the connection of synchronous data equipment in packet-switched networks
- X.28 – Interface functions and protocols for the connection of asynchronous data equipment to PAD functions in packet-switched networks
- X.29 – Procedure for the exchange of control information between a PAD function and synchronous data equipment in packet-switched networks
- X.31 – Support for packet-network terminals in ISDN
- X.32 – Interface between DTE and circuit-switched equipment (such as DCE) for terminals interconnected with packet-switched networks
- X.75 – Interface functions and protocols used between packet-switched networks

The following recommendations are jointly applicable to X.25 and other types of network:

- X.1 – List of transfer-rate classes
- X.2 – List of subscriber services
- X.87 – Design of subscriber classes
- X.96 – Status signals
- X.110 – Routing principles
- X.121 – Numbering plan
- X.180 – Administrative routines for closed user groups

2.2 ITU-T Recommendation X.25

X.25 is essentially the protocol for synchronous transmission across the DTE/DCE interface. The network's task is to transmit packets in the correct order and to the correct address.

The network serves a large number of subscribers, so ensuring the "correct order" and finding the "correct address" will be a central task for the exchanges (PSEs) that route the packets through the network. This means that the PSEs must also follow the rules of packet handling in X.25. In other words, the protocol will primarily be the concern of a DTE and its PSE. In addition to the packet handling functions, charging functions must also be provided for public virtual circuits between PSEs in the network.

Figure F1.2.1 X.25 seen as an interface protocol between DTE and DCE

In Recommendation X.25, layers are organised according to the OSI model. The recommendation describes three layers:

- Layer 1: The interface to the physical layer, DTE/DCE. X.21 and X.31 are suitable for use as layer 1.
- Layer 2: The link layer which defines the data flow over a link in the network and guarantees error-free transmission.

- Layer 3: The network layer (also called the packet layer) which defines the addressing and packaging of messages.

The division of X.25 into layers was one of the foundations of the OSI model. It is therefore logical that the three layers in X.25 are almost identical with the three lowest layers of that model.

Figure F1.2.2 shows a network-based application of the X.25 layers.

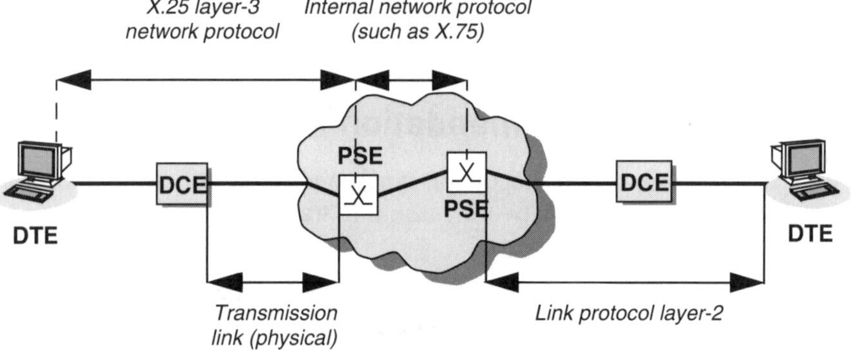

Figure F1.2.2 X.25 as a protocol between packet-handling units in the data network

To further clarify the division into layers, we will study the procedure for transmitting data in packets. The user equipment segments the information into suitable lengths for packets and provides the packets with a label containing an address or a logical channel number. Each user can be connected to several other subscribers in the network through one or more PSEs, as shown in *Figure F1.2.3*. Because the information is divided into packets, several users can employ the same link. Each interface may be said to have several logical channels.

The basic prerequisites for data transfer are:

- a bit stream on the physical circuit;
- a bit-transfer structure that enables the parties at both ends of the circuit to agree on when information bits, control bits, and the like should be sent (frame structure); and
- a method of packaging and addressing the information.

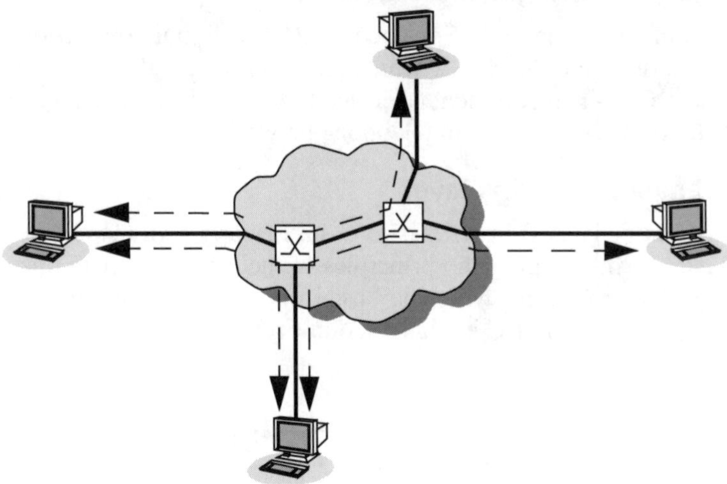

Figure F1.2.3 Any user in a packet-switched data network can simultaneously communicate with several other users

This explains the technical considerations behind the division into layers. Layer 1 gives a basic bit stream on the physical circuit; layer 2 divides the bit stream into manageable frames; and layer 3 allocates this physical circuit to a number of logical channels ("dynamic multiplexing").

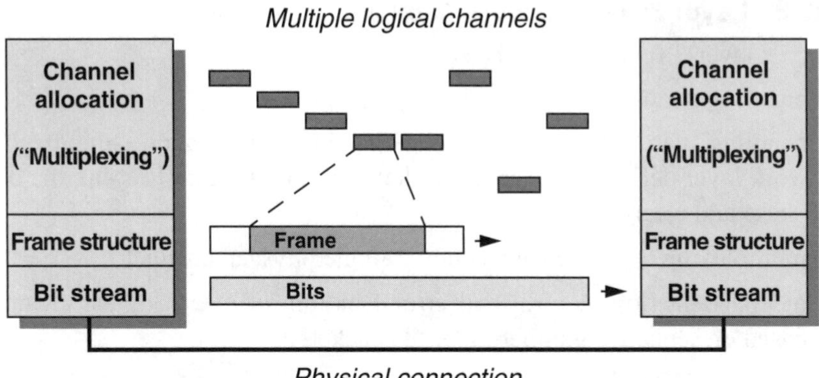

Figure F1.2.4 Logical channels in X.25

2.2.1 Layer 1: The physical layer

X.25 recommends the use of protocol X.21 for digital connections. If the transfer is not digital, X.21*bis* – which permits use of a V-interface between DTE and DCE – is recommended instead. X.21*bis* in data networks corresponds to the V.24 interface in telephone networks.

2.2.2 Layer 2: The link layer

The function of layer 2 in X.25 is to ensure error-free transport of packets from layer 3. X.25 applies the principles of the high level data link control (HDLC) link procedure, which is based on an ISO standard. The frame structure formed in HDLC is illustrated in *Figure F1.2.5*.

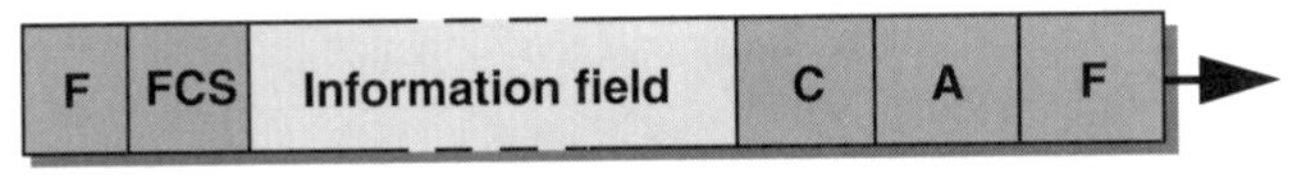

F = flag, FCS = frame check sequence, C = check, A = address

Figure F1.2.5 Frame structure in HDLC

The information field is used by data packets from layer 3. Only one packet can be transported in each frame. The flow control function in layer 2 is primarily intended for the link between a DTE and the PSE to which the DTE is connected. The frames are separated by one or more eight-bit flags.

2.2.3 Layer 3: The network layer

X.25's layer-3 functions can be summarised as follows:

- handling permanent virtual circuits;
- handling switched virtual circuits with point-to-point addressing; the network layer defines the various packet types used for call set-up, the data phase and clearing;
- multiplexing logical channels into a single physical channel;
- independent flow control and error handling of every logical channel, based on sequence numbering of the packets;
- transfer of interrupts;
- exchange of packet-size information between two DTEs.

Dynamic multiplexing is the method used to multiplex logical channels. Each virtual connection is assigned a logical channel number which identifies all packets belonging to that connection. The number consists of two parts, channel groups 0–15 and channel numbers 0–255, allowing a total of 4,096 possible logical channels.

2.2.4 Packet design and packet length

The design of a layer-3 packet depends on its contents (call request, call accept/connect, clear request, clear confirm, data packet). For layout and packet format, see *Figure F1.2.6*.

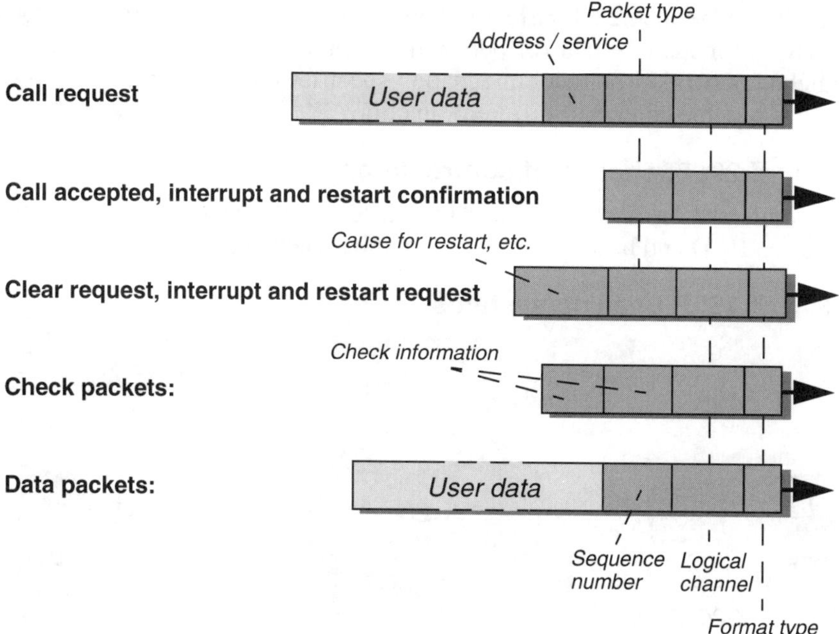

Figure F1.2.6 Example of packet design

The possible values for packet size are indicated as a number of octets. All X.25 networks must be able to offer "modulo 128", which is equal to a length of 128 octets, but considerably longer packets (about 1,000 octets) have been specified.

2.3 Other basic ITU-T recommendations for packet traffic

2.3.1 X.3: The PAD function

Asynchronous terminals must be connected via a PAD (see Chapter 5, Section 5.3). Recommendation X.3 ("The PAD function for asynchronous data equipment") describes 18 alternative parameter functions for such connections.

2.3.2 X.28: Interface functions

Recommendation X.28 describes the procedure for communication between an asynchronous terminal (or personal computer) and a PAD in a packet-switched network. The recommendation specifies transfer rates, set-up procedures and the control of different functions.

2.3.3 X.29: Exchange of control information

Recommendation X.29 describes how a terminal connected to X.25 can control a PAD and how data is exchanged between units.

2.3.4 X.75: Signalling systems

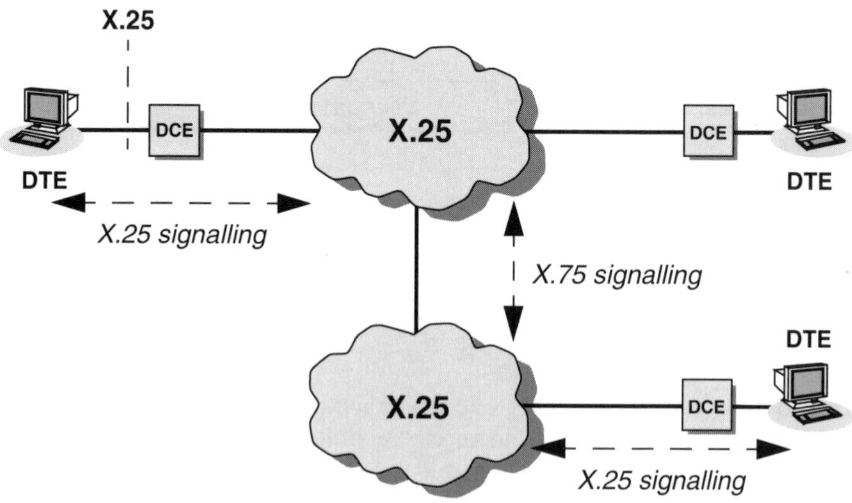

Figure F1.2.7 Packet switching over several data networks based on ITU-T Recommendation X.75

Recommendation X.75 deals with the interface functions and protocols used for signalling between packet-switched data networks. The main difference between a call request sent between DTEs in the network layer (X.25) and a call request that passes through two networks is the information contents of the call-request packets.

3 Switching and switch control

3.1 General

Switching and switch control are described in Volume 1, Chapter 3, Section 3.4. As we mentioned in Chapter 1, packet-switched networks use the store and forward method, which means that the whole frame is received before it is sent on.

3.2 Switching in X.25

Packets can be transmitted over VC and PVC connections (see Chapter 1, Section 1.3).

Virtual circuit

When a call is made over a VC, the nodes select the links to be used for the logical channel. Information on how to route the frames is stored in all nodes throughout the set-up phase. A VC is connected only for the duration of the actual transfer of data. After that, the information in the network is erased.

Permanent virtual circuit

Information on how the frames are to be transported between two subscribers in the network can also be permanently stored in the nodes, making a PVC. In this case, a subscriber need not state the B-subscriber's subscriber number before each transfer of data, because the B-subscriber already has a dedicated logical channel.

3.2.1 Logical channels

When a DTE is connected to a packet network, a number of logical channels are allocated to it. The channels are divided into 16 groups, at most, each group containing up to 256 channels. This means that 4,096 channels are available for communication. In practice, every DTE is given several channel numbers in one or more channel groups. When data is transferred over VCs, specific channel numbers and channel group numbers are allocated for use by all packets included in that transfer.

3.2.2 Example of hardware structure in a packet node

In principle, the exchanges in a packet network are computers with software and input/output devices for the connection of subscribers and lines.

In the example we are using here, the hardware has the modular structure shown in *Figure F1.3.1* and can be adapted to different capacity requirements. The main components are communication processor units, with computer modules and line modules, and a storage module. The computer modules in the exchange communicate over an inter-computer bus.

Each computer module controls a specific line module. For reliability, the exchanges are designed as communication processor units containing two computer modules (CMs) each plus the associated line modules (LMs). If traffic handling is disturbed, one of the computer modules can control the traffic through both line modules in the communication processor unit.

A PSE in a public network consists of at least one communication processor unit and one storage module. Up to 16 processor units (32 computer modules) can be interconnected in a PSE. If the exchange has more than one communication processor, one of them is master and handles central functions, such as:

- supervision of all processors;
- fault reporting;
- exchange configuration data; and
- automatic switch-over of the function for line-module control in case of computer malfunction.

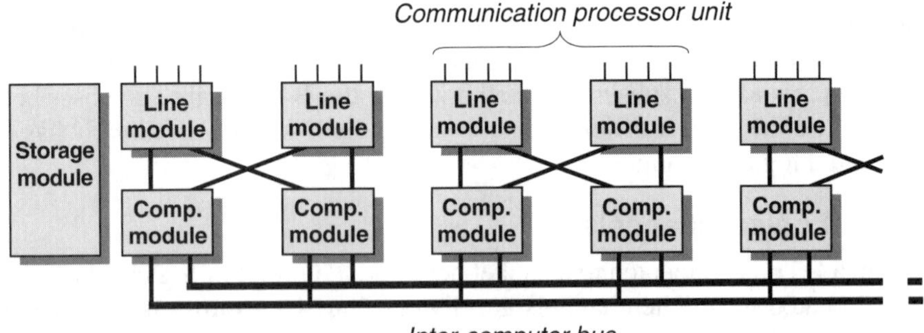

Figure F1.3.1 Hardware modules in a possible packet switching exchange

4 Transmission techniques

Two-wire, baseband communication on paired cable is a common method for transmission between a DCE and a PSE at low bit rates. Depending on the cable type and bit rate, the distance is limited to 10–20 kilometres. Modems are used for longer distances, and PCM channels for higher bit rates.

5 Trunk and access networks

5.1 General

In this chapter, we describe briefly the trunk and access networks for X.25 applications. The description applies mainly to public X.25 networks (PSPDNs).

5.2 Trunk network

The trunk network consists of the physical circuits that interconnect the switching nodes in a network. Normally, X.25 uses the common transport network as trunk network. X.25 circuits always occupy a number of time slots in PCM systems, in which other time slots are used for other logical networks, such as PSTN and ISDN.

The original structure of X.25 networks was "flat", with nodes at a single hierarchical level. Today, networks with special transit exchanges and international exchanges are more common.

5.3 Subscriber line

Terminals (DTEs) can be connected to an X.25 network in different ways. A subscriber may have his own direct line or a leased line to the PSE. Alternatives include physical connection of terminals through the PSTN or ISDN.

Synchronous terminals are connected according to the X.25 protocol, while asynchronous terminals are connected according to X.28. Because asynchronous terminals have no packet-handling functionality, PAD functions (a special type of network function) must be used for packet assembly and disassembly.

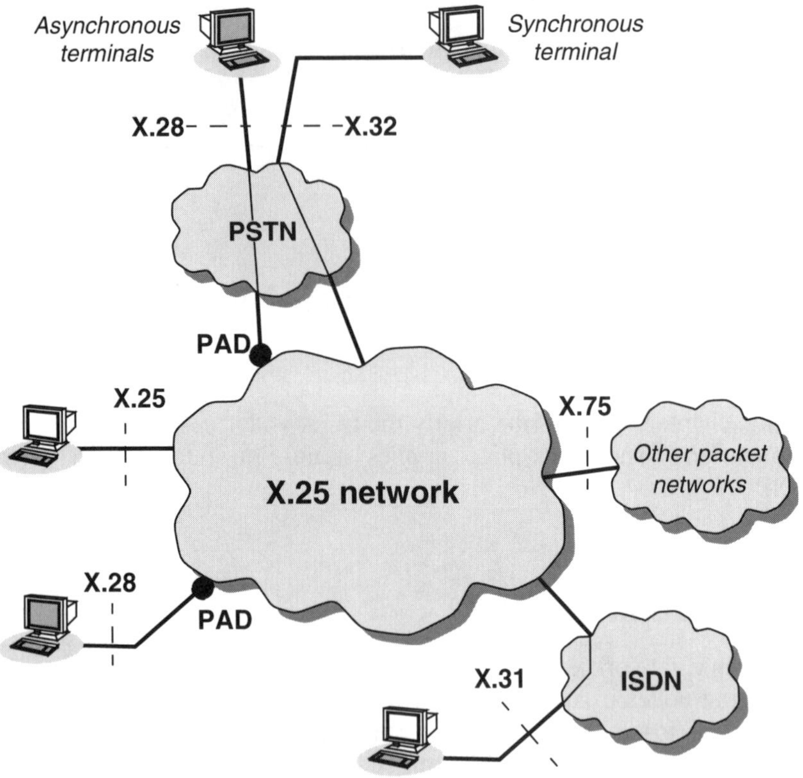

Figure F1.5.1 Paths for connecting terminals to an X.25 network

6 Network intelligence and value-added services

6.1 Network intelligence in X.25 networks

Unlike the PSTN, ISDN and PLMN, X.25 networks have no separate IN nodes. Hence, "network intelligence" in the sense of nodes is not applicable to X.25. However, intelligence is being added to X.25 nodes to facilitate the introduction of more services.

6.2 Supplementary services

Supplementary services in X.25 networks include:

- closed user groups to prevent unauthorised calls;
- group numbers;
- subaddressing;
- barring of incoming or outgoing calls;
- reverse charging; and
- services that reject unauthorised users, such as calling address validation, access identification and secure dial-back.

6.3 Value-added services

X.25 networks are used for information retrieval from databases and for electronic mail applications, such as those specified in Recommendation X.400.

7 Signalling

7.1 Introduction

There is a striking similarity between the call set-up procedures used in public data networks and those used in public telephone networks. Connection-oriented data networks must also be able to:

- identify subscribers as free or busy;
- react to calls and acknowledge them;
- receive selection information (the B-subscriber's address);
- set up connections through the network;
- attract the B-subscriber's attention;
- monitor traffic in progress;
- release the connection once communication ceases; and
- prepare and store charging data.

However, the need for signalling is greater in a data network than in a telephone network. Signals are required to identify the type of terminal, to synchronise the bit rate at both ends of the connection and to identify the beginning and end of characters or character sequences.

While data networks require more signalling, they also permit us to design more signals. This means that we can introduce a number of extra signals in data networks, such as information showing the cause of an unsuccessful set-up attempt.

7.2 Signalling packets

Signalling packets and ordinary message packets have the same basic design: they consist of a header, an information field and a control part. The information in the header determines whether it is a signalling packet or a message packet.

The following are examples of signalling packets:

- call request;
- call accept;
- ready to receive packets;
- cannot receive any more packets;
- clear request;
- clear confirmation;
- error messages;
- interrupt request; and
- restore sequence counter.

7.3 An example of traffic processing

Figure F1.7.1 shows two subscribers connected to separate PSEs in a packet-switched network. The routing information contained in each node determines the route selection.

The signalling diagram in *Figure F1.7.2* shows how the packets are exchanged. After the *call* packet has reached PSE 1, a route for all packets in the session (that is, the virtual connection) is selected. Then the *call* packet is sent on to DTE B, which responds by sending a *call accept* packet. The transfer of data packets can then start.

PSE 1
PSE 2
DTE A
DTE B

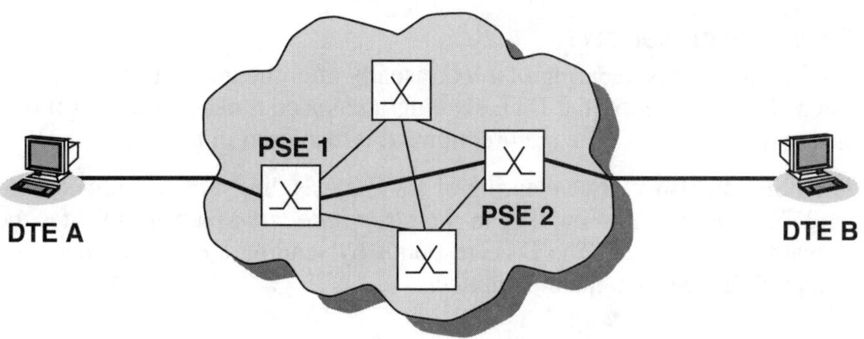

Figure F1.7.1 Subscribers A and B connected to separate PSEs

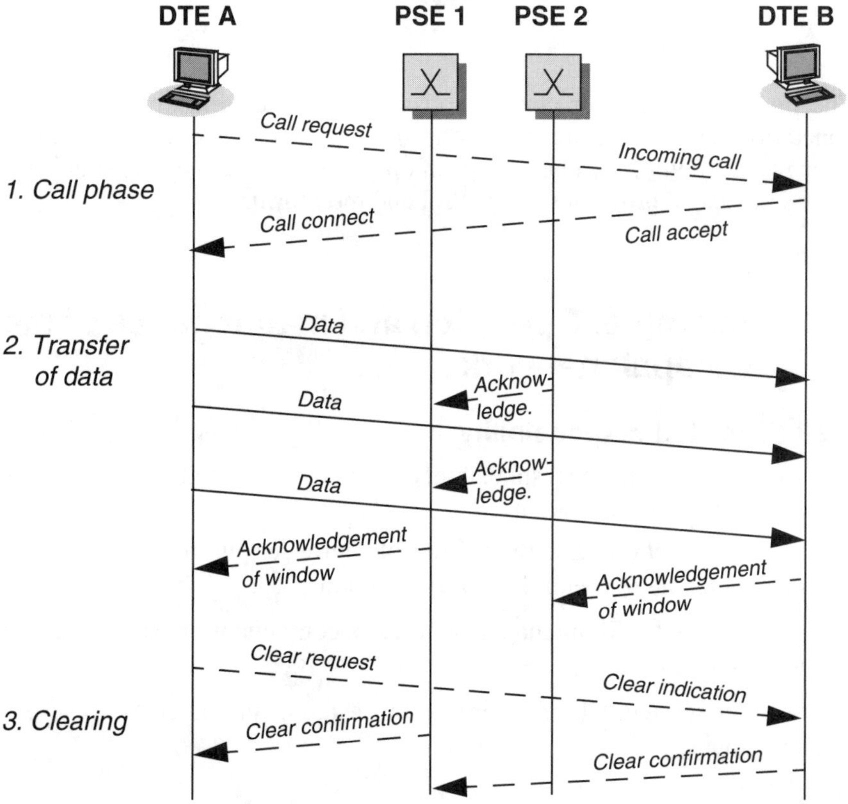

DTE A
PSE 1
PSE 2
DTE B
1. Call phase
Call request
Incoming call
Call connect
Call accept
2. Transfer of data
Data
Acknow-ledge.
Data
Acknow-ledge.
Data
Acknowledgement of window
Acknowledgement of window
3. Clearing
Clear request
Clear indication
Clear confirmation
Clear confirmation

Figure F1.7.2 Example of signalling and data transfer between two subscribers (window = maximum number of sent frames not yet acknowledged)

Clearing

Clearing at packet level

A DTE can request clearing of a VC, usually after the transfer of data is finished. This is done by the DTE sending a *clear* command in the form of a *clear request* packet. The *clear* command is also used in fault situations.

The PSE can also initiate clearing of a VC by sending a *clear indication* to the DTE. The channel number in the *clear indication* packet indicates the channel to be cleared. The DTE responds by sending a *clear confirmation* packet with the same channel number.

8 Network management

8.1 General

The traditional term for control and supervision of telecom networks is "operation and maintenance". Today the term "network management" is often used to denote the classic type of operation and maintenance but it also covers advanced processes for control and monitoring.

8.2 Example: Operation and maintenance of the Datapak network

8.2.1 Areas of responsibility

Three important areas of responsibility have been assigned to the operation and maintenance organisation:

- The NCC function: A network control centre serving the entire country and responsible for central network functions.
- Network service: Maintenance of network components, customer circuits and exchanges (PSEs).
- Customer service: Claims, elimination of faults and other forms of customer contact.

NCC function

The Datapak network is designed for centralised supervision. In brief, the main NCC functions include:

- monitoring the operating status of the network;
- deciding on actions that affect the operating status of the entire network;
- following up events in the network and mapping disturbances; and
- checking that service goals are attained.

The work is organised in two main areas: operation and monitoring and an expert function for fault analysis.

The network service function

The individual telecom areas are responsible for the network service function. The operative responsibility for Datapak PSEs, including circuits, modems and customer premises equipment, is delegated to specific personnel. The PSE personnel perform all fault locating and elimination. Work on serious faults or faults that affect several telecom areas is coordinated with the NCC function. The responsibilities of the PSE personnel are as follows.

- Connect new customers. Line up and reconfigure circuits.
- Supervise (during normal business hours) the PSE's own customers, exchange equipment and circuits to other exchanges.
- Troubleshoot and correct network faults. Report major repair assignments – which may require a concerted effort and particular care to secure the operation of other network functions – to the NCC.
- Participate in troubleshooting and repair work initiated by the NCC.
- Staff exchanges when major modifications are made to the network.

Maintenance functions must be readily available in the daytime. Outside normal business hours, fault-corrective measures must be initiated within two hours. To assist them in their work, the maintenance personnel will use a log describing planned actions and recording events and corrective measures. Other means of support are documents (such as system descriptions), alarm printers, operation terminals, line monitors and cable testers.

Every telecom area also has an organisation for local operations support. This organisation will:

- assist in the elimination of faults at the subscribers' or in the network;
- communicate with central support functions and the NCC function;
- plan local corrective action;
- monitor in-service performance; and
- prepare operating reports.

The customer service function

Customer service is a centralised function. The following are examples of tasks performed by this function.

- Monitor operations related to customer service.
- Register complaints and collect information related to such complaints.
- Analyse and delimit faults.
- Delegate fault-correcting tasks to personnel with the necessary competence.
- Provide customers with information about fault-corrective measures taken, and report on the completion of such measures.
- Provide customers with technical support in cooperation with the NCC. This requires personnel with a thorough knowledge of customer applications and customer systems.

The handling of customers' complaints has high priority and forms the basis of good service, while it wins users' trust in network functions. The customer service function is always responsible for the correction of faults, regardless of which departments take part in the corrective work.

8.2.2 Central operations support

Central operations support is made available if the resources provided by the local operations support and the expert group of the NCC function are inadequate. The expert group and the central operations support function decide jointly whether external operations support from the supplier is necessary.

8.2.3 External operations support

Agreements signed with equipment suppliers for the provision of external operations support usually contain rules stipulating the procedures for fixing hardware and software, for consulting personnel with broad knowledge of systems or expertise when introducing new program versions, when changing system components or when connecting key customers to the network.

9 Interworking between networks

9.1 Introduction

Interworking between networks is described in detail in Volume 1, Chapter 9. Hence, we confine ourselves here to a description of how the role of X.25 networks has changed over the past decade.

9.2 X.25 and other networks

Originally, the main purpose of public X.25 networks was to permit the transfer of data over great distances. In the 1970s and 1980s, X.25 networks usually served as backbone networks as well. Users were offered access either directly by means of X.25 or through other networks (such as the PSTN and ISDN). (See Chapter 5, Section 5.3, *Figure F1.5.1*.)

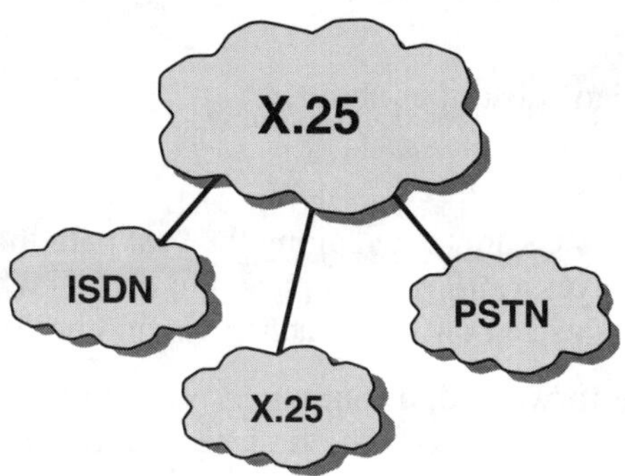

Figure F1.9.1 X.25 used as a backbone network in the 1970s and 1980s

Since the early 1990s, the use of X.25 as a backbone network has been declining, while the use of frame relay and ATM networks is rising.

10 Network planning

10.1 Types of X.25 network

Both private and public X.25 networks have been installed. As we mentioned previously, X.25 has the two categories of switched virtual circuits and permanent virtual circuits. In a public network, SVC is the standard category, while PVC is more of an alternative to leased circuits.

10.2 Fundamental technical plans

10.2.1 Numbering plan

The numbering plan used in X.25 networks adheres to ITU-T Recommendation X.121, which describes the format for addressing in public circuit-switched and packet-switched data networks. The format consists of four parts containing a total of up to 15 digits.

<PREFIX><DCC><NETWORK CODE><NTN>

- PREFIX is the first digit and indicates an international call
- DCC is the data country code
- NETWORK CODE indicates a specific network in the country of destination
- NTN is the dialled subscriber number

10.2.2 Routing plan

Calls over ordinary VCs are routed along the best path through the network. When the PSE receives a *call request* packet, it checks whether the recipient is connected locally or can only be reached via another PSE.

If the call must be forwarded, a routing case is activated – that is, a list of possible routes to the addressee. The first item on the list is the first-choice route, while the rest are called alternative routes and are used only in the event of a link fault or high traffic load.

Once a route has been selected, the *call request* packet is sent onwards, and a connection is set up. All packets in the message will follow the selected route through the network. One or more physical connections can be used between two PSEs. A multilink procedure (MLP) can be invoked to distribute the packets among several connections to equalise traffic load.

10.2.3 Charging plan

To illustrate the use of charging plans, we will study the price structure of Telia's X.25 service, Datapak. The cost of a "Unidata Datapak" subscription is divided into a non-recurrent fee, a periodic subscription fee and traffic-dependent fees.

Non-recurrent fee

The amount of the non-recurrent fee will depend on the mode of connection and – in the case of X.25 – on the distance class and the bit-rate class selected. The distance class is determined by the distance "as the crow flies" between the customer's connection point and the nearest network node. The following distance classes apply at present (1997): 0–3 kilometres, 3–100 kilometres, and 100 kilometres or more.

Subscription fee

The subscription fee is fixed and charged periodically. Its amount depends on the mode of connection, the distance class and the bit-rate class selected.

Traffic-dependent fee

The traffic-dependent fee consists of a call-request cost, a time-dependent cost and a volume-dependent cost.

- The call-request cost is charged for every request for set-up of a data connection, but subscribers are not charged for set-up attempts that fail due to faults in the network. The cost is the same for all connection modes, bit-rate classes and distances.
- The time-dependent cost is charged for each commenced minute of data transfer. The cost depends on the mode of connection but not bit-rate class or distance if a domestic call; the cost is related to distance for international traffic.
- The volume-dependent cost is proportional to the amount of data transferred. The cost of the Unidata Datapak Basic Service is unrelated to the bit-rate class and distance for traffic within Sweden but depends on distance for international traffic.

For traffic carried by PVC connections in the Unidata Datapak network, the time-dependent, volume-dependent and call-request costs are replaced by a fixed non-recurring fee and a fixed periodic fee.

For supplementary services, users pay a non-recurring fee and a subscription fee. Some services are free of charge.

Part F2 – Frame relay

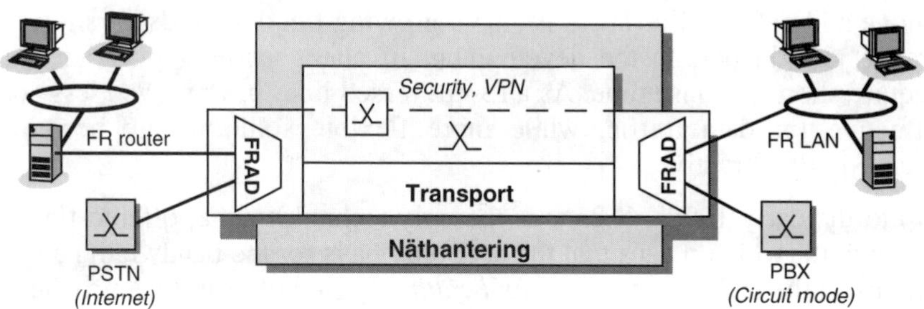

Figure F2.0.1 Reference model

1 User services, terminals

1.1 Introduction

Before the mid-1980s, *leased lines* were the standard solution for networks serving to bridge the geographical distances between a multi-site company's units. Since then there has been a substantial increase in the volumes of telephone and data traffic. There is also a growing trend towards burstier data traffic, due in part to the development of client-server applications that require short response time. As a result, leased lines have proved less cost-effective for data traffic, while more flexible solutions are becoming increasingly attractive.

Up to the early 1990s, X.25 was the only technology that offered flexible bandwidth (which means that the user only pays for the bandwidth he actually uses; the technical term is *bandwidth on demand*). But the introduction of new, sophisticated services demands higher network performance, and this has shown X.25 to be something of a bottleneck, mainly because of its limited transmission capacity – usually 64 kbit/s.

Frame relay was designed to meet the new requirements. One of the reasons for the success this technology met with was its timely launch – just as companies were beginning to look for cheaper and more effective solutions for their private networks.

Today, frame relay is probably the best and most cost-effective bearer network for interconnecting two LANs. The technology is commonly known as "the X.25 of the 1990s" and "a tuned-up version of X.25" but also as "the first international standard for data communication that really works".

The next major frame-relay application is being prompted by the growth of Internet traffic. We might say that frame relay is a very efficient concentrator of "home surfer" traffic over the interface between the PSTN/ISDN and the Internet. See also *Part H – The Internet*, Chapter 5.

The idea behind frame relay is to make optimum use of the flexible bandwidth of the packet-switched network and of the high bit rate and insignificant delay of the circuit-switched network. To achieve this objective, the designers had to sacrifice some functions, for example, functions for error correction and flow control. This makes frame relay best suited for installation in networks with high transmission quality and users who are "disciplined" as far as the generated traffic volume is concerned. The X.25 protocol will continue to be more efficient on circuits with high bit error rates (worse than 10^{-6}). That is why frame relay is usually associated with fibre transmission.

The protocol for frame relay is simple (it is active mainly at the two lowest levels of the open systems integration (OSI) model) with only a small amount of overhead. The transmission capacity is high – ≥2 Mbit/s – because the analyses made in the nodes are simple. A protocol capable of transmitting up to 50 Mbit/s has now been designed.

1.2 Services

The basic frame-relay service is called permanent virtual circuit (PVC). On a PVC, the network management system controls the routing of frames in the nodes. A more advanced service that supports subscriber signalling – switched virtual circuit (SVC) – will be introduced if the market so demands. Supplementary services include services for virtual private networks, access control and the like. (See Chapter 6.)

The good network economy demonstrated by frame-relay networks in LAN-to-LAN communication has resulted in a high rate of installation of these networks in Europe and the US. At the same time, the number of leased lines for LAN-to-LAN traffic is decreasing.

The frame used in frame-relay networks is long enough (<4096 octets) to be able to carry other protocols without these having to be divided into several frames. If we have TCP/IP-based protocols in the LANs connected, several LANs can be perceived as a single network. Frame relay is also suitable for "slower" protocols (such as X.25) and is adaptable to the protocols of the IBM world (such as SNA/SDLC). Frame relay, in turn, can be carried by ATM.

The term *legacy application* is often used to denote a configuration in which frame relay carries SNA, or equivalent, traffic between a front-end processor and a number of terminals or PCs installed in different places. Lately, operators have focused on the possibility of using frame relay for voice, Internet and multimedia communication. Voice communication in frame-relay networks is described in Section 1.4 of this Chapter.

1.2.1 Permanent virtual circuits

PVCs are logical point-to-point connections through the network and, as such, define the structure of the network. The circuits are connected when the customer's network is configured but can be modified later at the customer's request (including adding or disconnecting circuits). The network operator will usually need a couple of working days to introduce such modifications.

The main function of a PVC is to ensure that all its traffic is carried along the same path through the network. This guarantees that the frames will reach their destination in the right order.

Each PVC has only one user. It is not possible to borrow capacity from idle PVCs or to receive information sent on another user's PVC. This way of ensuring integrity is a much-appreciated feature.

However, since all traffic on a PVC follows the same path through the network, the circuits are vulnerable to faults caused by defective links. Many network operators set up backup circuits to be able to offer alternative routes, which, of course, increases the cost of the network.

1.2.2 Switched virtual circuit

In contrast to a PVC, which is a permanent point-to-point circuit, an SVC connection can be set up between any two users. All one needs is an access connection.

A connection initiated by a user is cleared when the data transmission phase is completed. As in the case of an ordinary telephone call, the connection is set up by means of subscriber signalling, which means that we need a numbering plan. Frame Relay Forum recommends E.164 or X.121.

An SVC does not support dial-up access to the frame-relay network. Users must connect their equipment either through fixed access or by setting up connections over ISDN, for example. (See Subsection 5.1.2.)

SVC can be of particular benefit to users whose traffic volume varies frequently and to users who have a fast-growing network. SVC connections make frame relay a highly flexible network.

Other advantages are simpler network management (because the network operator need not predefine all connections) and the possibility of eliminating the cost of redundancy in the form of stand-by PVCs.

Two factors discourage the use of SVCs. Many companies consider SVCs to entail security risks greater than the less flexible PVCs, and PVCs are also a cheaper alternative. Implementing signalling protocols for SVCs in all frame-relay nodes is also rather complicated. Even if one public operator invests in SVC equipment, it does not necessarily follow that other operators will do so, which would be a prerequisite for a universal frame-relay SVC network.

Although SVCs have been defined and available as a service for a long time, their implementation is limited so far. In fact, some experts doubt that public frame-relay operators will find SVCs suitable for implementation in the foreseeable future.

1.3 Terminals, network connection elements

For a user to be able to connect his terminal to a frame-relay network, he needs a frame-relay router, a frame-relay access device (FRAD) or a frame-relay concentrator.

1.3.1 Frame-relay router

As we have already mentioned, LAN-to-LAN communication is a popular frame-relay application. A FRAD in a LAN is usually combined with a router, which contains the specific protocols needed to communicate with a frame-relay network. The other end of the user-network interface (UNI) is equipped with a *frame-relay switch* (also known as a *frame-relay network device*).

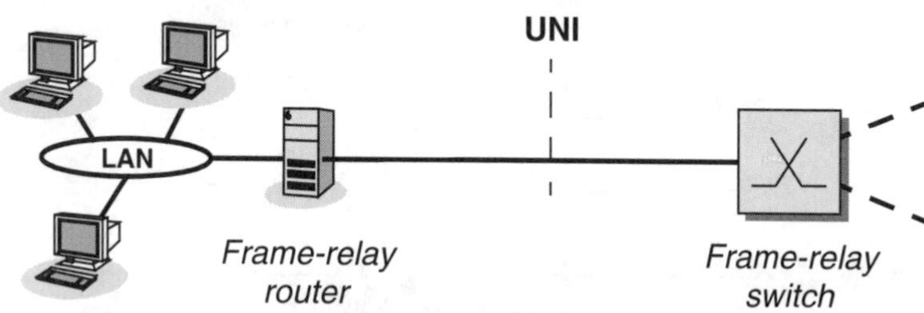

Figure F2.1.1 Frame-relay router used as access equipment

1.3.2 Frame relay access device

A FRAD is the frame-relay equivalent of a packet assembler/disassembler (PAD) in X.25 applications. The unit does not actually assemble data, though, so FRAD officially stands for frame relay access device.

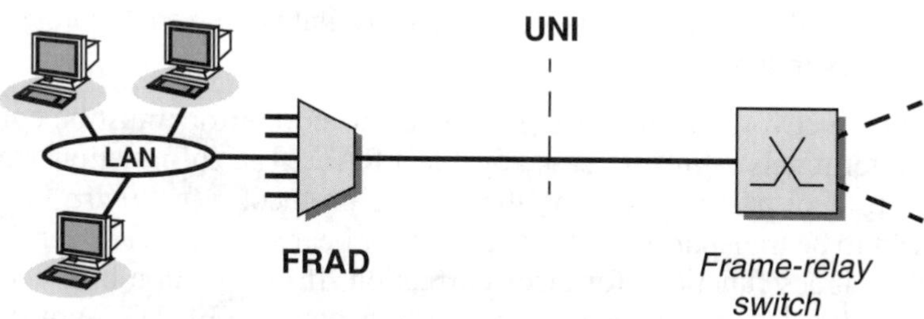

Figure F2.1.2 Frame relay access device used as access equipment

The FRAD has a multiprotocol interface which permits the sending of protocols other than the frame-relay variants over a frame-relay network. Since no standards for the design of FRADs are available today, each manufacturer markets its own solutions. However, the basic principle is always the same. A FRAD receives frames from an end-user, such as a PC or a workstation in a LAN, and maps them onto a logical connection – a data link connection identifier (DLCI) – for transmission to a FRAD in the receiving LAN.

Regardless of its manufacturer, every FRAD must contain three main functions: a multiprotocol handling component, a service protocol component, and a frame-relay component.

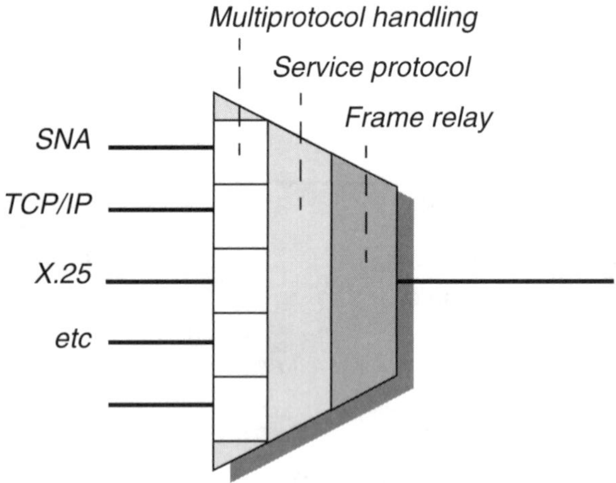

Figure F2.1.3 Frame relay access device – multiprotocol handling

The multiprotocol part handles different protocols, such as systems network architecture (SNA), X.25 and the Internet protocol (IP). The user should not be aware of the use of a frame-relay network but perceive the connection as completely transparent.

Since the network cannot ensure correct transport, errors must be corrected in the terminals – in this case, by the FRAD. The information from the multiprotocol part is nested by the service protocol (see *Figure F2.1.3*) to allow it to be transported by the frame-relay bearer service. The service protocol includes functions for error correction. If information bits have been discarded or become erroneous during transport, the FRAD – not the end-user – will request retransmission. Different manufacturers may design different functions, but in most cases they are based on X.25's link protocol.

The service protocol, in turn, will be handled by frame-relay software and assigned a DLCI value (logical address) and a checksum called frame check sequence (FCS). A flag at either end of the frame indicates its start and end.

1.3.3 Concentrator

A frame-relay concentrator is a special FRAD variant with no functionality for multiprotocols. In its simplest form, a concentrator only contains a frame-relay interface. Combined equipment (FRAD/concentrator) is also available, as shown in *Figure F2.1.4*.

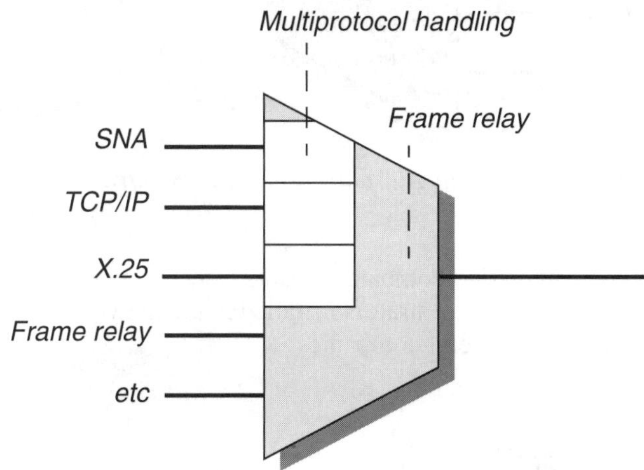

Figure F2.1.4 FRAD/concentrator

There are two types of concentrator:

- transparent concentrator, and
- guaranteed-delivery concentrator.

A transparent concentrator changes the routing address in the incoming frame-relay frames and sends the frames onwards. A guaranteed-delivery concentrator functions as a FRAD, except that it only has a frame-relay interface. All frames pass a service protocol which performs the same task as the corresponding protocol in FRAD: it offers functions for secure transport by means of flow control and error detection and correction.

Concentrators installed in the frame-relay network enable the operator to provide backup capacity for other traffic. However, the most common application is to install concentrators at companies that have several frame-relay interfaces, for instance, a company with several LAN routers.

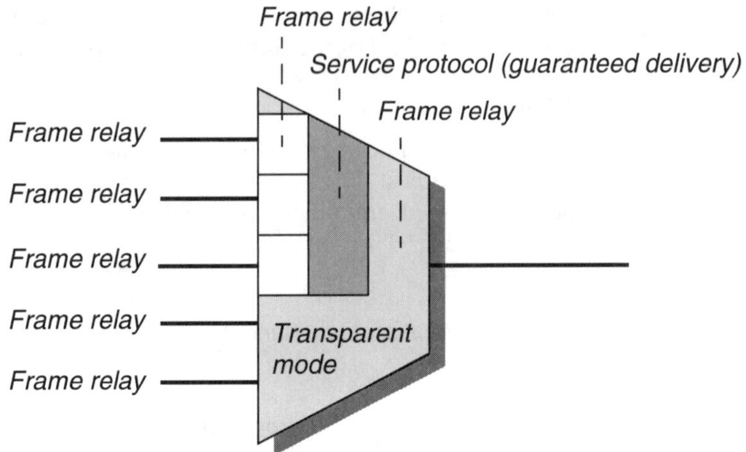

Figure F2.1.5 Transparent and guaranteed-mode concentrator

Many large and medium-size companies install concentrators for connecting several LAN routers. Concentrators installed in the network are used for "collecting" traffic from several companies.

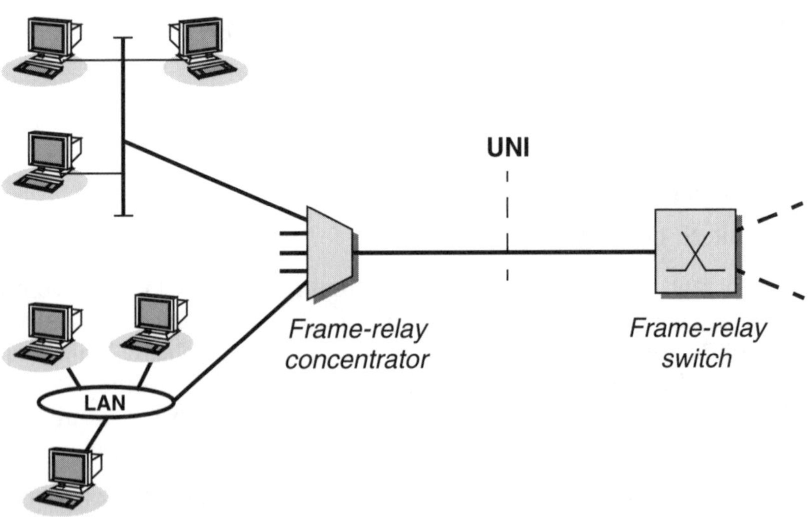

Figure F2.1.6 Frame-relay concentrator used as access equipment

Concentrators can also be used for converting traffic between different types of frame-relay protocol. Several types of local management interface (LMI) are available on the market. (See Chapter 2, Section 2.8.)

1.4 Voice transmission in frame-relay networks

Frame relay was originally designed for carrying data traffic. Due to the rapid increase in the number of frame-relay networks during the past few years, companies have also taken an interest in the transfer of other services – such as voice, fax, video and, eventually, multimedia services – over their frame-relay circuits.

The advantages offered by an integrated network for all types of service would be simpler network management and more efficient use of bandwidth, that is, better network economy.

It goes without saying that the introduction of isochronous services, such as voice, will make new demands on the network. Isochronous services are relatively insensitive to bit errors but extremely sensitive to delays and delay variations.

The frame-relay network must be able to guarantee a certain minimum bandwidth and a maximum delay of approximately 200 ms. In addition, it must be able to handle problems caused by echo. Setting up speech connections over a public frame-relay network also requires some type of common signalling.

Several factors affect the duration of delays:

- the number of switching nodes passed (more than four nodes will probably result in unacceptably low quality);
- the type of backbone network used (frame relay, ATM);
- the current degree of network load (number of users, type of traffic and so forth); and
- the coding method used (coding and decoding cause delays).

Pulse code modulation (PCM), with a voice coding rate of 64 kbit/s, is by far the most common coding standard today. However, voice routed over frame relay requires a more effective coding algorithm to reduce the probability of overload. Examples of other standards are 8 kbit/s algebraic code-excited linear prediction (ACELP, G.729) and 6.4 kbit/s multipulse maximum likelihood quantisation (MPMLQ, G.723.1).

Better utilisation of the conversation time is one way of reducing the voice bandwidth further. As a matter of fact, the periods of silence during a normal telephone call amount to 60% of the total duration of the call on average. If we use a compression method called digital speech interpolation (DSI), only the speech will be transmitted, while all "silent" time can be used for other traffic. If we combine DSI with ACELP, MPMLQ or some other compression technique, we will obtain an additional average compression of 2:1.

However, a completely silent telephone line would make the subscribers think the communication was broken. To cope with this problem, complete silence is replaced locally by faint background noise.

A prerequisite for properly functioning voice transmission in a frame-relay network is that the overwhelming majority of the traffic is data communication. If not, the priority-setting functions may be rendered inoperative.

Note also that current technology does not allow us to dial a telephone number in a frame-relay network; nor can we reach a telephone outside our own frame-relay network. Hence, the main area of application of frame-relay telephony is the interconnection of private branch exchanges.

2 Standards

The frame-relay standard has been described by the International Telecommunication Union-Telecommunications (ITU-T) and the American National Standards Institute (ANSI) and has been accepted by manufacturers and operators. It appeared as an independent protocol in 1989; before that, frame relay was part of the protocol for narrowband integrated service digital network (N-ISDN).

2.1 Frame Relay Forum

The prime mover in the development of frame-relay technology is the Frame Relay Forum. This body, consisting of manufacturers, operators, users and other relevant parties, assists the traditional standardisation organisations – the ITU-T, ANSI, the European Telecommunications Standardisation Institute (ETSI) and others – in preparing background data for standards.

The Frame Relay Forum, which was formed in January 1991, has well over 100 members. Its market committees arrange training courses and disseminate information about frame relay. A number of technical committees work out implementation agreements (IA), describing how frame relay should be implemented to permit cooperation between different types of equipment.

The ITU-T's frame-relay recommendations include Q.922, which describes the frame, and Q.933, which describes signalling.

2.2 Frame-relay connections and CIR

Although PVCs are normally used in frame-relay traffic, there is also a standard for SVC. A characteristic of both variants – which also applies to X.25 and most other wide area network (WAN) protocols – is that they are connection-oriented. All frames of a specific connection are sent along the same route through the network, thus ensuring the smallest possible amount of overhead in each frame.

To check the amount of information sent over the frame-relay network, the following user parameters have been defined:

- CIR – *committed information rate* – the average transmission capacity agreed on;
- Bc – *committed burst size* – the maximum amount of data that a user is allowed to transmit during a period Tc;
- EIR – *excess information rate* – the maximum permissible transmission capacity during short periods; and
- Be – *excess burst size* – the amount of data by which the user is allowed to exceed Bc during a period Tc.

Each PVC and SVC is assigned a CIR value which indicates the transmission capacity that has been agreed on for the service. CIR is equal to Bc/Tc. The same CIR value applies to both directions. Correspondingly, EIR is equal to Be/Tc.

The customer can select the CIR value (the available range is 0–2 Mbit/s, and typical values are 0, 8, 32 and multiples of 64 kbit/s). The zero value is used if the customer cannot make even a rough estimate of his future traffic structure, or if the traffic volume is insignificant. It is thus the CIR value that the customer pays for, and the network operator dimensions his network on the basis of all CIR values added together. Both simplex and duplex PVCs are supported, which means that the CIR in one direction need not be set to the same value as that in the other direction.

There is no relationship between the CIR value and the bit rate of the physical connection. A user may have a 2 Mbit/s physical connection but use a PVC with a CIR value of only 64 kbit/s. In other words, one and the same physical connection can carry several PVCs that have different CIRs.

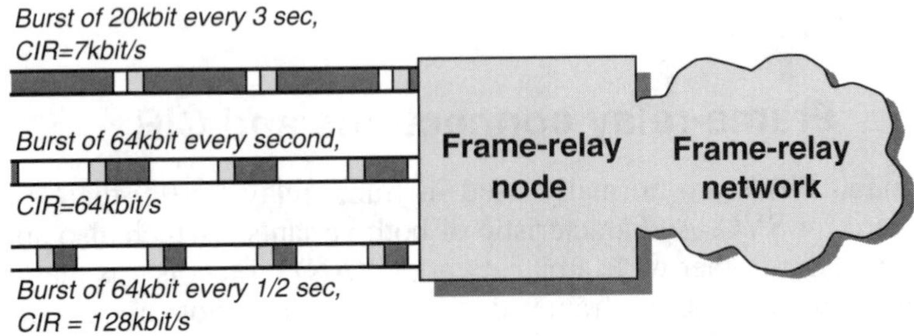

Figure F2.2.1 The CIR is adapted to each customer's needs

It follows from what we have just said that there is no way of guaranteeing a certain capacity through a frame-relay network; the CIR value is the average traffic specified by a user. The possibility of exceeding the CIR value up to the EIR value is of great advantage to the customer and makes frame relay particularly well suited for data traffic (where data is usually transferred in the form of bursts). This is what we call flexible allocation of bandwidth, or bandwidth on demand, in frame-relay applications. On the other hand, the operator may have difficulty in dimensioning his backbone network. If several users systematically exceed the CIR value agreed on, this will result in overload.

Although the network cannot prevent a user from exceeding the CIR, it includes functions for warning of near-problem situations and for "recommending" reduction of the transfer rate.

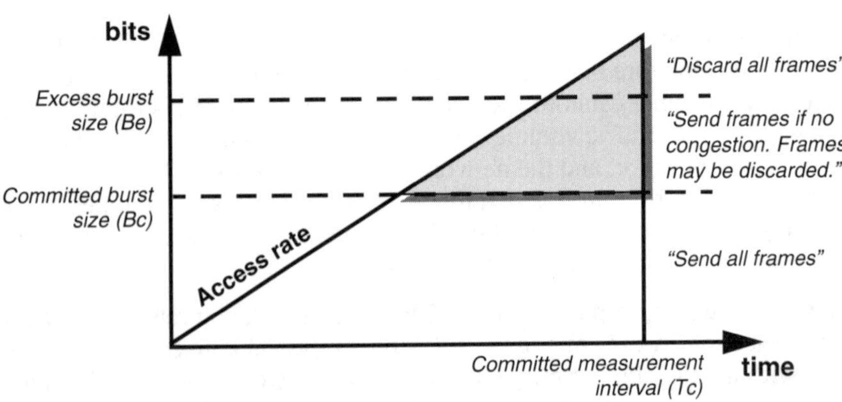

Figure F2.2.2 CIR is allowed to be exceeded up to a preset limit

What happens if overload occurs in the network? To cope with these situations, frame relay activates decision functions which result in the discarding of "problematic" frames. How then does the network know which frames exceed the CIR value and which ones comply with the value agreed on? A bit – the discard eligibility (DE) bit – in every frame is used for this purpose. The DE bit can be activated for frames that exceed the CIR, and these frames are the first to be discarded if a problem arises. For decision thresholds and actions, see *Figure F2.2.2*

2.3 Frame-relay protocols

In principle, the frame-relay network uses the two lowest layers of the OSI model. (For a description of the OSI model, see Chapter 2 of Volume 1.) Frame relay is a layer-2 protocol (data link layer) and comparable to the corresponding protocols for other networks, such as synchronous data link control (SDLC) for SNA networks, link access procedure balanced (LAPB) in X.25 and high-level data link control (HDLC) for OSI applications. In addition, there are a large number of LAN protocols in which layer 2 is somewhat differently structured.

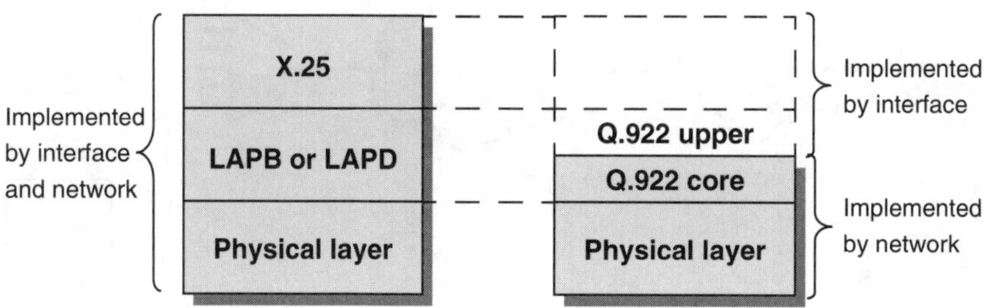

Figure F2.2.3 Comparison between the protocol stacks for X.25 and frame relay

Frame relay uses an adapted version of link access procedure on the D-channel (LAPD), which was originally designed for N-ISDN. In frame-relay networks, this version is called LAPF and is actually part of the complete LAPD protocol. LAPF, which is specified in Q.922, defines a number of core functions that must be provided in all frame-relay networks.

Recommendation Q.922 consists of two parts: Q.922 core, which describes all the core functions that all nodes in a frame-relay network must be capable of performing, and Q.922 upper, which contains functions for retransmission and flow control to ensure that the end-user receives correct information.

All nodes are involved in frame checking. They must be able to detect the start and end points of the frame and check that it is correctly formatted. All information is sent transparently through the nodes, which means that no node can draw any conclusions as to the contents of the information.

The nodes must also check the frames for transmission errors, for which the FCS checksum is used. Detected errors cannot be corrected by the network; erroneous frames are simply discarded.

Other typical layer-2 functions that are not performed by frame-relay nodes are frame sequencing, segmentation and different types of flow control (acknowledgement). On the other hand, this means that the frame-relay nodes can operate considerably faster.

Responsibility for these important network functions is transferred to a higher-order protocol in the receiving equipment, for example, a FRAD. If an error is detected, the FRAD will request retransmission along the whole path through the network.

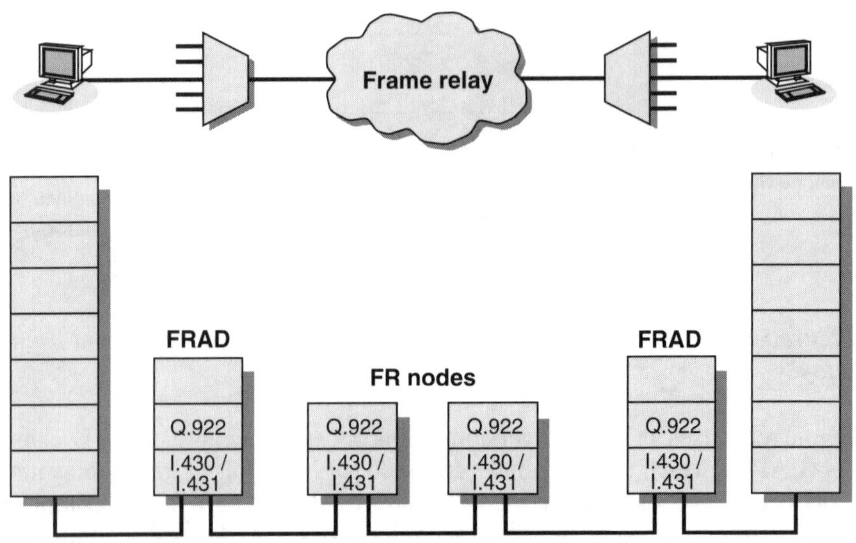

Figure F2.2.4 Example of protocols in a frame-relay network

There are no frame-relay standards for the bearer service that transports frame-relay frames. However, the Frame Relay Forum has presented an IA, which offers a number of alternatives, including I.430, I.431, V.35, G.703, G.704 and X.21.

2.4 Frame format

The frame structure in a frame-relay network is relatively simple. It consists of two flags indicating the beginning and end of the frame, an address field, an information field and a frame check sequence.

In addition to the address, the address field contains functions that warn of overload and indicate which frames should be discarded first.

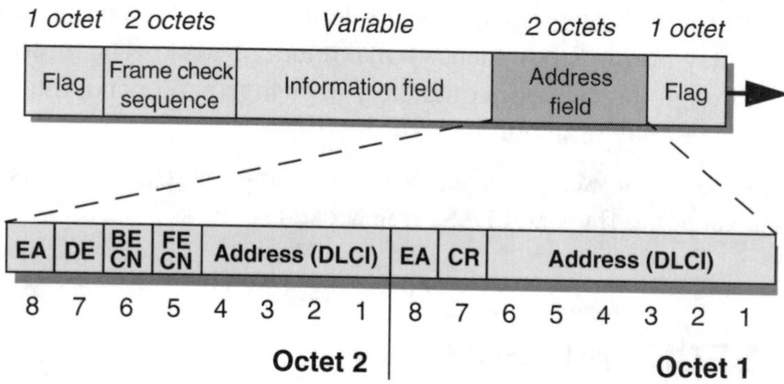

Figure F2.2.5 The frame-relay frame

- Flag: All frames begin and end with a flag consisting of an octet composed of a known bit pattern: a zero followed by six ones and a zero (01111110).
- Address: In the two octets in the address field, the first six bits of the first octet and the first four bits of the second octet are used for addressing. These 10 bits, which form the DLCI, select the next destination to which the frame is to be transported. (DLCI is described in Section 2.6.)
- CR: *command response* is not used by the frame-relay protocol. It is sent transparently through the frame-relay nodes and can be made available to users as required.

- EA: At the end of each address octet, there is an *extended address* bit which can allow extension of the DLCI field to more than 10 bits. If the EA bit is set to "0", another address octet will follow. If it is set to "1", the octet in question is the last one in the address field. No manufacturer of frame-relay equipment uses the EA today.
- FECN: If overload occurs in the network, *forward explicit congestion notification* is indicated to alert the receiving end. The network makes this indication, and end-users need not take any specific action.
- BECN: Similar to FECN, *backward explicit congestion notification* alerts the sending end to an overload situation in the network.
- DE: *discard eligibility* indicates that the frame is to be discarded in case of overload. This indication can be regarded as a prioritising function, although frames without a DE indication can also be discarded.
- Information field: This is where we find user information. The network operator decides how many octets the field is allowed to contain, but the Frame Relay Forum recommends a maximum of 1,600. The information passes through the network completely unchanged and is not interpreted by the frame-relay protocol.
- FCS: the *frame check sequence* checks the frame for errors. All bits in the frame, except the flags and FCS, are checked.

2.5 BECN and FECN

Flow control is an important function in all types of network, and frame relay is no exception. The purpose of flow control is to prevent the originating party from sending more information than the receiving end can accept. Sometimes a specific part of the network is overloaded because it cannot keep up with the overall pace.

If the network assumes the role of the receiver of information in these situations, flow control can be used to avoid serious degradation of network performance. This is where the BECN and FECN bits come into play. When a frame-relay node has been overloaded, all BECN and FECN bits in all frames on all connections through the node are flagged.

The purpose of the BECN and FECN bits is to inform the end-users of this overload. The party that is responsible for the transfer of information (either the sender or the recipient) must then reduce the transfer rate to allow the network to recover.

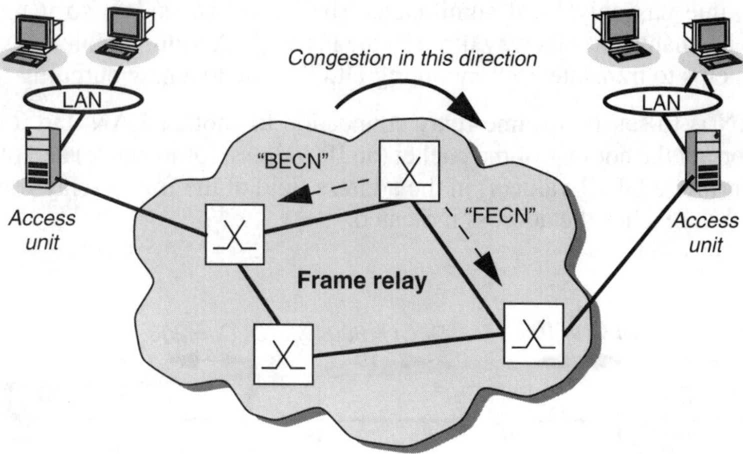

Figure F2.2.6 Backward explicit and forward explicit congestion notification

Unfortunately, only a few end-user protocols can interpret the BECN and FECN bits.

The TCP/IP protocol is designed for equally effective use on leased lines and in X.25, ATM or frame-relay networks. In other words, it should perform the same functions, regardless of which lower-layer protocol is used. That is why it is not considered practical to incorporate functions (such as BECN and FECN) that are unique to frame relay. However, network elements such as routers are often equipped with functions for interpreting BECN and FECN and for taking action to reduce the load – through temporary storage in buffers, for example.

2.6 DLCI

Every frame-relay connection consists of one or more data link connections (DLC), and each DLC – whether it is a PVC or an SVC – is identified by a data link connection identifier (DLCI). The DLCI values make up the logical connections between different frame-relay users. Since the DLCI field consists of 10 bits it can represent up to $2^{10} = 1024$ logical connections, many of which are reserved for special tasks. After deduction of these special-purpose connections, 992 different DLCI values are available for use in traffic.

By assigning different DLCI values to different frames, we can create several simultaneous logical connections on the same physical circuit. The DLCI value has only local significance (between two nodes) so it might have to be changed on its way through the network. A routing table in every switch helps to translate each incoming DLCI value to a new outgoing one.

If a LAN is to set up a frame-relay connection to another LAN, the router will interpret the address of the packet (an IP address, for instance) and place the appropriate DLCI value(s) in the address field of the frame-relay frame, so the PVC reaches the address indicated.

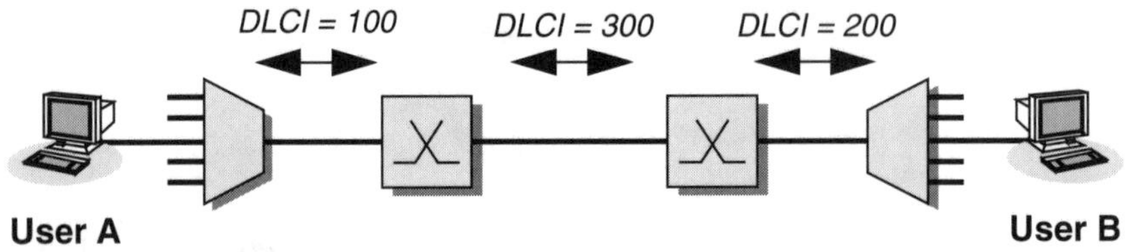

Figure F2.2.7 DLCI has only local significance; a logical connection changes DLCI values between the end points

2.7 UNI and NNI

Two types of interface are defined in a frame-relay network: the user-network interface (UNI) and the network-node interface (NNI).

UNI describes the user's interface to the frame-relay network, while NNI describes how different types of frame-relay network can be interconnected. Such interconnection may involve frame-relay networks run by different operators, or installed in different countries, or one private and one public frame-relay network.

UNI allows all users to communicate with all frame-relay networks. NNI, on the other hand, is unlikely to be used between all frame-relay nodes – only between different frame-relay networks. This is because the NNI protocol contains some procedures that will be redundant if the nodes involved belong to the same operator, and also because many supplier-specific NNIs include functions besides those of the standardised NNI interface. (See also Chapter 5, Section 5.2.)

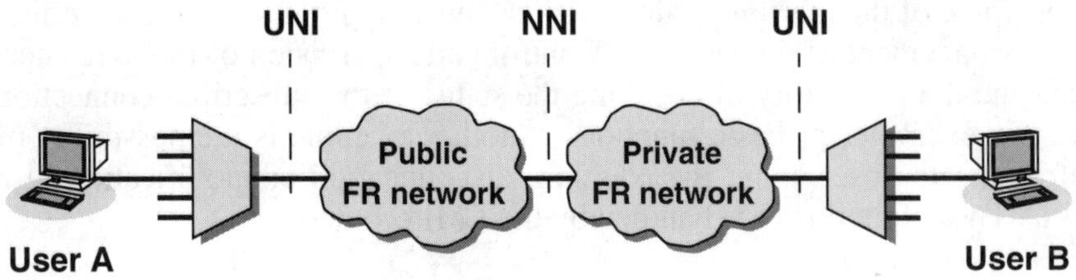

Figure F2.2.8 Structure of a frame-relay network – example

2.8 LMI

Since routers or other types of FRAD equipment usually belong to the user, while the frame-relay nodes form part of a public network, a standardised maintenance protocol will be required to permit the exchange of information between these units. In frame relay, the maintenance protocol is called local management interface (LMI).

DLCI values 0 and 1023 are reserved for the LMI. The reason for reserving two values is that two different LMI standards have been issued, one by the ITU-T and the other by ANSI. Pending a uniform standard, manufacturers must support both alternatives, and both DLCI = 0 and DLCI = 1023 must be reserved.

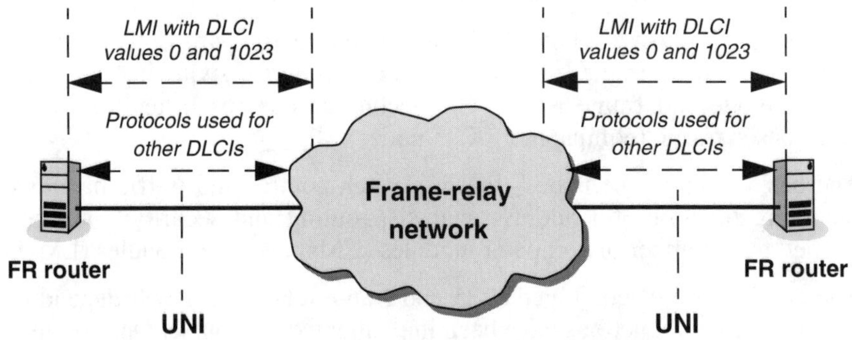

Figure F2.2.9 Local management interface

Many functions that are usually included in other WAN protocols have been deleted in the frame-relay protocol to make it as simple as possible. However, some of the missing basic functions must be provided to ensure effective management of the network. Control and supervision of the user interface and the possibility of checking the status of the subscriber connection are two examples of basic functions. Another example is the possibility of informing the user about the addition, disconnection or modification of a PVC. These functions are handled by the LMI protocol.

3 Switching and switch control

3.1 Environment and adaptation

The switching environment in a frame-relay network is more heterogeneous than that of public circuit-switched networks. We can use a frame-relay network for data traffic from public or private networks – such as the PSTN, ISDN or X.25 – and for private data traffic through LANs, legacy systems (such as IBM's SNA), TCP/IP or other private systems. Transfer of voice over private frame-relay networks is also becoming highly topical. The switching nodes in a frame-relay network often include a set of access modules for handling different protocols.

3.2 Combined switching nodes

Combining frame-relay switching with packet switching or IP routing is a practical solution in some cases.

Figure F2.3.1 illustrates how X.25 traffic in the central parts of the networks can be carried by frame relay by means of combined switching nodes for packet mode and frame mode. This technique ensures faster transfer of X.25-based traffic (compared to X.25 nodes).

The basic tasks of the node – that is, switch control and traffic handling, including functions for address analysis, routing and security – are performed by a number of computer modules (CMs) and line modules (LMs).

The architecture of combined X.25 and frame-relay nodes will depend on how the various functions have been implemented, of course. One solution, shown in *Figure F2.3.2*, is to have line modules for low-speed connections (<256 kbit/s medium-capacity line modules, LMM) and for high-speed connections (<2 Mbit/s high-capacity line modules, LMH). The LMHs are usually integrated into the computer modules.

All line modules are controlled by a number of computer modules, which are interconnected by an inter-computer bus (ICB). For reliability reasons, all computer modules operate in pairs, and the internal bus is duplicated for the same reason.

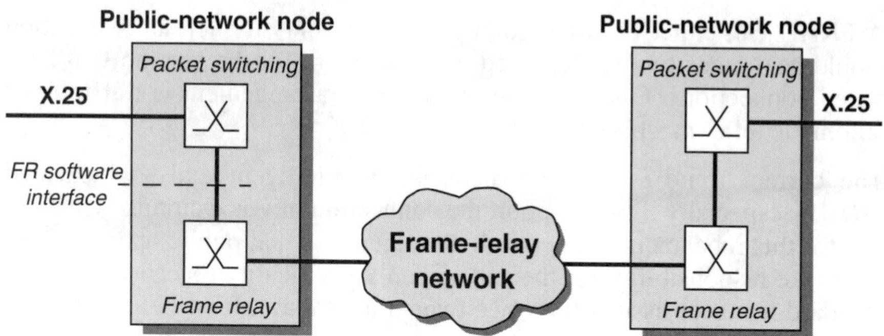

Figure F2.3.1 Combined X.25 and frame-relay switching nodes

Large nodes may consist of more than 30 CMs. In some implementations, PVC connections can be switched without the assistance of CMs, which gives very short switching time (about 2 ms).

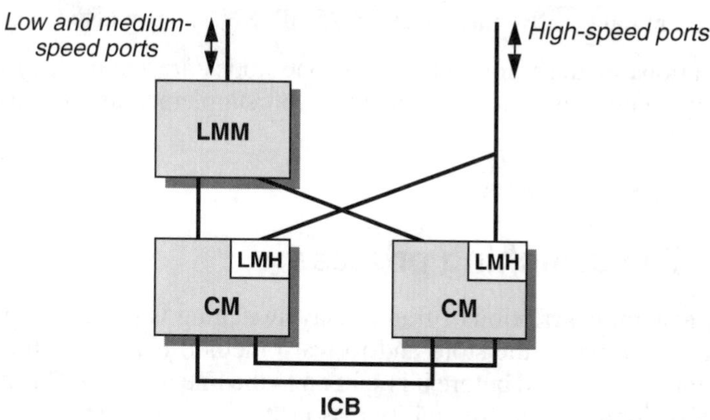

Figure F2.3.2 Example of combined X.25 and frame-relay node architecture

3.3 Hierarchy

Unlike circuit-switched networks, the frame-relay network does not divide switching operations into a hierarchical structure. The following network elements can perform switching operations:

- FRAD and
- frame-relay backbone switches.

A FRAD can either be installed at a company or – if such an installation would be too costly – be deployed in the network for the assembly of low-speed connections. One example of the latter arrangement is traffic from automatic teller machines.

The current trend is towards increasingly intelligent and sophisticated FRADs, especially if they support the connection of voice circuits. One reason for this rebalancing of network intelligence is that public operators seldom take responsibility for the end-to-end voice quality (because so far no standard has been issued for voice over frame relay). It is the suppliers of FRAD equipment who take the main responsibility for quality and provide the nodes with functionality for tasks such as:

- prioritisation (voice vs data);
- voice compression;
- echo cancellation;
- signalling;
- congestion control;

and different data-traffic interfaces (X.25, IP, SNA). (See also Chapter 1.)

The functions of the frame-relay backbone nodes are mainly restricted to switching operations and the execution of supplementary services (see Chapter 6).

3.4 The switching process

A short general description of frame-relay switching is given in Volume 1, Chapter 3. Normally, the store and forward method is applied; that is, the whole frame is received before it is sent on to the line modules. The modules are usually duplicated for reliability reasons.

Multicasting is an example of special switching functions.

4 Transmission techniques

Frame-relay systems are terminated in different types of equipment installed in the network or on a company's premises. Ordinarily, these points are connected by means of digital transmission systems with plesiochronous digital hierarchy (PDH) or synchronous digital hierarchy (SDH). Unlike ATM cells, frame-relay frames cannot be placed in STM-1 modules directly, but must pass through PDH systems (64 kbit/s, $n \cdot$ 64 kbit/s, 2 Mbit/s). As mentioned before, optical fibre is the preferred transmission medium.

5 Trunk and access networks

5.1 Access to frame relay

To be able to transfer data over long distances, the frame-relay customer (usually a company) must be connected to a frame-relay wide area network (FR-WAN) run by a major, global operator. If the operator has not installed a frame-relay node near the company, some kind of bridging will be necessary. Here, "access method" refers to the way in which a frame-relay customer connects his equipment to the nearest frame-relay node, the applicable type of transmission and topology and the type of connection (permanent or dial-up).

A company wanting to use frame relay for its internal, multisite data traffic cannot always select the preferred mode of connection but will rely heavily on the local operators' facilities.

5.1.1 Point-to-point access circuit to FR-WAN

A frame-relay customer can lease a point-to-point access circuit, either from the operator who offers the FR-WAN service or from a rival operator. A typical capacity range here is from 64 kbit/s to 2 Mbit/s, depending on the volume of traffic that will be carried through the network.

Of course, different corporate units can be connected over access circuits of varying capacity. A head office with a server that is in constant use needs more capacity than other corporate units.

For a company, the most economical solution will be to allow all traffic – voice, data and video – to use the same *channelised* access circuit. Some of the channels on a PCM link can be used for voice, and others for data in frame-relay format. For example, allocating six time slots to frame relay will give a 384 kbit/s frame-relay access circuit.

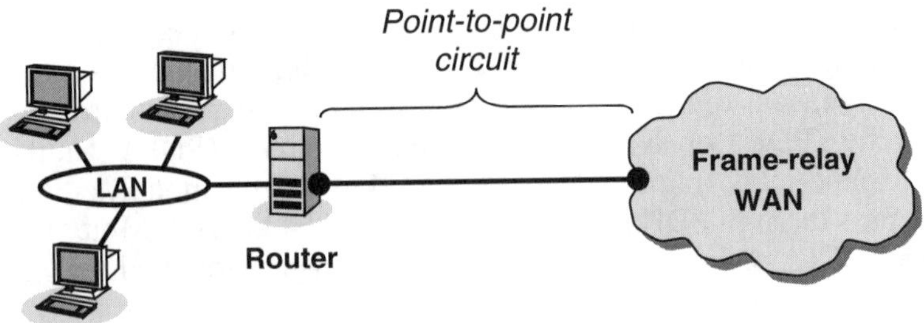

Figure F2.5.1 Point-to-point access

Frame-relay applications will benefit if the local operator installs optical fibre rings for his access networks. This is a relatively common arrangement (especially in big cities and industrial areas) that offers two advantages. First, optical fibre has excellent transmission characteristics; that is, the number of bit errors is very small. Second, ring topology means higher reliability since problems can be eliminated by rerouting the traffic in the ring.

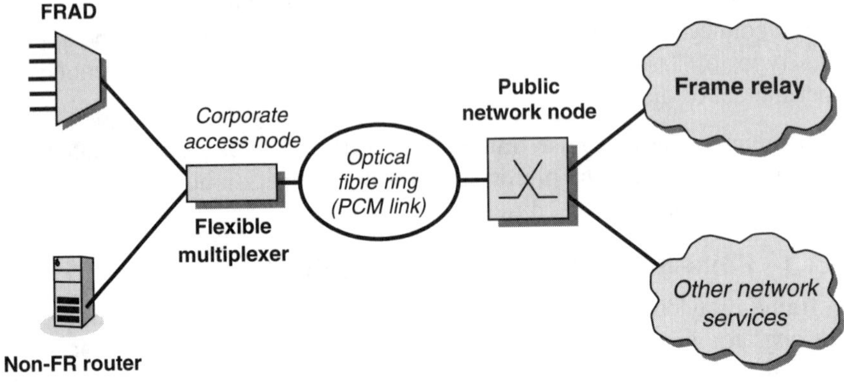

Figure F2.5.2 Integrated access over a PCM link

5.1.2 ISDN access

Originally, leased lines provided the only means of accessing a frame-relay network. Today, ISDN is an alternative method that offers dial-up access as a complement to leased lines. One reason why a company should choose a basic rate access (BRA) or primary rate access (PRA) subscription is that the price of ISDN connections has dropped considerably in recent years. BRA provides the company with two parallel 64 kbit/s connections, while PRA provides 30 such connections.

Dial-up access does not mean that the frame-relay service must be switched. In other words, the SVC service is not required: setting up a connection to a PVC service through ISDN is equally effective. Hence, we must distinguish between the two concepts "SVC" and "dial-up access".

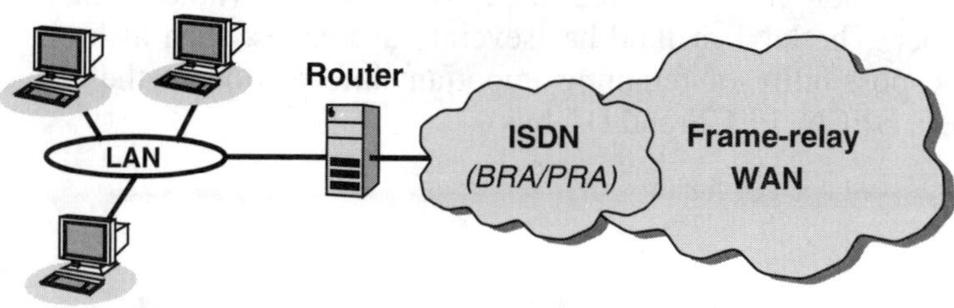

Figure F2.5.3 ISDN access

5.1.3 Local frame-relay access

Yet another way of connecting to an FR-WAN is via a frame-relay access service provided by the local operator. As a rule of thumb, there must be at least three corporate accesses to the FR-WAN for this alternative to be cost-effective. See *Figure F2.5.4*.

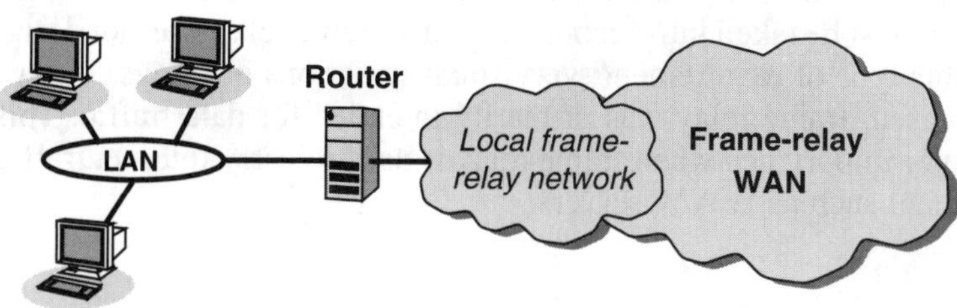

Figure F2.5.4 Local frame-relay access

5.2 NNI and gateway

NNI is the interface that enables two frame-relay network operators to exchange frames between their networks, even if they use equipment from different suppliers. However, the fact that a standard has been issued does not guarantee it is universally applied. This is a common situation as far as frame relay and NNI are concerned, mainly because the operators to a certain extent lose control of the services they provide.

For example, if a fault occurs in a local operator's network, the global operator can hardly do much more than report it.

Today, a simpler type of interface – called a *gateway* – is in common use between different frame-relay networks. The difference between a gateway and an NNI is that in a gateway the contents of a frame-relay frame are moved to a new frame, whereas the NNI moves the whole frame including its header. The NNI method has several advantages, such as higher speed and the possibility of retaining important information in the header (for instance, BECN, FECN and DE bits).

6 Network intelligence and value-added services

6.1 Introduction

The intelligence of a frame-relay network usually resides in the switching nodes. Typical supplementary services are those related to security and virtual private networks (VPN).

In the case of value-added services, any requirements for isochronous transmission must be taken into account, because frame relay was not designed to meet this type of requirement (very small variations in delays). As we have emphasised, frame relay was primarily intended for data traffic. This is of particular importance when frame relay is used to carry Internet traffic from equipment such as WWW servers.

6.2 Security

Typical security services are:

- closed user groups;
- calling address validation;
- access identification; and
- secure dial back.

6.3 Virtual private networks

VPNs can be created within a frame-relay network by using a procedure similar to the one used when creating a VPN in the PSTN/ISDN.

Examples of VPN services include:

- closed user groups;
- private, company-specific numbering plans;
- flexible routing for each company; and
- charging and settlement of accounts for each company.

6.4 Value-added services

Frame relay can be used for services such as database access, e-mail and Internet access.

7 Signalling

This chapter describes in broad outline the different types of signals that a frame-relay network must be able to handle. For a more detailed description, see Frame Relay Forum Implementation Agreement, FRF.4, and ITU-T Recommendation Q.933, which form the basis of frame-relay signalling.

7.1 "Signalling" on PVCs

Since PVCs have been established "once and for all" by the operator, they require no signalling. In other words, each PVC is locked onto one and only one final destination.

However, network management signals will be sent, including quality parameters (FECN/BECN), LMI information and information showing how the agreed average transmission capacity (CIR) is utilised.

The charging of traffic on PVCs does not require any signalling because the customer pays an amount corresponding to a preset CIR value.

7.2 Signalling on SVCs

The network management signalling on PVCs is also used on SVCs, but otherwise the two types of circuit differ greatly as far as signalling is concerned. SVC connections make much stricter demands on signalling because they are not permanent but set up when required. This means that we need routing tables in the nodes and we need a numbering plan.

The E.164 and X.121 numbering plans are supported by Frame Relay Forum. E.164 is usually the first choice in long-term planning, but the operator is free to choose any plan he prefers.

The network must first identify the subscribers to check authorisation and to determine which of them is to be charged. The charging function must also include parameters that take the duration of the set-up phase into account.

During the set-up phase, the three parties involved (the A-subscriber, the B-subscriber and the network) must negotiate a number of transmission parameters, such as the size of the information field, Bc and Be. The A-subscriber begins by sending a set-up message that specifies the desired quality of service (QoS) and other information. When the negotiation is concluded, communication can start.

8 Network management

8.1 Introduction

Frame-relay networks normally offer subscribers a very good QoS. However, an effective network management system must be provided to perform the necessary functions. The network management system is used to configure the network, to set up all types of connection and to supervise the network to ensure that it continues to operate as trouble-free as possible. Faults must be detected and reported by the operations system – preferably before the customer phones in his complaint. Another important function is the collection of statistics and information about operations, as a basis for long-term planning.

What then constitutes the main difference between a frame-relay network and other networks? Most obvious, probably, is the fact that a frame-relay network operator has only limited means of controlling the traffic volumes that subscribers are sending through his network.

8.2 Operation and maintenance

The International Organization for Standardization (ISO) has proposed a network management structure for OSI-based networks. This structure is also used by many other types of network management system. The OSI model elucidates every aspect of network management – operator-related as well as user-related considerations. The model consists of five function areas. (See also Volume 1, Chapter 8, Subsections 8.3.3 and 8.5.2–8.5.5.) The requirements that a frame-relay network places on network management can also be described on the basis of these function areas, namely fault management, performance management, configuration management, accounting management and security management.

8.2.1 Fault management

Activities performed in this function area normally include the reporting of different events in the network: fault localisation, fault isolation, alarms and – where applicable – correction of faults affecting equipment and software. When an alarm is issued, the network management system must be able to decide whether it was primarily caused by a local problem or whether it ensues from a problem elsewhere in the network. It must also be possible to collect statistics on events.

Alarm reports fall into two categories: those generated when a fault occurs and those generated when a threshold value is exceeded. An example of the latter category is an alarm report indicating that too many frames are being lost. Threshold values are set for such alarms to keep the number of alarm reports at a manageable level.

To be able to deal with a fault, the system may have to reconfigure the network, reroute traffic or load new software.

8.2.2 Performance management

This function area comprises the handling of different types of quality parameters for measuring the QoS offered to the user. Typical frame-relay data collected are the number of frames sent and received, the number of FECNs and BECNs and the number of discarded DE frames and non-DE frames, respectively. Some quality parameters are associated with an alarm supervisory function, which is activated if a user exceeds the CIR value agreed on. This type of alarm may not result in the operations system taking immediate action, but recording how often the alarm limit is exceeded is important nevertheless.

8.2.3 Configuration management

Configuration in this context means making an inventory of all elements in a frame-relay network: hardware, software and external connections. Tools for modifying all these elements are also provided. Different network parameters must be defined to ensure reliable and flexible operation, including CIR values and the maximum permissible number of data bursts. An important characteristic of a frame-relay network is that the network operator must be able to make modifications in real time so as to minimise downtime. Being able to make modifications in real time – and assigning different priorities to users – will always involve a risk: the system may reject low-priority users even if they themselves have not caused any faults.

8.2.4 Accounting management

Tools must be provided for the generation and collection of charging information in a frame-relay network as well as for the creation of a register of customers. On the whole, charging is much simpler than in packet-switched networks. In X.25, each packet is charged, whereas frame-relay customers pay an amount corresponding to a preset CIR value and a preset maximum bandwidth: Be/Tc. Charging and accounting is more complicated if several frame-relay networks are involved. In such cases, uniform charging rules must be agreed on.

Another requirement that must be met by a frame-relay network is the possibility of varying the charging rate through the use of day-of-the-week and time-of-day tariffs. For instance, the system may offer a higher CIR value at the same rate during certain periods (weekends, for example) or a lower rate at unchanged CIR value during certain periods of the day (off-peak hours). Naturally, this applies to PVCs only. An operator who offers SVCs must introduce parameters that take the duration of calls into account.

8.2.5 Security management

This area comprises the handling of information that shows which subscribers are authorised to access the operations system, the frame-relay network and – in more specific terms – to which applications they should have access. Unauthorised users must not be allowed to log on and tamper with information or functions. Security is not all that important in a private network but comes to the fore as soon as there is a link to a public network.

We distinguish between operational security and user security. Because today's frame-relay networks are mostly made up of PVC connections, and because all connections are controlled by the network management system, operational security has priority over user security. When SVC connections become more common, it will be necessary to revise the rules for user security.

8.2.6 SNMP-based network management systems

An OSI-based network management system can be rather complex. Hence, most suppliers will probably design individual solutions for their own frame-relay equipment, including suitable interfaces to network management systems at higher levels.

A result of the expansion of local networks is that network management systems based on the simple network management protocol (SNMP) have become popular. This, in turn, has resulted in the design of standardised interfaces between SNMP and large public network management systems. SNMP's simplicity is its greatest strength and its greatest weakness.

The Frame Relay Forum has standardised an SNMP protocol adapted to network management in frame-relay networks, both in terms of functions and requirements.

The advantages of using SNMP in a frame-relay network can be summarised by describing it as a simple and easy-to-handle protocol that is well suited to LAN/WAN environments and by stressing the fact that standards are available. As for disadvantages, there are no directives governing the compilation and interpretation of information, and the built-in security functions are far too few. Even so, it seems likely that SNMP will continue to form the basis of network management in frame-relay networks. For more information about the SNMP, see *Part H – The Internet*.

9 Interworking between networks

9.1 Introduction

Since frame relay was designed as an upgraded X.25 network, interworking with X.25 was natural at the initial stage. As we have seen in Chapter 3, switching nodes can be designed for use with both frame relay and X.25. However, the future of frame relay will be determined to a much greater extent by its ability to interwork with ATM and the Internet. Because frame relay, ATM and the Internet have different characteristics, they can be assigned different tasks in the total network. In most cases, it will not be a matter of choosing between the networks but of ensuring that they can interwork in an efficient manner.

9.2 Interworking between networks and service interworking

Interworking between networks means that frame relay either transports data in transparent mode for another network (X.25, for instance) or that frame relay is transported by another network (such as ATM).

Service interworking means that the terminal points belong to different networks – for example, a FRAD communicating with an ATM terminal – without any of the terminals having to be equipped with special software. Conversion between frame relay and ATM is performed by separate equipment: the interworking function (IWF).

9.2.1 Interworking between networks

Interworking between X.25, frame relay and ATM networks is illustrated in *Figure F2.9.1*. Tunnelling, nesting and stratification are examples of terms used in this context. (See Volume 1, Chapter 9, for a description of this type of interworking between networks.)

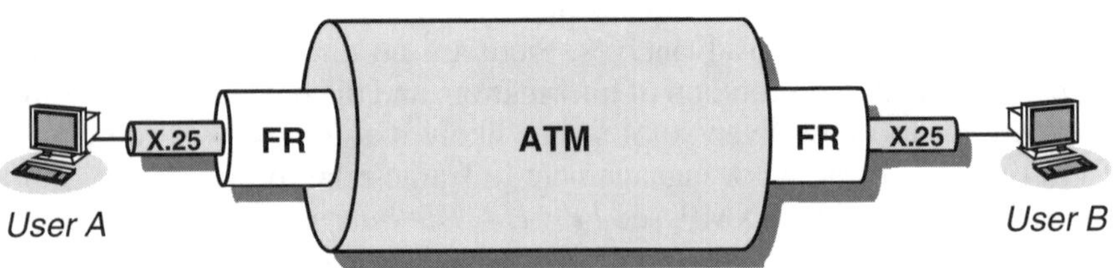

Figure F2.9.1 Interworking between networks (tunnelling)

9.2.2 Service interworking: frame relay – ATM

Interworking between frame relay and ATM networks includes protocol conversion in the interface (IWF) between the two networks. The frame-relay user sends traffic over a PVC through the frame-relay network to a service IWF, which maps the traffic onto an ATM-PVC. (There is always one ATM-PVC for each frame-relay PVC.) The service IWF is usually integrated with a frame-relay or ATM node but could be a stand-alone conversion unit. A service IWF translates the frame-relay address, and an ATM adaptation layer 5 (AAL 5) performs conversion on the ATM side. (See *Part G – ATM and B-ISDN,* Chapter 2, Subsection 2.5.1.)

9.3 Dial-up access: N-ISDN – frame relay

Using N-ISDN as a carrier of frame-relay traffic is another form of interworking between networks that is becoming increasingly common.

10 Network planning

10.1 Different types of frame-relay network

As we have seen, frame-relay networks can be either public or private. A subscriber in a public network based on a PVC will have access to some 1,000 DLCI values, while the number of addresses in a public network based on an SVC may be "unlimited". Frame-relay connections can also be carried by ISDN or "tunnel" through ATM.

For some time now, two special applications of frame relay have been in focus:

- frame relay as a bearer of Internet traffic, and
- frame relay as a bearer of voice.

Voice traffic in this case mainly refers to intra-company communication. The fact that both applications have great growth potential may decide how and where frame-relay networks will be built.

10.2 Fundamental technical plans

10.2.1 Numbering plan

Frame relay has no numbering plan of its own. X.121 (which is used for X.25) or E.164 (which is used for the PSTN and ISDN) are recommended for this purpose. Each PVC is identified by a network terminal number (NTN) and a DLCI for originating and terminating DTEs. (See Section 2.6.) The network selects DLCIs between end points.

10.2.2 Routing plan

The routing functions of frame relay, which closely resemble those of X.25, are based on routing tables with alternative routes.

10.2.3 Transmission plan

High-quality transmission is a prerequisite for high-performance frame-relay operation. If the bit error rate exceeds 10^{-6}, frame relay will not be as effective as X.25. Fibre-optic FRAD-to-FRAD transmission is the best way of avoiding congestion and retransmission caused by bit errors.

If the operator uses the frame-relay network for isochronous services, such as voice, many requirements will be stricter than those applicable to data transmission. Voice traffic does not tolerate long delays or great variations in delay. (The maximum permissible delay is about 200 ms, and the maximum permissible variation is about 100 ms.) A secondary effect of long delays is unacceptable echo. To avoid such degeneration, voice should not be buffered in the same way as data. If there is a risk of temporary overload, voice traffic should be given priority, and this can be done in a FRAD. Echo cancellers will also be required. Delay variations can be adjusted by means of *frame fragmentation.* (See also Chapter 1, Section 1.4.)

Another way of levelling out delay variations is to reduce the number of switching points along the path. Experience shows that voice quality starts to deteriorate if the number of nodes exceeds four.

Variations in delay can also be counteracted by using delay buffers in the FRAD.

If frame-relay connections are transported in an ATM network, the fast switching in the ATM nodes may help to reduce the overall delay.

10.2.4 Charging plan

The following are important parameters in the charging plan:

- PVC or SVC;
- bit rate (CIR);
- distance; and
- one-way or two-way.

For an SVC, charging can be based on the time during which the connection is actually used, whereas a PVC can be charged according to the flat-rate method.

10.2.5 Signalling plan

Signalling is required in networks containing SVCs. SVCs rather than PVCs may be used in large networks to facilitate configuration and network management. SVCs are also preferable in mesh-shaped networks. A disadvantage of an SVC is its vulnerability to wire-tapping (compared to a PVC).

10.3 Dimensioning

Examples of basic dimensioning parameters are "maximum 80 ms delay in interactive TCP/IP traffic" and requirements for availability.

Configuring a frame-relay network entails four main steps:

- Drawing a PVC map. This applies in particular to companies that are going to introduce frame relay. It may be advantageous to install central hubs in the network instead of an "all-to-all" PVC configuration.
- Determining the traffic volume for each PVC. Traffic requirements can be asymmetrical, which means that the volume is dependent on the direction.
- Determining a CIR value for each PVC. Here we can use the mean holding time – plus an adequate margin – as a basis.
- Determining the bit rate on the transmission link for each corporate unit.

Part G – ATM and B-ISDN

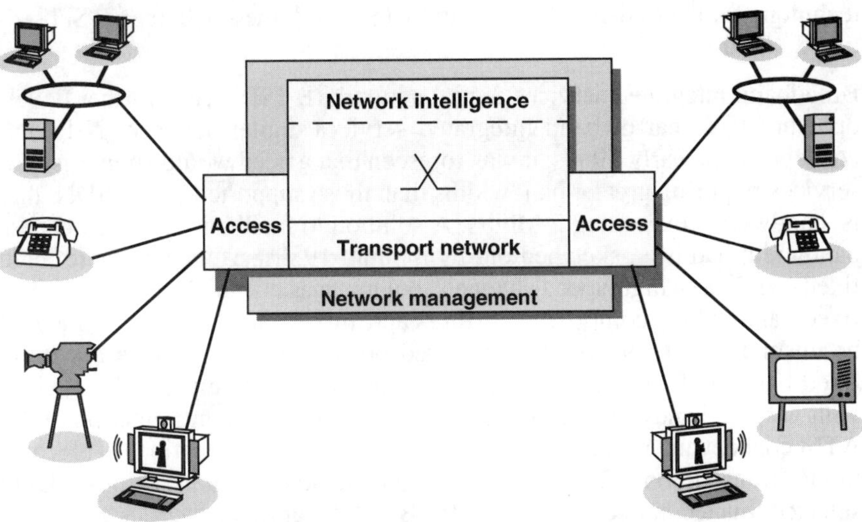

Figure G.0.1 Reference model

1 User services, terminals

1.1 ATM and B-ISDN – An introduction

Asynchronous transfer mode (ATM) is a connection-oriented, cell-based technique for the transfer of information. (See Volume 1, Chapter 2, Subsection 2.10.10.)

Broadband integrated services digital network (B-ISDN) is a further development of the narrowband integrated services digital network (N-ISDN) concept. In the early 1980s, it was foreseen that a need would soon arise for services requiring greater bandwidths than those supported by N-ISDN, that is, bandwidths exceeding 2 Mbit/s. A solution to facilitate increased access bandwidth had been sketched out by the mid-1980s. At its core were three fixed-bandwidth high-speed channels, but this was not an ideal solution. The fixed bandwidths (comprising 2 Mbit/s and 140 Mbit/s, for example) would be unsuitable for services that required other capacities. Above all, these fixed-bandwidth channels would not be able to effectively handle services with varying bandwidth requirements. As a result of the introduction of the ATM concept and its apparent bit-rate flexibility, the International Telecommunications Union – Telecommunications Standardization Sector (ITU-T) selected this technique as the basis for B-ISDN services.

N-ISDN and B-ISDN differ in two vital respects:

- *Bandwidth.* N-ISDN employs a switched bandwidth of $n \cdot 64$ kbit/s up to 2 Mbit/s. B-ISDN can switch different bit rates, from 64 kbit/s and lower to rates exceeding 100 Mbit/s.
- *Degree of integration.* N-ISDN specifies a range of transfer modes, all of which must be managed by the network operator. B-ISDN utilises only one mode – ATM – that can offer all services. (See also Volume 1, Chapter 3, Section 3.5.)

The ATM cell is a small packet having a fixed length of 53 octets, five of which comprise the header. The remaining 48 octets make up the information field.

The fact that the information field is just 48 octets is the result of a compromise that was arrived at during the standardisation process. The US wanted a 64-octet information field and the Europeans wanted one that contained 32 octets. A short cell is better suited to real-time services, which are sensitive to network delays – telephony being the most typical example. Filling a cell with speech from an individual call connection takes about 6 ms. If the cell is too long, the entire information field cannot be utilised for services that are sensitive to delays, which results in poor utilisation. On the other hand, a longer cell is more effective for different types of data communication service because it has less "overhead", that is, data-management information.

ATM can be utilised for the transfer of audio, video and data at the right quality and over all distances, covering the entire range from local area networks (LANs) to wide area networks (WANs). A service-integrated broadband network will open up new opportunities for operators, notably in the area of new teleservices.

Future broadband networks will be capable of handling multimedia calls in which at least two connections make up the "call", for example one data and one video connection. And it will very likely be possible to vary the combination of services while the call is in progress.

Broadband networks will also be expected to manage point-to-multipoint connections, which are of interest for distributive services, such as TV applications. In the long run, it should even be possible to set up multipoint-to-multipoint connections. Conceivable applications are virtual LANs or videoconferencing. What will then be the roles of ATM and B-ISDN in these future broadband networks?

ATM's strength as a transfer mode lies in its hardware-based, extremely fast broadband switching that is superior to current router techniques and ordinary circuit-switching techniques. However, ATM is regarded as weaker in multiplexing capability because of the larger amount of overhead in cell-based transmission systems compared to packet-based X.25 and frame-relay networks. This factor will become less important over time, as transmission costs continue to decline.

The switching characteristics of ATM are extremely well suited to both public and large business networks. ATM can therefore evolve into a unified transfer mode "from desktop to desktop".

As mentioned in Volume 1, Chapter 2, Subsection 2.10.6, cell-based transmission systems may become commonplace, if cell mode becomes generally accepted as the prevalent transfer mode. However, operators now investing in trunk and access networks are choosing synchronous digital hierarchy (SDH), the predominant transmission technique.

ATM can provide residential subscribers with services like video-on-demand and broadband Internet access. Telephony can also be integrated into these systems. Several transmission solutions are possible – chiefly cable-TV modems and asymmetrical digital subscriber line (ADSL) technique.

ATM is an excellent access alternative for large and medium-sized businesses. LAN interconnect, videoconferencing, private branch exchange (PBX) interconnect and broadband Internet access are viewed as services important for the business sector. A possible development scenario is explored in Chapter 10, Section 10.3.

The widespread use of B-ISDN is still a long way off. It would seem today as if the Internet may turn out to be a worthy competitor in the struggle for supremacy in the multimedia market. There are naturally other scenarios, in which interworking between ATM and Internet protocol (IP) networks figure largely. (See Chapter 9, Subsection 9.2.2.)

1.2 Service classes

All user services can be subdivided into two groups, regardless of the technique used: interactive and distributive services. (See Volume 1, Chapter 1, Subsection 1.3.2.) Services may then be further classified in accordance with their particular transfer requirements.

ATM has a service-dependent layer – the ATM adaptation layer (AAL) – that adapts user information to the ATM layer so as to make it service-independent.

Audio, video and data are the services that operators would like to transfer in one and the same network. They make different demands on the network and require different adaptation functionality. The result is three different parameters or requirements:

- the need for synchronisation between the sender and the receiver;
- constant or variable bit rate; and
- connection-oriented or connectionless transfer.

Four service classes – A, B, C and D – have been defined on the basis of these parameters. The services within each of the classes place similar demands on the ATM network.

Four protocols – designated AAL 1, AAL 2, AAL 3/4 and AAL 5 – support the different service classes.

1.2.1 Class A

Service class A includes constant bit rate (CBR) services for connection-oriented transfer with end-to-end synchronisation. Protocol AAL 1 supports service class A.

Examples of class A services are voice coded using pulse code modulation (PCM), circuit-emulated connections having a bit rate of $n \cdot 64$ kbit/s or $n \cdot 2$ Mbit/s and video signals coded for constant bit rate.

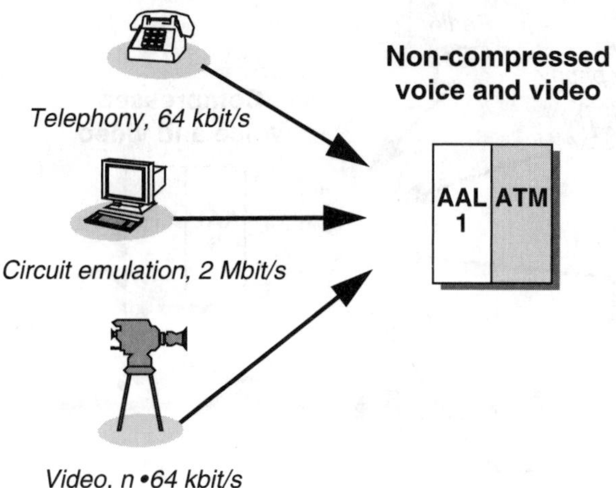

Figure G.1.1 Class A services

Circuit emulation is explained in more detail in Chapter 9, Subsection 9.3.1.

1.2.2 Class B

Service class B includes variable bit rate (VBR) services for connection-oriented transfer that demands end-to-end synchronisation. An example is the transfer of VBR-coded video signals.

To facilitate effective transfer of digital video, the bit stream must be compressed. The method that will be used is referred to as MPEG2 (specified by the Motion Picture Experts Group); it reduces the bit stream by a factor of 20, from 120 to 5–6 Mbit/s. The problem is, the greater the movement in a picture, the greater the need to transmit more information bits. This problem could be solved by providing a connection whose bit rate can be varied as required but which is synchronised to ensure that variations in the transfer rate are the same at both ends.

As seen in *Figure G.1.2*, several services can be made more efficient through the use of data compression. Using the adaptive differential PCM (ADPCM) technique, voice can be transferred at bit rates below 64 kbit/s. Services such as video-on-demand and music-on-demand might be future class B services.

Protocol AAL 2 was originally intended for these services. However, AAL 5 will be used instead, because AAL 2 has not yet become a standard. The future of AAL 2 is very uncertain.

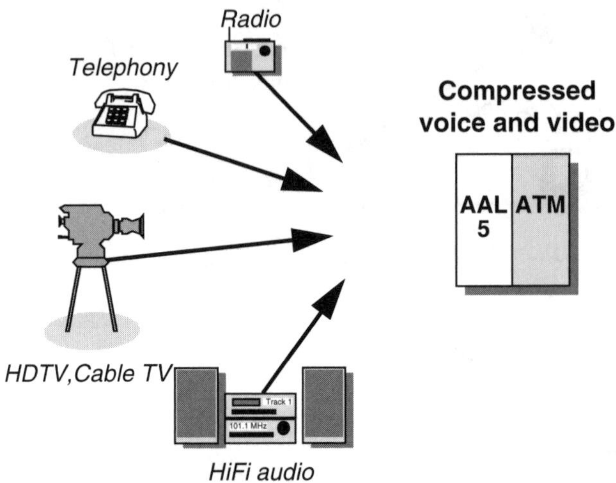

Figure G.1.2 Class B services

1.2.3 Class C

Service class C includes VBR services for connection-oriented transfer without any requirements for end-to-end synchronisation. Class C services (data services) can be supported by AAL 3/4 or AAL 5.

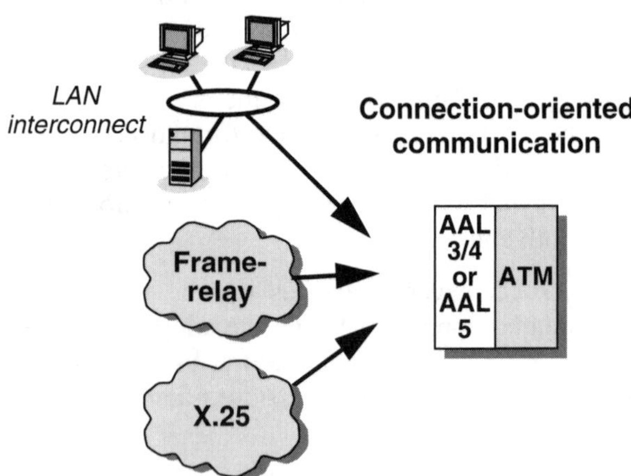

Figure G.1.3 Class C services

1.2.4 Class D

Service class D includes VBR services for connectionless transfer without any requirements for end-to-end synchronisation. Class D services can be supported by AAL 3/4 or AAL 5. LAN interconnect, switched multimegabit data services (SMDS) and especially the Internet with TCP/IP are examples of class D services.

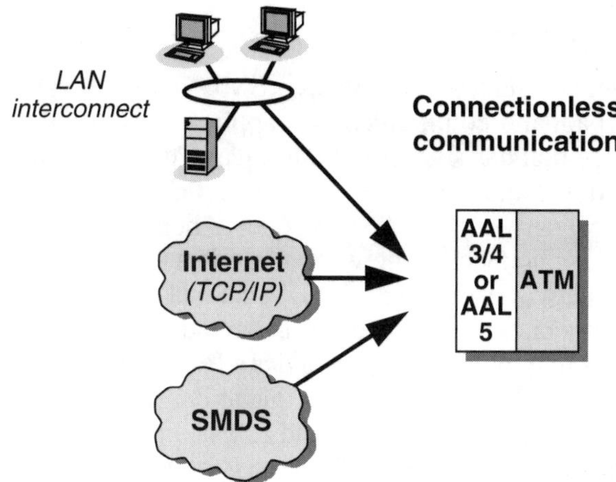

Figure G.1.4 Class D services

1.3 Public ATM services

The following section describes a number of public broadband services. Chapter 9 contains descriptions of circuit emulation (Subsection 9.3.1) and LAN emulation (Subsection 9.3.2).

1.3.1 ATM cell-relay services

Services of the cell-relay type provide direct delivery of ATM cells. The basic types of ATM connection are:

- Permanent virtual circuits (PVC) that are set up by the operator with the aid of a network management system.
- Switched virtual circuits (SVC) that are controlled by user signalling. B-ISDN requires SVC.
- Both SVC and PVC can be established in the form of virtual path connections (VPCs) or virtual channel connections (VCC). Companies wanting to create a private virtual ATM network can opt to lease a VPC in the form of a PVC and to manage their own virtual channels.

- Point-to-point connections and point-to-multipoint connections, which can be either of the PVC or the SVC type. Point-to-point connections can either be unidirectional or bidirectional, and the bidirectional connections can either be symmetrical or asymmetrical (the same bit rate or different bit rates in the two transmission directions). Point-to-multipoint connections are unidirectional virtual-channel circuits.

1.3.2 SMDS over ATM

Switched multimegabit data service access (SMDS) was developed in the US as the first broadband communications application – a public connectionless data service that has a specified interface to the user. The service is primarily intended for the effective interconnection of different private LANs. Today's local networks can be perceived as being "islands" of broadband communication; connection between these islands consists of significantly slower data networks or leased lines. What makes SMDS particularly interesting is its association with the world of data communication. The interfaces to SMDS that have been specified are IEEE's 802.6 metropolitan area network (MAN) solution, distributed queue dual bus (DQDB), which provides a natural connection to MANs and LANs, and AAL 3/4. Connectionless broadband data services (CBDS) is the European version of SMDS.

1.3.3 Interworking between networks over ATM

As mentioned in sections 1.2.3 and 1.2.4, ATM can support a diversity of data communication protocols, such as IP, frame relay and X.25. For more information, see Chapter 9.

2 Standards

2.1 Introduction

This chapter will deal with:

- standardisation organisations and cooperation between them;
- ATM interfaces and B-ISDN reference configurations; and
- protocol reference models.

ATM will be the dominant subject of this chapter. ATM's basic characteristics are described in Volume 1, Chapter 2, Subsection 2.10.11, where the distinction between B-ISDN and ATM is also addressed.

2.2 Standardisation organisations dealing with ATM and B-ISDN

Two types of organisations are engaged in the specification and standardisation of ATM and B-ISDN: formal standardisation bodies and industrial organisations.

The more notable formal standardisation organisations are the ITU-T, the European Telecommunications Standardisation Institute (ETSI) and the American National Standards Institute (ANSI). They primarily direct their efforts to areas dealing with ATM for public networks, for example B-ISDN.

The most notable industrial organisations are:

- ATM Forum;
- Frame Relay Forum;
- SMDS Interest Group;
- Internet Engineering Task Force (IETF); and
- Digital Audio Visual Council (DAVIC).

These organisations consist of users, vendors, operators and experts who represent universities and colleges of advanced technology. They are engaged in developing standards to ensure interoperability between equipment supplied by different vendors. The organisations concentrate on current standardisation issues to develop ATM solutions that the ITU-T can use as a basis for their recommendations. Being backed by large industrial organisations, these solutions quite naturally can be expected to have significant impact.

2.2.1 ATM Forum

The ATM Forum is a non-profit international organisation. It was established for the purpose of promoting the early use of ATM products and services through the timely development of interoperability specifications.

At its start in 1991, the ATM Forum had four members. Today the organisation consists of more than 700 members who are primarily engaged in the application of ATM to private networks or to business services.

The ATM Forum consists of one world-wide technical committee and three marketing committees, covering North America, Europe and the Asia-Pacific region. The Enterprise Network Roundtable is an additional forum in which ATM users are welcome to participate.

2.3 Standards and recommendation sources

B-ISDN and ATM are specified in ITU-T recommendations. However, it is the ATM Forum's recommendations that are initially implemented in ATM equipment.

The following working groups have been organised under the ATM Forum:

- Broadband Inter-Carrier Interface (BICI) and Interworking among ATM Networks (IAN);
- LAN Emulation (LANE);
- Multiprotocol Over ATM (MPOA);
- Network Management (NM);
- Physical Layer (PHY);
- Private Network to Network Interface (PNNI);
- Residential Broadband (RBB);
- Service Aspects and Applications (SAA);
- Security (SEC);
- Signalling (SIG);
- Testing (TEST);
- Traffic Management (TM);
- Voice and Telephony over ATM (VTOA); and
- Wireless ATM (WATM).

The ITU-T releases ATM and B-ISDN recommendations as they are completed. The recommendations are included in the I series.

2.4 Network interfaces and reference configurations

2.4.1 ATM network interfaces

The access interface is referred to as the user–network interface (UNI), and the interface between network nodes is referred to as the network–node interface (NNI). In the case of private networks, *private NNI (P-NNI)* denotes the interface between nodes or between different private networks. The interface between the public networks of two operators is referred to as a broadband inter-carrier interface (B-ICI).

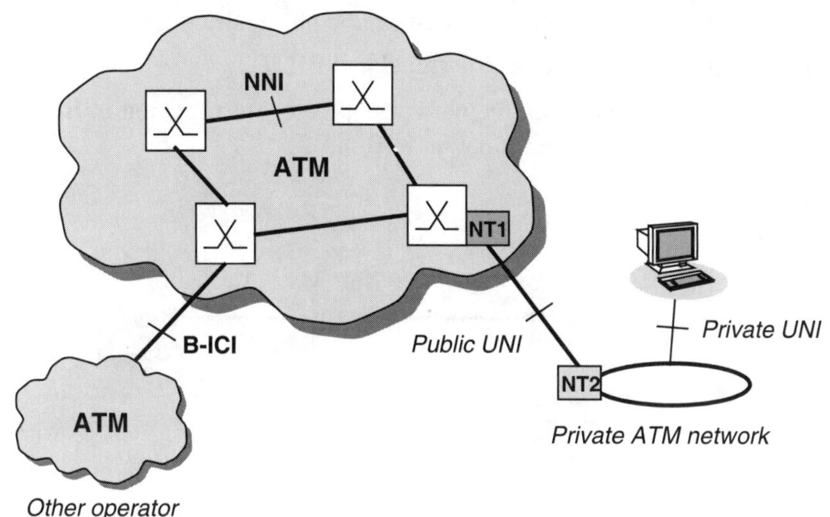

Figure G.2.1 ATM network interfaces

2.4.2 B-ISDN UNI reference configuration

Figure G.2.2 shows the reference configuration for B-ISDN access. (It is analogous to the corresponding configuration for N-ISDN.) A reference configuration is a general description in the form of a block diagram and is based on:

- *functional groups:* units having a distinct standardised function;
- *reference points:* points that demarcate the boundaries between functional groups;
- *B-TE:* a terminal that terminates all protocols that are employed between the users;
- *B-NT 2:* network termination (a private exchange or a private computer network, for example) that manages cell synchronisation, concentration, buffering and local switching;
- *B-NT 1:* network termination that primarily performs functions in the lower protocol layers, such as the termination of the transmission system and its operation and maintenance channels;
- *TE 2:* a terminal for N-ISDN; and
- *B-TA:* an adapter for broadband terminals.

The R, S, T and U reference points are indicated in *Figure G.2.2*. Only two of them are specified as interfaces that can be physically implemented:

- S is the interface between the terminal and B-NT 2;
- T is the interface between the network operator (termination in B-NT 1) and a private network (termination in B-NT 2).

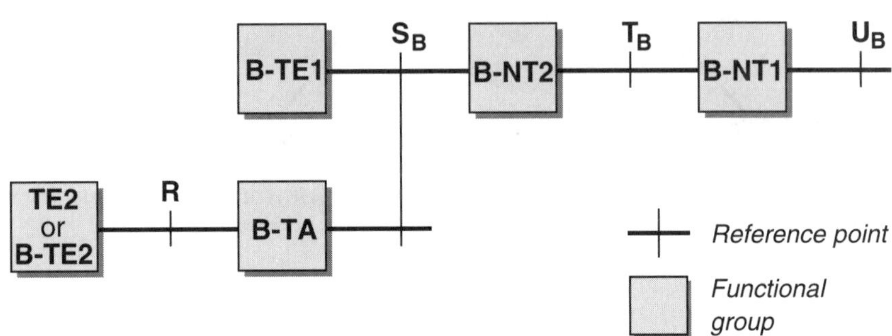

Figure G.2.2 Reference configuration for B-ISDN user-network interface

2.5 Protocol reference models

The ITU-T has standardised a layered protocol reference model greatly similar to the open systems integration (OSI) model. To allow the system to handle the data transfer rates associated with broadband, ATM protocols must be simple, low-level protocols. The various functions that can be included in the protocol stack, as well as their placement in the stack, are also addressed.

The model differs from OSI in that the different layers have also been divided into a number of planes, as shown in *Figure G.2.3*. The portion of the model which deals with the transfer of data between users is referred to as the user plane; the part supporting signalling is referred to as the control plane. The subdivision applies to protocols residing in AAL and above. A management plane deals with the control of ATM nodes.

See Volume 1, Chapter 2, Subsection 2.10.10, for a summary description of the protocol reference model for ATM.

AAL adapts the flow of information as it arrives from the user and segments the information so that the ATM layer can manage the flow in a service-independent manner. At the receiving end, AAL reassembles the information flow again so that the receiver can manage it. For isochronous services, any variations in the delay of the received cells are compensated for.

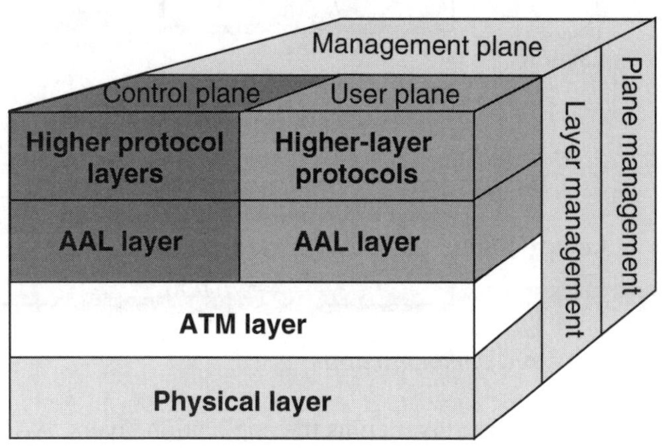

Figure G.2.3 Protocol reference model for B-ISDN

The ATM layer creates ATM cells by adding headers to the packets received from AAL, thereby providing the switching and multiplexing capabilities required of a transfer mode.

The task of the physical layer is to transport the ATM cells that were created in the ATM layer.

2.5.1 Layered communication – An overview

In layered communication, a layer (N) performs services called for by the layer just above it (layer N+1) and utilises the services provided by the layer just below it (layer N-1). (See *Figure G.2.4.*) Layer N receives (payload) data from layer N+1.

A protocol data unit (PDU) is involved in layered communication. An (N+1) PDU contains information that is to be sent to layer N+1 at the receiving end.

A service data unit (SDU) is also involved. The N SDU contains information for the service to be provided by layer N.

A number of functions are performed in layer N. The SDU may be processed (for example, segmented) before a header – and possibly a trailer – is added to create an N PDU. The combination of header and trailer is referred to as the *protocol control information (PCI).*

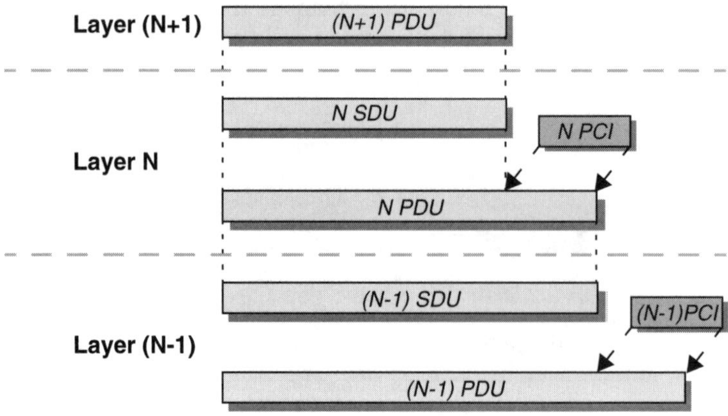

Figure G.2.4 Layered communication

ATM is made up of three layers plus the application layers. AAL communicates with the higher layers and with the layer just beneath it (the ATM layer). An AAL PDU corresponds to an ATM SDU.

All AAL PDUs have a length of 48 octets.

2.5.2 ATM adaptation layer

The AAL consists of a number of different protocols, each of which is specialised in the support of services found in the four service classes – A, B, C and D. The four most important AALs are described below.

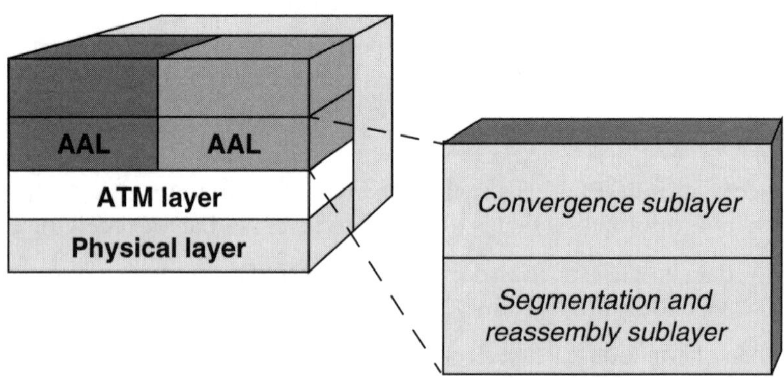

Figure G.2.5 Two AAL sublayers

The AAL is subdivided into two sublayers: the convergence sublayer (CS) and the segmentation and reassembly (SAR) sublayer. The CS performs the convergence functions required to map both connection-oriented and connectionless bit streams from higher layers onto the SAR and ATM layers. The function of the SAR sublayer is to deliver 48-octet packets from the higher layers to the ATM layer. SAR also reassembles the information flow that is sent through the network.

AAL 1

The purpose of AAL 1 is the realisation of circuit-switched connections with constant bit rate and minimal delay. In other words, AAL 1 supports class A services.

User information, delivered to AAL 1 at a constant bit rate, is placed in a segmentation and reassembly protocol data unit (SAR-PDU) that is made up of 48 octets. The information is subdivided into packets containing 47 octets and a one-octet SAR header. The packets are then forwarded to the ATM layer, where they will fill out the cell's information field. (See *Figure G.2.6.*)

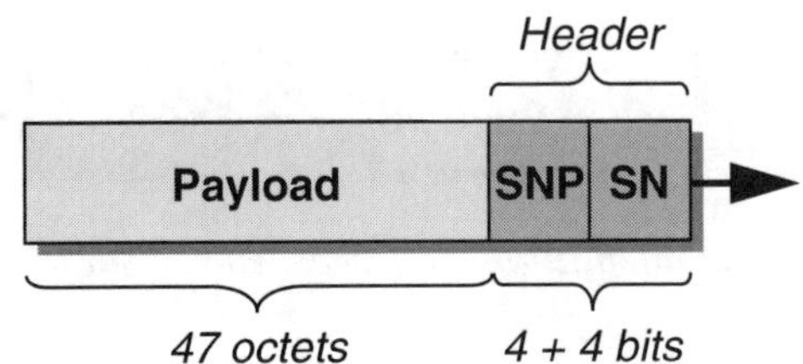

Figure G.2.6 AAL 1 segmentation and reassembly sublayer protocol data unit

The SAR-PDU has a header consisting of eight bits, four of which make up a sequence number (SN) used to detect lost or misinserted cells. The remaining four bits provide for sequence number protection (SNP) – used when performing a checksum control for the four SN bits. No error checking is performed on the remaining 47 octets of the information field, since occasional bit errors in data transfer for these types of service are not critical.

It is not necessary for all 47 octets to be utilised for the payload. The number of octets actually used is determined by the delay that the service in question is able to tolerate. The delay is caused by the fact that it takes a finite amount of time to fill a cell (6 ms in the case of voice).

The following functions can be performed by the CS layer:

• error correction in some audio and video applications;

• synchronisation; and

• the handling of lost and incorrectly addressed (misinserted) cells.

AAL 2

The purpose of AAL 2 is the realisation of circuit-switched connections with variable bit rate and minimal delay. In other words, AAL 2 supports class B services. AAL 2 has not yet been completely specified.

AAL 2 places the bit stream from higher layers into a 48-octet SAR-PDU that is then forwarded to the ATM layer. In this case, the size of the packets sent can vary from time to time and can even exceed the size of the ATM cell. If so, the packets will be distributed over a number of cells.

The ITU-T has recommended the structure shown in *Figure G.2.7* for the AAL 2 SAR-PDU.

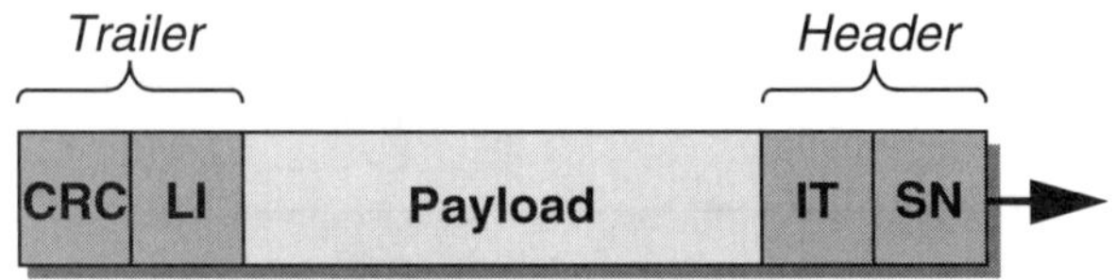

Figure G.2.7 AAL 2 segmentation and reassembly sublayer protocol data unit

SN is a four-bit cyclic counter that is used to keep track of lost and incorrectly addressed cells.

The information type (IT) can assume three different values:

- Beginning of message (BOM) indicates that the SAR-PDU contains the beginning of a longer message;
- Continuation of message (COM) indicates that the SAR-PDU contains the continuation of a previous data packet and that more data is to follow; and
- End of message (EOM) indicates the end of a data packet.

These fields receive their values in the sending terminal and are used by the receiving terminal to indicate that a number of cells are to be combined into a larger packet before being handed over to the next higher layer.

Class B traffic often contains its most significant information at the beginning of the information packets. The AAL can then request that the ATM layer assign higher priority to those cells that contain the most significant information. *Information payload* refers to the actual space allotted to the payload. As in the case of AAL 1, it is not necessary that all octets be utilised.

The length indicator (LI) is used to indicate how much of the space allotted to the payload is actually utilised.

The cyclic redundancy check (CRC) field is used for the correction of bit errors wherever they occur within the SAR-PDU, which is not the case for class A traffic. It is vital that all bits are correctly transferred in the case of class B traffic, since they are often generated by a compression algorithm (an example is the differential coding of video signals) where the effects of sporadic bit errors are multiplied and may cause serious disturbances.

The CS layer primarily performs the same functions as those performed for class A services.

AAL 3/4 and AAL 5 – Introduction

AAL 3/4 and AAL 5 support both class C and class D services, in other words, connection-oriented or connectionless services with variable bit rates and no end-to-end synchronisation. Consequently, we are speaking here of data communication services.

Originally, AAL 3 and AAL 4 were two separate protocols intended for class C and class D services, respectively. During the specification phase it was discovered that the two protocols were similar to one another, and they were therefore combined into AAL 3/4.

AAL 5 was specified when AAL 3/4 had been found to be too complex for certain services.

The CS layers of both AAL 3/4 and AAL 5 have been divided into two sublayers: a service-specific convergence sublayer (SSCS) and a common part convergence sublayer (CPCS). As is evident from the sublayers' names, as many common class C and class D functions as possible were selected for specification in the CPCS. Functions that are unique to a specific service have been placed in the SSCS. Hence, a special SSCS exists for each service.

There are special SSCSs for connectionless services.

AAL 3/4

AAL 3/4 is primarily used the for the connectionless SMDS and CBDS services. (See Subsection 1.3.2.)

Information packets of varying sizes are sent to the CS layer, which packs them into a protocol data unit: CS-PDU. The CS-PDU is then forwarded to the SAR layer, where it is subdivided into 48-octet SAR-PDUs, which are in turn handed over to the ATM layer.

The CS-PDU consists of an information field having a maximum length of 65,532 octets, a header and a trailer, each containing four octets. The header and trailer contain information used for the allocation of receiver buffer space and for error detection. The *PAD* field is a padding field of 0, 1, 2 or 3 octets, the purpose of which is to adjust the length of the CS-PDU to a multiple of 32 bits (four octets).

Two modes – message mode and streaming mode – are defined in the CS; both are used for transfer with or without mechanisms for retransmission and flow control. Running in message mode, the AAL-SDU is sent as a coherent block; in streaming mode, it will be subdivided into a number of smaller parts and its transmission can therefore be initiated before it has been received in its entirety by the AAL. This is described in ITU-T Recommendation I.363.

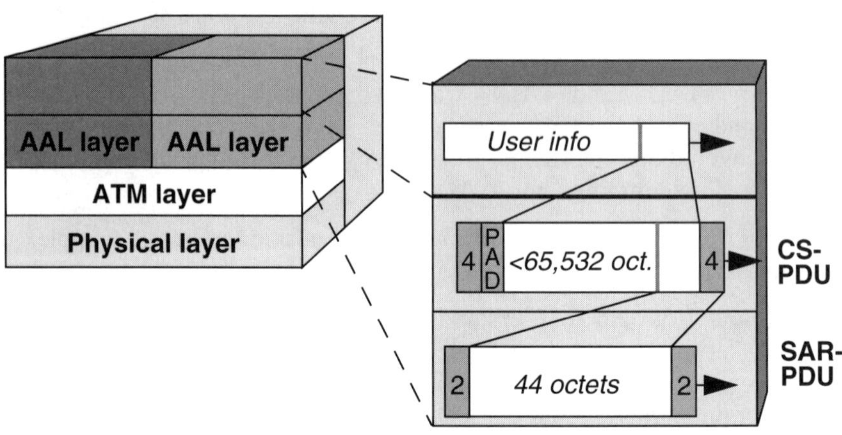

Figure G.2.8 Segmentation of the AAL 3/4 convergence sublayer protocol data unit

The CS-PDU is transferred from the CS layer to the SAR layer where it is divided into one or more SAR-PDUs. The structure of the AAL 3/4 SAR-PDU is illustrated in *Figure G.2.9*.

Segment type (ST) is a two-bit field that can assume one of four values. It is used to indicate whether the SAR-PDU contains:

- BOM;
- COM;
- EOM; or
- Single-segment message (SSM), which means that there is sufficient space for the entire CS-PDU in one SAR-PDU.

SN serves the same purpose in AAL 3/4 as in AAL 1.

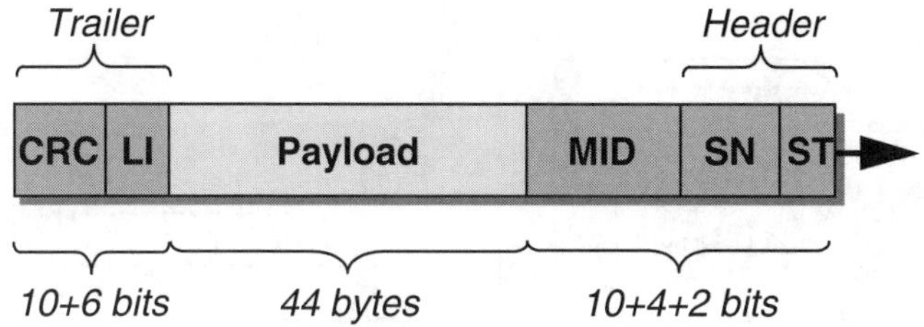

Figure G.2.9 AAL 3/4 segmentation and reassembly sublayer protocol data unit

Multiplexing identification (MID) is a 10-bit field used to distinguish between the different CS-PDUs that are concurrently transferred over one and the same ATM connection. SAR-PDUs belonging to the same CS-PDU have the same MID value.

The information payload consists of 44 octets and makes up segments of the corresponding CS-PDU.

The LI is used to indicate how many of the 44 octets contained in the information payload actually contain user data (portions of the CS-PDU). Neither EOMs nor SSM SAR-PDUs are required to be composed of exactly 44 octets. The value of LI must be a multiple of 4.

CRC is a 10-bit checksum. Bit-error checking is performed on the entire SAR-PDU.

As we mentioned, AAL 3/4 is a complex protocol.

AAL 5

One disadvantage of the AAL 3/4 protocol is its relatively large overhead and the resulting low efficiency. For that reason, designers developed AAL 5, which is less complex but provides more reliable bit-error checking. Its simplicity and efficiency have led to AAL 5 being named *simple and efficient adaptation layer (SEAL).*

AAL 5 is used for frame relay, LAN emulation and signalling. It is limited to the handling of message mode without the use of any retransmission mechanisms.

AAL 5 defines a CS-PDU that communicates with the SAR function. Like AAL 3/4, the CS-PDU information field can consist of a maximum of 65,532 octets. The CS-PDU – which has a trailer of eight octets including information for error detection and error handling – is filled by the PAD field with up to 47 octets so that a multiple of 48 is achieved.

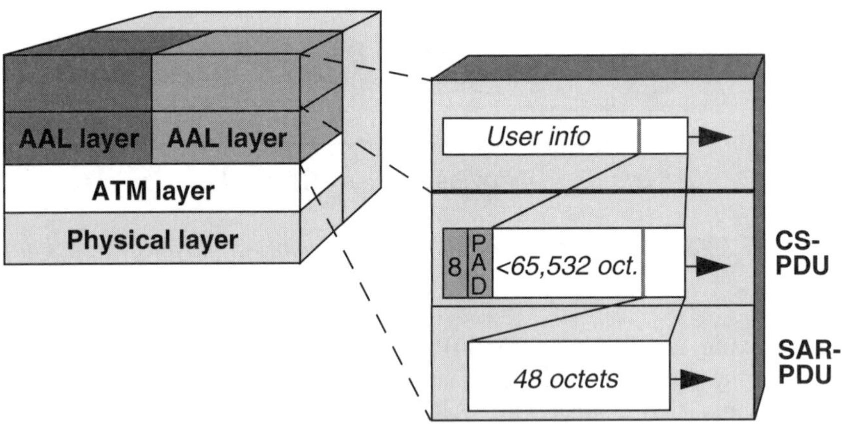

Figure G.2.10 Segmentation of the AAL 5 convergence sublayer protocol data unit

Using the PAD field allows all SAR-PDUs to be filled, doing away with the need for the LI. On the other hand, since no field exists that corresponds to the AAL 3/4 ST field, it must be possible to detect the start and end of CS-PDUs. The payload type identifier (PTI) field in the ATM cell header is therefore used to indicate the arrival of the last cell from a CS-PDU, so that the CS-PDU can be reconstructed in the receiving equipment.

Buffer allocation at the receiving end is made complex by the fact that AAL 5 does not indicate the length.

In spite of these problems, the standardisation of AAL 5 represents a significant advance. There now exists a complete standard for class C services that favours the development of both private ATM switch modules and ATM chips.

Connectionless services employing AAL 3/4 and AAL 5

Both AAL 3/4 and AAL 5 are intended to support class D services, that is, connectionless services. How then can a connection-oriented technique such as ATM support connectionless services?

The answer lies in the fact that the operator employs a connectionless server (CLS). The CLS terminates the AAL protocol and performs tasks related to connectionless transfer.

All connectionless packets are sent to the CLS over the ATM links. The server then forwards the data packets to their correct destination address, via a number of CLSs if necessary. It is highly probable that dial-up connections will be used to connect a user to a CLS when user signalling is introduced. Each time a connectionless packet is to be sent between a user and the server, a new ATM connection will be established.

Today's user has a fixed connection to the CLS. Connections between different CLSs will very likely be established as semipermanent connections.

There are situations in which connectionless transfer is preferable; for example, when one wishes to avoid the delay caused by the connection set-up phase in a node or when the communication in question is less frequent and very brief. Connectionless transfer is preferable if a company has two separate LANs/MANs and wants them to be perceived as a single network.

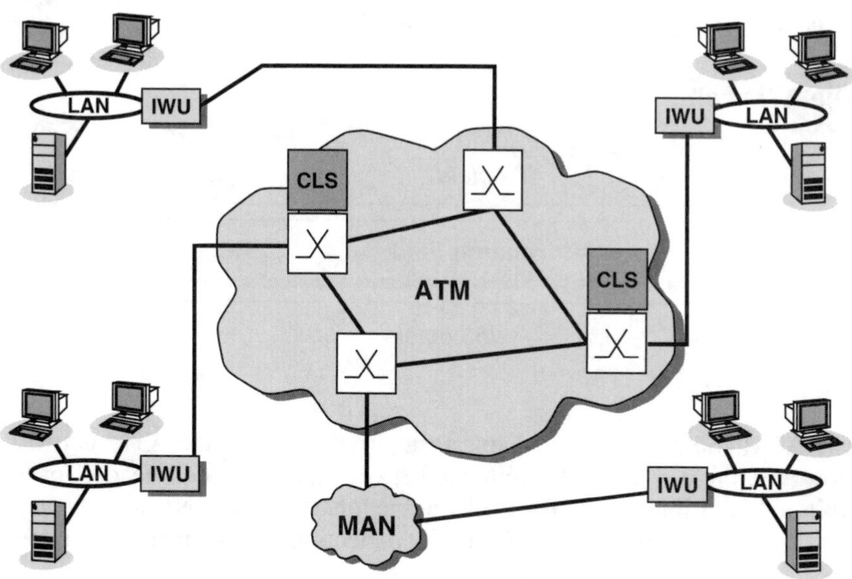

Figure G.2.11 An ATM network with connectionless servers

2.5.3 The ATM layer

The ATM layer handles ATM cells. As mentioned earlier, an ATM cell consists of a header composed of five octets and an information field of 48 octets. It is important to note once again that only the cell header is processed in ATM nodes. The information field is unaffected and is sent transparently through an ATM network.

In addition to cells containing user information and those used for signalling, the ATM layer also handles certain unassigned cells, as well as operation and maintenance cells.

Functions of the ATM layer

The principal functions of the ATM layer are as follows:

- To create the ATM cell by adding a header to the information field that is received from the AAL. At the receiving end, the ATM layer removes the cell header before the cell is received by the AAL.
- To multiplex and demultiplex the cell flows from different connections. The connections are identified by the virtual channel identifier (VCI) or virtual path identifier (VPI) values contained in the cell headers.
- To read and interpret the information fields in the cell header. The VCI/VPI is read and translated in the ATM nodes to ensure that cells are sent to the correct address.
- To provide mechanisms for flow control.

The ATM cell

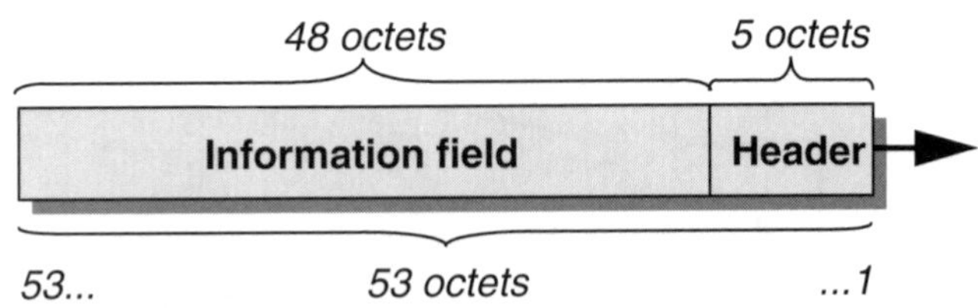

Figure G.2.12 The ATM cell

The ATM cell maintains the same structure throughout the ATM network. However, there is a slight difference between the ATM cell headers of the UNI and NNI interfaces. The VPI field is longer in the NNI, which can be motivated by the greater need of trunk connections between network nodes.

The octets of the cell are sent in number sequence (1 to 53), as shown in *Figure G.2.12*. The individual bits within each of the octets is sent in reverse number sequence in accordance with *Figure G.2.13*. Simply stated, one may say that the bits are transmitted in the same order as when reading text from a page.

We will now turn to an analysis of the roles of the various fields in the cell header.

- Generic flow control (GFC) is a four-bit field that is defined in the UNI interface. Flow control functionality in the user interface may make use of the GFC field. The objective is to ensure that the bandwidth, assigned to each service, is not exceeded. The four bit positions will assume a value of "0" if empty cells are sent. GFC is not yet completely standardised.
- VPI is a field used to identify virtual paths. The VPI field consists of 8 bits in the UNI interface and 12 bits in the NNI interface. An empty cell assumes a VPI value of "0" for all bits.
- VCI is a field consisting of 16 bits used to identify virtual channels. Empty cells assume a value of "0" for all bits in the VCI field. Other VCI values may be reserved for information such as signalling channels. In their recommendations, the ITU-T has reserved the first 16 VCI values in every virtual path for special purposes. Similarly, the ATM Forum has reserved the first 32 VCI values in every VPI.

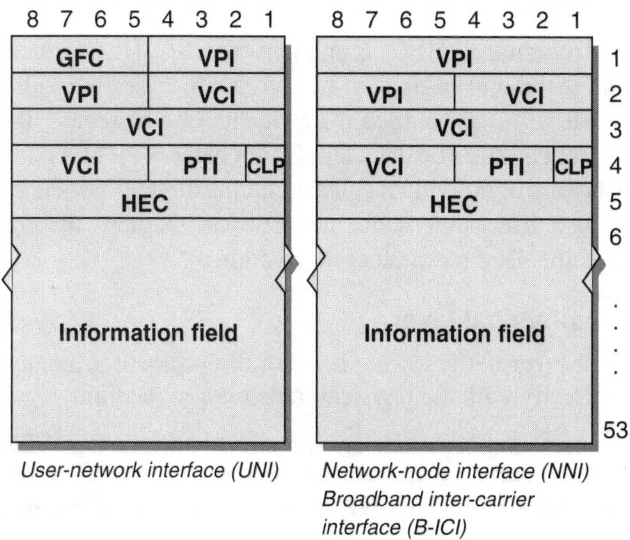

Figure G.2.13 ATM cell header for user-network interface and network-node interface

A broadband terminal connected to an ATM network uses a VPI/VCI address when requesting – via the nearest ATM exchange – that a connection be set up across the network. A virtual connection is created consisting of numerous links through the ATM network, all the links having different addresses (VPI/VCI). The VPI/VCI in the cell header is thus changed in the ATM switches. The same link addresses apply in both directions.

- PTI is a three-bit field used to indicate the type of load being transferred and to indicate whether or not the network has been overloaded during the transfer of the cell. Examples of load type are operation and maintenance cells, signalling cells, idle cells, and, naturally, cells containing user information.
- Cell loss priority (CLP) is a bit that can be used to set the priorities of different cells in an overloaded network. If the bit is set to "1", the cell may be discarded if the network becomes overloaded. If the bit is set to "0", the cell has higher priority. An example of its use is the transfer of video-coded signals. For this type of transfer, the compression algorithm operates such that the first five octets have greater significance than the other octets and thus are placed in a cell with higher priority. In certain situations, even the ATM network can affect the CLP bit. If a connection exceeds its negotiated bandwidth, the ATM network can "penalise" the user (regardless of whether or not the link has sufficient capacity) by giving lower priority to the cells associated with the connection.
- Header error control (HEC) is an eight-bit CRC. HEC can correct single-bit errors that occur in the cell header. Multi-bit errors will be detected, but the cell will be discarded if they cannot be corrected. It is important that header cell errors be detected. Errors in the VPI/VCI address not only lead to the loss of individual cells, including all data associated with them, but will also affect other cells in the flow if the new, incorrect VPI/VCI value is being used for another connection.

2.5.4 The physical layer

The physical layer is the lowest layer of the protocol reference model and interfaces directly with the physical transmission medium.

The layer's principal functions are to collect and organise ATM cells from the ATM layer and to transport them to the physical medium. Aided by HEC and cell synchronisation, the physical layer is responsible for the correct transfer of ATM cells.

The functions of the physical layer are divided into two sublayers:

- the physical medium sublayer, which handles and adapts bits as they are fed to the physical medium, for example, optical or electrical conversion; and
- the transmission convergence sublayer, which converts the flow of cells from the ATM layer into a continuous bit stream.

This conversion involves:

- the adaptation of ATM cell speed to the transmission system's bit rate (cell rate decoupling);
- cell synchronisation, that is, determination of the position of the ATM cell boundaries in the bit stream (cell delineation);
- mapping of cells into the payload of the transmission frame; and
- the calculation and verification of HEC.

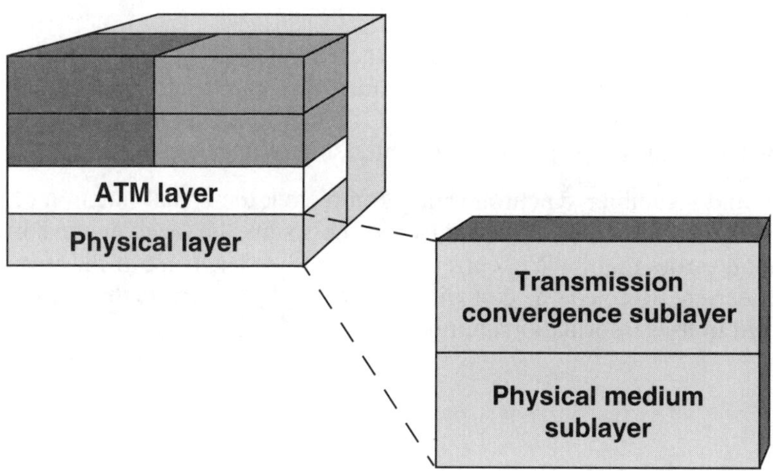

Figure G.2.14 The physical layer

The flow of cells is adapted to the transmission system's bit rate through padding with idle cells. The receiving end removes the idle cells, which it detects with the aid of a reserved cell pattern: VPI = 0, VCI = 1. The information field of an idle cell contains 10101010 in every octet.

Transmission systems that transmit bits in a framed structure must contain functionality that allows them to keep track of where the transmission frame starts. This applies to transmission systems based on SDH and plesiochronous digital hierarchy (PDH) but does not apply to cell-based systems.

A checksum – HEC – is transferred in the last octet of the five-octet cell header. The receiver uses HEC for three functions that must be performed in sequence:

1. The receiver calculates the checksum for four consecutive octets in the cell flow and compares the result with the value contained in the next octet to arrive. If the calculated value is equal to the value contained in the fifth octet, then the cell header has been identified, and the receiver can expect the next cell header to appear 53 octets later. If the calculated value is not equal to the fifth octet, the receiver will shift one bit position and repeat the calculation and the subsequent comparison. Bit after bit are summed and compared until the cell header has been identified. The receiver calculates the checksum for every 53 octets to verify that cell synchronisation has been attained.

This function makes it possible to transmit ATM cells transparently over different types of transmission system without the necessity of having a transmission frame that identifies the start of the cells.

2. The information field is scrambled (ordered randomly) to prevent any user from imitating, intentionally or unintentionally, a cell header in the information field. Two of the eight bits in the HEC field are used to inform the receiver as to where in the bit pattern the scrambler's random generator starts.

3. Cell and scrambler synchronisation completed, the actual function of the HEC field can be activated. Aided by the checksum, the receiver can correct single-bit errors that have occurred in the cell header. If multi-bit errors in the header are detected, the cell will be discarded. Any errors that may have occurred in user information are not corrected.

3 Switching and switch control

ATM switching is described in Volume 1, Chapter 3, Subsection 3.6.2. The following is only a short summary.

ATM networks are connection-oriented; that is, data transfer is preceded by a signalling procedure.

A logical connection through the network is defined by switching tables in the switching nodes. Signalling is performed using ATM cells.

In an ATM switch, ATM cells are transported from an incoming logical channel to one or more outgoing logical channels. A logical channel is designated by identities:

- the number of the physical link; and
- the logical channel number, that is, the incoming channel's VPI/VCI.

To execute the transfer of cells, an association must be established between the two identities of the incoming and outgoing channels. This is performed with the aid of tables.

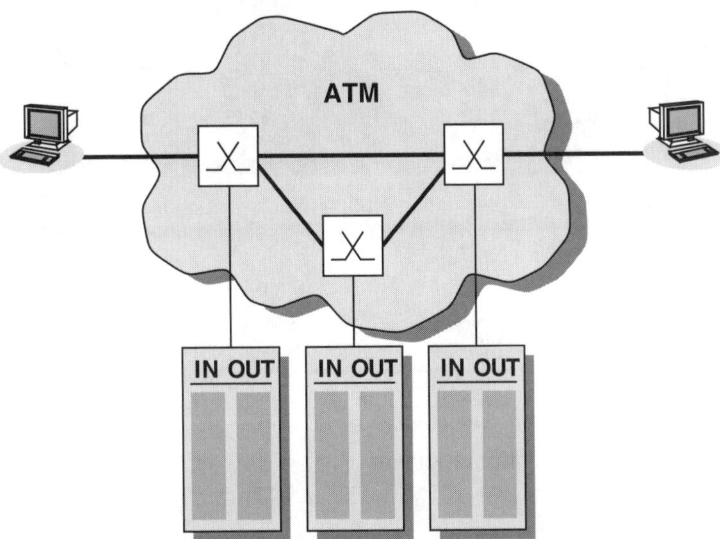

Figure G.3.1 Tables control routing through switching nodes

Since no time slots are used in ATM switching systems, problems can arise in combination with space switching, when two or more inputs simultaneously attempt to send cells to one and the same output. To avoid this situation, buffering must be introduced in the switch, thereby allowing the queuing of cells that cannot be immediately sent to the output. Since buffer size must be limited, cells can be lost in situations where buffer size is insufficient.

Figure G.3.2 illustrates a schematic example of how an ATM switch can be designed. The figure shows a switch module that has one input and three outputs. The switch core, which may be designed in the form of a matrix, a ring or a bus, has sufficient bandwidth so that no congestion can occur. This means that cells can be switched from all inputs to one and the same output and within the span of one "cell time" without any cells colliding at the output. "Cell time" is the time required for a cell to pass through the switch core.

In addition, buffers at the outputs allow cells to be multiplexed out onto the physical link in a continuous flow, using idle cells where necessary.

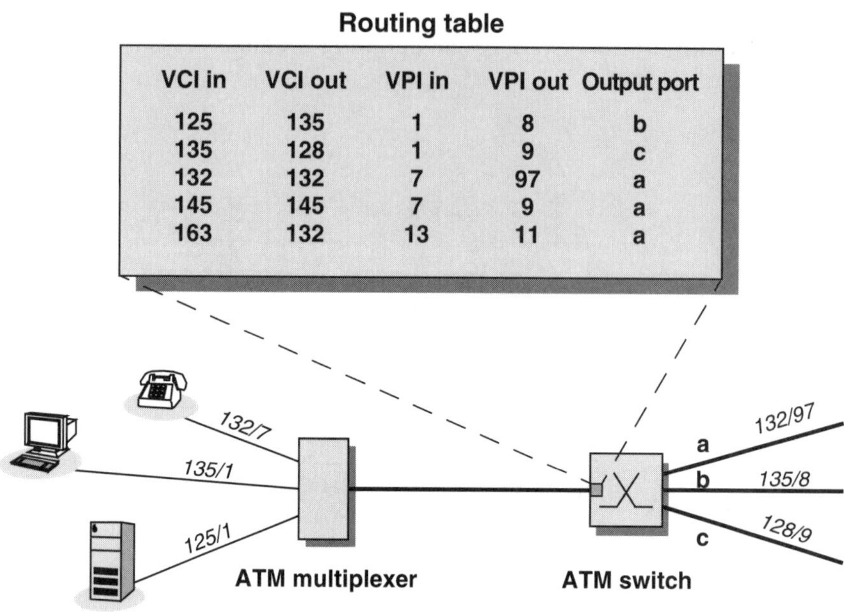

Routing table
VCI in
VCI out
VPI in
VPI out
Output port
125
135
1
8
b
135
128
1
9
c
132
132
7
97
a
145
145
7
9
a
163
132
13
11
a
132/7
135/1
125/1
ATM multiplexer
a
b
c
132/97
135/8
128/9
ATM switch

Figure G.3.2 Schematic diagram of an ATM switch

A function at the module's input reads the current logical channel number and then – in a table that is unique to every input – retrieves the output to which the cell should be switched and the new logical channel number that the cell is to be assigned on the next link. Cells are directed through the switch with the aid of a label that indicates the output port. The implementation of this label, which is only found in the switch, is not standardised.

We differentiate between virtual path and virtual channel switching. A virtual path switch handles only virtual path addresses, which means that VCI values pass unchanged through the switch. The switch may be regarded as an ATM cross-connect since it is controlled by the operator. Virtual channel switches handle both VPI and VCI addresses. *Figure G.3.3* illustrates virtual path and virtual channel switching. Note that only logical switching is illustrated, not physical switching.

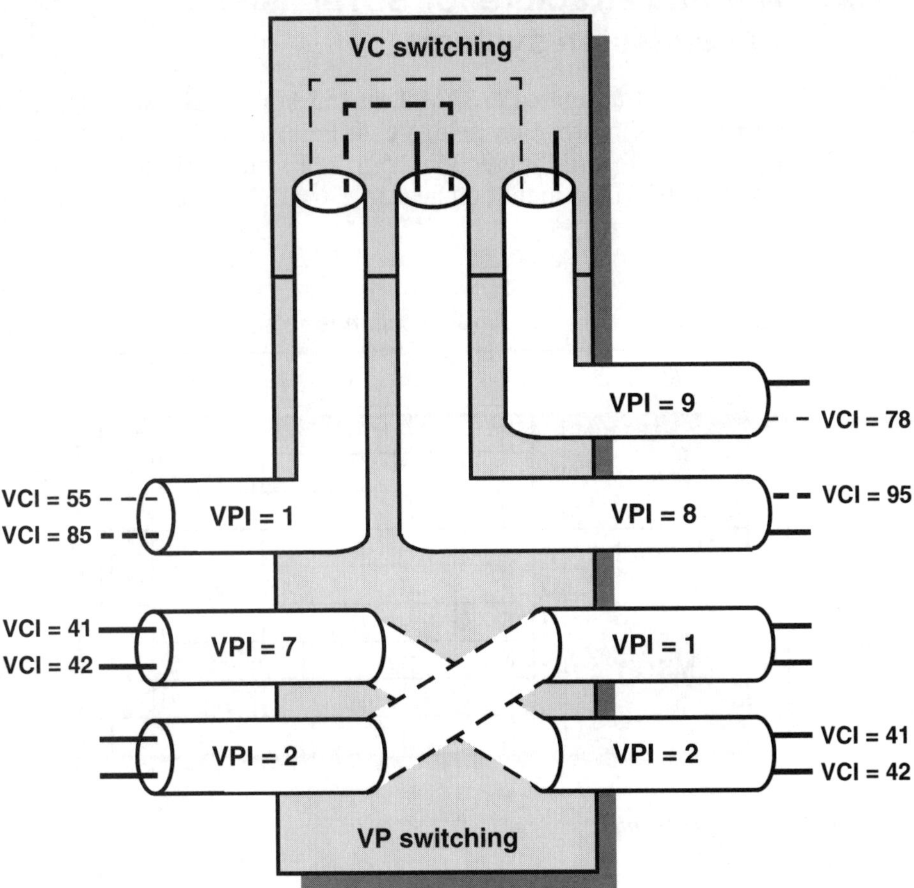

Figure G.3.3 Virtual path and virtual channel switching

4 Transmission techniques

4.1 Introduction

ATM transmission is generally based on PDH or SDH but can also be cell-based. In the latter case, a continuous flow of cells is transmitted.

The interfaces can be used asymmetrically. For example, a user can receive at 622 Mbit/s and send at 155 Mbit/s.

4.2 A frame structure for SDH-based transmission systems

When ATM cells are transmitted in STM-1 (at 155 Mbit/s) they are mapped into the SDH frame's information field, VC-4. Pointers indicate where the VC-4 starts. As described in Subsection 2.5.3, cell synchronisation is performed using the HEC field in the cell header.

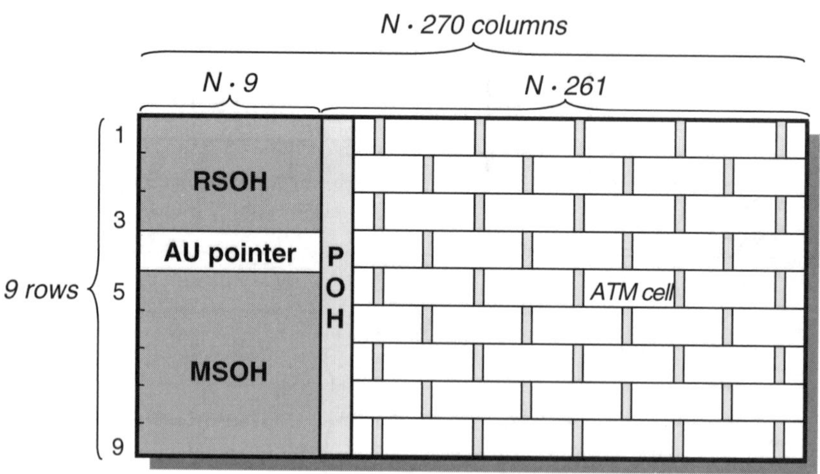

Figure G.4.1 SDH frame

When ATM cells are transmitted in STM-4 (at 622 Mbit/s) they are mapped into four concatenated information fields (VC-4–4c). Concatenation means that a number of virtual containers (VC) are linked together to create a larger virtual container that has the same capacity as the sum of the incorporated VCs. VC-4–4c represents four VC-4s that have been linked together. They are byte-interleaved, and a pointer points to the first VC-4. Through concatenation, the cell flow from many users can be multiplexed together and boost the efficiency of bandwidth utilisation.

Figure G.4.2 illustrates an STM-4 that has four VC-4s with ATM cells, and *Figure G.4.3* illustrates an STM-4 with four concatenated VC-4s.

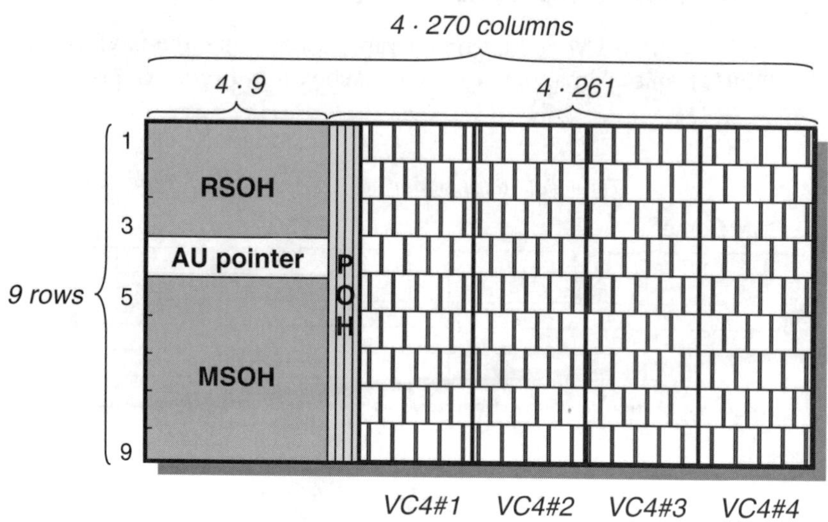

Figure G.4.2 ATM cells in an STM-4 having four VC-4s

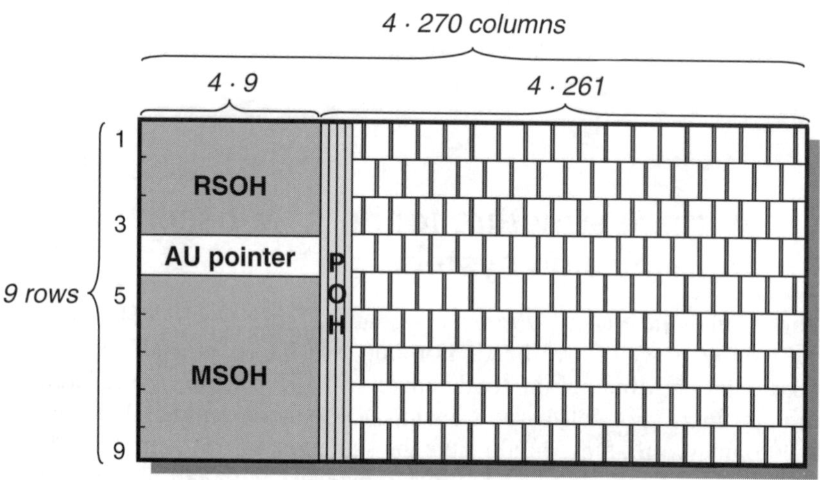

Figure G.4.3 ATM cells in an STM-4 having four concatenated VC-4s

4.3 A frame structure for a PDH-based 2 Mbit/s transmission system

Needless to say, the ATM cell is considerably longer than the payload of a PCM 2 Mbit/s frame. A mapping example is shown in *Figure G.4.4*.

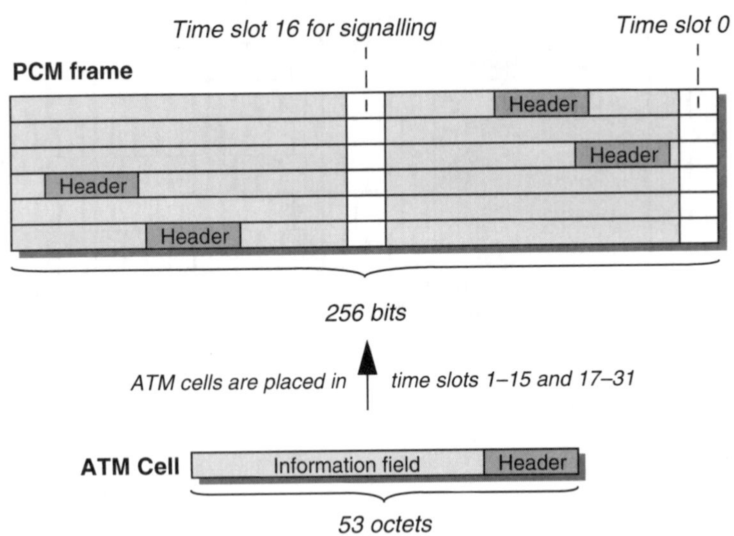

Figure G.4.4 ATM cells as they are transported in a 2 Mbit/s PCM system

4.4 A frame structure for an ATM-based transmission system

As shown in *Figure G.4.1*, *Figure G.4.2* and *Figure G.4.3*, STM modules contain quite a bit of overhead. For one STM-1, overhead amounts to approximately 6 Mbit/s of the total capacity of 155.2 Mbit/s, corresponding to one part in 27. For cell-based transmission systems and SDH systems to be able to interwork, they should have the same amount of overhead. That is the reason why a cell-based system reserves every 27th cell for such information.

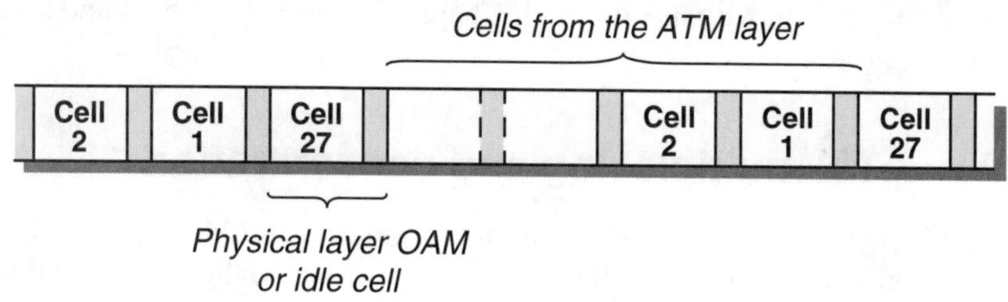

Figure G.4.5 ATM-based transmission system

5 Trunk and access networks

5.1 Trunk networks

ATM trunk networks are predominantly intended to be SDH-based; the design of ATM is based on it drawing maximum benefit from the functions SDH provides. ATM can also be carried by PDH, but monitoring functionality is much less effective in this case.

5.2 Access networks

The following public access interfaces have been standardised:

- 2 Mbit/s (PDH-based)
- 34 Mbit/s (PDH-based)
- 100 Mbit/s (FDDI standard)
- 155 Mbit/s (SDH-based)
- 622 Mbit/s (SDH-based)

Private ATM networks also support an access bit rate of 25.6 Mbit/s.

All existing transmission media can support the transfer of ATM cells: copper pairs, coaxial cable, optical fibre and radio. For access over copper pairs, digital subscriber line alternatives, such as ADSL, can be suitable. Hybrid fibre coax (HFC) can be used for access via coaxial cable. ADSL is addressed in Volume 1, Chapter 4, Subsection 4.4.3, and all the above access techniques are dealt with in Volume 1, Chapter 5, Subsections 5.14 and 5.15.

5.3 ATM multiplexing and concentration

An ATM access link carries a continuous flow of ATM cells which is adapted to the fixed bit rate of the link. The cell flow is achieved by feeding idle cells into the link when the number of user cells is not sufficient to fill it. All access links that reach an ATM multiplexer or concentrator are therefore filled to capacity. Idle cells are removed by the multiplexer, and user cells are multiplexed together on a new link. Due to the effect of multiplexing bursty traffic, the multiplexed flow will be less bursty than the tributaries. (See Volume 1, Chapter 5, Section 5.1, and Chapter 10, Subsection 10.2.2, of this Part.) Because idle cells are removed, the new link may have a lower bit rate than the sum of the incoming links' bit rates.

Since the combined flow of user cells is still uneven (and the cell flow maintains a lower bit rate than that of the SDH link being used), the new link must also be fed with idle cells.

6 Network intelligence and value-added services

ATM networks are primarily designed as being high-capacity connectivity networks. In the area of value-added services, the present trend is towards client–server networks, such as the Internet.

The Internet is perfectly suited to value-added services, such as information retrieval. Many of the value-added services that were originally intended to be used in conjunction with B-ISDN are available today via the Internet.

The most talked-about broadband value-added service for ATM is video-on-demand, illustrated in *Figure G.6.1*.

ATM and the Internet may also be viewed as complementing one another. In this case, value-added services are normally carried by the Internet.

Network intelligence will be a prerequisite for broadband virtual private network (VPN) services and mobile ATM communication.

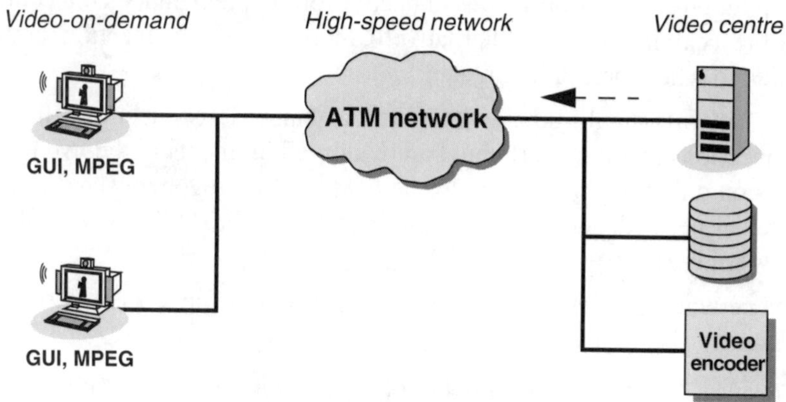

Figure G.6.1 Video-on-demand

7 Signalling

7.1 Introduction

Parts B, C, D and E of this Volume include descriptions of *circuit-switched networks* and their signalling. The following major trends are addressed:

- More powerful signalling between subscribers and the local exchange – to be performed on a separate channel. Example: The signalling performed on the D-channel in N-ISDN.
- More powerful signalling between exchanges and between exchanges and intelligent network nodes. In this case, a separate signalling network is used as the transport system (bearer network).

An ATM network differs from a circuit-switched network in many respects:

- The network is cell-based. Signalling must therefore also be cell-based.
- The network is divided into virtual channel and virtual path connections. Virtual channel connections are comparable to the access and trunk lines of a circuit-switched network. Virtual path connections are somewhat similar to the routes and leased lines of a circuit-switched network that are handled by a management system.

- The network is especially designed for multimedia communication. This may require the set-up or disconnection of supplementary connections during a call in progress. Alternatively, more than one connection may be required when the call is initiated.
- The network should be able to handle asymmetric connections; that is, connections that have different bandwidth requirements in the two transmission directions. It should also be possible to signal between different types of network service, for example, between TCP/IP and N-ISDN or between B-ISDN and non B-ISDN.
- The network handles different services in different ways when there is an imminent risk of cell loss or delay.

The result is that there are a number of significant differences between the signalling in an ATM network and that in circuit-switched networks:

- Signal messages are transmitted connectionless, without any requirement for end-to-end synchronisation (service class D). They are therefore broken down into ATM cells via AAL 5.
- A virtual channel is allocated in every virtual path to serve as a control channel for configuring signalling channels to satisfy users' needs for point-to-point or point-to-multipoint connections (broadcast/multicast).
- Current trends indicate development towards separating the call and connect functions, where – ideally – a path is only set up after it is certain that the network or the receiving terminal is capable of handling the service in question. The service-related phase is referred to as the "call", and we differentiate between call signalling and connect signalling. Call signalling is related to the signalling protocol described in Subsection 7.2.2, and the connect functions are related to the service-specific protocols in the AAL, described in Subsection 7.2.3.
- Negotiation on traffic characteristics is performed in the manner described in Chapter 8, Subsection 8.2.2.

7.1.1 Signalling on virtual channels

Signals are transmitted via signalling virtual channels (SVC) that consist of ATM cells. Several types of SVC have been specified:

- Meta-signalling virtual channels (MSVC) – one per interface – are bidirectional, 64 kbit/s, permanent signalling channels that can be connected or disconnected as required. The channel identified as having VCI = 5, VPI = 0 is reserved for MSVC. Meta-signalling is not used at present.

- Point-to-point signalling virtual channels (PSVC) are bidirectional and are used to connect, monitor and then disconnect VC and VP user connections. It should also be possible to establish VC and VP connections without the use of signalling, namely through a management system (subscription). Meta-signalling might be used to set up a PSVC; but MSVC (VCI = 5, VPI = 0) can also be employed directly for point-to-point connections.
- Broadcast signalling virtual channels (BSVC) are unidirectional from the network to the user and may be used for the transmission of signal messages to signalling points. It is possible to select the signalling points that are to be addressed, for example, to users who have a particular service profile. A BSVC can be set up using meta-signalling.

At present, VPI = 0, VCI = 5 is the channel on which all signalling is performed. PSVC and BSVC are not used. At some time in the future, it may be possible that VPI = 0, VCI = 5 will be used as a meta-signalling channel for the set-up of either PSVC or BSVC, depending on the type of connection to be established.

7.2 Signalling protocols – An overview

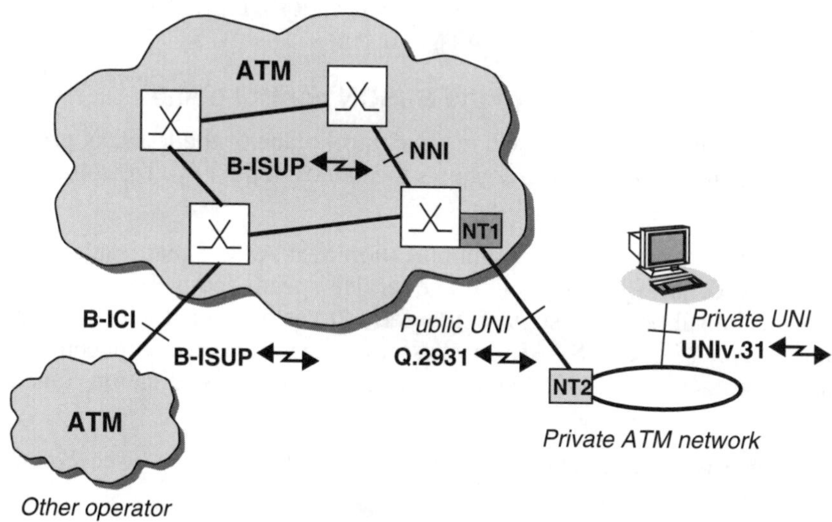

Figure G.7.1 Signalling protocols in an ATM network

Figure G.7.1 illustrates the various signalling protocols that are used in an ATM network.

7.2.1 Access network signalling

The ITU-T's Q.2931 is the protocol that specifies B-ISDN signalling across ATM UNI. UNI signalling for B-ISDN uses a system called digital subscriber signalling system No. 2 (DSS2). (See Subsection 7.3.1.)

The ATM Forum's protocol, AF UNI v3.1, specifies signalling for private UNIs. The signalling part of the protocol has been harmonised with the ITU-T's DSS2 specification. (See Subsection 7.3.2.)

7.2.2 Signalling between nodes and between networks

The ITU-T's broadband ISDN user part (B-ISUP) is based on signalling system no. 7 (SS7) and is used for signalling between the nodes of a public ATM network, that is, across an NNI. (See Subsection 7.4.1.)

B-ICI is a special version of B-ISUP used for signalling between public ATM networks that are run by different operators.

The ATM Forum's P-NNI specifies signalling between the nodes of a private ATM network. P-NNI signalling is based on UNI signalling. The PNNI protocol is primarily a routing protocol. (See Subsection 7.4.2.)

The specifications for these protocols are not complete at present.

The greater part of the signalling specifications currently being implemented are those issued by the ATM Forum.

7.2.3 The architecture of the B-ISDN control plane

Signalling functions are shown in the control plane of the B-ISDN protocol reference model. *Figure G.7.2* shows the names of the ITU-T recommendations that describe the signalling.

Signalling is based on data communication over AAL 5 that results in special ATM cells (signalling cells). The service-specific convergence sublayer is a special sublayer for signalling, referred to as the signalling ATM adaptation layer (SAAL). SAAL consists of a service-specific connection-oriented protocol (SSCOP), and a service-specific coordination function (SSCF).

MTP in *Figure G.7.2* stands for message transfer protocol. (See *Part E – The signalling network.*)

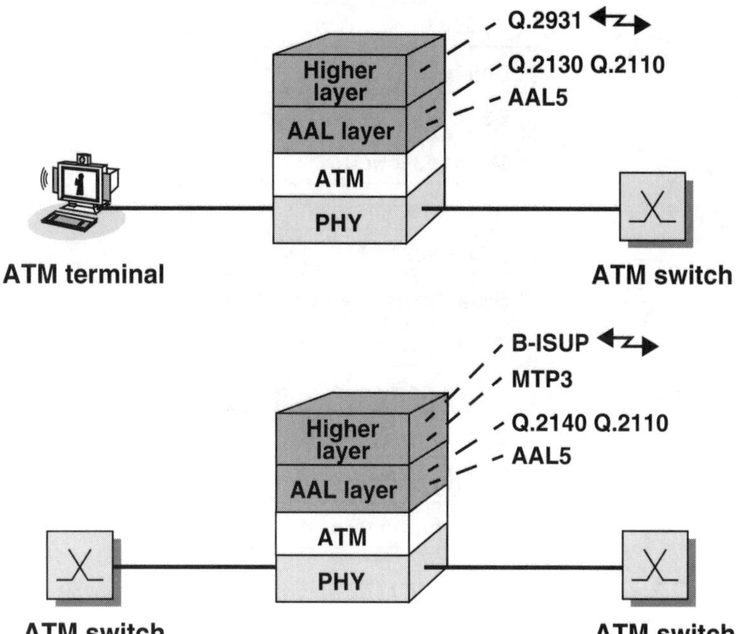

Figure G.7.2 Overview of the control plane architecture

7.3 Access network signalling

7.3.1 Q.2931

B-ISDN's approach to access network signalling is based on a modified form of the D-channel signalling used in N-ISDN (DSS2, specified in ITU-T Recommendation Q.2931). Naturally, signals must be capable of carrying more parameters than is the case in N-ISDN.

Figure G.7.3 illustrates the parameters included in a SETUP message. As can be seen in the illustration, the source's traffic characteristics (*ATM user traffic descriptor*) and the user's *quality of service (QoS)* are included for the connection. The first four fields of the message are mandatory for all types of signal message.

These four fields contain information on the protocol that is used, the call reference, the message type and the length of the message. *Call reference* identifies the call to be set up.

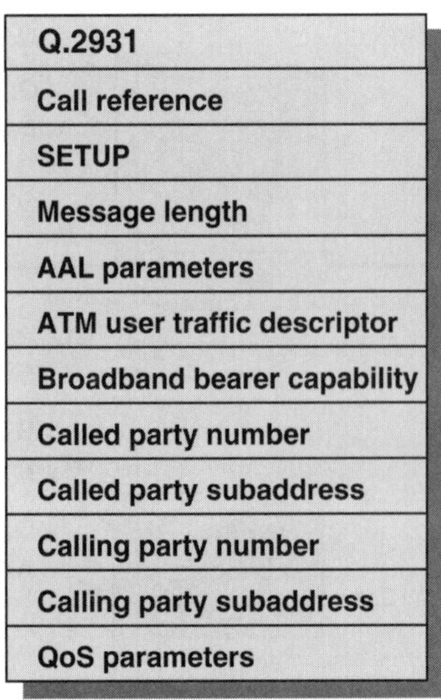

Figure G.7.3 Parameters in a SETUP message

Point-to-point calls and multimedia calls

A point-to-point call is set up with the aid of Q.2931 in the same way as any ordinary ISDN call.

A multimedia call consists of a number of connections between two points. The connections may be set up and disconnected independently of one another. All connections of a multimedia call belong to one and the same call. Connection number two is set up as usual, but the SETUP message specifies a call reference associated with the connection that was originally set up.

Point-to-multipoint calls

Subscriber signalling must also be capable of handling point-to-multipoint connections, which are unidirectional and employ one transmitter and many receivers.

The first connection in a point-to-multipoint call is set up in the same way as in a point-to-point call. The "root" (the calling terminal) can then add "leaves"; that is, the calling terminal can connect additional recipients to the call by sending an ADD PARTY message. Each of the new recipients will receive a SETUP message. This method assumes that the leaves have indicated they wish to be connected – they might have subscribed to receive all matches televised during the World Cup in football.

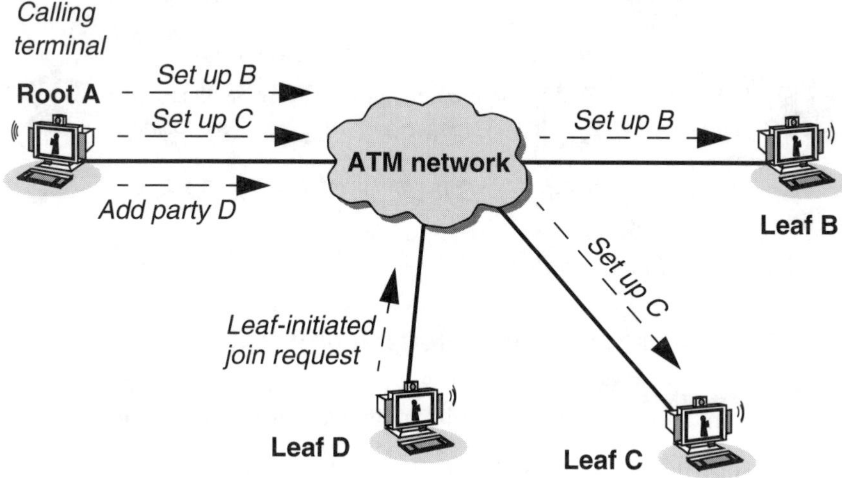

Figure G.7.4 Signal messages in a point-to-multipoint call

Upon request, a recipient can be connected to an ongoing point-to-multipoint call. As illustrated in *Figure G.7.4*, leaf D sends a *leaf-initiated join request* to the network. The network can respond to the request in one of three ways: 1) the network can add a new leaf to the ongoing call, 2) it can add the leaf to the call and inform the root of this addition, or 3) it can request the root's permission before adding the leaf to the call.

7.3.2 ATM Forum's user-network interface

Like practically everything else in the world of telecommunications, the ATM Forum's UNI standards are being developed in stages: UNI 3.0, UNI 3.1, UNI 4.0. UNI 3.1 bears the greatest resemblance to ITU-T Recommendation Q.2931. UNI 3.1 is not backwards compatible with UNI 3.0.

7.4 Interexchange signalling

7.4.1 Broadband ISDN user part protocol

Interexchange signalling is based on SS7. A new signalling protocol, B-ISUP, has been created, and the demands made by new B-ISDN services have influenced the development of this protocol, of course.

The channel identified by VCI = 5, VPI = 0 is used for signalling between network nodes.

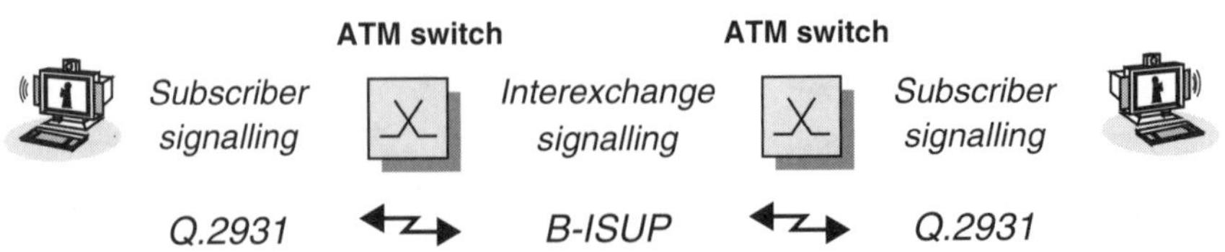

Figure G.7.5 B-ISUP signalling

7.4.2 Private network node interface protocol

P-NNI is a routing protocol that defines the signalling required to set up point-to-point and point-to-multipoint calls over an ATM network.

Until the specification of P-NNI is complete, the interim inter-switch signalling protocol (IISP) can be used. IISP is based on UNI 3.1, with minor modifications. Both P-NNI and IISP are ATM Forum protocols.

Routing supported by P-NNI is addressed in Chapter 10, Subsection 10.1.3.

8 Network management

8.1 Introduction

An ATM-based network can offer its users great flexibility, and the operator can benefit from a high degree of utilisation. To avoid any potential contradictions in these attributes, the operator must have a well-developed system for the management of its network resources. The majority of the solutions presented in this chapter may not as yet have been implemented on a large scale, but the mechanisms we describe play a central role in enabling effective network utilisation.

An ideal ATM-based network should make it possible for the user to transfer any amount of traffic, at any level of quality he may choose and at any time suitable to him. The price that must be paid for such flexibility is the increased complexity in the management of available network resources.

Cells are transported, in an ATM switch or multiplexer, from an input port to one or more output ports. A buffering function will be activated if an output port receives cells at a rate that exceeds the outgoing transfer rate. The buffer will overflow and cells will be lost if this state lasts too long.

Buffer overflow is unavoidable in a cell-based network, but the level of quality that the operator and the user have agreed on may apply nevertheless. When the number of lost cells becomes excessive or when cell delay reaches an unacceptably high level, the network is said to be overloaded.

It is the resources of the network that determine network performance and how well user services function. Operators depend on the performance of their networks to gain customers, and users (the operators' customers) are concerned that the services they use operate satisfactorily and at a reasonable cost.

Operators must be able to optimise their usage of network resources and to supervise and maintain their networks.

8.2 Resource management

Resource management involves maintaining the negotiated quality of all network connections, by using the appropriate resources and an optimally dimensioned network. Operators can optimise network usage by anticipating and checking the traffic pattern of new calls and by introducing functions that measure traffic load. No network – be it today's PSTN or tomorrow's ATM – need be dimensioned so as to allow all subscribers to use it simultaneously.

The fact that an ATM network is capable of carrying so many different types of traffic – such as file transfer, video and voice – makes it difficult to optimise its use from the outset. Uncertainties as to traffic patterns, in combination with complex network structures, will cause the development of methods for resource management to evolve in stages.

8.2.1 Which resources should be managed?

The most important network resources are bandwidth, buffers, the number of virtual channels and processor capacity to be used for signalling and routing.

- Bandwidth can be specified per connection (in cells per second) or per transmission link (in bits per second).
- The buffers in the multiplexers and switches offset variations in bandwidth. Buffer size also affects the quality of a connection. A totally filled buffer will result in cell loss; variations in cell delay will occur when the buffer is being filled and emptied. Note that buffers need not be completely filled for the occurrence of such variations.

- The number of virtual connections is large. Every virtual path contains 65,536 virtual channels. The UNI has sufficient capacity for 256 virtual paths (an eight-bit VPI), and the NNI has sufficient capacity for 4,096 virtual paths (a 12-bit VPI). This results in 16,777,216 virtual connections in the UNI and 268,435,456 in the NNI.

Resources should be optimised so that they can handle as much traffic as possible in accordance with the quality agreed in the traffic contract.

8.2.2 Traffic contract – Quality of service and traffic parameters

In preparing to set up an ATM connection, the operator and user will negotiate a number of technical details. These negotiations ordinarily culminate with the creation of a traffic contract, specifying the characteristics of the user's information, his requirements in terms of allowable network delays and the transfer quality that the operator undertakes to maintain. This is a contract in the strict sense of the word. If the user breaks his commitment (for example, by sending too large a burst of cells), then the operator can take actions that will counteract any negative effects experienced by other connections in the network.

The quality that the operator is committed to delivering is defined as quality of service (QoS), that is, the level of network performance offered by the operator. QoS is described in terms of a number of parameters (described under "Measures of ATM network performance" in this Subsection).

The characteristics of the user's information are specified in the ATM source traffic descriptor. A connection's traffic descriptor consists of a set of traffic parameters that are sent when requesting a connection. They specify, for example, peak cell rate and the length of that state (peak duration).

The contracted parameters need not be specified symmetrically; that is, they need not be the same for both directions of the connection.

Quality of Service classes

The ATM Forum has defined two QoS classes for ATM:

- No traffic parameters specified. This class deals with best-effort services, for which the operator makes no quality commitments.
- Traffic parameters specified. The operator undertakes to meet the agreed service level.

Types of service

The ATM Forum has also defined five different types of service:

- Constant bit rate (CBR): corresponds to class A services for AAL 1, that is, connection-oriented CBR services that require synchronisation.
- Variable bit rate, real-time (VBRrt): corresponds to class B services for AAL 2, that is, VBR services that require synchronisation.
- Variable bit rate, non-real-time (VBRnrt): corresponds to class C and class D services for AAL 3/4 and AAL 5, that is, bursty data communication services.
- Unspecified bit rate (UBR): allows the user to send information through the network without any guarantees as to when or in what condition the information will arrive at the receiving end. This type of service utilises the capacity available after CBR and VBR services have consumed the capacity they require.
- Available bit rate (ABR): utilises the network capacity available after CBR and VBR services have consumed the capacity they require. There are network functions that indicate instantaneously available network capacity. This enables the sender to adapt the transmission rate to the availability of the network and thereby avoid cell loss and retransmission.

UBR and ABR are best-effort services.

ATM traffic parameters

Parameters in the traffic descriptor describe the source's traffic characteristics when a connection is requested.

The only parameter that has been clearly defined so far is peak cell rate (in cells per second). With only this parameter specified in the traffic descriptor, an operator has very limited possibilities of utilising his network optimally. The following are a number of common parameters whose definitions have not yet been agreed by the members of the ATM Forum:

- average cell rate (in cells per second);
- burstiness (the relationship between the highest and the average cell rates);
- peak duration of the highest cell rate; and
- source type, that is, the type of application generating the traffic (for example, telephone or videophone).

Measures of ATM network performance

A preliminary ITU-T Recommendation, I.356, specifies network performance parameters for the transfer of ATM cells. A cell that is sent may arrive intact or corrupted or may not arrive at all. A received cell may have originated in another connection, if its address field has been corrupted. These suppositions underlie the following definitions:

- Cell error ratio (CER): the relationship between the number of errored cells and the total number of cells transmitted.
- Cell loss ratio (CLR): the relationship between the number of cells that have been lost and the total number of cells transmitted.
- Cell misinsertion rate (CMR): the number of received cells with corrupted address fields divided by the measurement time. Since a cell with a corrupted address field has its origin in a connection other than the one being measured, any relationship to the number of cells received is irrelevant.
- Severely errored cell block ratio: the relationship between the number of cell blocks with faulty contents and the total number of blocks. The number of cells contained in a block has not been defined, but 1,000 is a plausible figure. The purpose of this parameter is to prevent bursts of cell losses from affecting other parameters in an unpredictable manner.
- Mean cell transfer delay: average cell-transmission delay between the points being measured.
- Cell delay variation (CDV): the difference between the delay observed for a specific cell and the average delay for the connection.

Flexibility – A key concept in ATM

Flexible quality is a concept key to ATM. The process of allocating bandwidth to users is to be characterised by flexibility, and users should also be offered flexibility in their selection of transfer quality.

The interpretation of what is actually meant by high and low CLR has varied during the past few years. Today, a majority perceive a CLR that is guaranteed better than approximately 10^{-8} as being high quality. Even an "economy class" must be able to guarantee a basic level of quality, for example, CLR $< 10^{-5}$.

There are no clearly defined rules for variations in cell delay. In principle, we can imagine data traffic handled by network elements with buffers for approximately 10,000 cells, and we can also imagine this traffic to be insensitive to delay variations of 10,000 cell times. But buffers in audio and video connections should not cause longer delays than 100 cell times.

8.2.3 Resource management functions

Resources are managed during the various stages of a call. When setting up a call, the appropriate functions must check the availability of sufficient network resources to ensure that the call can be handled. When a connection has been established, a "police" function must check that the user does not misuse his traffic contract and jeopardise the quality of other connections. If a problem arises in the network, nodes can selectively discard low-priority cells. *Traffic shaping* may be performed if a user's data burst has an instantaneous bit rate that is too high. The term is clarified later in this subsection under "Police function actions".

Each individual network operator decides whether or not the functions described in this chapter will be implemented.

Connection admission control

Connection admission control (CAC) includes those actions that are taken by the network – before setting up a connection – to check whether it can be accepted or not. CAC bases its decision on the source's traffic description and on network performance parameters.

Usage parameter control and network parameter control

Usage parameter control (UPC) and network parameter control (NPC) perform the same tasks but for different interfaces. The UPC function is performed at the UNI, and the NPC function at the NNI. UPC is usually referred to as a police function, or cell-flow control, while NPC is often referred to as cell-flow control.

UPC and NPC functions are necessary as a means of ensuring that users do not exceed the traffic intensity specified in their traffic contracts. One individual user's contract violation may adversely affect the quality of all connections in a network. Cell flow must be checked for each and every connection, at every network inlet to which a user may connect.

Priority control

Different network elements can selectively discard cells of low priority. The priority of all cells in a connection (VP/VC) can be set via the CLP bit in their respective cell headers. Cell priority can also be assigned on a selective basis.

Network resource management

Network resource management includes functions that separate traffic streams according to traffic characteristics and quality requirements. The ATM technique provides network operators with the possibility of grouping traffic, but such functionality has not yet been standardised.

Fast resource management

Many theories have been presented as to how network operators can reserve bandwidth or buffer space to compensate for short and large bursts that occur during the time it takes for signal messages to traverse a network. The ITU-T has not yet come to agreement on a practical solution to this problem.

Figure G.8.1 illustrates the location of the different functions involved in resource management.

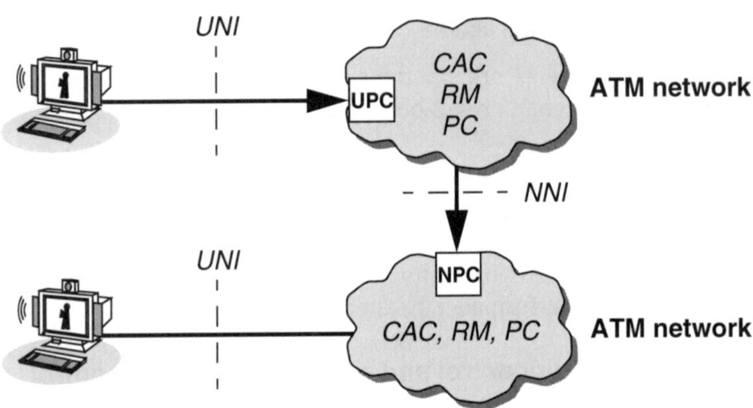

Figure G.8.1 Model of resource management functions

Police function actions – usage parameter control

The operator of an ATM network must supervise the cell flows that have access to the network. Actions must be taken in the event of user traffic contract violations.

Using UPC as a police function to get a correct impression of user cell flow poses a problem. On the one hand, the network operator should not accept more cells than the flow specified in the traffic contract. On the other hand, the measurement process must have sufficient margin so that no negotiated cell flows will be wrongly discarded.

Possible actions that the police function may take in cases of contract violations are:

- Allow the cells to pass. If there is ample network capacity and there is no risk of overload, then the police function may allow the cell flow to pass unhindered through the network.

- Convert the cell flow using traffic shaping. If the density of user cell flow (the rate at which cells arrive) is too high, the police function may opt to buffer the cells and send them at a lower density. The risk of cell loss is imminent if cell buffers become filled as a result of unusually heavy cell bursts.
  Generally, traffic shaping is performed in the user's equipment to fulfil the traffic contract.

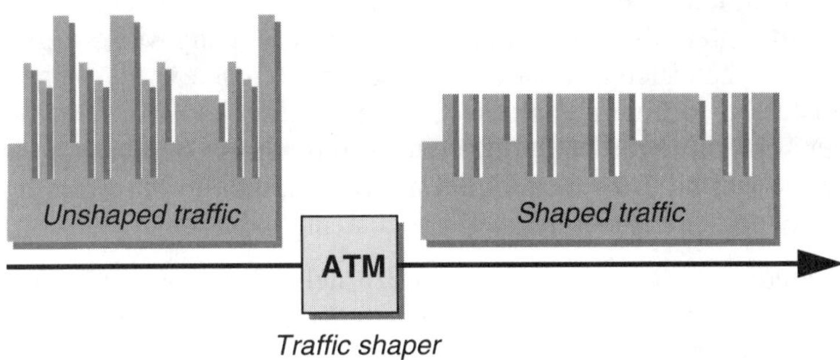

Figure G.8.2 Traffic shaping

- Label the cells. Cells may receive lower priority as a result of the police function modifying the CLP bit. This means that they will be discarded if the network becomes overloaded.
- Discard the cells.
- Clear the connection. The connection may be cleared if the user repeatedly violates the contract.

Network overload actions – Network parameter control

A number of actions are conceivable in the event that a network becomes overloaded. The first approach is to discard low-priority cells. Priority can either be specified per connection or per cell. By specifying priority on a per-connection basis, it is possible to select priority in the switching node with regard to both cell delay and cell loss.

To specify priority on a per-cell basis, the CLP bit of the cell header is set to either "0" or "1". But the user will probably not be able to assign a low priority to a particular class of cells. Using the CLP bit, the network operator can then reduce the priority of the cells being transmitted by a user who is transmitting more traffic than that specified in the request for a connection.

Explicit forward congestion indication means that the overloaded network element is sending a message to the receiving terminal to the effect that an overload situation exists (or is about to arise). The indication amounts to the setting of a bit in the cell header when the number of cells in the buffer have reached a predefined level. The actions that can be taken by the receiving terminal and its options for influencing the network's load situation are still being negotiated by standardisation groups.

Cell losses

In a well-dimensioned ATM network, cell losses will occur relatively seldom – with intervals of up to many hours or even many weeks between incidents. But when such a situation does occur, one can expect many instances of cell loss to occur in rapid succession. Network performance therefore implies something radically different from the noise of analog networks or the occasional bit error of a digital network (although bit errors in optical-fibre networks are also perceived as occurring in bursts).

The boundary between cell loss and cell delay is a floating boundary. If a cell has been sufficiently delayed, then the higher-level protocol will sooner or later consider it to be lost.

8.3 Operation and maintenance

8.3.1 General

ITU-T Recommendation I.610 describes the functions for the operation and maintenance of the physical layer and the ATM layer, that is, supervision at the bit and cell levels. The objective is to guarantee effective supervision of the UNI. In the case of the ATM layer, a portion of an ATM connection (VPC or VCC) can be supervised, that is, the portion which passes through a particular operator's network.

The functions offered by underlying transmission networks – primarily the operation and maintenance functions available in SDH – are used for supervising the physical layer and the transmission system. Special operation and maintenance (OAM) cells have been defined for an ATM-based transmission network.

The ATM layer is constantly supervised using OAM cells. The operation and maintenance of the layers above ATM (the AAL and above) have not been addressed in the ITU-T recommendations published so far.

8.3.2 Five levels – Five independent information flows (F1-F5)

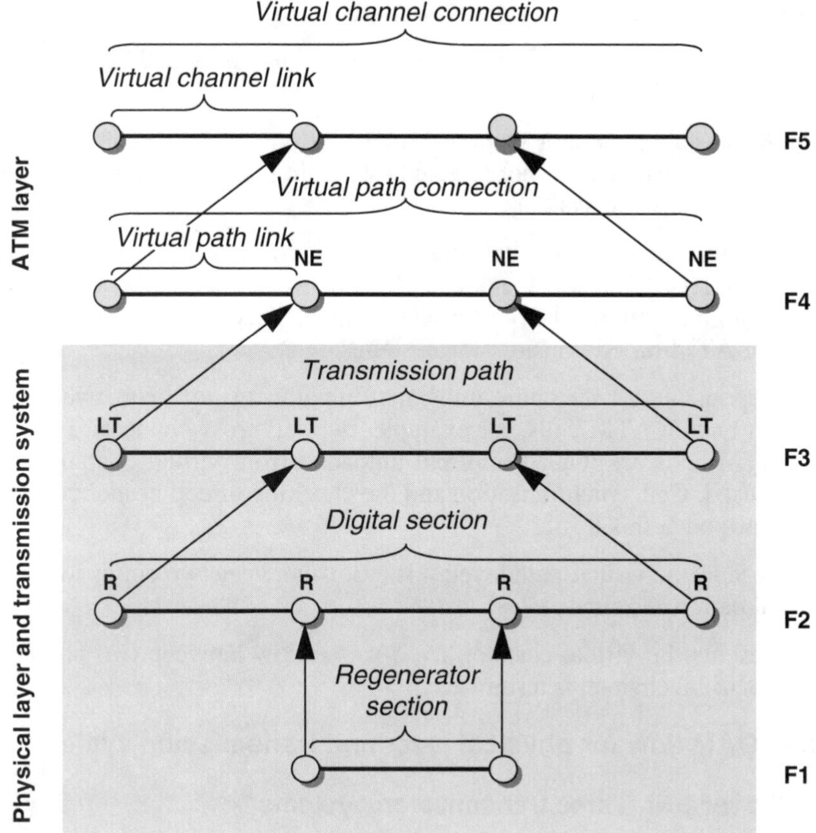

Figure G.8.3 Five independent maintenance levels, including network elements, line terminals, and regenerators

Five hierarchically separate levels are used for the OAM functions of an ATM-based network. A basic principle is that the OAM functions related to a particular level are independent of the operation and maintenance of other levels. Each level is capable of handling its own information – for example, information related to quality and alarms – and can also communicate its status to the OAM centre in the telecommunications management network (TMN) via a Q interface.

Figure G.8.3 should be read as follows: A virtual channel connection can be seen at the top of the illustration. This channel consists of virtual channel links. Every virtual channel link is a virtual path connection consisting of virtual path links. Every virtual path link is a transmission path. Every transmission path consists of one or more digital sections. Every digital section consists of one or more regenerator sections.

The OAM functions of the five levels communicate via the cell flows F1–F5. All flows are bidirectional.

F1 represents a regenerator section, a transmission path between two regenerators. The SDH frame is not affected by passing through a regenerator of an SDH transmission system.

F2 covers the digital section between two line terminals (LTs). In SDH systems, the LT is the network element (NE) where virtual containers can be loaded into and unloaded from the SDH frame. This level is of no significance for ATM-based transmission systems.

F3 is responsible for the entire transmission path. It is a flow between two NEs that handle ATM cells, for example, two VP cross-connects. In these NEs, ATM-cells are loaded into and unloaded from virtual containers, if SDH is used. Cell synchronisation and the checking of cell header contents are performed at this level.

F4 represents the virtual-path level; it is a flow between two points in which a virtual path is terminated.

F5 represents the virtual-channel level; it is a flow between two points in which a virtual channel is terminated.

8.3.3 OAM flow for physical layer and transmission system

F1–F3 over UNI: Three transmission systems

Three types of transmission systems are feasible for connecting a user to the network:

- Transmission systems based on SDH

The OAM flows F1 and F2 are sent in the octets specified in *section overhead* (*SOH*). F3 is carried by the octets for *path overhead* (*POH*). The messages used are the same as in the case of SDH.

- Transmission systems based on ATM

The OAM flows F1 and F3 are sent in special OAM cells. As mentioned in Chapter 4, one OAM cell (or idle cell) is sent in every group of 27 cells.

If the bit rate is 155 Mbit/s – which corresponds to STM-1 – then the OAM information-handling capacity is the same as that of an SDH system. This is an important factor for interworking between networks.

An alarm will be triggered if the maximum allowable separation between OAM cells is exceeded. The alarm indicates that the maintenance flow has been lost.

- Transmission systems based on PDH

The OAM flows F1 and F3 are sent in the header of the PDH frame.

8.3.4 Alarms for the physical layer and the ATM layer

The F1 and F2 flows monitor the underlying transmission system; that is, they handle the transfer of bits. The F3 flow monitors functions that handle cells and their mapping to an underlying transmission system.

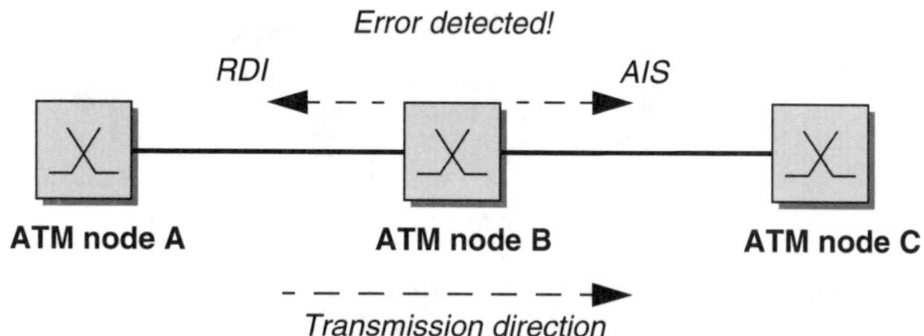

Figure G.8.4. Error detected in node B

Two types of alarm are sent when an error is detected in any of the flows F1, F2 or F3:

- Alarm indication signal (AIS) sends a message in the same direction as that of the signal, to the effect that an error has been detected.
- Remote defect indication (RDI) sends a message to the transmitting terminal that an error has been detected. RDI is also referred to as the far-end reporting failure (FERF).

Alarms related to the physical layer are indicated using path AIS/RDI. Virtual path AIS/RDI and virtual channel AIS/RDI are also generated for the ATM layer.

8.3.5 Operation and maintenance of the ATM layer

Special OAM cells (F4 and F5 cells) are used for the control of virtual paths and virtual channels with regard to their performance and availability. For example, the number of lost cells may be detected by transmitting these OAM cells along the various connections.

F4 cells are used to monitor a VPC, F5 cells for a VCC. OAM cells in the F4 and F5 flows are used for monitoring a segment of the network and end-to-end monitoring.

Two reserved VCI values are used to identify both types of OAM cells in F4 flows. OAM cells in F4 flows have the same VPI as that of the connection being monitored.

Two reserved values in the payload type identifier are used to identify OAM cells in F5 flows. OAM cells in F5 flows have the same VCI as that of the connection being monitored.

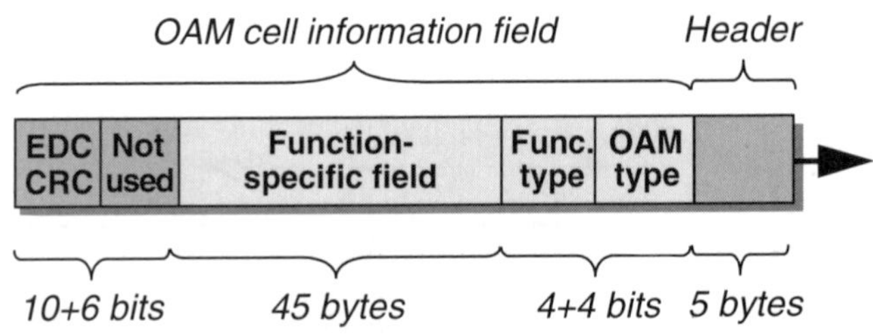

Figure G.8.5 Operation and maintenance cell

The operation and maintenance cell

All OAM cells that pertain to the ATM layer contain the following functions (the OAM cells of the physical layer have a different appearance):

- Header: Two VCI values are reserved for the identification of the OAM cells of the F4 flow, one for the monitoring of network segments and one for end-to-end monitoring. Two PTI values are reserved for the identification of OAM cells of the F5 flow, one for the monitoring of network segments and one for end-to-end monitoring. These values are specified in ITU-T Recommendation I.361.
- OAM type: Specifies the type of operation and maintenance function being referred to, for example, error handling, performance measurement, activation or deactivation.
- Function type: Specifies which function the OAM cell is supporting among the class of functions specified by "OAM type", for example, transmitting AIS or RDI or monitoring the network.
- Function-specific field: Used when performing the various OAM functions.

- Error detection code (EDC): An error correction code (CRC-10) based on the contents of the information fields in the OAM cells, used for error detection.

8.3.6 Operation and maintenance functions of the ATM layer

The following functions apply to both the F4 and the F5 flows; that is, they can be performed for both VC and VP connections.

Fault management

The AIS and RDI messages of the F4 and F5 flows are sent to the other network nodes via the VPC or the VCC to which the message refers. The AIS and RDI have the same meaning here as they have in the case of the physical layer. The type of error and its location can be indicated in the OAM cells.

Continuity checking is another fault management function. To check whether a VCC that has been idle for a period of time is still functioning, the network elements can send continuity-check cells along that VCC.

Performance management

At fixed intervals, OAM cells are transmitted in both directions to notify other network elements of any detected errors. The messages can be transmitted in either the F4 or F5 flows or in another connection.

Activation/deactivation

Activation/deactivation of monitoring can be initiated by the operation and maintenance centre (via the TMN) or by the user.

9 Interworking between networks

9.1 Interworking between network operators

In these times of deregulation, the users of different operators' ATM networks must be capable of communicating with one another. Such communication requires agreements between operators as well as a protocol for the transfer of information between the networks. This could be problematic, because operators are not inclined to divulge their network strategies to their competitors. The B-ICI is just one such protocol that the ATM Forum is considering. It is based to a great extent on the ITU-T's protocol for the NNI and uses B-ISUP for signalling.

9.2 ATM interworking with other networks

9.2.1 General

There are two different types of interworking for ATM networks:

- Interworking over an ATM network. Example: ATM is the bearer of frame relay or X.25.
- Interworking with an ATM end system. Example: A frame-relay user communicates directly with an ATM user.

Interworking over an ATM network

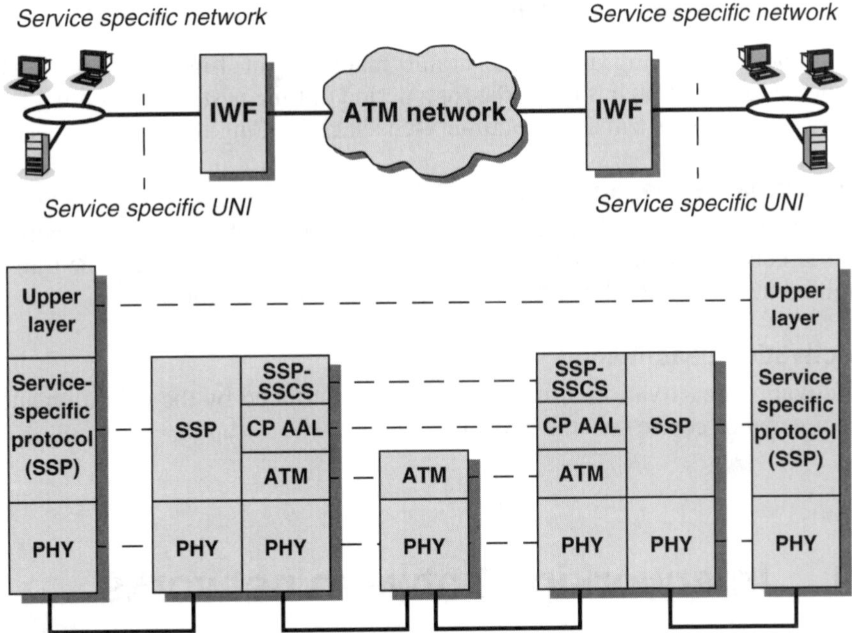

Figure G.9.1 Network interworking over an ATM network

Figure G.9.1 illustrates a conceivable physical configuration in which ATM is the bearer of another network service. The logical protocol stacks for the various interfaces are also included. The service-specific network may be frame relay, X.25 or N-ISDN.

From the left in *Figure G.9.1*, we see a service-specific network with its service-specific protocol (SSP) and its user interface (service-specific UNI). Interworking with the ATM network requires the use of an interworking function (IWF). The ATM portion of the IWF must include an AAL that can manage the specific service (frame relay, X.25 or N-ISDN) by employing the service-specific convergence sublayer of AAL that is adapted to the service in question (SSP-SSCS). The packets from frame relay, X.25 or N-ISDN are segmented, assigned headers and then transmitted as cells to an IWF having the same functionality as the one just mentioned. The IWF converts the ATM cells into the format of the service-specific network.

In this type of interworking between networks, the non-ATM service-specific systems need never know that their information is being borne by ATM.

Interworking with an ATM end system

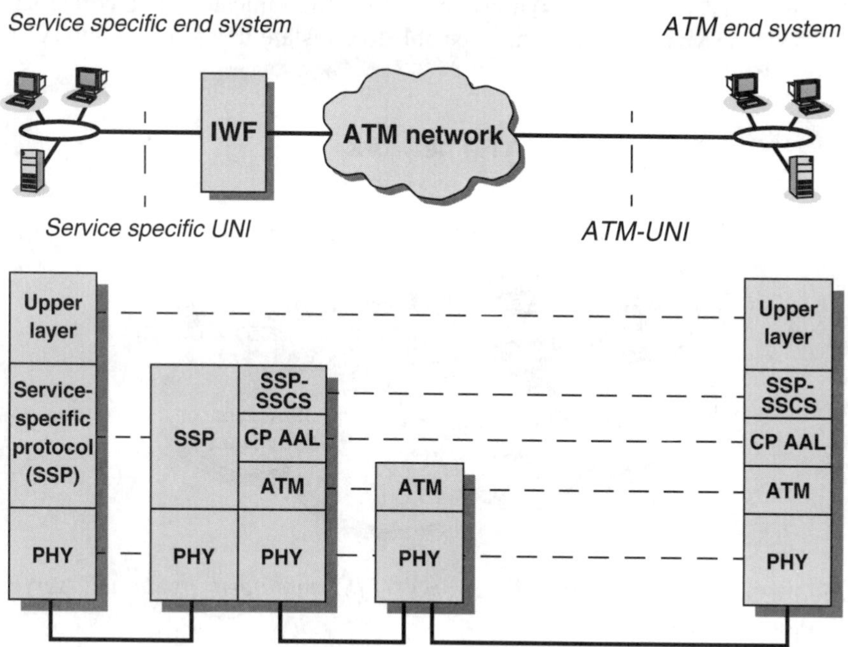

Figure G.9.2 Network interworking with an ATM end system

An IWF is used when interworking is to be achieved between two different end systems.

From the left in *Figure G.9.2* we see the service-specific system connected to an IWF for conversion into ATM. The ATM network carries the cells to the recipient: an ATM user in this case. The user's AAL (SSP-SSCS and common part AAL) must be equal to that of the IWF; in other words, adapted to the service in question.

There is also a third case referred to as *service interworking*. In that, the ATM or frame-relay user need not be aware of the fact that different protocols are involved. IWF manages the entire conversion process.

9.2.2 ATM – Internet

The IETF has developed a protocol called "*Classical IP and ARP over ATM*. The function of the protocol is to create point-to-point links between routers or IP links to terminals.

It is possible to create logical IP subnetworks (LIS) that are carried by ATM. Every LIS is handled by an IP server that keeps track of all LIS clients. Each client maintains contact with the IP server via the ATM node. All LIS units (clients, servers and routers) must be able to communicate with all other LIS units via ATM, and all units must be able to translate IP addresses into ATM network addresses.

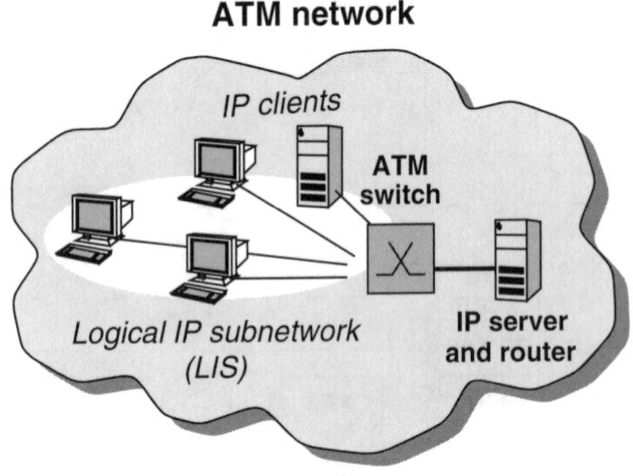

Figure G.9.3 Logical IP subnetworks (LIS) managed by an IP server through an ATM node

A number of LISs communicate with one another via routers. The objective of the router is to find a path between the users of different LISs.

An ATM node is capable of managing more than one LIS, creating a single ATM interface to the router. *Figure G.9.4* shows a configuration in which three LISs share one IP server. Here, the IP server is co-located with the router.

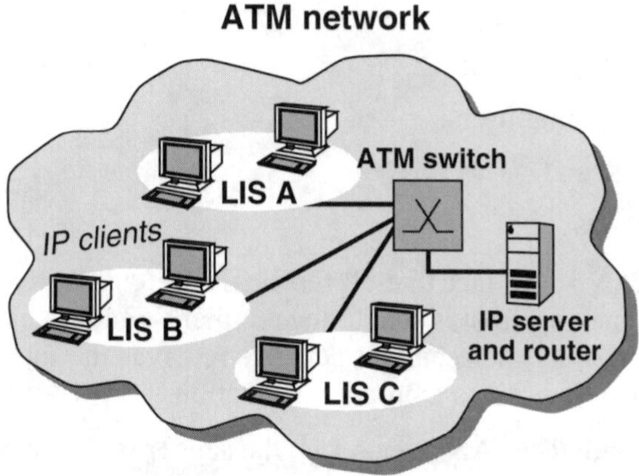

Figure G.9.4 The communication between more than one LIS is performed with the aid of a router

9.3 Emulation

"Emulation" means faithful imitation. By circuit emulation, in this context we mean that ATM imitates a circuit-switched network so well that end systems need not "know" that ATM is involved at all. Following the same line of reasoning, LAN emulation is a process in which the terminals of the emulated network never register the fact that they are not connected to a genuine LAN.

9.3.1 Circuit emulation

Circuit emulation can be performed for 64 kbit/s channels and 2 Mbit/s links over AAL 1. There are functions in AAL 1 for the transfer of synchronisation information for the emulated bit stream and for error detection. Errors – for example, the fact that an ATM cell of the emulated flow has been lost – can be detected with the aid of the sequence numbering of the SAR-PDUs. The loss of a single cell of the emulated bit stream means the loss of 47 octets. In an emulated 2 Mbit/s link, an ATM cell corresponds to more than a complete PCM frame.

9.3.2 LAN emulation

The ATM Forum has developed an implementation specification for LAN emulation (LANE), designated *LAN Emulation over ATM,* or af-lane-0021.000. Via LAN emulation, connectionless communication can be established over ATM even though ATM is connection-oriented.

LAN emulation makes communication possible between:

- ATM users;
- ATM and Ethernet users;
- ATM and token ring users;
- Ethernet users; and
- Token ring users.

Typical of a LAN is the fact that all terminals are constantly connected to one another. A message that is sent to the recipient's address is perceived by all terminals, but only the recipient actually receives the message. In contrast to ATM, LANs possess a broadcast function.

To be able to emulate a LAN over ATM, the sender must create a broadcast function (a function that allows one terminal to address all others in the network) and a multicast function (addressing a number of specific terminals). LAN emulation requires the use of three different servers. (See *Figure G.9.5*.)

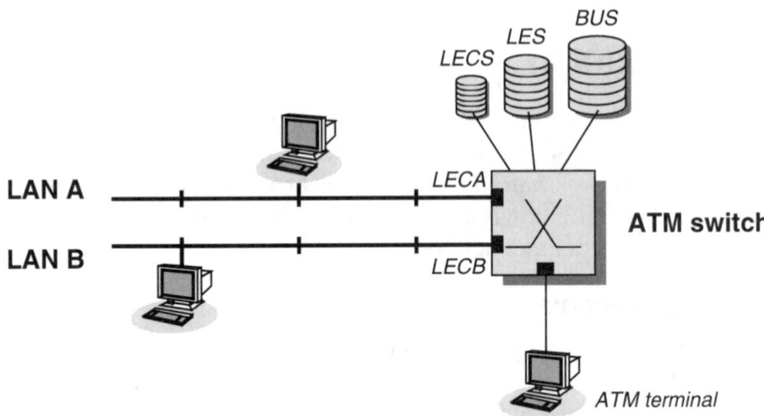

Figure G.9.5 LAN emulation aided by a LAN emulation server (LES)

Every unit of an emulated LAN (ELAN) is identified as a LAN emulation client (LEC). LAN A and LAN B in *Figure G.9.5* are LECs.

An ATM terminal may belong to more than one ELAN, in which case it needs an LEC for each ELAN. A LAN emulation client server (LECS) determines the ELAN to which an LEC will belong. An LECS is configured by the network operator. A LAN emulation server (LES) coordinates the ELAN by translating LAN addresses into ATM addresses. A broadcast and unknown server (BUS) handles broadcast and multicast functions.

10 Network planning

10.1 Fundamental technical plans

Like all other public networks, ATM-based networks require fundamental technical plans as the basis for network planning. (See also Volume 1, Chapter 10, Subsection 10.8.5.)

10.1.1 Numbering plan

The numbering plan for B-ISDN is referred to as E.164. It is the same numbering plan as that used for the PSTN/N-ISDN.

The ATM Forum allows two additional address formats, namely the data country code (DCC) and the international code designator (ICD). The actual address format used is specified in the first octet of the address field of the signal message.

10.1.2 Transmission plan

Transmission plans stipulate transmission quality requirements in terms of cell loss, delay variation and bit errors.

It is indeed a challenge to achieve acceptable quality for the services included in class B, that is, isochronous services with variable bit rate, such as the bit rates produced in the differential coding of video signals. Class B cells should have small and constant delay and should be error-free when delivered to the user. Optical transmission is recommended to maintain a low bit error ratio. However, radio transmission for ATM in the access network will become more common.

To avoid cell loss, networks must be dimensioned so that buffer overflow never occurs. (See also Chapter 8, Subsection 8.2.2.)

10.1.3 Network topology and routing plan

Network operators often make use of servers to facilitate the offering of different ATM network services. Examples include:

- connectionless servers for SMDS/CBDS;
- LANE for LAN-emulation;
- IP servers for Internet over ATM; and
- telephony servers for the transmission of telephony over ATM networks.

Operators can use transmission techniques such as ADSL or HFC to facilitate the delivery of ATM services to residential users and small businesses.

Large corporations are connected via SDH or PDH. In such cases, the ATM network functions as the bearer network for the services in question.

An ATM network is highly complex, handling the traffic of many different types of service, all having their specific traffic characteristics. PSTNs are developing, as mentioned earlier, towards increasingly flatter networks, and the same trend is apparent for ATM networks.

Nodes can be classified as access nodes for the connection of subscribers or as core network nodes. Core nodes can handle significantly more traffic than that handled by PSTN nodes (commonly expressed in Gbit/s). As a result, only a few such nodes are required even in large cities.

At the access network level, nodes can be grouped into clusters in areas having many ATM sources. For redundancy purposes, these clusters have two links to the core level.

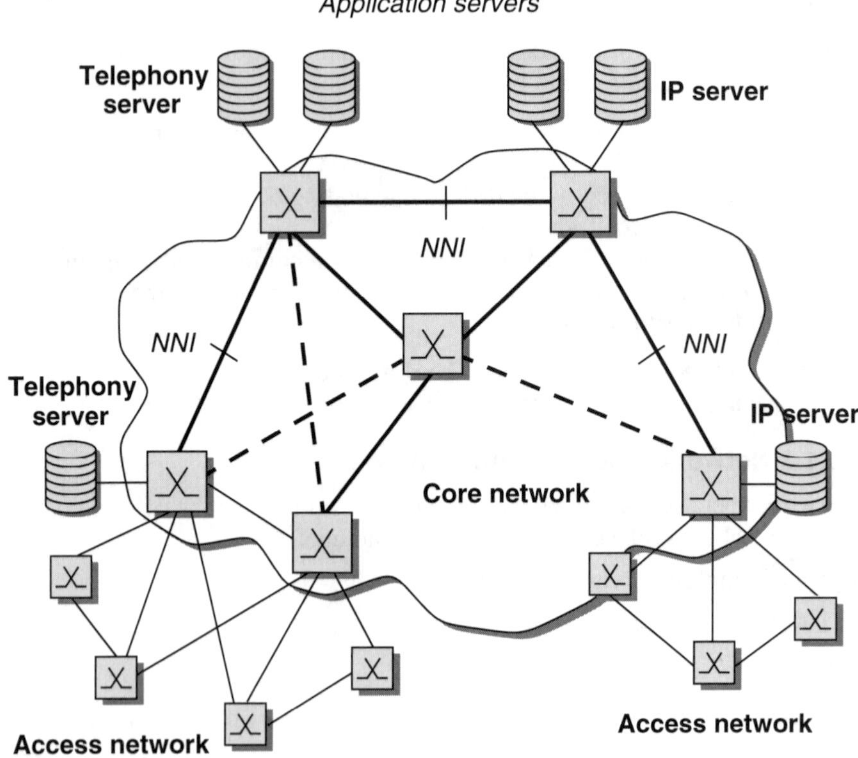

Figure G.10.1 ATM network

Routing techniques

Either an NNI or P-NNI can be used between the nodes of the core network or between the nodes in the access clusters.

The NNI is used for B-ISDN. It presupposes the existence of routing or routing tables that have been set up by the operator in each of the network's nodes (static routing). When setting up a connection with the aid of B-ISUP signalling, the connection is routed step-by-step between the calling subscriber and the recipient: each node finds its way to the next node aided by its routing table. Rerouting, if any, is based on a predefined alternative route and on the status of the network.

The P-NNI can replace the NNI for ATM bearer networks. The P-NNI has a well-defined routing protocol, and routing tables are produced and updated automatically. This is a function found in router networks, such as the Internet. The nodes of a network using the P-NNI communicate with one another, and the nodes of a cluster keep track of the connection links used by the other nodes. To limit the time taken for connection set-up, a cluster must not contain more than 20–50 nodes, otherwise the routing tables, located in each of the nodes, would become unmanageable.

Source routing is used by an ATM network employing the P-NNI. This means that when setting up a connection, the first node selects the entire path to the recipient instead of using the step-by-step procedure used in B-ISDN. The optimum path may be selected based on customer cost, operator cost, connection set-up time, the traffic load on the various network links or some other factor of importance. If a link becomes functionally inoperative, the "crank-back" function may be used to reroute traffic: the network determines a new route, starting from the node just preceding the faulty link.

10.1.4 Synchronisation

Synchronisation can be performed at a number of different levels:

- At the service level: Class A and class B services (isochronous services) require end-to-end synchronisation. The AAL should provide user services with a transparent path through the network, so this layer must provide for synchronisation, for example, in the case of circuit emulation.
- At the network level: The network elements which handle the transmission of bits of the cell flow must be synchronised. This normally applies to SDH and PDH networks.
- At the cell level: It must be possible at the receiving side to detect all cells contained in a cell flow and to locate the cell boundaries (cell delinea-

tion). This is performed using the HEC field described in Chapter 2, Subsection 2.5.4.

10.1.5 Charging plan

It is feasible to charge for calls processed by an ATM network on a cell basis. Alternatively, charging may be based on the quality and average bandwidth required by the user and on the duration of the established connection. UBR services ought to be less expensive than ABR and VBR services. CBR services are more expensive than UBR and ABR services. (ABR, CBR, UBR and VBR are service types described in Chapter 8, Subsection 8.2.2.)

10.2 Dimensioning

Dimensioning is thoroughly addressed in Volume 1, Chapter 10. As stated in Subsection 10.9.6, the theories and models applied to the dimensioning of ATM networks are not yet completely developed. The following provides a summary of the salient concepts and a more detailed description of dynamic (statistical) multiplexing and effective bandwidth.

10.2.1 General

An ATM network is capable of carrying many different services. Each connection in the network exhibits specific traffic characteristics – such as burstiness and maximum required bandwidth – and different quality requirements with respect to delay and allowable cell loss. Additionally, different services exhibit different traffic behaviour in terms of holding time, the time of day that they are used and call frequency.

All these factors must be taken into account by an operator when dimensioning links, buffers and switching elements.

10.2.2 Dynamic multiplexing and effective bandwidth

Multiplexing, performed either directly in a multiplexer or in the output port of a node, can be static or dynamic. Static multiplexing refers to the reservation of a bandwidth that corresponds to the sum of the maximum bit rate of all tributaries. In the case of dynamic multiplexing, it is sufficient to reserve a bandwidth that exceeds the sum of the average bit rate of all tributaries. Dynamic multiplexing is suitable in cases of a large number of traffic sources with comparable bit rates.

A large number of traffic sources having different bit rates are shown at the top of *Figure G.10.2*.

Static multiplexing is displayed at the bottom left: the sum of the maximum required bandwidths of a few traffic sources has been calculated, and the link has been dimensioned accordingly. As is obvious from the diagram, a significant portion of the link's bandwidth is not used.

Dynamic multiplexing, involving a large number of sources, is displayed at the bottom right. The dynamic effect is considerable in such cases: the probability that many sources will exhibit simultaneous bursts is small. This leads to a "smoothing" of the accumulated bit rates compared to the bit rate from one single source or a few sources. Note that the scales of the y-axes of the upper and lower diagrams are not the same.

Due to the "peak-smoothing" effect brought about by the multiplexing of many sources, links need not be dimensioned for maximum bit rates. It is sufficient to make use of "effective bandwidth". This effective bandwidth is service-dependent and is also a function of the number of sources that may be multiplexed over a given link. The larger the link is, the lower the effective bandwidth, because many sources may be multiplexed resulting in a greater dynamic effect.

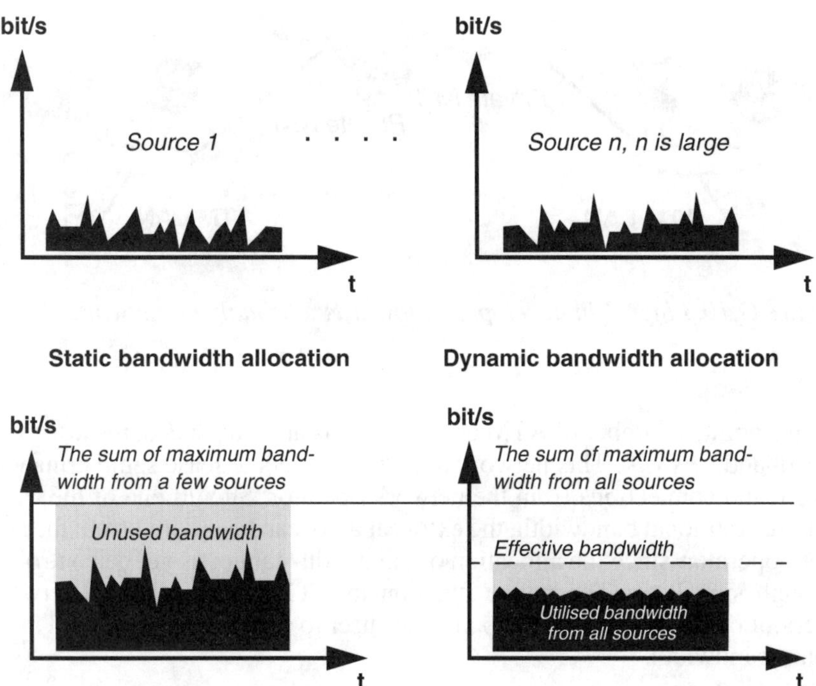

Figure G.10.2 Multiplexing

10.3 Building a network with ATM

This section describes a plausible course of development towards a broadband network.

The first three steps illustrate how large enterprises and organisations may begin to use public broadband networks. The subsequent steps deal with how private customers may gain access to these broadband networks and how operators may utilise them.

10.3.1 Step 1

A company has an ATM LAN installed at two sites, connected by a leased line. This configuration does not require the services of a public ATM network. The company would probably be interested in the LAN interconnect service.

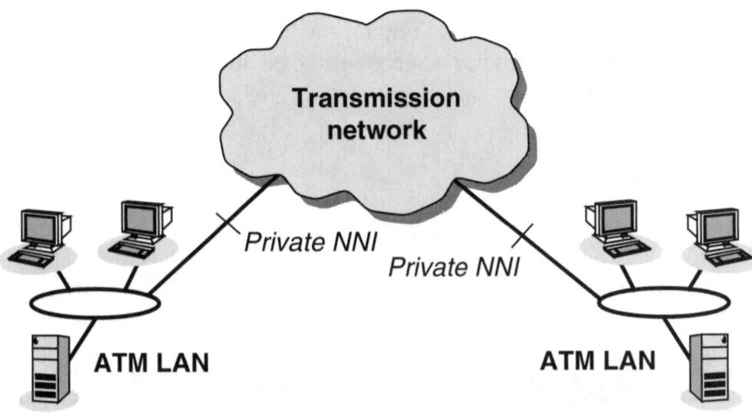

Figure G.10.3 Step 1 in development towards a broadband network

10.3.2 Step 2

At this point, a number of ATM cross-connects are introduced, resulting in a broadband network. This network allows two users to lease semipermanent broadband connections from the network operator. Should one of the users require additional bandwidth, the extra capacity can be ordered from the network operator, since the allocation of bandwidth cannot as yet be controlled through signalling. The police function in ATM will notify the network operator of any attempt on the part of the user to exceed the negotiated maximum bandwidth.

Let us assume that the company uses its semipermanent broadband connections for LAN interconnect and videoconferencing between the two sites. Since the company already has an ATM connection – for audio, video and data – then PBX traffic may also be carried by the ATM connection with the help of circuit emulation.

A large business can be connected to the ATM network via its own ATM multiplexer. A company whose need of communication is relatively limited will use an ATM multiplexer that belongs to the network operator. ATM multiplexers can be equipped with interface boards, which make it possible to connect a LAN or a PBX to them.

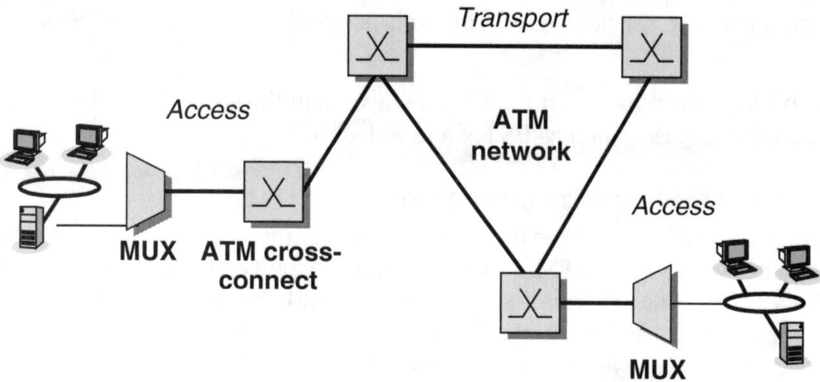

Figure G.10.4 Step 2 in development towards a broadband network

10.3.3 Step 3

The next step is the introduction of ATM nodes controlled by signalling, which would allow users to establish broadband connections by means of signalling. The number of ATM nodes is determined by the number of users connected.

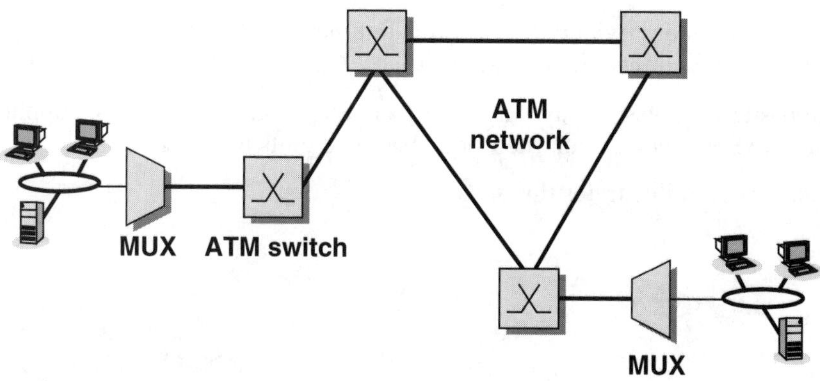

Figure G.10.5 Step 3 in development towards a broadband network

10.3.4 Step 4

Residential users and small businesses

New techniques must be implemented in existing access networks if residential users and small businesses are to be connected to broadband networks that support ATM access. There are two alternatives: use ADSL or very high bit rate digital subscriber line (VDSL) over the copper wires used for telephony or rebuild the cable-TV network for HFC. These techniques would make it possible for ATM cells to carry information to residential users, enabling services like video-on-demand and high-speed Internet access.

An ATM multiplexer with IWF can also handle subscribers in circuit switched networks, such as PSTN and N-ISDN.

Large and medium-size businesses

Many large businesses have their own ATM multiplexers that can access the public network via an STM-1 or something less powerful, such as a 2 or 34 Mbit/s leased line. Medium-size businesses and organisations may either have their own ATM multiplexers or direct access to an ATM multiplexer owned by the operator. In the latter case, they can utilise the operator's LAN emulation or circuit emulation services.

To enable users who are connected to a broadband network to communicate with subscribers who have PSTN/ISDN connections, an IWF is required between the ATM network and the PSTN/ISDN in question.

Service providers

A variety of service providers can utilise an operator's ATM network to offer their services – video-on-demand, for example – with the aid of video servers.

Internet service providers (ISPs) offer Internet access via their servers and IP routers for connectionless traffic. (See *Figure G.10.6.*)

Multi-site businesses may subscribe to LAN emulation services, supplied via LANE servers, to link their organisational units together.

Figure G.10.6 illustrates this scenario.

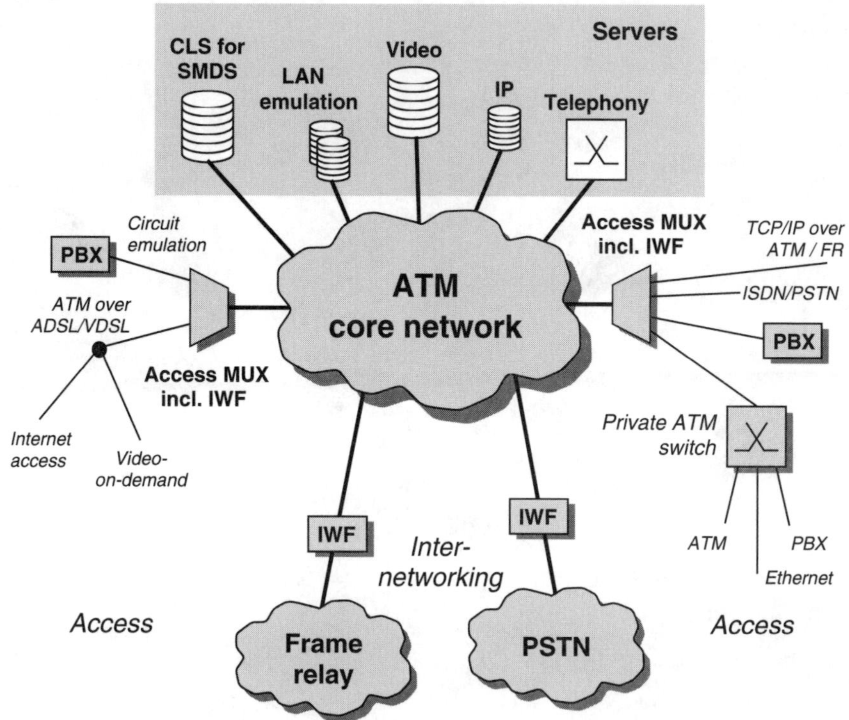

Figure G.10.6 Step 4 in development towards a broadband network

Part H – The Internet

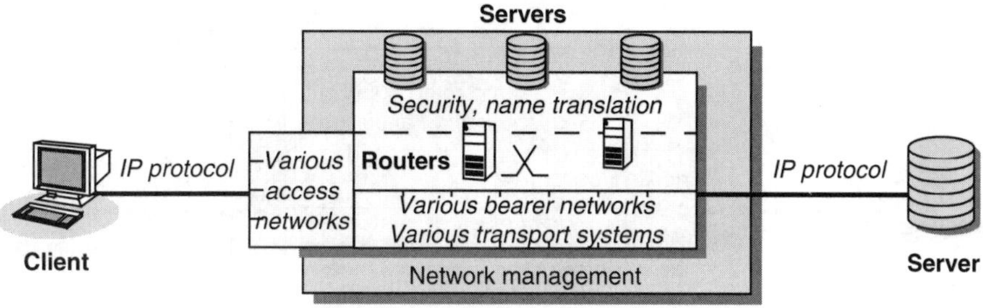

Figure H.0.1 Reference model

1 User services and terminals

1.1 Introduction

This chapter deals with the various Internet services available, the terminals used to access them, and some of the players who offer public services linked to the Internet.

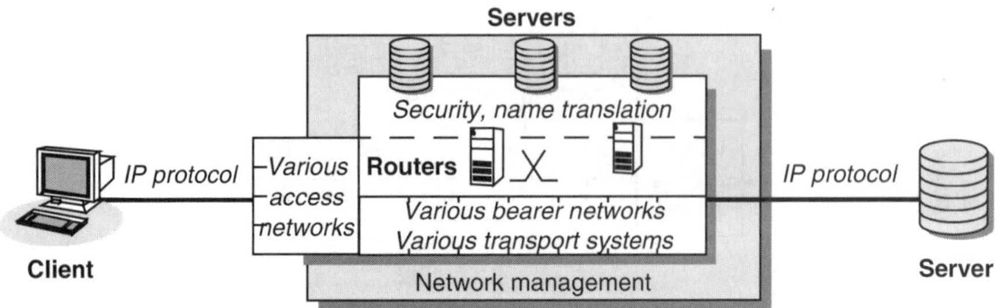

Figure H.1.1 The Internet

The name "Internet" has different connotations for different user groups, depending on the context. Our books define the Internet as follows:

The Internet (derived from *internetworking*) is the global network formed by the interconnection of thousands of subnetworks that all make use of

- the TCP/IP protocol suite (TCP = transmission control protocol, IP = Internet protocol); and
- a common address structure.

At present (the late 1990s), this packet-oriented "network of networks" is growing faster than any other network in existence. Astonishing as it may seem, this is going on when the number of transfer techniques has reached an all-time high (never before have so many different transfer techniques been available to the public telecommunications market):

- the PSTN, ISDN and PLMN, which are optimised for fixed and mobile voice transfer (ISDN also addressing multimedia applications);
- X.25 and frame relay, which are optimised for data transfer; and
- asynchronous transfer mode (ATM), which is designed for multimedia communication (but which, for the time being, is primarily used for data communication).

How then does one explain the Internet's enormous success – a success that has surprised even network operators and equipment vendors? As is often the case with unexpected developments, the answer is a combination of factors.

1.1.1 A global network

The above definition provides an important bit of information – namely that the Internet is a global network. Unlike transfer techniques such as X.25, frame relay and the majority of ATM applications, the Internet is an end-to-end application extending all the way to the user's computer. The communication protocol (TCP/IP) is an integrated entity of the user's computer system. Hence, the Internet provides the same prerequisites for world-wide services that fixed and mobile networks do for telephony services. The Internet's ability to interconnect computers globally is attributable to the fact that it can be designed as an overlay network (consisting of a number of interconnected subnetworks) on top of all the other transfer techniques, including leased line and local network techniques such as Ethernet and token ring.

Network operators view the Internet's ability to "surf" on other networks as an especially attractive attribute. The introduction of Internet capabilities is a simple matter of upgrading an existing network and not a replacement for some other technology in which an operator has already invested. ATM, on the other hand, feels more like a replacement than an upgrade.

It should be noted that use of the Internet protocol (IP) does not require the underlying (switched) bearer networks. IP possesses the qualities required of a transfer mode; that is, multiplexing and switching functionality (referred to as *routing functionality* in Internet terminology).

1.1.2 Attractive applications

Having global accessibility is half the challenge, the other half being the ability to offer attractive applications. We will first discuss these applications from a broad perspective. Someone once said that the Internet protocol "carries everything over anything" (see *Figure H.1.2*). This is a half-truth. For instance, the Internet cannot support high-quality broadband multimedia communication unless network performance is enhanced in terms of bandwidth and protocols.

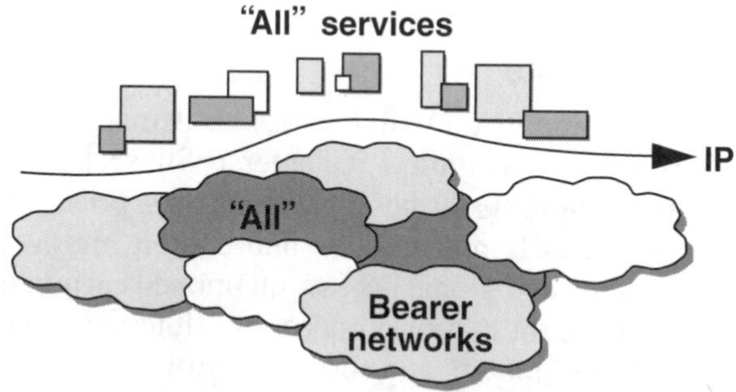

Figure H.1.2 The Internet carries "everything over anything"

Early applications such as e-mail and information retrieval systems (World Wide Web, WWW) have met great success, which is evidence of the fact that they fulfil a genuine need. When "the Web" was first introduced in the early 1990s, the number of users mushroomed. Commerce and banking services via the Internet will surely be the next success story, and real-time services (video and telephony) are bound to follow.

1.1.3 Every man's property

Browsers, or web readers, and the graphical user interface (GUI) make the Internet user-friendly and exciting. The two most common Web browsers are Netscape Navigator and Internet Explorer. The days when the Internet was used by a select group of technicians who employed a number of complicated commands is gone and almost forgotten. Today, the Internet can be used by just about anyone, and many regard this as the main force now driving expansion.

1.1.4 Reasonable pricing

Pricing of Internet calls has been very reasonable compared to the pricing of telephone calls over the PSTN, especially for long-distance communication.

1.1.5 The Internet – a global resource

The Internet represents a global resource in the form of information and knowledge and provides a platform for cooperative ventures. This has resulted in the establishment of a wide variety of information service providers. Unfortunately, the Internet has also seen the establishment of a number of unwholesome service providers, such as those dealing in child pornography and extremist propaganda. Perhaps we are oversimplifying, but there is good and bad information. Information can also be categorised in another way: as open or internal information, with security measures required to protect the latter category. Finally, information can be categorised based on its value. One may thus differentiate between information primarily intended for advertising purposes and that classified as premium rate information (having a value that the caller is willing to pay for).

1.1.6 Success factors

Let us also make a comparison with the various demands made on teleservices that we discussed in Volume 1, Chapter 1, Subsection 1.1.2. Teleservices should satisfy a real need, be sufficiently low priced, have sufficient coverage, be user-friendly and reliable and exhibit high availability. The first four requirements and global access, mentioned earlier, make the Internet a winner. Information is a basic necessity, Internet prices are low, the number of installed computers and servers is growing by leaps and bounds and the access bandwidth is increasing, for example in the PSTN through modem refinements. Web readers and GUI offer a high degree of user-friendliness.

1.2 Overview

A number of important questions may be formulated on the basis of what we have described so far.

- There are thousands of Internet service providers. How do they cooperate and how does the continuous and rapid standardisation process proceed? This issue is addressed in Chapter 2, which also includes a brief description of the major standards, especially the TCP/IP protocol suite.
- What about traffic routing in the Internet? There is obviously a need for a number of routing points and an address structure that can be used by everyone. To a certain degree, router characteristics determine both the services that are possible in the Internet and the maximum bandwidth for those services. The manner in which such routers interact and their respective roles in the network are other related aspects. Although this topic is addressed in detail in Chapter 3, a short introduction is called for here.
  Unlike traditional bearer networks, the Internet is *not* based on a strict hierarchical structure – its topology is rather flat. However, the trend is towards increasingly hierarchical designs. The Internet's address structure is indeed subdivided into a number of levels, but this subdivision does not reflect the geographical layout of the network, which makes routing a complex process. *Figure H.1.3* is a schematic diagram of the Internet structure including a great number of LANs connected to the network.
- How does one connect to the Internet? How is IP able to use other networks for access purposes to offer communication between the user's own computer – the client – and a server located, for example, in another country? (The terms *client* and *server* are explained in Chapter 2, Subsection 2.3.4.) Access issues are addressed in Chapter 5.
  Bandwidth is a determining factor for data communication via the PSTN, ISDN and PLMN. The Internet has created a demand for greater bearer network bandwidth. The PSTN has responded with higher-speed modems, and the PLMN is being upgraded.
  ISDN already has a comparatively broad bandwidth (128 kbit/s in its 2B+D version). Will these circuit-switched networks eventually become less important as Internet access networks? This is only one of many exciting questions for the future.

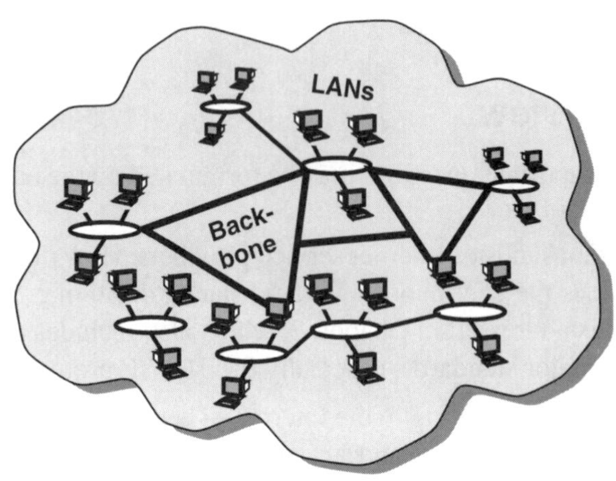

Figure H.1.3 Structure of the Internet

- There are many types of server in the Internet. What needs do they cater to? In Chapter 6, we differentiate between servers that primarily provide communications services (especially those that support routing and vital security aspects) and servers that provide information services and support e-mail and commerce. Functionally, we recognise a certain relationship to the PLMN (authentication and locating the B-subscriber). This division of server functionality corresponds to the division between network intelligence (IN) and value-added services that is so often alluded to in our books.
- Does signalling exist in the Internet? This issue is addressed in Chapter 7. Some sort of processor communication is undoubtedly required if a service is to be established between a client and a server.
- The organisation of the Internet's network management, interworking between networks and network planning is discussed in Chapters 8, 9 and 10.

1.3 How did the Internet arise?

The origins of the Internet lie in experimentation surrounding the packet switching of data traffic performed during the 1960s. Such experimentation was financed by the Advanced Research Projects Agency (ARPA), an office of the United States Department of Defense. The first experiments were performed in 1966, and the first communications terminals were put into operation in 1969. It was not at all self-evident that packet switching was to become a successful telecommunications technique; many critical voices could be heard from the establishment. But ARPA was persistent and ran the projects openly, without any veil of secrecy.

The embryo that gave rise to the Internet was a network called ARPANET, named after its financier. Four ARPANET nodes existed in 1969. In the early 1970s, more and more people became convinced that packet switching was an effective and dependable method of data transfer. ARPA started a number of experimental projects employing packet switching for shipping and satellite communication. One of the projects was the celebrated Hawaiian Aloha project that employed packet switching via radio.

The technique used by the Aloha project was further developed into what is now known as Ethernet – the technique most commonly used for local data networks. Ethernet is not a competitor to the Internet but rather one of the techniques used to carry Internet traffic.

The protocols that are now the basis for Internet communication were developed during the 1970s and early 1980s. The requirements made on these communication protocols were that they should provide for a dynamic and robust network. Since the research was sponsored by the Department of Defense, the objective was a network that would continue to function even if a number of nodes were destroyed as a result of a nuclear assault. The protocol suite was named TCP/IP, after two of the most important protocols: transmission control protocol and Internet protocol.

1.4 How has the Internet developed?

The ARPA experiment that started some 30 years ago has developed into a global network serving many millions of users. Originally aimed at linking the various military research organisations together, the network broadened to include communication between universities. It has now become commercialised – an open network for everyone.

The Internet can be used for a wide variety of services, information retrieval probably being the most common service. Real-time and interactive services and various forms of multimedia seem to be the next large categories to emerge.

1.5 The Internet in brief

Transfer mode:	Packet switching, connectionless
Access bandwidth:	A function of the underlying networks
Maximum switched bandwidth:	Often a function of the underlying networks – broadband routers are being developed and set the limit if underlying switched networks are not used
Types of service:	From today's data to multimedia
Security:	Firewalls, encryption, authentication
Terminal mobility:	Using a mobile system as a bearer in the access part
Support for private networks:	Intranets; Extranets; Virtual private networks (VPNs)
Network management:	Simple network management protocol (SNMP)

Figure H.1.4 The Internet in brief

1.6 User services

The wide selection of services is one of the reasons for the astounding spread of the Internet. There's something here for everyone. Services such as e-mail and information retrieval via the World Wide Web are currently the most common services. But many other ways of using the Internet are already in existence, and there is nothing to indicate that the creation of new applications will slow. The following describes some of the most important services and, in some instances, the protocols they employ. More detailed descriptions of the actual protocols are available in Chapter 2.

1.6.1 The original services

The services that were used in the Internet immediately after its inception were primarily intended to make use of the greater possibilities made available by a network as opposed to stand-alone computers: resource-sharing and the exchange of messages. Three application protocols were developed – e-mail, file transfer and remote logon. (See *Figure H.1.5.*)

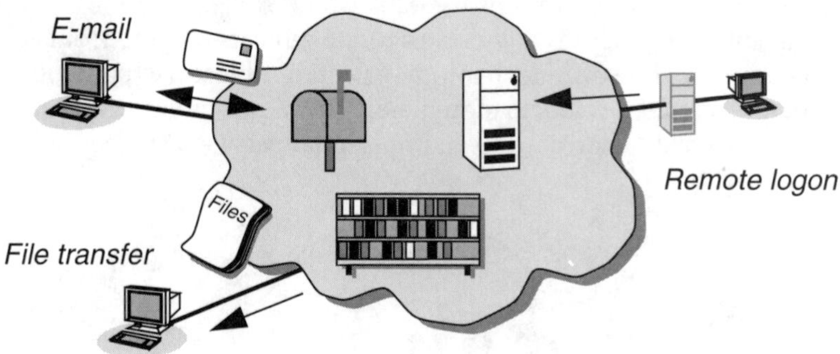

Figure H.1.5 The original Internet services

Electronic mail

Electronic mail, or e-mail, is one of the original applications of the Internet. It is based on the simple mail transfer protocol (SMTP) and the post office protocol (POP) and is used for the transmission of short text messages between two users. E-mail is certainly one of today's major Internet teleservices.

File transfer

The purpose of the file transfer application is to provide a number of users with the possibility of sharing common storage resources from which files can be retrieved when required – with or without some form of authorisation control (for example, user name and password). Transfer is normally performed using the file transfer protocol (FTP).

Retrieving files from different file archives is a popular service. Some file archives function as *anonymous FTP servers,* meaning that no special authorisation is required to gain access to the material stored there.

Remote logon

Remote logon enables users to connect to other computers and use their resources. This service originated at a time when computers and processing power were in short supply but in great demand. The protocol for the service is called TELNET.

1.6.2 Discussion groups

The Internet has not only made worldwide data communication possible but has also made it simple and inexpensive. The most common communication service is e-mail, but the Internet can also be used as a meeting place where users can "congregate" and discuss issues of common interest.

News groups

Internet news groups are forums for debate and exchange of information on different subjects. There is a wide variety of subjects ranging from cooking to programming; however, technology-oriented subjects (in particular those related to computer science) dominate. The news-group service can be described as e-mail addressed to an impersonal party – a subject field.

Figure H.1.6 The Internet as a meeting place

Discussion groups are not based on real-time communication. Instead, users submit their articles or questions after which a response may be entered by other members of the group. The various questions and answers are saved in a catalogued structure so that they can be read at a time convenient for the reader. The advantage of this arrangement is that users have access to topics discussed earlier, although it is somewhat difficult to maintain a concise overview of the structure.

The network news transfer protocol (NNTP) is used for the transfer of information to and from discussion-group members.

Chat

Chat is a sort of discussion forum in which members converse – via a text-based interface – over a network of interconnected servers. Numerous users can communicate with one another at the same time. A channel is created when the first user connects and ceases to exist when the last user terminates communication. A message that is written by one user and then sent over the channel is immediately distributed to all other users connected to that channel. Unlike news, chat is based on real-time communication.

The protocol that connects the servers with one another, and the individual clients with their respective servers, is called the Internet relay chat (IRC) protocol.

1.6.3 Information retrieval

Information retrieval over the Internet has almost become synonymous with the World Wide Web (WWW). The Web represented an enormous breakthrough for the Internet and is probably the application that has been most instrumental in the rapid spread of the Internet around the world. Ironically, the Web is also responsible for a good portion of the criticism that has been aimed at the Internet. There is an enormous amount of information making it more or less impossible to maintain a simplified overview, and dramatic increases in Internet traffic have also led to lengthy response times.

Information retrieval is greatly facilitated by the use of *search engines* (such as Alta Vista or Yahoo!), which help locate the desired type of information by browsing through millions of pages in hundreds of thousands of servers. A search engine can search on titles, uniform resource locators (URLs, described in Chapter 6, Subsection 6.5.3), key words and phrases.

See Chapter 6 for further details on the Web.

1.6.4 Commerce

Commerce over the Internet represents one of the most interesting application areas for future Internet services. One idea is for the Internet to be used as a sort of gigantic, continuously updated mail-order catalogue containing products and services. The physical delivery of ordered software and information will be performed directly over the Internet. (See Chapter 6, Section 6.8 for more information.) The international features of the Internet will make it suitable as a tool for commerce across national borders, with the ensuing problems relating to customs and value-added tax collection. Here, the US has taken the initiative in exempting Internet commerce from taxation.

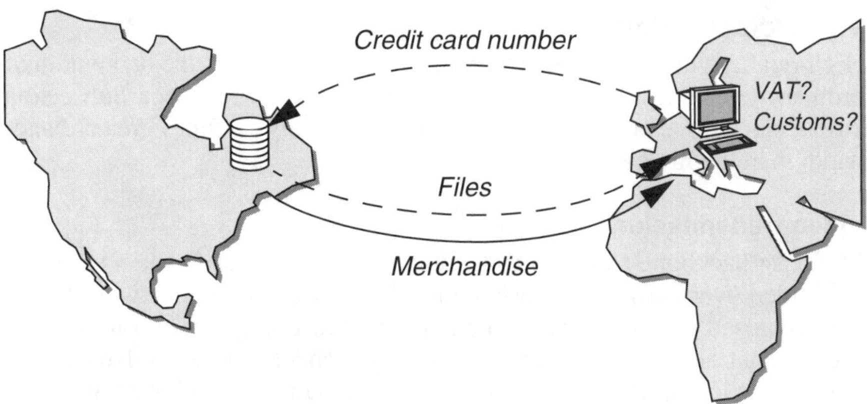

Figure H.1.7 The Internet as marketplace

1.6.5 Telephony

Telephony over the Internet is a more recent service. An important advantage of this service is the low price. Users only pay for the connection set-up to their Internet service supplier – usually the price of a local call – and can then call other users anywhere in the world. The disadvantage is that the Internet, as a packet-switched network, is not designed for the transfer of services that are sensitive to delays and delay variations, in particular. Delays can become significantly large (in the range of seconds) and can also vary with time. Moreover, no common standard exists. This means that parties wishing to carry on telephone conversations over the Internet must install the special telephony software from the same supplier. Demonstration copies of this software can be downloaded from the Internet free of charge.

When these problems are solved, the Internet can become a significant complement to the already established networks for voice transfer (PSTN/ISDN and PLMN), with a forecast 10 million or so subscribers in the year 2000.

1.6.6 Multimedia services

Multimedia

Multimedia is a term often used in connection with the Internet. Which services one includes in this category depends on how multimedia is defined. The definition used here is the following: A service that employs at least two of the three service types *voice*, *data* and *video* and also entails a certain degree of interactivity. (See Volume 1, Chapter 1, Subsection 1.3.2.) The term "voice" can be expanded to include audio in general. Data traffic is currently the primary traffic type transmitted over the Internet, but the transmission of sound and video is increasing. A reasonable prediction is that the Internet will be carrying large volumes of multimedia traffic in the near future.

Videoconferencing

High-quality videoconferencing requires at least six times the bandwidth of ordinary telephony. It works best if run over an *intranet* (see Subsection 1.6.7), since these networks can offer approximately 10 times greater bandwidth than the Internet can.

Video transmission

Multicast backbone (Mbone) and streaming video are used when transmitting video over the Internet. Mbone is a logical, broadband network that is superimposed on the ordinary Internet network. It consists of a number of servers that support multicast, that is, one sender and several receivers. Although some Internet routers do not "understand" IP multicast, they can be used for Mbone traffic if the traffic is encapsulated in normal TCP packets by means of special Mbone computers.

The streaming video technique employs a high degree of video information compression and display of information at the receivers' concurrent with the transfer of subsequent information. The flow is smoothed by a buffer in the receiving equipment.

1.6.7 Business services

Companies have a number of alternatives when employing the Internet or Internet technologies in their internal networks.

Intranets

An intranet is a company network based on the use of Internet technology. The prime advantage of an intranet is a possibility provided by WWW techniques: having a common interface for different information formats. Information can be disseminated quickly and in a uniform manner. Employees can use the same software that they use when retrieving information directly from Internet sources. An intranet can be used to retrieve information from databases, to distribute company news or for special Web pages that serve as bulletin boards. An intranet is ordinarily protected by a *firewall* to prevent intrusion (unauthorised access). (See Chapter 6, Subsection 6.3.1.)

An *extranet* is a solution whereby a company offers certain external individuals (customers and subcontractors) limited access to the information available on the company's intranet.

Virtual private networks

A company can interconnect local data networks to form a virtual private network (VPN) by using the Internet. The service is offered by Internet operators in the form of a "public intranet", a term which in itself is a contradiction. Internet operators can provide better quality of service (QoS) via a public intranet than in the public Internet.

1.7 Terminals and interactivity

1.7.1 Terminals

Terminals play a key role in the spread of the Internet to those who are not comfortable using computers. Most striking in today's rapid development of terminals is the fact that prices are dropping while functionality is increasing. Users are getting more for their money. Interesting characteristics are mobility, speech recognition and smart agents – programs that collect information according to a user's preferences.

Personal computers and workstations

The Internet has inherited many features from the UNIX world. Until a few years ago, the workstation was the most common terminal used when connecting to the Internet. Today, the PC is the predominant terminal.

However, the Internet's relationship with UNIX and workstations is still of interest, because the Internet was to a great degree designed in a UNIX environment, and its methods, rules and terminology are evidence of these roots. Hence, a user with basic knowledge of UNIX can more easily understand how the Internet was created and has developed.

You need a network card or a dial-up modem plus software that supports TCP/IP communication to connect to the Internet. The operating systems that support workstations have built-in TCP/IP support, as do the majority of new PC operating systems.

TV set with set-up box

By means of remote control, a keyboard and a set-top box, a TV set can be used as an Internet terminal for services such as WWW browsing and e-mail. Upstream communication initially uses the PSTN/ISDN.

Network computers

Work is under way to develop special network terminals with a minimum of hardware and only a small hard disk (or none at all). These terminals – called network computers (NC) – can only function when they are connected to a network from which software is downloaded. They are inexpensive to manufacture and can be administrated and have their software updated more easily. On the other hand, they contribute to an increase in data communication in a network.

1.7.2 Support for interactivity

Interactive services require a dialogue between a WWW server and a user. The host computer offering the service sends a form to the user, who fills it in and returns it. Depending on the user's response, the host computer will send certain parameters to a transaction processor. The resultant response from the processor indicates to the host computer the next step to be taken in the dialogue.

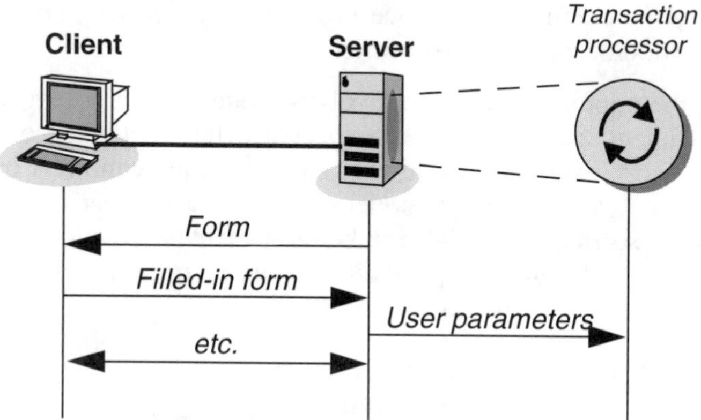

Figure H.1.8 Interactivity

Java

The Java programming language, which was developed by Sun Microsystems, is intended to support interactive network applications. Instead of doing all the executing itself, the host computer called delivers Java code together with the requested document. The application code is then executed locally on the user's computer.

Java is platform-independent; in other words, the computer operating system is irrelevant. Java creates a "virtual" processor that executes on top of the operating system. This virtual processor supports the same operations regardless of whether it is executing in a PC Windows-based environment or in a UNIX-type workstation environment. In other words, Java code can be freely moved between computers and operating systems, but hardware performance will naturally depend on the computer itself.

1.8 Service providers

1.8.1 Internet service providers

An Internet service provider (ISP) provides its subscribers with access to one or more Internet services.

ISPs fall into several categories: as a function of the types of services they offer; as a function of the size of their core networks (and whether or not they have any core network at all); and whether they are commercial companies or public institutions. Previously, the Internet was primarily offered by universities to researchers and students. In step with recent deregulation developments, commercial service providers are carrying an increasingly greater portion of total Internet traffic.

Much of the ongoing discussion revolves around ISP problems in offering users sufficient capacity. The unexpectedly large number of users has caused network overload, resulting in slow communication. A critical portion of the network has been modem pools: The number of modems has often been insufficient during peak hours. However, development is under way to alleviate the situation, and all ISPs are working intensively to boost the capacity of their networks.

1.8.2 Information service providers

Universities, companies and private individuals are offering large amounts of information over the Internet. This information covers a multitude of subjects, and although the emphasis is still on the natural sciences, the amount of other types of information is growing rapidly. An ISP can also be an information service provider when offering on-line services, which involves access to special information, to chat groups and to games.

Considerable effort is being invested in the legal aspects of regulating information flow. The objectives are to eliminate hard-core pornography and documents of the type "Pointers for budding terrorists". Many within the established Internet community protest vigorously, arguing that we have at last arrived at a "democratic" medium in which everyone has a right to make his or her voice heard. They feel that censure is a threat to freedom of speech.

1.8.3 Product providers

Product providers are companies that sell their products over the Net, employing either electronic payment or cash on delivery (COD). Selling via the Internet is not a booming industry today, but it may become an effective means for a vendor to market his company and to gain experience in the use of the Internet as a sales medium.

2 Standards

Internet standardisation activities are being conducted with a great degree of openness, thereby allowing all interested parties the opportunity to present their viewpoints. Before a technical solution can be approved as a standard, it must be implemented and tested in a number of different systems. The objective is to arrive at mature and stable standards that are widely accepted by the Internet world. The standardisation process also strives towards clear and easily understood documentation and quick and effective administration. The Internet should be developed in step with the advent of new requirements and be compatible with new techniques.

The standardisation process is performed within the framework of the Internet Society (ISOC). It is organised and driven forward by the Internet Architecture Board (IAB) and the Internet Engineering Steering Group (IESG). Standards and other documentation of common interest are published as Requests For Comments (RFCs).

2.1 Organisations

Internet Society

The ISOC is a non-profit international organisation for global cooperation and coordination of Internet-related activities. It is a free-standing organisation with headquarters in Reston, Virginia, in the US.

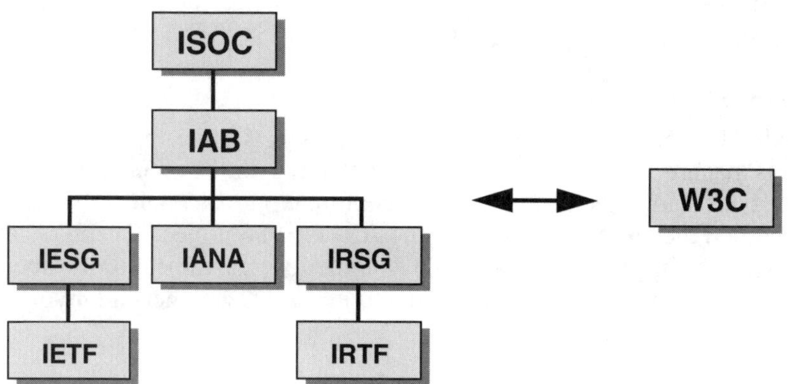

Figure H.2.1 Internet standardisation organisations

The objectives of the ISOC are:

- to maintain and develop Internet standards;
- to expand and develop Internet architecture;
- to develop effective administrative processes for the operation of the Internet; and
- to promote the development of and accessibility to the Internet.

ISOC membership has grown steadily since the organisation was formed in 1992. Today, members include government agencies, other non-profit organisations, private corporations and private individuals.

Internet Architecture Board

Formerly the Internet Activities Board, the Internet Architecture Board (IAB) consists of 13 members, each of whom has one vote. IAB members are not appointed on the basis of any specialist competence but rather because of their broad overall knowledge of the Internet. Issues addressed by the IAB often deal with future strategies and international cooperation. The objective is results that can be used as guidelines by the IESG.

The IAB, which is a technical reference group affiliated with the ISOC, publishes Internet Official Standards on a quarterly basis.

Internet Engineering Steering Group

The IESG is responsible for the technical control of the Internet Engineering Task Force's (IETF's) efforts and all Internet standardisation activities. The IESG is a member of the ISOC and oversees the standardisation process in accordance with a set of established rules.

The IESG consists of the IETF's area directors and the IETF's chairman, who is also chairman of the IESG.

Internet Engineering Task Force

The IETF's most important function is to assign priorities to the various protocols that are to be developed and integrated into the Internet protocol suite. The IETF started as a forum for the coordination of technical matters that concerned the various suppliers to the ARPA 1986 project. The association has since then grown into an open, international organisation of network designers, network operators, manufacturers and researchers all involved in the development of the Internet.

The IETF's objectives are:

- to identify and suggest solutions to technical operational problems arising in the Internet;
- to specify the development and use of protocols and architecture;
- to be a forum for the exchange of information between manufacturers, users, researchers and network operators.

All technical work is carried out in working groups, each being responsible for a particular area – for example, applications, network management and security. Each of the areas has an area director.

The IETF nominates future members of the IESG and the IAB.

Internet Assigned Numbers Agency

Protocol specifications contain parameters (such as port numbers and error codes) that must be uniquely defined. The IAB is responsible for this undertaking but delegates the task to the Internet Assigned Numbers Agency (IANA), which publishes the defined parameters in a periodic RFC under the title Assigned Numbers.

Internet Research Steering Group

The Internet Research Steering Group (IRSG) functions as the decision-making group for the Internet Research Task Force (IRTF). It has the same relationship to IREF as that existing between the IESG and the IETF.

Internet Research Task Force

The IRTF, which does not directly participate in the standardisation process, investigates subjects that are considered too uncertain, advanced or insufficiently scrutinised to be included in the standardisation process. The IRTF's efforts may then lead to specifications of sufficient maturity to become a standard.

World Wide Web Consortium

The World Wide Web Consortium (W3C) promotes the use of the World Wide Web by developing specifications and products. Different member companies finance W3C operations. However, the products that are developed are free of charge and can be used freely by anyone.

2.2 Documents

Requests for Comments

Requests for Comments (RFCs) is a series of documents that serves as the official publications channel for Internet standards and other documentation produced by the IESG, IAB and the rest of the Internet world. Each new version of a document is published as a separate RFC. In other words, a document titled "RFC 1100 version 2" cannot exist – the new document will receive a unique RFC number. One must therefore check that the RFC being used has not been replaced by a new version.

RFC 1 (Host Software) is dated 7 April 1969. The number of RFCs passed the 2,000 mark in 1996 and is currently increasing at a rate of one new document every other day.

An RFC can contain anything from formal protocol standards to articles of a general nature. The procedures dealing with the Internet standardisation process are described in RFC 2026.

Documents that may receive RFC status are referred to as Internet drafts and are published by the IETF via a special on-line library. An Internet draft will be deleted in the event that the document has not been recommended for full RFC status within a period of six months. The document is not official and may be modified during the publishing process.

Internet standards

Some RFC documents are also Internet standards, in which case they are referred to as *STD documents.* The majority of Internet standards deal with various protocols, for example, TCP and IP. Documents must pass through three stages to be adopted as an Internet standard: proposed standard, draft standard and standard. To advance to the next stage in the standardisation process, a document must be recommended by the IESG.

Proposed standard

As a proposed standard, the document will be published for the Internet world, and viewpoints will be solicited. Documents will remain in proposal status for a period of six months to allow all viewpoints to be gathered and processed. Advancing to the next stage requires two independent implementations as well as proven interoperability.

Granting a protocol the status of proposed standard is a significant step. This brands the protocol as a candidate for the subsequent status of draft standard and possibly future standard.

Draft standard

The status of a draft is the last stage before a specification becomes a standard. It is an important stage, indicating that the specification is mature and usable. To attain the status of draft standard, specifications must be "well understood" and recognised as being stable. In spite of this, additional tests may be required, because products or functions that have been proposed for standardisation may exhibit unforeseen behaviour following large-scale implementation.

A standard draft is generally considered a "finished" specification. If any changes are introduced before the specification is finally approved as a standard, they usually deal with solutions to certain specific problems. Although still at the draft stage, such specifications are often implemented commercially.

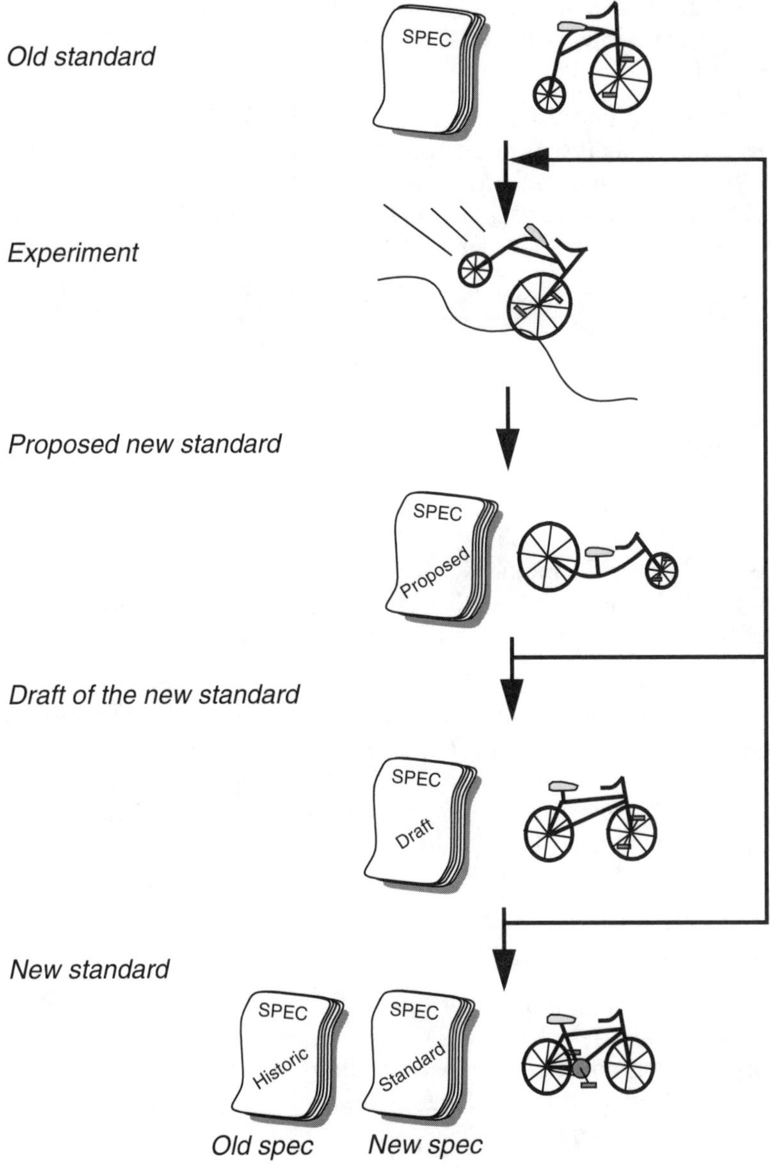

Figure H.2.2 Internet standardisation – flowchart

Standard

A draft standard may be elevated to the status of standard after having first been sufficiently implemented with positive operational outcome. An Internet standard must be a stable and coherent specification, implemented in many independent systems and contributing significant value to all or parts of the Internet.

New versions of old Internet standards are subjected to the entire standardisation process, just as if they were completely new specifications. When a new specification attains standard status, it usually replaces the older standard, which then receives the designation *historic*. In some cases, versions are allowed to exist in parallel in order to protect systems already implemented.

Specifications for which no standardisation procedures have been proposed are classed as prototypes, experimental, informational or historic.

2.3 Protocols

The following deals only with the protocols included in the TCP/IP protocol suite. This designation, or just TCP/IP, is the collective term for the IP itself, as the network protocol, and the various transport and application protocols related to the IP. We will start our discussion with a presentation of the overall structure of TCP/IP and the functions of the various layers, followed by a review of some of the most common protocols.

As in the case of the open systems integration (OSI) model, TCP/IP operates according to the principle of layered communication. Lower layers offer services to the layers above them, and adjacent layers communicate across an interface. Protocols defining a set of rules are used for communication between layers at the same level in different nodes.

A given TCP/IP function is not as strictly bound to a specific layer as is the case in the OSI model. (See Volume 1, Chapter 2, Sections 2.9 to 2.12, for more information about layered communication.)

The TCP/IP and the OSI models differ in other respects, too. These differences are due in part to the fact that TCP/IP was developed to solve a particular problem (data communication between units of the US defense research community), while the OSI model was developed to serve as a reference for future protocol development.

TCP/IP attaches great weight to internetworking, that is, communication between units that are not connected to the same network (not even necessarily connected to the same type of network). TCP/IP communicates in a connectionless manner (meaning that no connections are set up through intermediate nodes, even if a logical connection is established between the client and the server). This results in decreased sensitivity when communicating over interconnected networks. Even the approach taken by the two models to network management differs.

TCP/IP is much more widespread than the protocols of the OSI model. On the other hand, the value of the OSI model as a reference model is indisputable. (See Volume 1, Chapter 2, Subsection 2.9.7 for more information on the OSI model.)

TCP/IP's approach to communication is based on three parties being involved – processes, hosts and networks. (See *Figure H.2.3.*) Processes – those units that communicate with one another – are executed in host computers which are in turn interconnected by the networks. The network elements that bind the networks together are described in Chapter 3.

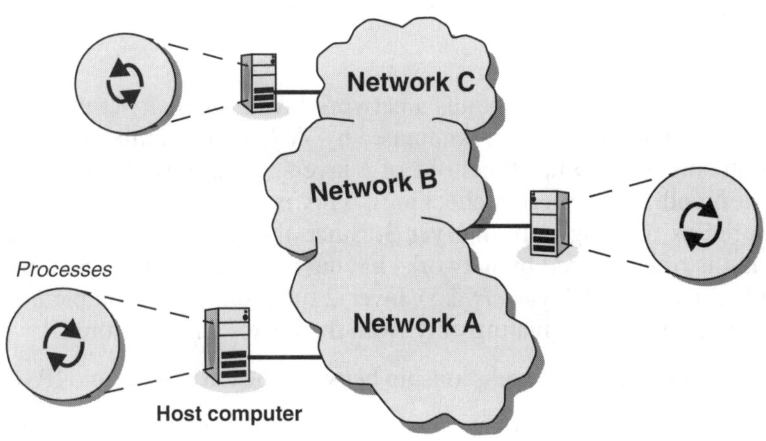

Figure H.2.3 Processes, host computers and networks. Data packets are addressed using the host computer's address and are then sent along to the correct process.

Although the TCP/IP protocol suite is named after its two most well-known protocols, a number of different protocols are included in the suite.

Note that TCP does not have to be used when we communicate with the aid of the TCP/IP protocol. It would perhaps be more correct to call it *the IP suite.* As a matter of fact, the term *IP technique* is increasingly being used instead of TCP/IP.

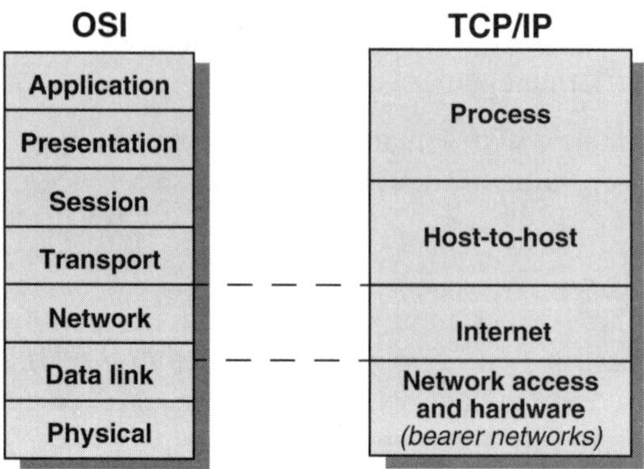

Figure H.2.4 Comparison between the OSI model and TCP/IP. Note that IP contains portions from both the network and data-link layers. The network access and hardware layer is defined in Subsection 2.3.1.

In OSI terms, the IP suite contains a network layer, dominated by the Internet protocol; a transport layer, dominated by TCP; and a number of application protocols. IP also has functions of a layer-2 type (discrimination, segmentation and IP-label error checking). This is often forgotten, and IP is considered as residing only in layer 3. Since the IP suite has no physical layer and is often carried by networks having a two-layer structure (see the example illustrated in *Figure H.2.5*), layer-2 functions in the complete stack are often defined as originating only from the bearer and not from IP.

Figure H.2.4 illustrates the relationship between the OSI model and IP suite.

Figure H.2.6 provides an overview of the IP suite protocols that will be addressed below. (Resource reservation set-up protocol (RSVP), which supports isochronous services over the Internet, is addressed in Chapter 10.) A number of bearer networks have also been added.

The TCP/IP structure is briefly described in Volume 1, Chapter 2, Section 2.12.

The lowest layer in the TCP/IP stack is in turn subdivided into layers. See *Figure H.2.5*, which illustrates a "connection" employing IP routers. However, the subdivision into data-link and physical layers is of no interest in this Part. For a more detailed description of these layers, see those Parts that address the various bearer networks.

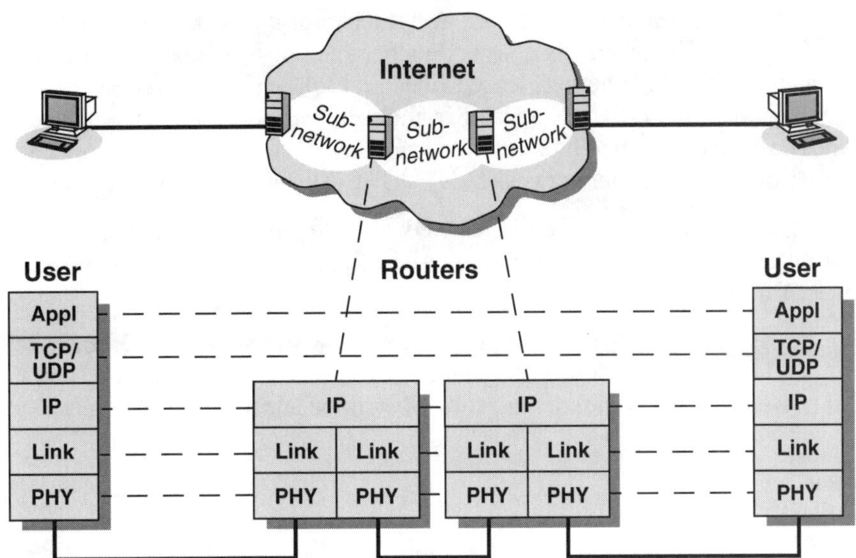

Figure H.2.5 An "Internet connection". Since the Internet is connectionless, the communication path may change from one packet to another.

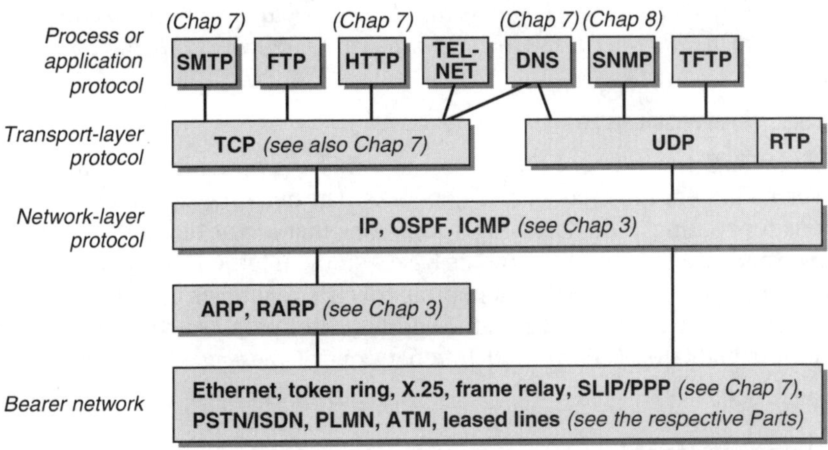

Figure H.2.6 Protocols described in Chapter 2 and their interrelationship.

2.3.1 Network-access and hardware layer – Bearer networks

The network-access and hardware layer contains the protocols that provide access to a specific bearer network and the bearer network itself, for example, Ethernet. The protocols deliver data between hosts that are connected to the same network. Ethernet, leased lines and token ring are predominantly used for local networks; X.25 and frame relay can be used for longer distances. Fibre distributed data interface (FDDI) is used in local networks and in metropolitan area networks (MAN). ATM is used in all types of network.

The fact that the IP suite can be carried by so many networks is one of the reasons for the global use of the Internet. Special standards exist for each type of interworking.

It is not our ambition to describe private data networks such as Ethernet, token ring and FDDI. X.25, frame relay and ATM are addressed in Parts F and G. No bearer network standards or protocols will be addressed in this Part.

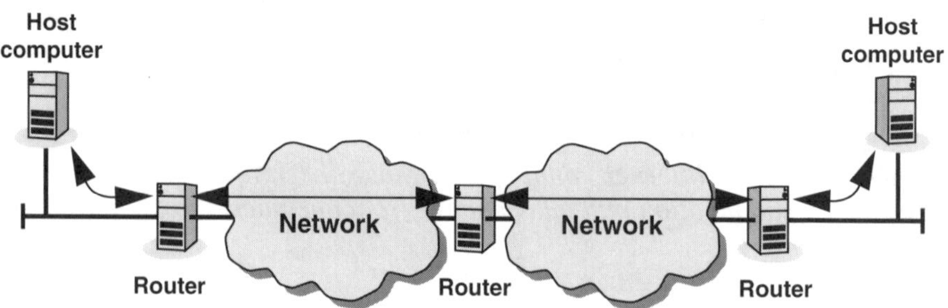

Figure H.2.7 The network-access and hardware layer is responsible for the transport of data over LANs, metropolitan area networks (MANs) and WANs

2.3.2 Network layer

The layer-3 functions of the IP protocol make it possible to communicate over a number of interconnected networks. The network layer includes functions for routing and addressing – functions that are of fundamental importance because the entire Internet is based on the interconnection of different networks. In addition to the main protocol (IP), a number of auxiliary protocols are included, in particular, the address resolution protocol (ARP), open shortest path first (OSPF) and Internet control message protocol (ICMP). (See Chapter 3.)

Internet protocol

IP is the core protocol of the Internet. It is designed to be simple and adaptable to different underlying bearer networks. IP provides a service for the transfer of data units – datagrams – between the host computer and the router as well as between routers. The source and destination are identified through the use of fixed-length IP addresses. IP is also responsible for the fragmentation and recombination of datagrams. IP has no functions for increasing reliability of transfer; in other words, flow control, sequencing or retransmission. This is left to higher-level protocols. However, a checksum is computed for the IP header to allow transmission errors to be detected and any erroneous datagrams to be discarded. At the IP level, each datagram is handled as a separate transfer and not as part of a larger data set.

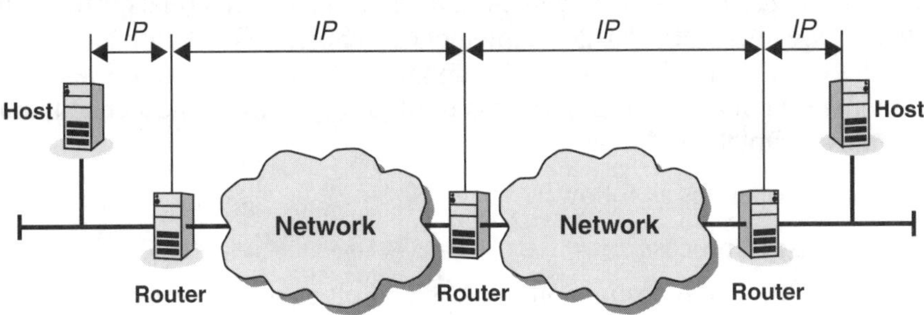

Figure H.2.8 The network layer is responsible for the routing of data

IP is a required standard in every host computer that communicates with the Internet and in every gateway or router that interconnects the various networks. An IP header is illustrated in *Figure H.2.9.*

1 … 8 (bits 1–4)	(bits 5–8)	16 (bits 1–8)	24 (bits 1–8)	32 (bits 1–8)
Version	IHL	Service type	Total length	
Identification			Flags	Fragment offset
Time-to-live		Protocol	Header checksum	
Source address				
Destination address				
Options				Padding
User data (fragment)				

Figure H.2.9 IP header (IPv4) with user data

Version specifies the IP version being used – in this case, version 4. The *Internet header length (IHL)* is the size of the header as the number of 32-bit words. *Service type* indicates datagram priority. *Total length* specifies the number of octets in the datagram; the maximum size is 65,535 octets. (All host computers must be capable of receiving datagrams at least 576 octets in length.) *Identification* is used for the recombination required after fragmentation. *Flags* indicate that the datagram has been fragmented. *Fragment offset* shows where in the datagram a specific fragment belongs. *Time to live* is the maximum lifetime of a datagram in the network. Units are in seconds, and every node that handles the datagram must reduce time to live by at least one unit. *Protocol* specifies the IP user (for example, TCP) that the user data is to be delivered to. *Header checksum* is computed on the basis of the IP header. *Source address* is the IP address from which the datagram was sent. *Destination address* is the IP address that is the datagram's final destination. *Options* are different forms of supplementary choices. For example, the path which the datagram must follow through the network can be indicated here. Options need not be used. *Padding* is used to fill out the IP header so that it contains complete 32-bit words.

In short, IP operates as follows:

The sending IP process

- receives data, the destination address and other parameters from higher layers, for example, TCP (see *Figure H.2.13*);
- creates a datagram header and positions it in front of the data that has been received (see *Figure H.2.9*), and determines the address of the next node along the path to the final destination. The address can be an Ethernet address of an the Internet router connected to the same Ethernet as the sending host computer; then
- forwards the datagram and the bearer network address to the underlying network, for example, Ethernet.

The routing process

- receives the datagram from the underlying network, computes and compares the checksum and reads the IP address;
- determines the next bearer network address; then
- forwards the data and the new bearer network address to the underlying network.

The receiving process

- receives the datagram from the underlying network and computes and compares the checksum;
- removes the IP header; then
- delivers data to the specified user, for instance, TCP or UDP (the IP user is determined by the contents of the *protocol* field in the IP header).

The routing process is explained in detail in Chapter 3.

IP addresses (IPv6)

Some form of addressing is required for the information to arrive at the correct host computer. In TCP/IP, this is provided for through the use of IP addresses. An IP address is four octets in length (in IPv4, see the comparison between IPv4 and IPv6 below) and consists of two parts: the network portion and the host computer portion. (IP addressing is described in more detail in Chapter 3, Section 3.2.) One of the Internet's growing pains is that IP addresses are becoming scarce.

1		8	16	24	32
1 2 3 4	5 6 7 8	1 2 3 4 5 6 7 8	1 2 3 4 5 6 7 8	1 2 3 4 5 6 7 8	
Version	Prio	Flow label			
Payload length			Next header	Hop limit	
Source address					
Destination address					

Figure H.2.10 IPv6 header

IP version 6 (IPv6) has been developed primarily to alleviate the address shortage problem and the handling of real-time services that require guaranteed QoS. IPv4 is predominant today. (Version 5 was an experimental version that never became standard.)

Address length is increased in IPv6, from 4 to 16 octets. Other objectives are:

- to simplify the IP header and protocol handling; the IP header has been given a fixed length, and redundant functions in version 4 have been removed;
- to make it possible to guarantee the user a certain level of transfer quality with respect to delays; and
- to achieve backward compatibility; because IPv4 is already installed in many systems, the two versions must be able to coexist.

Version specifies the IP version; in this case, version 6. *Prio* indicates datagram priority. *Flow label* is used to support real-time services by identifying IP datagrams belonging to the same flow. *Payload length* specifies the length of the payload in number of octets. *Next header* identifies the next header (corresponds to the *protocol* field in IPv4). *Hop limit* is counted down by one for every node that forwards the datagram. *Source address* is the IP address from which the datagram was sent. *Destination address* is the IP address of the final destination.

IPv4 is described in RFC 791 and represents STD 5. IPv6 is described in RFC 1883.

2.3.3 Host-to-host layer

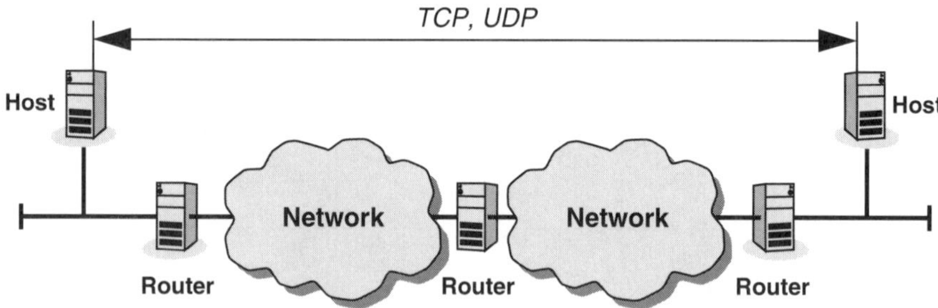

Figure H.2.11 Host computers are interconnected with one another at the host-to-host level

The host-to-host layer delivers data between communicating processes located in different hosts. Functionality is available for error control and flow control. Different protocols are used depending on the user's transfer service requirements in terms of sophistication and dependability.

There are primarily two protocols available at the host-to-host level: the TCP and the user datagram protocol (UDP). TCP is the more advanced of the two.

Transmission control protocol (TCP)

TCP is a dependable process-to-process protocol. It is connection-oriented inasmuch as it sets up logical connections between different processes in the network. On the other hand, packets do not traverse any predetermined path since routing is controlled by IP, which is connectionless. The service offered by TCP is dependable communication between processes executing in different host computers located in interconnected networks.

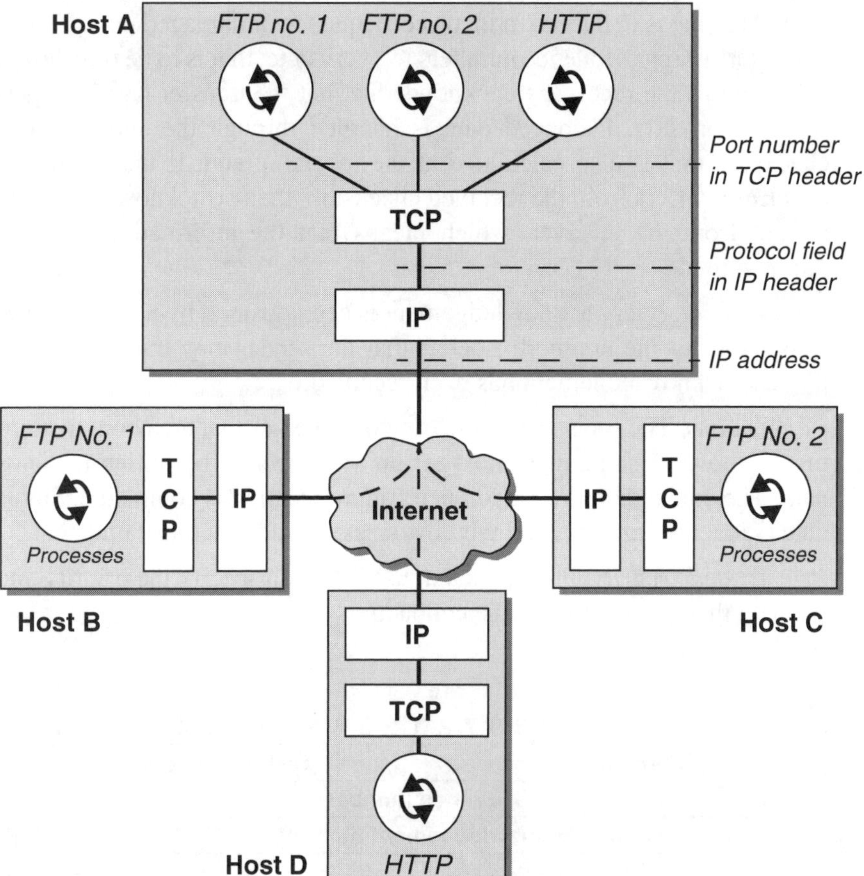

Figure H.2.12 Addressing and multiplexing via TCP

To enable the delivery of a secure transfer service, TCP contains functionality for:

- *Basic data transfer*. TCP is capable of transferring a continuous stream of data in both directions by packaging a number of data octets into segments that can be delivered to the underlying layers for subsequent transmission.
- *Addressing and multiplexing*. Several processes in one and the same host must be able to use TCP simultaneously. This requirement is met through the use of port numbers in addition to the IP addresses. A port number unambiguously identifies an IP user. (See *Figure H.2.12*.)

- *Dependability*. TCP must be able to tolerate loss of data, duplication of data, data that is delivered in incorrect sequence or damaged data. To this end, TCP assigns sequence numbers to every octet that is to be transferred and requires the receiver to acknowledge that the transfer has been performed correctly. Damaged data is handled through the addition of a checksum that is also calculated at the receiving end. If the calculated checksum differs from the received checksum, then no acknowledgement is sent from the receiver, which means that the information must be retransmitted.
- *Flow control*. Every acknowledgement is accompanied by a *window size*. This indicates the number of octets that the sender may transmit before the next acknowledgement has been received.
- *Connections*. The transport layers of two processes that are about to communicate with one another must set up a connection by initiating status data. The connection is cleared once communication is completed. Status data (sequence numbers and window sizes) are continuously updated.
- *Priority and security*. Processes that use TCP can specify the priority and security that are to apply to the connection.

1 8 16 24 32

1 2 3 4 5 6 7 8 1 2 3 4 5 6 7 8 1 2 3 4 5 6 7 8 1 2 3 4 5 6 7 8

<table>
<tr><td colspan="16">Source port</td><td colspan="16">Destination port</td></tr>
<tr><td colspan="32">Sequence number</td></tr>
<tr><td colspan="32">Acknowledgement number</td></tr>
<tr><td colspan="4">Data offset</td><td colspan="6">Reserved</td><td colspan="6">Control bits</td><td colspan="16">Window</td></tr>
<tr><td colspan="16">Checksum</td><td colspan="16">Urgent pointer</td></tr>
<tr><td colspan="24">Options</td><td colspan="8">Padding</td></tr>
<tr><td colspan="32">Data</td></tr>
</table>

Figure H.2.13 TCP header

The *source port* is the port used by the sending process. The *destination port* is the port number of the receiving process. The port number is used for identifying the session to which the segment belongs and the process to which it is to be delivered. For this to function properly, "standard" or familiar port numbers are used; for example, 25 would be used to denote SMTP – whereby the receiver is correctly informed of the process that the message is intended for. The *sequence number* is the sequence number of the first octet in the segment; TCP handles segments as portions of a connection. The *acknowledgement number*, used to avoid segment loss, specifies the next segment expected to be received. *Data offset* is the number of 32-bit words contained in the header, thus also indicating indirectly where the payload starts. *Reserved* is not used ("reserved for future use"). *Control bits* of different types are used for acknowledgement and other purposes (see Subsection 7.3.3). *Window* specifies the number of octets that the sender may transmit from this instant and until the next acknowledgement of reception. The *checksum* is calculated on the basis of the contents of the header and the payload. The *urgent pointer* is an extension of the URG bit; if the URG bit is set, then the urgent pointer indicates the start of "urgent data". *Options* allow optional parameters; for example, the maximum size of the TCP segments for a connection can be specified. *Padding* is used to fill out the IP header so that it contains complete 32-bit words.

TCP is used by a multitude of different application protocols, such as the simple mail transfer protocol (SMTP) and the file transfer protocol (FTP).

TCP is described in RFC 793 and represents STD 7, which is recommended but not mandatory.

User datagram protocol

UDP is the most common alternative to TCP at the host-to-host level. UDP offers a transmission service with a minimum of protocol handling. There are no guarantees that the message will arrive at the correct destination, nor are there any guarantees against duplication. No connection is established with the receiving end. The UDP header consists of four parts only, as shown in *Figure H.2.14*.

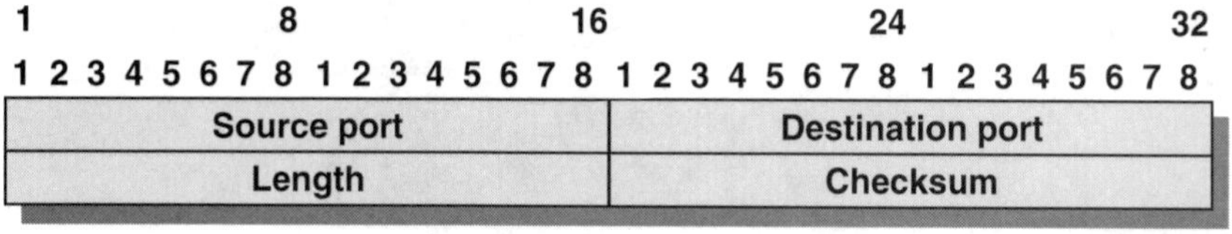

Bits 1–16 (1 2 3 4 5 6 7 8 1 2 3 4 5 6 7 8)	Bits 17–32 (1 2 3 4 5 6 7 8 1 2 3 4 5 6 7 8)
Source port	Destination port
Length	Checksum

Figure H.2.14 User datagram protocol header

The *source port* and *destination port* unambiguously identify each individual connection with the aid of IP addresses (the sender and receiver are included in the IP header). The port number is used to indicate – to UDP – the application that the message is intended for. *Length* is the number of octets contained in the packet. *Checksum* is calculated to determine whether or not an error has occurred during transmission. The checksum is calculated on the basis of the contents of the header and the payload. In the event of an incorrect checksum, the received segment is discarded and no further action is taken. Checksums need not be transmitted. If not transmitted, the field is set to 0.

UDP is used by the domain name system (DNS) and the simple network management protocol (SNMP). UDP is also used for many real-time applications that cannot handle retransmission, although they may have a high tolerance to bit errors.

UDP is described in RFC 768. It represents STD 6, which is the recommended standard.

Real-time protocol

The design of real-time protocol (RTP) – a transport protocol for providing real-time services – makes it independent of underlying protocols. RTP uses UDP to communicate in a TCP/IP environment. RTP cannot reserve resources in the network, nor can it guarantee a specific level of service quality. RTP is described in RFC 1889.

2.3.4 Process or application layer

The process layer contains the various application protocols (for example, protocols for e-mail and file transfer) that make use of the underlying layers for performing the actual transfer service. (See *Figure H.2.15.*)

The number of available application protocols is increasing in step with the development of new applications. A number of the most prominent protocols will be addressed below. SMTP, POP, Internet message access protocol (IMAP), hypertext transfer protocol (HTTP) and DNS are described in Chapter 7. SNMP is described in Chapter 8.

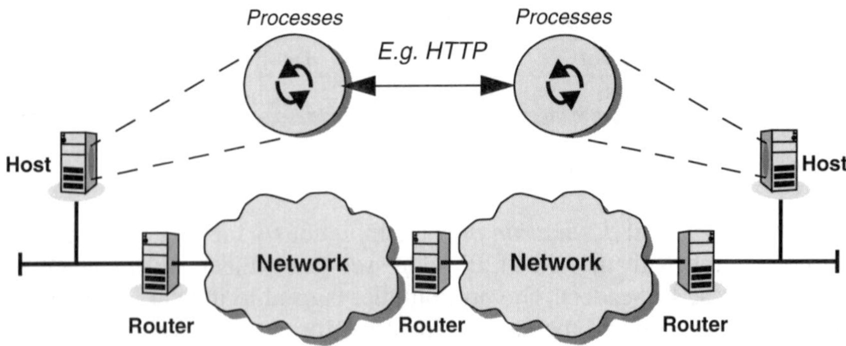

Figure H.2.15 Process layers interconnect application processes with one another

File transfer protocol

FTP is an application protocol used for the transfer of files between different computers. The objective is to provide users with access to file systems in other computers. The user should be able to view a remote computer's file catalogue and then request the transfer of any files of interest.

FTP is described in RFC 959 and represents STD 9.

Trivial file transfer protocol

Trivial file transfer protocol (TFTP) is a simpler version of FTP. FTP contains functions for the handling of compression and various file types – a handling method that is necessary when operating in an environment containing many interconnected networks. Simpler functionality is sufficient for local networks, which are targeted by TFTP. TFTP makes use of UDP, while FTP uses TCP.

TFTP is described in RFC 1350 and represents STD 33.

TELNET

The TELNET protocol was developed as a standard method for communication between terminals and terminal-oriented processes executing on a host computer. The principle is that the user can log onto a host computer rather than onto his desktop computer.

TELNET is based on the network virtual terminal (NVT) concept. An NVT may be said to represent a standard terminal and a standard set of the services offered. This makes work much simpler for those who use different terminals in their work. The standard combination of terminal and services can then be extended for each individual connection set-up, depending on the capacity of the terminal and that of the host computer.

TELNET is described in RFCs 854 and 855 and represents STD 8. Several application protocols are based on TELNET, such as SMTP.

Network news transfer protocol

NNTP supports Internet news groups (see Chapter 1) and includes functions for distribution, queries, downloading and the entry of new articles or of responses to previous articles.

NNTP is described in RFC 977.

Hypertext transfer protocol

HTTP is an application protocol primarily intended for client–server communication. A client is an application program that sets up a connection so it can send queries. A server is an application program that accepts requests for the set-up of connections over which queries can be answered.

HTTP is the most common application protocol on the WWW. See Chapter 6 for more details about the WWW, HTTP, hypertext mark-up language (HTML) and URL. HTTP is described in RFC 1945.

Simple network management protocol

SNMP is a protocol for the transfer of network management information between the elements of a network and the network management centres. SNMP contains no functionality for the actual management of the network; it just handles the transfer of information. SNMP is described in RFC 1157 and represents STD 15.

See Chapter 8 for more detailed descriptions of SNMP and SNMPv2.

3 Routing

3.1 Introduction

As a result of the widespread use of the Internet, large-scale connectionless communication has been introduced into the public network. Each packet is individually routed through the network, independent of the preceding packet. See also Volume 1, Chapter 2, Subsection 2.10.8, where the differences between connectionless and connection-oriented communication are discussed. Signalling system no. 7 is another network that handles connectionless communication (see *Part E – The signalling network*).

The advantage of individual routing of packets is twofold: a robust network (if one connection is out of order, then packets will take alternative paths), and no waste of capacity (all capacity is used for “commercial” traffic). A disadvantage is that there is no way of completely preventing delays. Transfer takes longer if the network becomes heavily loaded. This is the motivation for the development of protocols that are capable of reserving capacity, for example, the resource reservation protocol (RSVP).

In this Part, the heading “Switching and switch control” has been replaced by “Routing”. This term harmonises much better with Internet terminology when used to describe the functionality of network elements (routers) which “switch” connectionless traffic. (When the term *routing* is used in connection with circuit-switched networks, its meaning is restricted to “directing” or “route selection”.)

A dynamic control function is required to enable routers to determine the specific output port to which an incoming packet is to be sent. Such dynamic routing – a common Internet concept – is based on adaptive routing algorithms; that is, the router takes into account changes in network topology and the network load. Delay, throughput or availability and cost may be controlling parameters. When routing long-distance transit traffic, the routing process can sometimes be based on entirely different factors, even political. Routing information is compiled in routing tables.

The dynamics of the control function require continuous updating and supervision. Special protocols have been developed for this purpose, such as OSPF for updating between routers and ICMP for supervision.

The basis for the routing process is a carefully prepared numbering plan and some form of segmentation or hierarchical layering of the network. These aspects are addressed in Sections 3.2 and 3.3.

As mentioned in Chapter 1, the ability to "surf" on other networks is one of the most important reasons for the success of the Internet. (See *Figure H.3.1.*) But there are two sides to every coin. Surfing (or stratification) requires associations between addresses in the networks involved. The solution to this problem is discussed in Subsection 3.6.1, which deals with address translation, and Subsection 3.6.2, which describes the address resolution protocol (ARP) and the reverse address protocol (RARP).

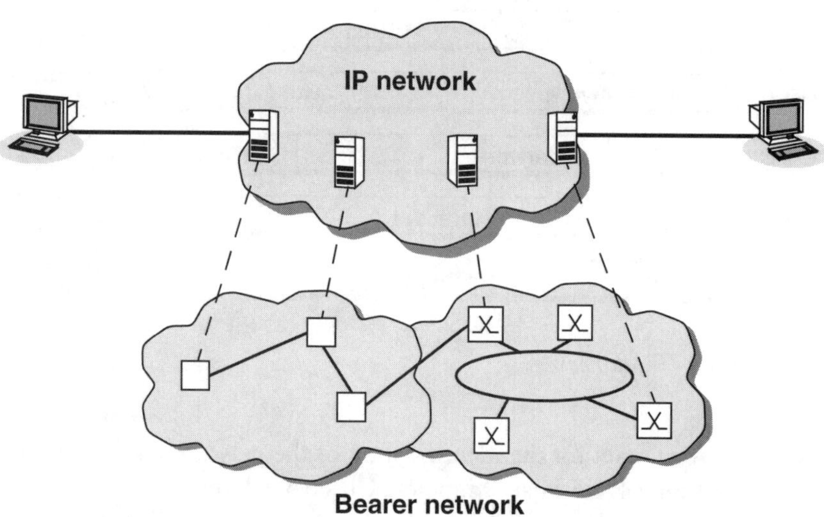

Figure H.3.1 Internet routing and stratification

Interworking between the Internet and ATM and their respective roles are not completely self-evident. One extreme is that ATM (like Ethernet and X.25) assumes a subordinate role as a simple point-to-point bearer. The other extreme is that ATM's switching and QoS characteristics are utilised to the full. To illustrate the interworking options, this chapter closes with a special routing and switching scheme based on ATM.

3.2 IP addresses and domain names

3.2.1 IP addresses

Each Internet host computer and router has an IP address. All addresses have a length of 32 bits. The addresses are placed in the IP packet's source address and destination address fields.

The addresses of IPv6 will be considerably longer.

Only a portion of the address is used for the actual routing process, namely the network address. The length of the network address is a function of the class of the IP address. Five classes exist: A, B, C, D and E. (See *Figure H.3.2.*)

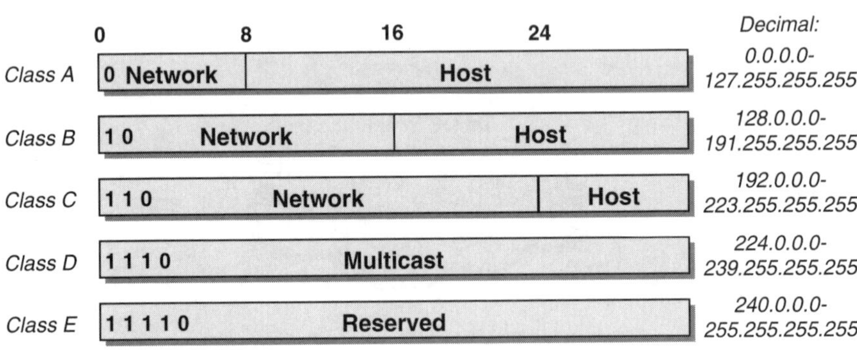

Figure H.3.2 IP addresses

- *Class A:* one octet for the identification of the network and three for the identification of the host computer. Class A addresses are suitable for very large networks; three octets allow more than 16 million host computer addresses per network. Class A addresses have "0" as the first bit.

- *Class B:* two octets for the network and two for the host computer. Class B addresses are only assigned to large networks. The assignment of new class B addresses is nowadays highly restrictive, because they are becoming scarce. One solution to this problem is to assign several class C addresses instead of one class B address. Class B addresses start with "10".
- *Class C:* three octets for network identification and one for host-computer identification. Class C addresses are still plentiful. They are suitable for small networks having less than 256 host computers per network (in reality, somewhat fewer, because certain addresses are reserved). Class C addresses start with the bit pattern "110".
- *Class D:* used for multicast, that is, one sender and many receivers. Class D addresses start with the bit pattern "1110".
- *Class E:* reserved for testing. Class E addresses start with the bit pattern "11110".

The notation used for IP addressing consists of decimal numbers for every octet, separated by periods; for example, 197.45.98.230.

Continued rapid expansion will probably result in all IP addresses being used up early in the 21st century. Theoretically, some four billion addresses are available. In practice, the number is significantly lower, because for practical reasons networks cannot utilise all addresses that have been assigned to them. Only complete network addresses are assigned, which means that even if the network to be connected only contains 15 host computers, it receives a class C address. This principle is especially problematic in the case of class A and class B addresses.

Companies with internal networks can use dynamic address allocation. This means that one set of addresses is used within the internal network (not necessarily IP addresses). The assigned set containing official IP addresses is used as a pool for those users who wish to access the Internet. A user is assigned an IP address to work over the Internet, then, after completion of the user's task, the IP address is returned to the pot and made available to other users.

Dynamic address allocation is also used by ISPs to serve customers communicating over the Internet via dial-up access.

Dynamic address allocation provides access to a larger internal address range than that officially assigned. The Internet address in *Figure H.3.3* starts at 130 (10000010 in binary notation). In other words, it is a class B address.

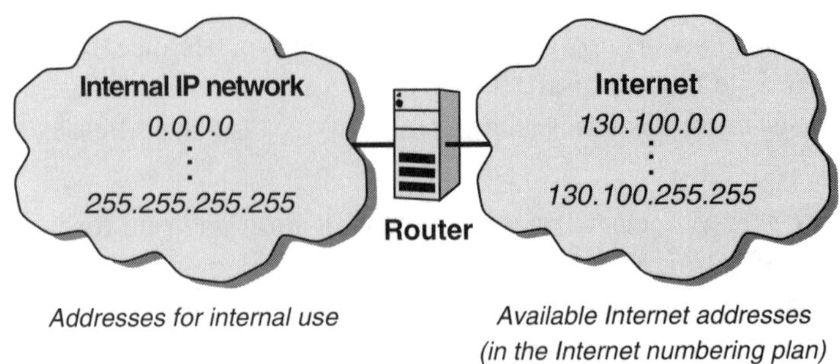

Figure H.3.3 Dynamic address allocation

3.2.2 Domain names

The Internet's IP addresses are not especially user-friendly, so domain names are used in parallel with IP addresses. The relationship between IP addresses and domain names is managed by a DNS. The DNS is a hierarchical database distributed to servers all over the Internet.

The *root* is located at the top of the hierarchy, followed by the upper domain layer. The database root is implemented in a limited number of root servers, the majority of them located in the US.

The upper domain layer is normally either a country or an organisation description. The original organisation descriptions were:

- *com* - commercial companies;
- *edu* - educational institutions;
- *gov* - state agencies (US only);
- *mil* - military agencies (US only);
- *net* - organisations that support Internet operators;
- *org* - other organisations; and
- *int* - international organisations.

Added to the upper domain layer are new domains, such as *firm*, *store*, *web*, *arts*, *rec* (recreation), *info* and *nom* (nomenclature).

A company that has been assigned a domain name is free to organise a hierarchy of domains (for example, coinciding with the company's organisational structure) beneath its assigned domain name. A complete hierarchy is shown in *Figure H.3.4* including an example of the domain names assigned to various departments.

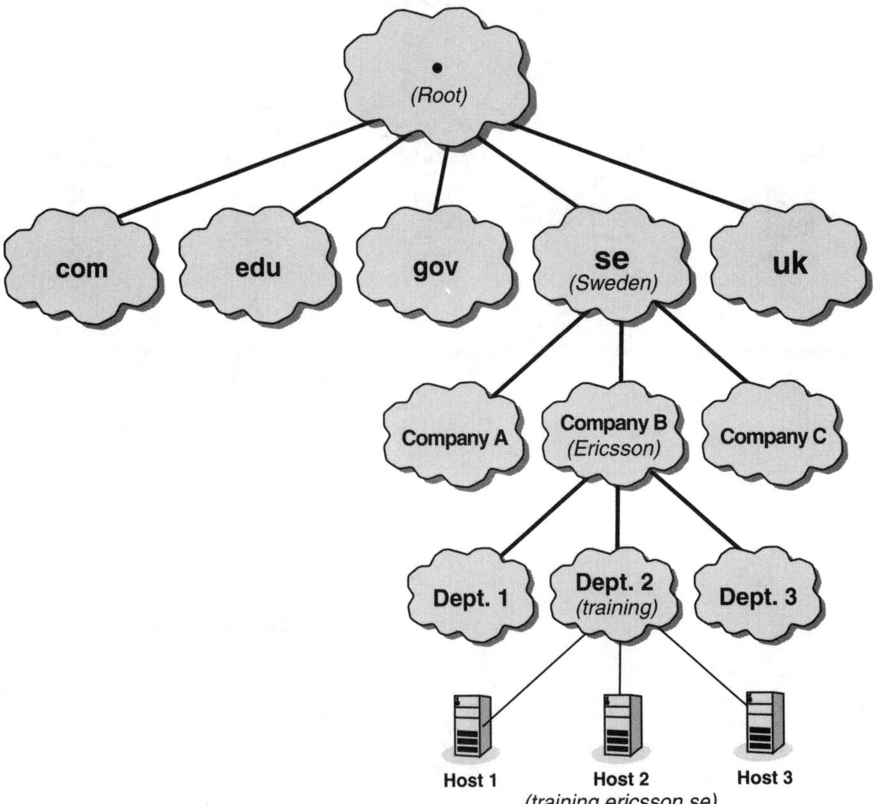

Figure H.3.4 Domain name system

The addresses are stored in the DNS servers that form a distributed network in which each server is responsible for one or more domains.

If the requested address is not known by the local DNS server, the query is sent higher up the hierarchy. The address query results in the receiver's IP address. Addresses are saved in the originating server for a period of time to avoid unnecessary querying. However, due to network modifications, they cannot be saved permanently.

DNS is described in RFCs 1034 and 1035 and represents STD 13. (See also Chapter 7, Section 7.4.)

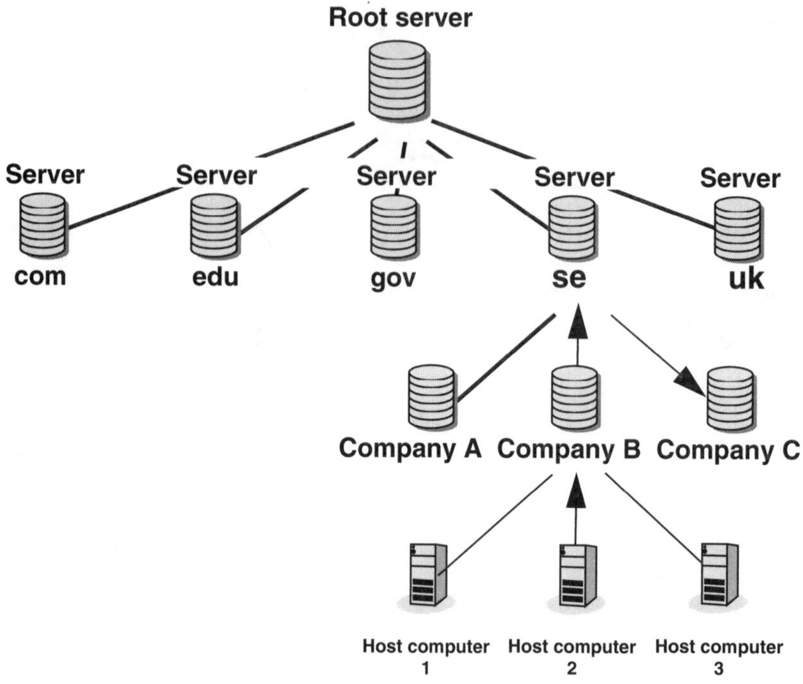

Figure H.3.5 Address identification with the aid of a domain name system

3.3 Internet segmentation

Many factors have influenced the ambition to segment the Internet into subnetworks. These subnetworks can either be at the same hierarchical level (forming a flat network) or at different levels.

- The Internet is run by many operators who naturally desire to design their subnetworks as autonomously as possible, for example, when choosing a routing algorithm.
- Considering the rapid growth of the Internet, the routing process in the router network must be simplified. If this is not done, routing tables (see Section 3.4) are bound to become all too complex, and the number of hops will become so great that delays will render isochronous services impossible. Thus a hierarchical structure is required.

- Gateways must exist between the various operators. This requirement, too, calls for a hierarchical structure.

These factors have produced several results.

- The creation of autonomous systems having one or more networks under one and the same administration. Routers in an autonomous system are equipped with protocols – referred to as interior gateway protocols (IGPs) – that allow the routers to exchange information with one another, as shown in *Figure H.3.6*. An example of an IGP is the routing information protocol (RIP, RFC 1723) and the open shortest path first (OSPF, RFC 1583). (See Section 3.5 for more information about OSPF.)
- Special routers, aided by exterior gateway protocols (EGPs), are used for the exchange of information between different autonomous systems. EGP is described in RFC 904. An example of an EGP is the border gateway protocol (BGP) which is optimised for transit traffic using other BGP routers. Here, technical, commercial and political aspects can influence routing.
- The creation of special networks for transit traffic: core networks.

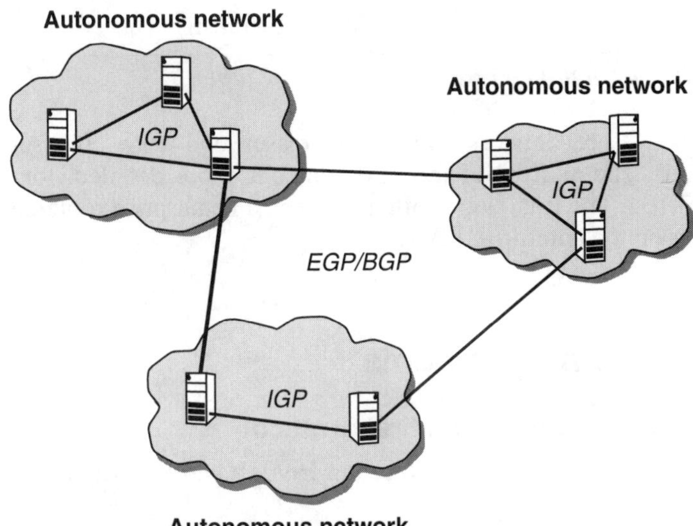

Figure H.3.6 Autonomous systems and the exchange of routing information between them

- The emergence of interexchange points or Internet exchange points. (See Chapter 9.) Here operators and/or network hierarchies are connected to one another.

3.4 The routing process

(See also the description of IP in Chapter 2, Subsection 2.3.2.)

Using the destination's IP address as a basis, a path for each packet is selected in each router (provided the router is not bypassed; see Section 3.7). The next hop is determined after consulting a routing table which is continuously updated. (See *Figure H.3.7.*)

The purpose of the routing process is to find an optimal path through the Internet, either directly to the terminating network (subnetwork) or via one or more transit networks. The IP destination addresses used for transit routing are usually related to subnetworks and not to all host computers, thus reducing the load on the routing process.

IP destination network	Next router
A	X (the home network, for example)
B	Y
C	Default / Z (transit)

Figure H.3.7 Simplified example of a routing table

A, B and C are networks whose addresses end with "0", such as in 123.10.0.0. The address of the next router is more detailed, for example 15.94.23.104. The final hop is often between an enterprise router and a host computer on the enterprise LAN.

3.5 Routing protocols

3.5.1 Open shortest path first protocol

The OSPF protocol was standardised in 1990. It was to fulfil a considerable number of requirements:

- It would be open.
- It would be dynamic, capable of rapid adaptation to changes in topology.
- The algorithm would base its routing choice on a number of parameters, especially distance and type of service.
- It would distribute traffic across a number of routes.

- It would support a hierarchical network to facilitate routing.

The last requirement is supported by network configurations having one or more core network routers within one and the same autonomous system.

OSPF messages may consist of HELLO messages, when a router is "getting acquainted" with its neighbours, or of link-status messages that are used when calculating the shortest path to other nodes.

3.5.2 Internet control message protocol

ICMP is used especially for communication between the router and sending host computers. See *Figure H.3.8*.

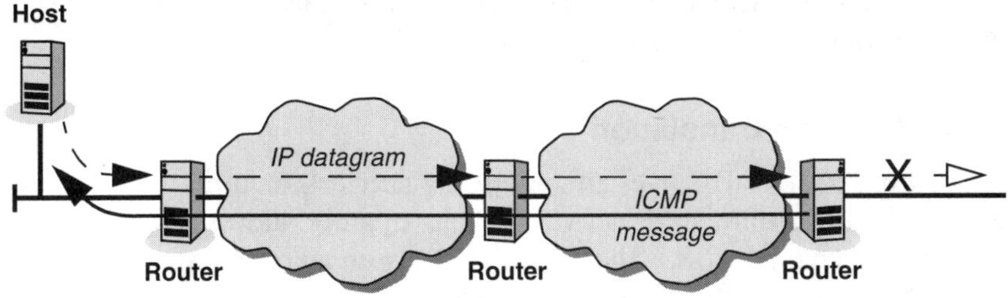

Figure H.3.8 Internet control message protocol

ICMP makes use of IP as if ICMP were a higher-layer protocol; in reality, it is integrated into IP. ICMP must be implemented in every network element that is equipped with IP.

An ICMP message is identified by the fact that the *protocol* field in the IP header is set to 1.

Communication problems lead to the discarding of the IP datagram. The sender may then receive an ICMP message to that effect.

The message generated by ICMP can be:

- *Destination unreachable*. The IP address set as destination in the IP header cannot be reached. The cause may be that the receiver is not active or that the IP datagram can only be sent if fragmented – in spite of the fact that the no-fragmentation-allowed flag is set.
- *Time exceeded*. The maximum time to live set in the IP header has been exceeded.
- *Parameter problem*. A problem has arisen when handling an IP header; for example, an incorrect options argument has been detected.

- *Source quench.* The receiver is not keeping up with the processing of incoming datagrams, or a switching gateway does not have room in its outgoing buffer. This message informs the sender of the fact that transmission speed should be reduced.
- *Redirect.* A gateway finds that the sending host computer and the next destination are connected to the same network (according to the routing table). The sending computer receives an ICMP message recommending that datagrams having this address be routed directly to the other node.

3.6 Associations between Internet and bearer network addresses

3.6.1 Address translation

The routing of IP traffic over an underlying network requires address translation. Routing within an IP network results in an IP address pointing to the next router. That address is then translated (by an address translator located in the IP network) to a corresponding address in the underlying network. If this network is connection-oriented (such as frame relay or ATM), then IP will order a connection that functions as a route between IP and the next router.

3.6.2 Address resolution protocol

ARP is used in LANs for the interconnection of physical local network addresses and IP addresses. IP addresses are logical and not strictly connected to any given computer. However, when a message is to be sent over the local network, the sender must know the physical address of the receiver. ARP uses broadcasting; that is, messages are received by all connected hosts. The sender transmits an ARP message that contains the receiver's IP address, and the appropriate receiver responds with his physical address. The sender saves the physical address to avoid having to repeat this procedure. See *Figure H.3.9*, in which a computer having the IP address 130.100.75.13 queries the network for the identity of the computer having the address 130.100.75.19.

RARP is used by terminals when querying their own IP addresses. This may be necessary when a terminal without any hard disk or other local storage medium is started. The terminal sends a physical address over the network and receives its own IP address in reply.

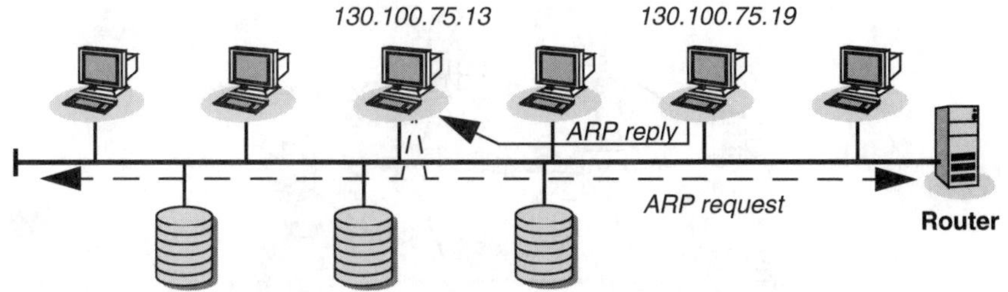

Figure H.3.9 Operation of the address resolution protocol

3.7 ATM routing and switching options

As we have mentioned in Section 3.1, the individual roles played by the Internet and ATM (for Internet traffic) are not completely self-evident. ATM is particularly well suited for use in central network sections (core networks) where traffic demand is great. Large capacity, rapid switching and guaranteed QoS are attractive ATM characteristics, notably in the case of multimedia traffic. The Internet's IP routers are certainly advancing in terms of performance but cannot match ATM nodes as yet.

The rapid ATM technique can be utilised if the IP addresses are translated into destinations in the ATM network. Such a destination should be located near the destination host or server. It will then be possible to bypass a number of routers between the access routers of the parties involved and use a "direct" ATM virtual circuit as traffic carrier. The technical terms used for this type of arrangement are *routing over large clouds* and *next hop resolution protocol.*

Another technique is based on the introduction of *edge routers* which attach a small information block – a tag – to the IP packets that are to be sent through the faster ATM network. The tag guides the datagrams through the ATM network to another edge router. There the tag is removed, and the packet is processed as if it were an ordinary IP packet on its way to its final destination. See *Figure H.3.10*. Tag switching over ATM can be used for combinations other than TCP/IP.

A third technique is based on the use of flow control. A combination of a router and an ATM node can alternate between plain ATM switching (*cut through*) and IP/ATM (*store and forward*). Plain ATM switching is used for traffic that has been classed as a *flow;* that is, a traffic connection lasting longer than a preset limiting value (it must be "long-lived"). The flow traffic is assigned its own virtual connection through the ATM network.

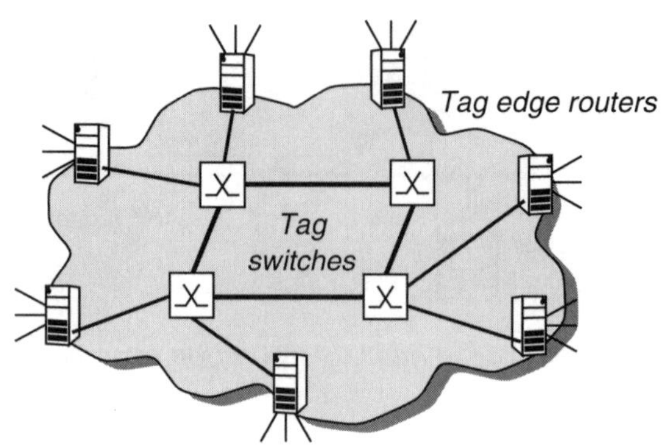

Figure H.3.10 Principle of tag switching

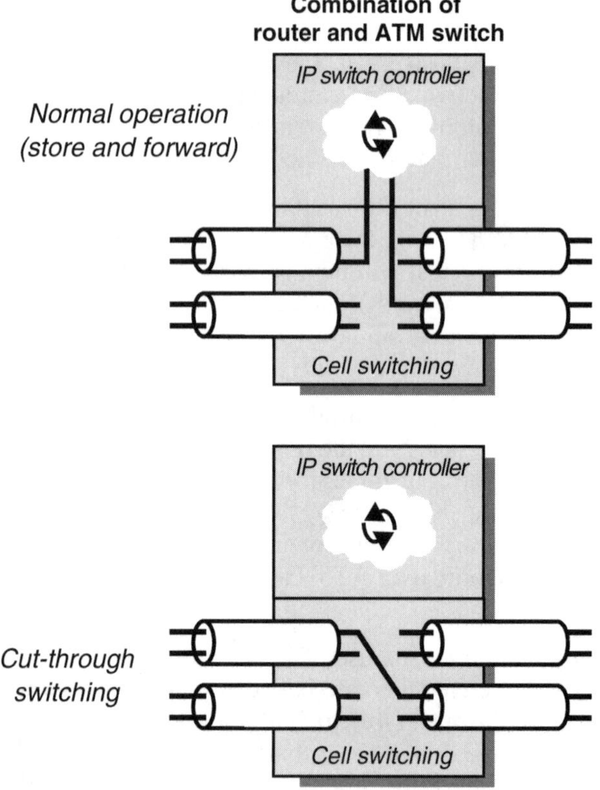

Figure H.3.11 Flow control

4 Transmission techniques

As we mentioned previously, Internet traffic can be carried by other switched networks or transmitted over fixed lines. In the first case, TCP/IP is regarded as just a load in the underlying switched network and its transmission technique. In the second case, IP over PDH (plesiochronous digital hierarchy) is common. Some experts foresee substantial growth of IP over SDH (synchronous digital hierarchy) or SONET (synchronous optical network).

5 Access and transport

5.1 Development

In the Internet structure that evolved during the 1980s (mainly in the US), a distinction was made between core networks and regional networks. Universities and government authorities connected their own campus networks to the regional networks and thus gained access to the Internet. Both core and regional networks consisted of leased lines and routers. Typical bit rates were in the 56 kbit/s to 1.5 Mbit/s range. Since then the Internet has developed in many respects, not least in the access and transport areas.

One effect of the almost unbelievable growth in the number of Internet subscribers is the large variety of access networks now being used, for both dial-up and fixed access. As a consequence, Internet traffic and other types of traffic often have to share the access facilities available. At the same time, this helps explain the success of the Internet: It can use different types of bearer network, in what is called stratification. This ability is also utilised in the core network, which basically corresponds to the transport network.

5.2 Access cases

Access networks are expensive – especially when used to serve thinly scattered residential subscribers – while core networks are cheap. Access network costs account for 50% to 60% of an operator's total investment. The economy of the core network benefits from the gradually decreasing cost of fibre transmission.

The availability of access facilities is critical to the development of a new network such as the Internet. Internet users communicate by means of computers using TCP/IP protocols; they prefer high-speed data communication and in some cases access to functions that allow mobility. The preference for mobile access applies in particular to Internet users who travel often and use portable computers.

For economic reasons, several access cases have appeared:

1. Internet access shares the transmission medium, the frequency band and a concentrating function (switching) with an established network (PSTN, ISDN, PLMN).

2. Internet access shares the transmission medium and the frequency band with an established network.

3. Internet access shares the transmission medium with an established network.

4. Internet access is a dedicated access.

IP is used in all these cases.

In cases 1 and 2, an Internet call may block the established service. One way of overruling such blocking is to convert the established bearer service (for example, the PSTN) to Internet technology and to terminate both services in the computer. This solution is described in Chapter 9, Subsection 9.5.1. A less complicated solution – time division multiplexing (TDM) – can be used in ISDN.

Case 3 is interesting for several reasons:

- Adverse effects on the existing network (such as holding times of 20 to 30 minutes) are avoided.
- Internet traffic creates a more advantageous business case for the access concerned, because revenue is generated on other frequency bands of the medium (*full-service access*).
- The operator will not have to rely on the bandwidth characteristics of another network, as in cases 1 or 2.
- Internet traffic does not pass any of the charging points of the established network (*bypass*).

Cases 1 and 2 are only discussed briefly here. For a more detailed description, see *Part B – PSTN*, *Part C – N-ISDN* and *Part D – PLMN*.

5.3 Dial-up access (case 1)

The access network for dial-up access connects the subscriber to the Internet operator's connection point: the point of presence (PoP). Well-established Internet operators have one or more PoPs in each routing number area of their PSTN/ISDN. The dial-up access for a call addressed to the Internet via PSTN/ISDN is charged according to the local tariff. (Special terms may be offered if the access operator is also an Internet operator.)

Dial-up access is used mostly by residential subscribers and small companies. The options available to these subscribers are shown in *Figure H.5.1*. Dial-up connections require the exchange of special protocols between the user terminal and the Internet supplier's equipment. These protocols are called serial line IP (SLIP) and point-to-point protocol (PPP). SLIP is specially designed for carrying IP packets, while the more universal design of PPP allows transfer of other data packets too. (See also Chapter 7, Subsection 7.3.5.)

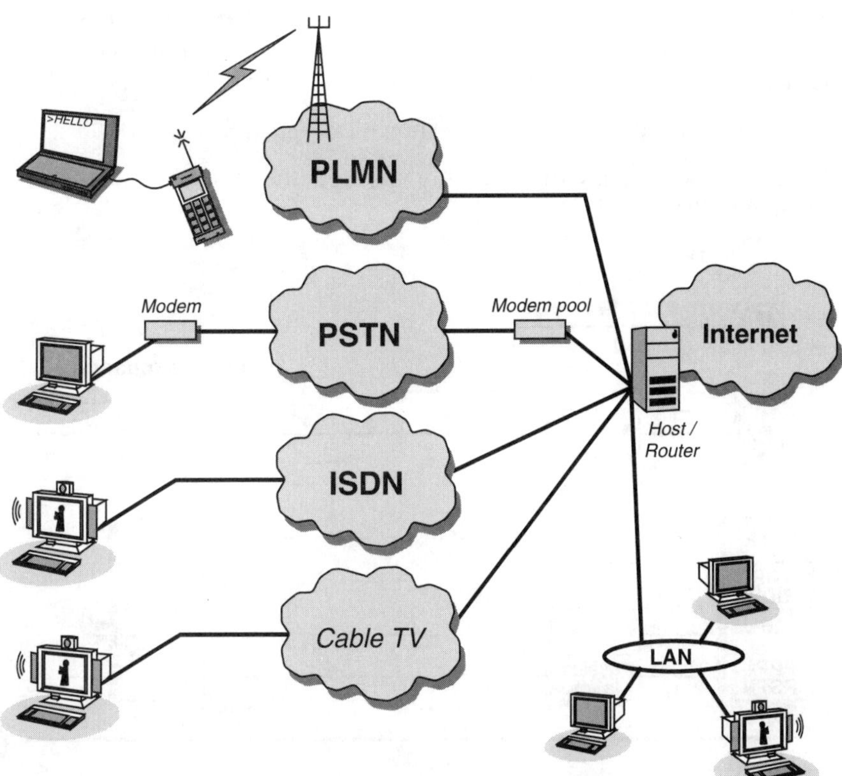

Figure H.5.1 Dial-up access to the Internet

The PSTN is the option most frequently used. However, modems are required, because the PSTN has analog subscriber lines. When leaving the PSTN, the original digital information is recreated by a modem of the same type as the one used by the subscriber.

The modems are arranged in pools to ensure efficient use. PSTN modems can handle up to 33.6 kbit/s, or – with asymmetric design – 56 kbit/s downstream and 33.6 kbit/s upstream.

In the case of ISDN, the bandwidth is the single most attractive feature. Basic rate access offers a maximum of 128 kbit/s.

Mobile access to the Internet requires the mobile network (for example, GSM) to be capable of transferring data. The mobile terminal must be equipped with a PC card to allow connection of a computer to the mobile network.

A disadvantage of mobile access is the low transfer rate (9.6 kbit/s in GSM, 19.2 kbit/s in NMT). High-speed circuit switched data (HSCSD) allows several time slots to be used for one and the same connection but it has not yet been implemented on a large scale. For a brief description of accessing the Internet via GSM, see *Part D – PLMN*, Chapters 1 and 2.

The protocols for dial-up access are shown in *Figure H.5.2*.

Internet protocols pass transparently through the modem and the local exchange in the PSTN.

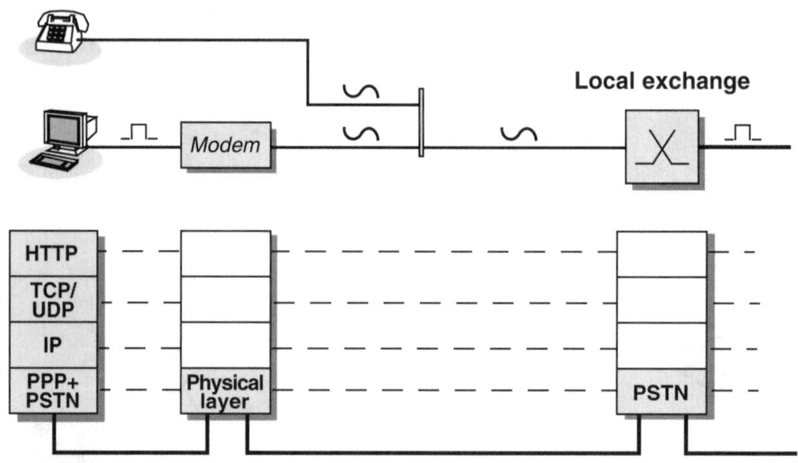

Figure H.5.2 Common protocols for dial-up access via the PSTN

5.4 Shared use of the transmission medium (case 3)

5.4.1 Copper pairs

As we mentioned in Volume 1, Chapter 4, Subsection 4.4.3, new transmission systems for copper access are being developed. This family of systems is called xDSL, where *DSL* stands for digital subscriber line, and *x* denotes "high bit rate", "asymmetrical", and so forth. *Figure H.5.3* shows asymmetrical digital subscriber line (ADSL), very high bit rate digital subscriber line (VDSL) and the maximum line lengths at different bit rates. The allocation of different frequency ranges to telephony and data communication enables simultaneous telephony and data traffic over the same copper pair. These access systems are connected directly to the Internet or to an intermediate access network (see below). A typical application is the connection of teleworkers to their company's LAN.

The length of a shared circuit in a copper network can vary between a couple of hundred metres and 3 to 4 km.

ADSL and VDSL are based on the use of advanced modems.

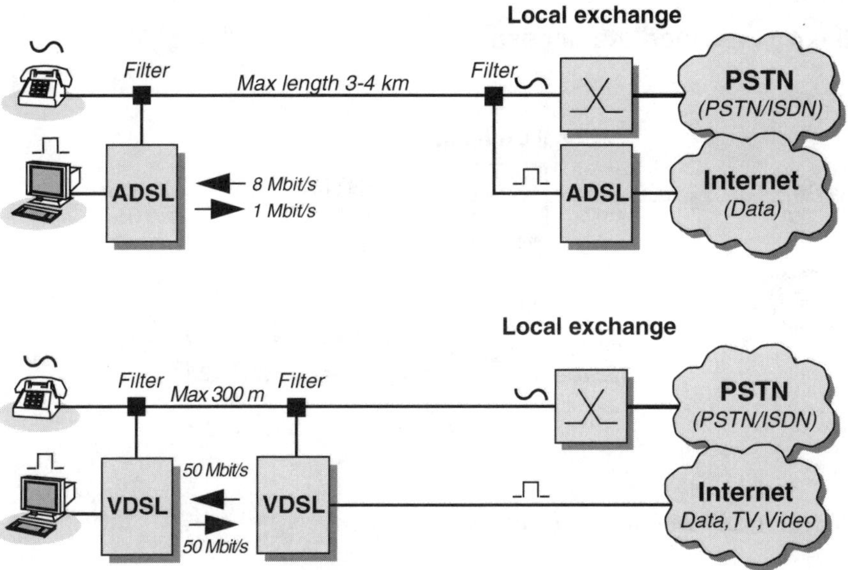

Figure H.5.3 New transmission systems for copper access

5.4.2 Coaxial cable (or fibre) for cable TV

(See also Volume 1, Chapter 5, Section 5.7.)

Using the cable-TV network for telephony and Internet traffic is an attractive option. The network is designed for broadband transmission, and coaxial cable can handle a much larger bandwidth than the paired cable that normally connects users to the telephone network. The trouble is that cable-TV networks are designed for one-way communication (TV channels are distributed from a central point). This problem can be solved either by making the network bidirectional or by using the PSTN for carrying traffic upstream (from the user). Users will then send their commands and requests over the telephone network, and the desired information will be delivered via the cable-TV network.

Cable-TV access supplemented with cable modems will allow a downstream rate of approximately 30 Mbit/s and an upstream rate of 3 Mbit/s.

5.4.3 Radio

The radio medium can be used to a much greater extent than it is today. Development is very rapid. Cellular systems using frequencies in the 2 GHz band and upwards and having a bandwidth of 2 to 8 Mbit/s will soon become a reality. (See also *Part D – PLMN*, especially Chapter 2, Section 2.6.)

5.4.4 Intermediate access

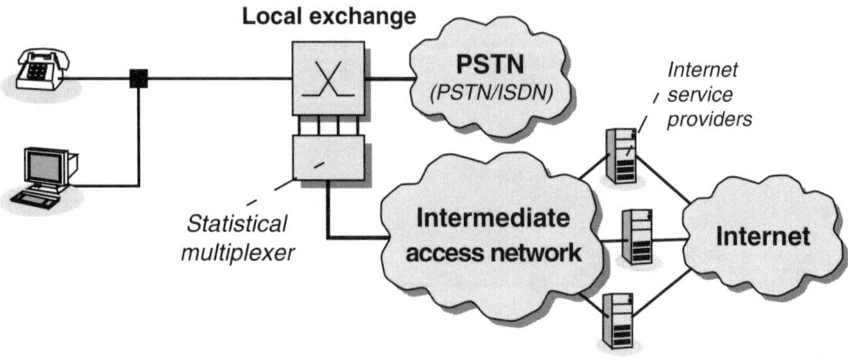

Figure H.5.4 Intermediate access

For several reasons it should be possible to extract bursty Internet traffic from the circuit-switched networks (PSTN/ISDN and PLMN) at an early stage of the client-server connection. If only one or a few exchanges in an area have ports to the Internet, the load on these exchanges – and on the networks around them – might be so heavy as to cause congestion. If Internet traffic is extracted at the local exchange level, an intermediate access network may be needed between the local exchange and the PoP. Such a network can benefit from transfer modes intended for bursty traffic, for example, frame mode and cell mode.

The characteristics of these transfer modes make them especially suitable for statistical multiplexing, which reduces the need for transport capacity. See *Figure H.5.4*.

5.5 Fixed access

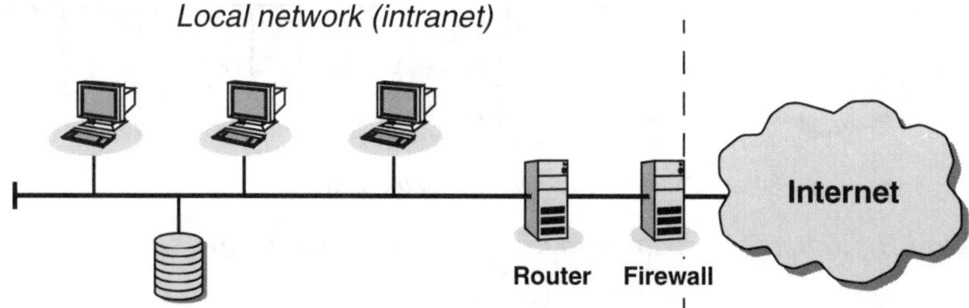

Figure H.5.5 Fixed connection to the Internet

Fixed access is almost exclusively used by companies. Since no dialling is needed, the TCP/IP packets are sent directly via frame relay, ATM, Ethernet or just by means of a transmission system.

Fixed access – which actually forms part of the Internet (the access operator is bypassed) – is offered by major Internet operators. The bit rate can be considerably higher than 2 Mbit/s.

Ordinarily, a LAN – not individual computers – is connected, as shown in *Figure H.5.5*. The local network can be based on different techniques; Ethernet is the technique most commonly used.

Needless to say, companies must protect themselves against various forms of intrusion. One way of doing so is to install a firewall; that is, a network element that prevents unauthorised users from accessing the network. (See Chapter 6, Subsection 6.2.1.)

5.6 Transport networks

The Internet uses different bearer networks and leased lines to transport IP datagrams. Most Internet core traffic is carried by dedicated transport network facilities, but on some sections of the transmission paths it is carried along with traffic in other public bearer networks. (See *Figure H.5.6* and Chapter 10.)

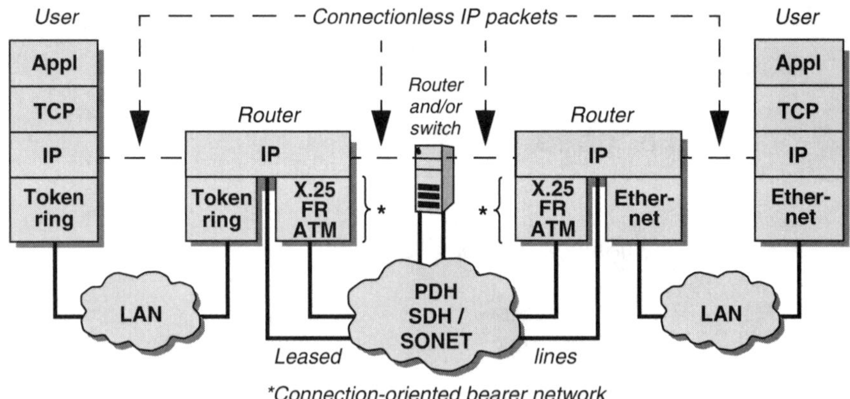

Figure H.5.6 Bearer networks in the transport network part

6 Server services

6.1 Introduction

Most IN and value-added services available over the Internet are located in servers. The concepts of IN and value-added services are used here to enable comparison between the Internet's architecture and that of other networks. Even though the Internet *network* may be both complex and "intelligent", the clients and the (information) servers, with their application protocols, are the dominant entities in Internet communication. The network's less prominent role as compared to other networks is illustrated in *Figure H.6.1*.

The Internet's "network intelligence" can be divided into three categories:

1. Server services needed prior to the communication phase:
   - authentication and authorisation (user identity, smart card, password)
   - logon from any terminal, with an individual service profile

- encryption (of credit card numbers, for example)
- DNS services (see Chapter 7)
- resource control in connection with access, if a specific QoS has been requested
- firewalls

2. Server services needed during the communication phase:
   - encryption
   - firewalls
3. Server services needed after the communication phase:
   - charging (depending on the charging system used in each case)

As you can see, many services are related to security.

Virtual private networks, multimedia mail, home shopping, and information, education and entertainment services are examples of IN and value-added services on the Internet.

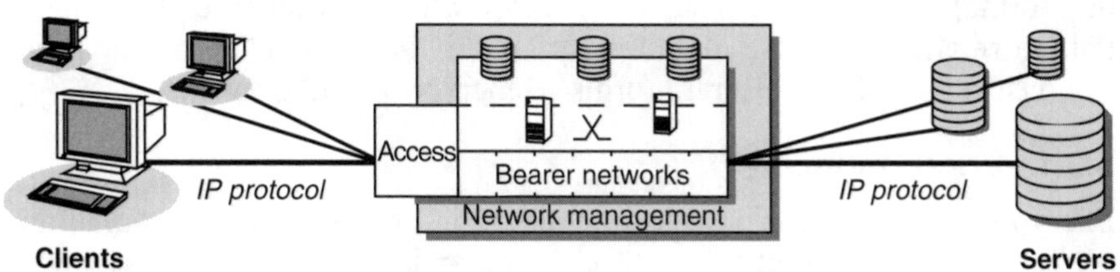

Figure H.6.1 The terminating network elements in the Internet play a more significant role than those in other networks

6.2 Example of server configuration

Figure H.6.2 shows a possible configuration of an ISP's point of presence (ISP PoP).

The terminal server ensures that the PSTN/ISDN subscriber who dials in (and who is an Internet subscriber) is temporarily connected to a LAN equipped with server and router functions. After the subscriber has logged on through the authentication server, he can use the services available through his subscription (such as e-mail and WWW access).

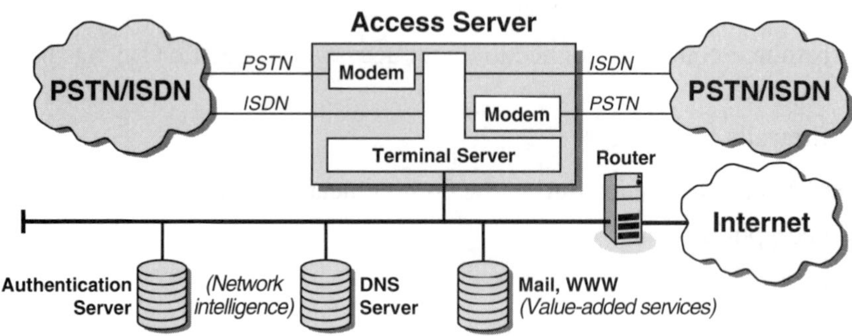

Figure H.6.2 Example of server configuration

6.3 Security

Preventing unauthorised users from entering a network is very difficult. This is particularly true of the Internet because of its "something for everybody" character. It is available not only to those who provide and make use of information and services but also to those who try to get hold of confidential information or whose intentions are purely destructive. Available security measures include different forms of encryption and firewalls.

6.3.1 Encryption

Encryption refers to the process of converting information into unintelligible form. Keys are used for the encryption and decryption of information. Development in this area is advancing rapidly.

6.3.2 Firewalls

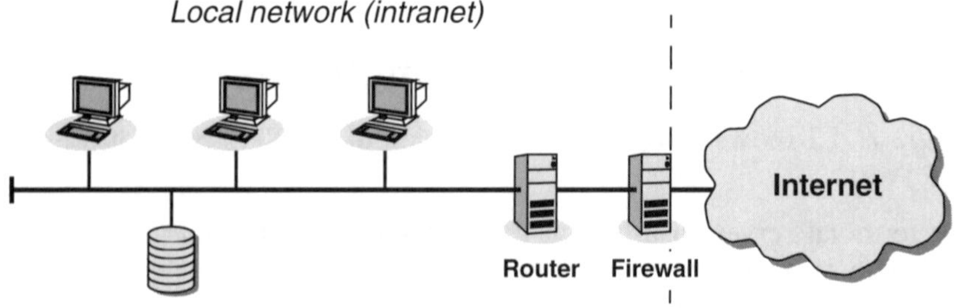

Figure H.6.3 Location of a firewall

In most cases, a firewall will suffice as protection against intrusion. The firewall separates the user's own network from the Internet by screening off at a single point all connections to and from the Internet, thus facilitating monitoring and security.

A firewall can be implemented in many ways – in hardware or software – and meet various security objectives. The general rule is that the objects to be protected as well as the protective measures must be clearly defined. The text that follows describes two of the most frequent implementations of authentication checks: IP-level filtering and application-level or proxy-type filtering. (See *Figure H.6.4*.)

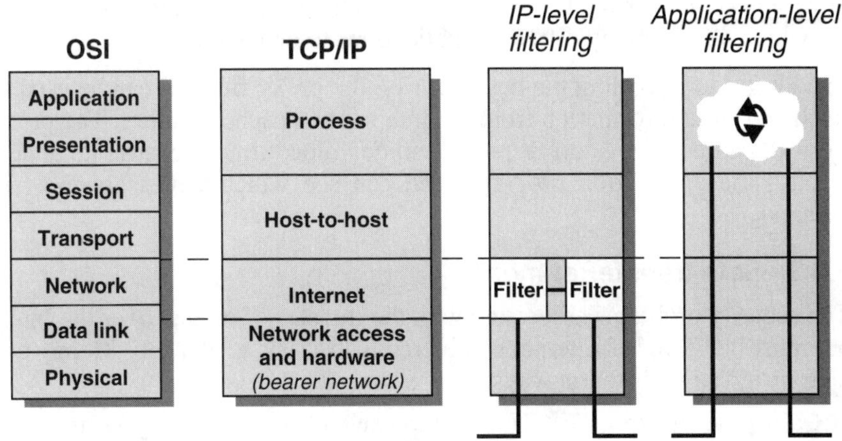

Figure H.6.4 Filtering at different levels

IP-level filtering

A firewall for IP-level filtering reads the labels of the IP packets and decides whether or not the packets should be allowed to pass between client and server.

One drawback of this method is that the information on which the firewall should base its decision is far from complete. The client's and server's authentication is checked against IP addresses, which makes the result less reliable than that obtained when a user states his identity and password. Hence, IP-level filtering is not a safe method for use by companies that want some of their customers or salesmen to have access to company servers, that is, in an extranet.

Application-level or proxy-type filtering

A firewall that filters information at the application level blocks all IP traffic between the private network and the Internet. No IP packets from the clients or servers of the private network are allowed to enter or leave the Internet.

Instead, this type of firewall operates according to what is referred to as the *proxy principle*. This means that internal clients set up connections to the firewall and communicate with a proxy server. If the firewall decides that the internal client should be allowed to communicate, it sets up a connection to the external server and performs the operation on behalf of the client. This method solves many of the security problems associated with IP.

Each proxy server uses a particular application protocol, such as *http-proxy* or *ftp-proxy*. The proxy firewall uses a combination of different proxy servers which allows many different applications to be handled.

In addition to providing the best security, the proxy firewall can be used to fetch and store information from the Internet in a cache memory. The proxy firewall can achieve short response and download times because it "understands" the application programs and can see which URLs are most in demand.

6.3.3 Safe transfer of money

The security problems associated with the transfer of money over the Internet must be solved if Internet commerce is to grow as planned. Money can be transferred in different ways:

- Cash payment (e-cash). This method, which will probably be used for minor transactions only, requires some form of guarantee to ensure that the amount transferred corresponds to its designated value.
- Payment by credit card (electronic funds transfer). Standardisation in this area is progressing steadily thanks to cooperation between major credit-card companies. The basic idea is to use different code keys (both public and private) when encrypting sensitive information, such as the credit-card number.

Many of the companies concerned – including VISA, MasterCard and IBM – are working on a specification for credit-card payment called secure electronic transactions (SET). The system works as follows:

The customer has an account with the credit-card company and sends his credit-card number (which is encrypted automatically) when he wishes to make payments via the network. The credit-card number is still encrypted when it is received by the payee, who checks with the issuing bank that the card is valid and that the customer is the authorised holder of the card. This check is automatically performed via the network by means of a special code allocated to the payee. The procedure is based on an encryption program called data encryption standard (DES).

SET is built into the Web browsers and the payees must add new software to their Internet servers to be able to use the new funds transfer function.

6.3.4 Anonymity

A person who wishes to be anonymous or give a false name on the Internet can use a special e-mail server that deletes the sender's name from a message before it is sent to the addressee. As a rule, one should not take it for granted that all Internet users operate under their actual identity.

6.4 Virtual private networks

VPNs consist of router and bearer-network resources (including switching capacity and transmission resources) defined in software.

In the world of the Internet, these networks – sometimes called "public intranetworks" – form a closed part of the public Internet where an ISP offers its customers security and QoS. In a public intranetwork, the operator can also offer its customers value-added services, and a VPN of this kind can have global coverage.

6.5 Information retrieval

Information retrieval, notably in the form of the World Wide Web, is the prime driving force behind the development of the Internet. Of course, "surfing on the Net" is the best way of getting to know the WWW, but one should also be familiar with some basic concepts.

The Web was developed at CERN in Switzerland in the early 1990s, with a view to creating an effective system for internal dissemination of information. To succeed, engineers had to design a system that would be capable of handling many different information formats and methods of transfer. Important contributions were the HTML, developed for the design of hypertext documents, and HTTP, developed for the transfer of these documents.

6.5.1 HTML

HTML is a page-descriptive language allowing the user to navigate through a text with the help of links.

An HTML document is created by providing different parts of the text with markers, for instance <TITLE>. Pictures and links to other documents can also be marked and included in an HTML document. Special word-processing programs make it possible to type a document in the usual manner.

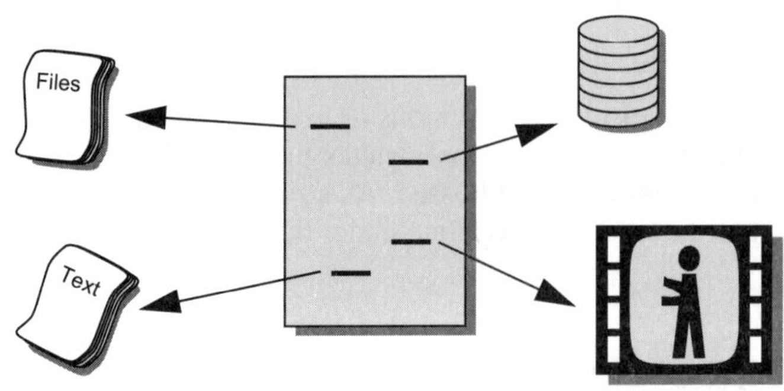

Figure H.6.5 A hypertext document allows the user (reader) to move between different types of information (such as explanations and digressions) by means of links

6.5.2 Virtual reality model language

The virtual reality model language (VRML) is used to describe three-dimensional objects. A real-estate agent may use VRML to depict a flat or house on the Web and invite prospective buyers to "tour" it in real time – regardless of whether it is next door or on the other side of the globe.

6.5.3 Uniform resource locator

For the WWW to work as intended, resources must be identified in a uniform manner. A uniform resource locator (URL) is used to indicate where a specific resource is found and which protocol should be used to fetch it. The user interlinks different documents by inserting a URL in the HTML document. *Figure H.6.6* shows the composition of a URL.

Figure H.6.6 Uniform resource locator

Protocol indicates the protocol to be used for the transfer. *Host computer* is the computer that contains the resource. *Search path* indicates the position of the resource in the internal structure of the host computer. Thanks to the WWW's large tool-box, FTP, Gopher or other protocols can also be used. The concluding "html" indicates that the information is probably written in the hypertext mark-up language (HTTP uses different information to select the application to be used when reading the document).

A Web browser is software that uses HTTP or some other protocol to fetch and display information. It can handle many information formats and can be modified by the installation of "plug-ins". A plug-in is auxiliary software run by the browser when a special format is to be read; for example, a short video sequence or a document written in a special word-processing format.

6.6 On-line services

On-line services are offered for an extra charge to a specific group of subscribers. Such users can normally connect their terminals to the public Internet but they will also have access to information that is not universally available. Most on-line services have open standards for user interfaces.

The services offered include those mentioned in Chapter 1, Section 1.6 (chat, information retrieval and so on). Unique features of on-line services are their content (which is often exclusive) and the way in which they are encapsulated. Since the user's authorisation is checked when he logs on, even services that are subject to special security requirements can be offered. America On-Line, CompuServe and Microsoft Network are a few on-line services.

Today, many on-line service providers are focusing on particular professional users rather than marketing to the general public. The reason is the huge cost of marketing to build a profitable subscriber base. Revenues are not sufficiently great to make a mass offering profitable.

6.7 Electronic mail and directory services

SMTP is the TCP/IP world's equivalent of the X.400 protocol of the OSI model. Electronic mail (e-mail) is an application used all over the world. To find the address of an individual user, directory services (such as Whois and Whois++) are available, as are address services based on the ITU-T's Recommendation X.500.

The user can send a complete file together with an ordinary text e-mail by "attaching" a picture or word-processing document. Mail communication is described in Chapter 7, Section 7.4.

6.8 Home shopping

Home shopping (or, more appropriately, on-line shopping) on the Internet promises to become one of the most interesting services available. The idea is to use the Internet as a gigantic, continuously updated mail-order catalogue for products and services. Software or information can be delivered directly to a user's terminal.

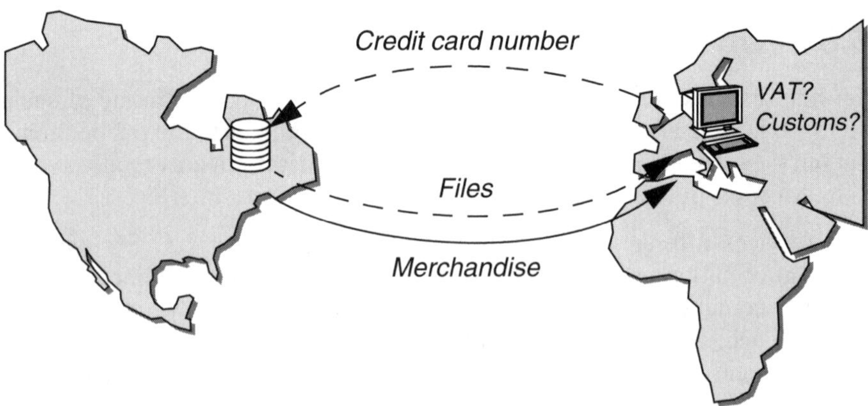

Figure H.6.7 The Internet as marketplace

The products offered via the Internet fall into two categories: information (software) and traditional products. Trading in software is quite common already. Software can be sold directly, but companies can also distribute products to their retailers or present beta issues; that is, software at the development stage that users receive free of charge for evaluation. Trading in traditional products resembles conventional mail order. Products are delivered by mail or by delivery firms.

Companies can offer their products and services through their own Web sites or rent space in virtual shopping malls or Web hotels.

The key restrictive factor today is the difficulty in finding a generally accepted method of electronic funds transfer.

7 "Signalling"

7.1 Introduction

"Signalling" on the Internet refers to the exchange of information between clients and servers which takes place at the TCP and application levels when setting up communication sessions.

The exchange of information may involve the establishment of a TCP session, the sending of an HTTP request (followed by a reply) in Web applications or the set-up of an e-mail connection.

TCP/IP communication at lower levels is supported by bearer networks, whose signalling is dealt with in other Parts of Volume 2, and by the Internet protocol, which is connectionless and thus requires no set-up "signalling".

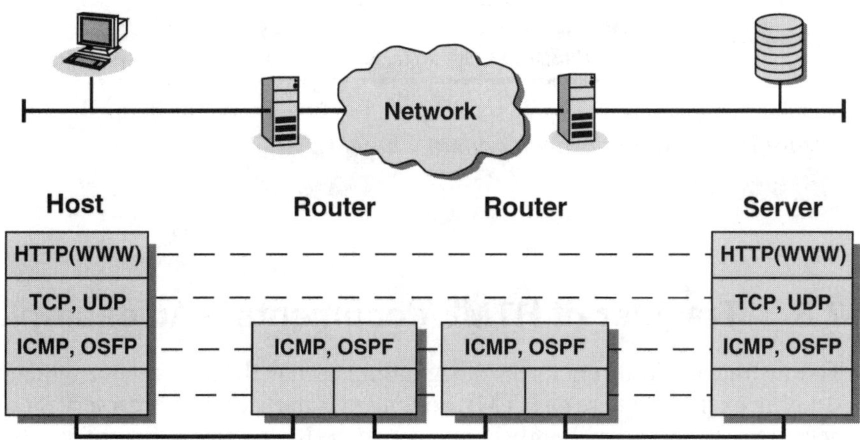

Figure H.7.1 Communication between protocols at different levels

7.2 Protocols and protocol layers

The following protocols are dealt with here:

- HTTP;
- TCP;
- SMTP, with IMAP and POP.

The layers of these protocols are shown in *Figure H.7.2*.

When describing HTTP, we include DNS communication and the setting-up of "PPP links". PPP is used for transferring Internet traffic over the PSTN, ISDN, PLMN and other types of network.

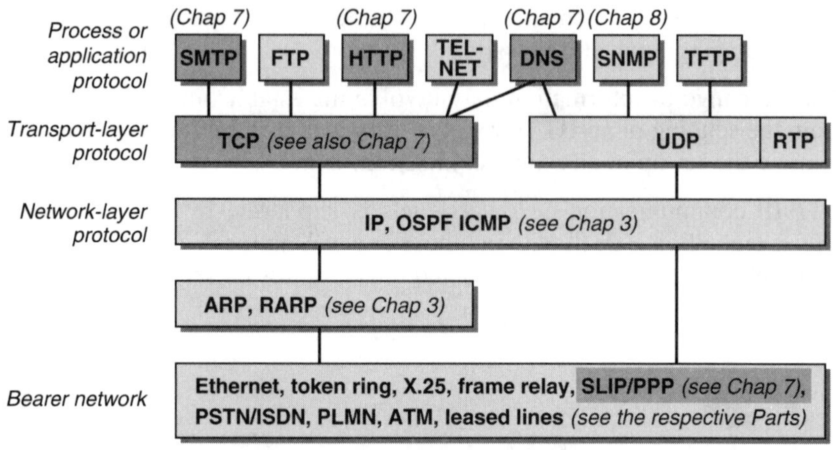

Figure H.7.2 Protocols dealt with in Chapter 7

7.3 Transfer of HTML documents – An example

To illustrate the different forms of signalling used in the Internet, we will now study an example where an HTML document is transferred from a server connected to a LAN (permanently connected to the Internet) to a dial-up user (client). This user does not know anything about the document except that its URL is *http://www.university.edu/public/courses/internet.htm.*

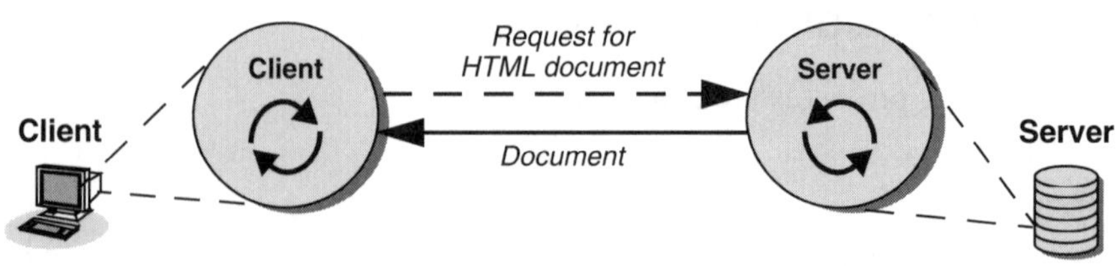

Figure H.7.3 Transfer of an HTML document from server to client

Of course, transfer of the document requires a connection between the client and the server. In this case, the connection is set up over the client's analog telephony circuit, via the PSTN, to the Internet point-of-presence, and via the Internet to the server.

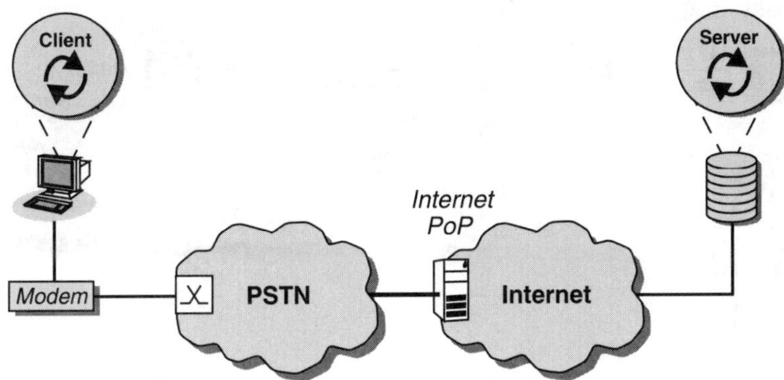

Figure H.7.4 Client-server connection

Let's study the exchange of signals between the different protocols and their counterparts when the different forms of "connection" are set up. We start at the highest level, that is, the application protocol, which is HTTP in our example because we are going to transfer an HTML document.

7.3.1 DNS communication

Before HTTP can set up a connection, the domain name (the only address the user knows) must be translated into an IP address that can be used when sending data to the addressed server. The domain name part of the URL – *www.university.edu* – is sent to the local DNS server. If that server does not know the IP address associated with the domain name, a request is sent to one of the root servers (several parallel root servers contain the same information). The root server returns the address to the next DNS server in the chain. (See (3) and (4) in *Figure H.7.5.*)

The procedure is repeated until the proper DNS server has been found. That server sends the IP address to the user's local DNS server, which forwards it to the user's application process.

Ordinarily, UDP is used for requests to a DNS server. If the length of the reply exceeds the capacity of a UDP datagram (512 bytes), the request is repeated but sent via TCP.

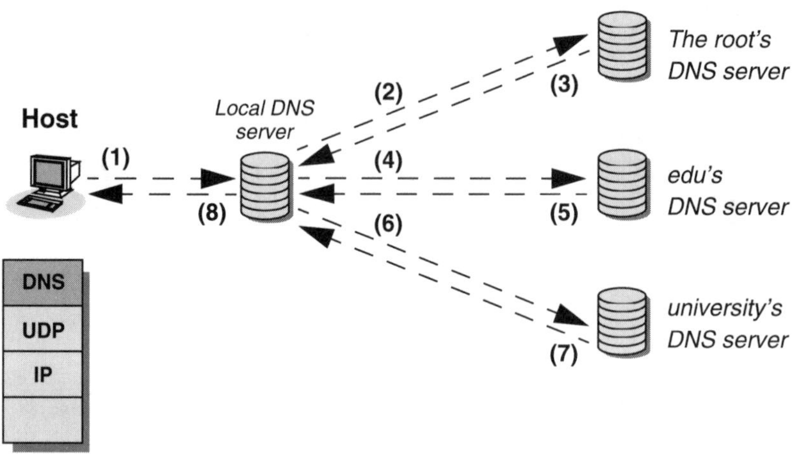

Figure H.7.5 Translation of a domain name into an IP address

1. IP address of www.university.edu?
2. IP address of www.university.edu?
3. IP address of the edu DNS server
4. IP address of www.university.edu?
5. IP address of the university.edu DNS server
6. IP address of www.university.edu?
7. IP address of www.university.edu
8. IP address of www.university.edu

Once the translation is finished, the client has everything required to initiate the set-up of "connections" at different levels. We will not follow the chronological order in which connections are set up but study one layer at a time, from top to bottom.

7.3.2 HTTP communication

Our application protocol, HTTP, is based on the principle of client–server communication, which means that it enables a client to set up a connection to a server and send a request. The server accepts the connection and replies to the request.

An HTTP request identifies the resource that the client is interested in and tells the server how to use it. HTTP enables users to fetch different kinds of resources (such as text, pictures or sound).

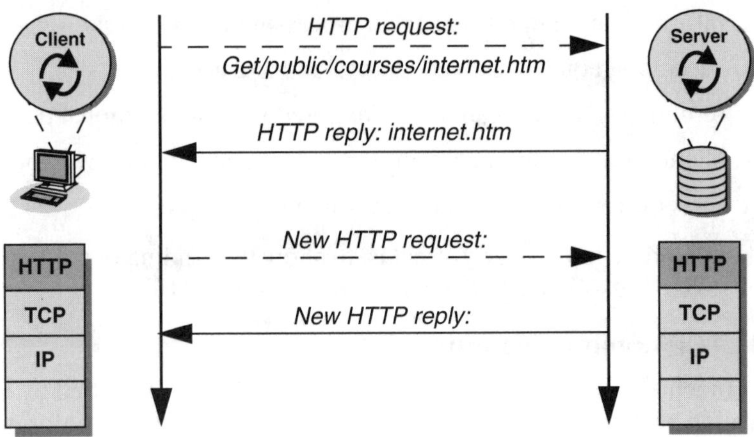

Figure H.7.6 Procedure for HTTP requests and replies

Requests and replies consist of a header (containing information about the resource) and a body (containing the actual resource, or document) according to RFC 822, Standard for the format of ARPA Internet text messages. The following requests are used:

- *OPTIONS:* Helps the client find out which possibilities and requirements are associated with a specific resource or server.
- *GET:* Indicates that the client wants to fetch the specified resource (in our case, the *internet.htm* file).
- *HEAD:* As *GET,* but in this case the server's reply need not contain any message body (according to RFC 822). This may be useful for clients which do not need the resource (document) itself but which only want to know when it was last updated.
- *POST:* Adds information to a specified resource; for instance, questions or items of information to a news group.
- *PUT:* Shows whether the enclosed material is to be stored in the stated location (URL) or whether it should replace existing material related to that location. In other words, this is a way of writing Web pages and putting them on a remote server.
- *DELETE:* Tells the server that the specified resource is to be removed.
- *TRACE:* Enables the client to follow the path along which the message was sent.

The replies to the requests are three-digit status codes. The first digit of a status code indicates how the request was received:

- 1xx: information – request received, processing in progress;
- 2xx: success – request received, understood and accepted;
- 3xx: rerouting – request cannot be answered without additional data;
- 4xx: client error – request contains errors that make it unanswerable;
- 5xx: server error – server cannot reply to a valid request.

For HTTP to function properly – that is, to allow the sending of requests and replies – TCP must first set up a connection "below" HTTP.

7.3.3 TCP communication

TCP's function is described in Chapter 2, Section 2.3. TCP is used by many application protocols (for example, SMTP and FTP) and for information retrieval on the WWW.

Figure H.7.7 illustrates the basic procedure for creating a TCP session. To set up a connection, one of the sides (in this case, A) sends a packet on which the SYN flag is set. If the other side (B) accepts the set-up, it returns a packet on which the ACK and SYN flags are set. (ACK and SYN are included in the control bits shown in *Figure H.2.13* in Chapter 2, Subsection 2.3.3.) ACK acknowledges receipt of the packet, and SYN sets up a session in the opposite direction. Side A responds with ACK to confirm that the packet has been received. The procedure is now finished, and data can be sent in both directions.

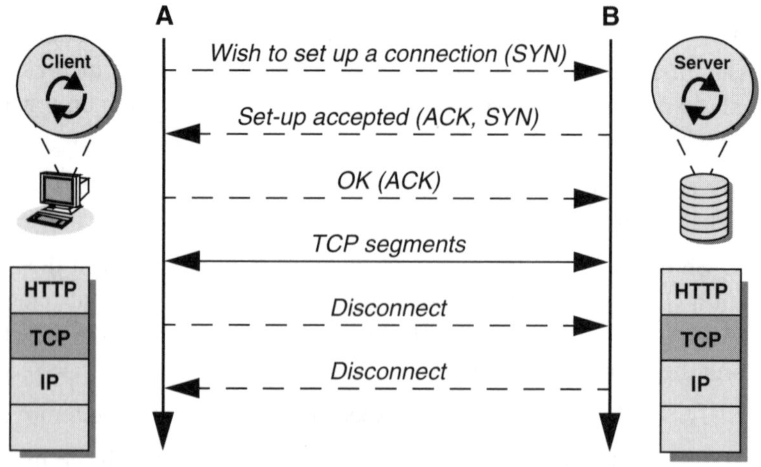

Figure H.7.7 Creating a TCP session – Basic principle

HTTP normally uses TCP port 80. For HTTP/1.0, a new TCP connection is set up for each HTTP request, whereas in HTTP/1.1 the same TCP connection can be used for several requests. These are the two "layers" of end-to-end connections that are set up. To enable set-up, the two bottom layers must allow the end points to communicate with each other.

7.3.4 IP communication

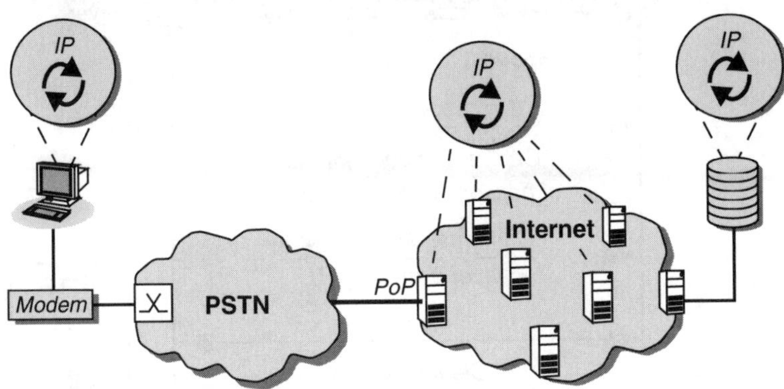

Figure H.7.8 Parties in our example that contain IP. Since the Internet is connectionless, the packets may follow different paths through the router network.

The fact that IP is connectionless means that no connections can be set up between network elements at the IP level. Packets are forwarded according to the best-effort principle, and if anything goes wrong, the layer immediately above or below IP must request retransmission. IP is implemented at the end points and in all network elements (routers) that affect the routing of IP packets (see *Figure H.7.8*). See also Chapter 3 for more information on routing.

7.3.5 Bearer networks

Although IP itself is connectionless, the networks that carry IP traffic may be connection-oriented. We are now going to study the implications of this fact, both in the case of serial connections (dial-up connections and leased lines) and in the case of switched networks (frame relay and ATM).

We will begin by studying the connection between the user and the ISP's PoP. This is an ordinary serial connection, and we need a protocol to open a link for data transfer and to encapsulate our IP packets. A modern protocol for this purpose is the point-to-point protocol (PPP, RFC 1661-63); an older alternative is serial line IP (SLIP, RFC 1055, 1144).

SLIP encapsulates the IP datagrams over the serial connection to prevent any disturbances on the line – before or after the datagram – from being interpreted as information belonging to the datagram. PPP, on the other hand, adds error checking and a link control protocol for the set-up, configuration and testing of the link. PPP can also carry protocols other than IP.

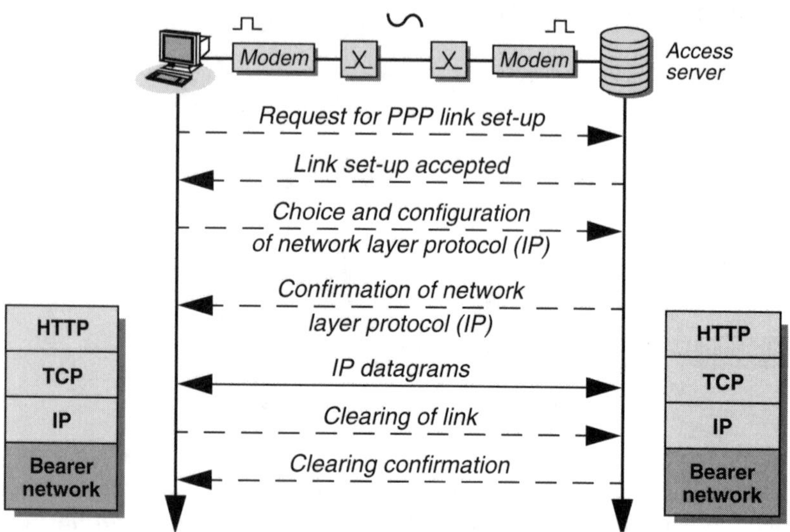

Figure H.7.9 Procedure for setting up a point-to-point protocol link (between a user and the ISP's point of presence)

In a typical case, traffic is then converted into Ethernet frames in the ISP's PoP. *Figure H.7.10* shows a possible configuration of a PoP. The task of the terminal server is to adapt dial-up subscribers so that they are treated like ordinary Ethernet users connected to the local network.

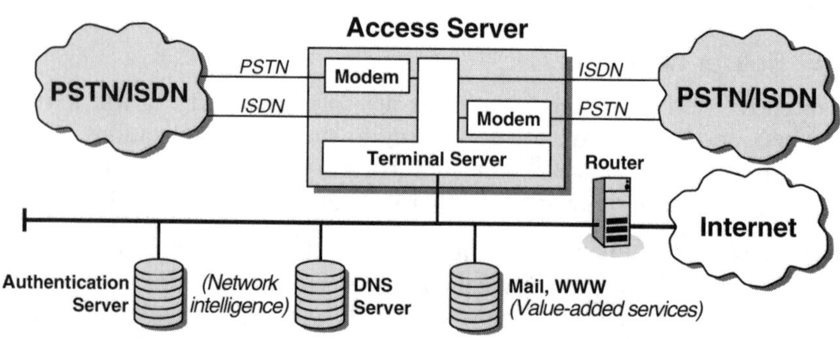

Figure H.7.10 Configuration of an Internet point-of-presence – Example

After passing the PoP, the traffic enters the Internet proper and is transported from one router to another. The routers may be interconnected over different kinds of leased lines, using PPP or SLIP as described above; the only difference being that two routers communicate with each other in this case. The routers may also be interconnected by different kinds of switched networks. The signalling used to set up and terminate connections in such a configuration is described in Chapter 7 of each Part of our books. (See, for example, *Part F2 – Frame relay* and *Part G – ATM and B-ISDN*.) The routers actually operate as ordinary subscribers in the respective bearer networks.

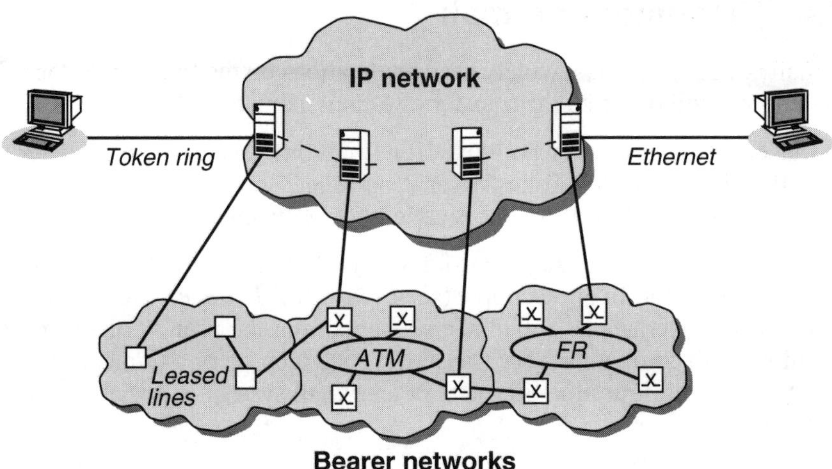

Figure H.7.11 Network elements involved in the transport of Internet traffic

Summary

The following operations must be performed (in the order stated) to enable a dial-up subscriber to fetch resources from a server connected to the Internet:

1. A data link is set up between the user's computer and an ISP's PoP, via PPP (or SLIP). The user is given an IP address which is used during the set-up phase.

2. The user orders a special resource to be fetched from a host (server).

3. The server's domain name is translated into an IP address.

4. A TCP connection is set up.

5. Requests are sent to the server (over the TCP connection).

6. Replies are received.

7. Any additional requests are sent to the server.

8. Any relevant replies are received.

9. The TCP connection is cleared.

Items 2–9 are repeated between the client and other servers as necessary.

10. The PPP link is cleared.

7.4 Transfer of e-mail

E-mail is one of the most widely used applications on the Internet. In the following, we will describe the transfer of e-mail using SMTP.

In our example, user A (who works for Ericsson) sends an e-mail letter to user B (who works for Telia). User A is logged on to a computer called *alpha.ericsson.se*. B's computer is called *beta.telia.com.*

Some other nodes – message transfer agents (MTA) – will also take part in the e-mail transfer. In our example (see *Figure H.7.12*), each user has a local MTA which operates as a mail server, containing the user's "mailbox". In addition, both companies have transit MTAs which serve a number of local MTAs. This configuration is typical of an e-mail system, especially in large companies.

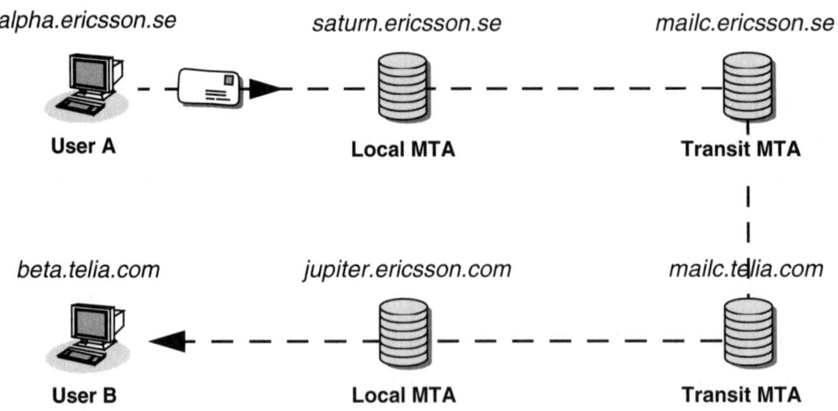

Figure H.7.12 Parties to an e-mail connection when sending an E-mail from user A to user B

Producing the letter

First of all, A must write his letter in his application program. Besides the text of the message, the letter must have a header which may contain several fields depending on the type of item to be sent. The most common fields are: To: – addressee, in our case *B@beta.telia.com*. A letter may have several addressees; From: – sender, in our case *A@alpha.ericsson.se*; Reply to: – used if a reply is to be sent to a party other than the sender; and CC: – "carbon copies", if parties other than the addressee should receive information copies. After filling in the header, A sends the letter by pressing SEND.

"A" and "B" in front of the @ symbol are local names which are unique in the local network only.

Sending the letter

A's application program contacts SMTP in his computer and orders the letter to be sent. SMTP sets up a TCP connection to the local mail server. The procedure for setting up a TCP connection is described in Subsection 7.3.3.

In the bearer network, the frame format and addresses of that network are used. IP addresses and IP packets (datagrams) are used at the IP level. The *protocol* field in the IP header routes the payload of the IP datagram to the appropriate higher-level protocol (TCP or UDP). TCP uses the port numbers to identify the appropriate application process (SMTP).

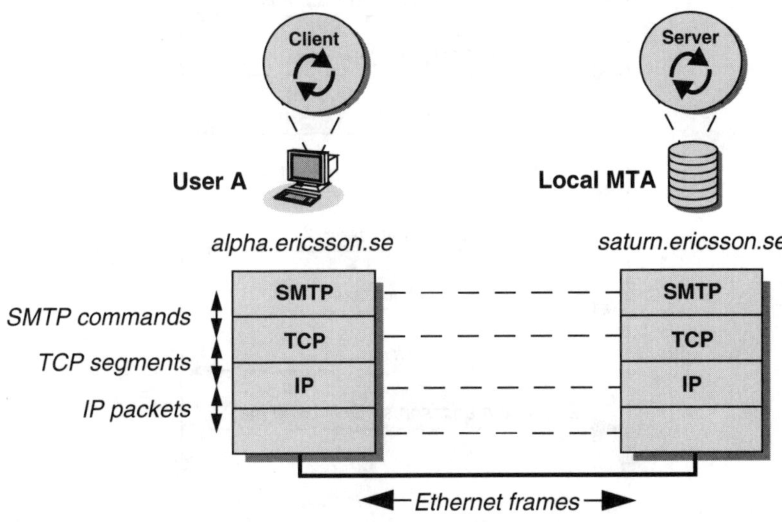

Figure H.7.13 Protocols used in a simple mail transfer protocol session

Figure H.7.14 shows what is sent between the client's SMTP process and the server's SMTP process after the TCP connection has been set up.

The server identifies itself and signals that it is ready to communicate with the client (*220 saturn.ericsson.se*). Then the client identifies itself (*HELLO alpha.ericsson.se*), and the server sends an acknowledgement to indicate that the client is accepted (*250 OK*). The client signals that it wants to mail a message and gives the identity of the originating user *(MAIL From: <A@saturn.ericsson.se>)*. This request is accepted by the server (*250 <A@saturn.ericsson.se>*). Then the client gives the identity of the addressee (*RCPT To: <B@jupiter.telia.com>*), which is also accepted by the server (*250 <B@jupiter.telia.com>*). If several addressees are stated, each one of them is acknowledged.

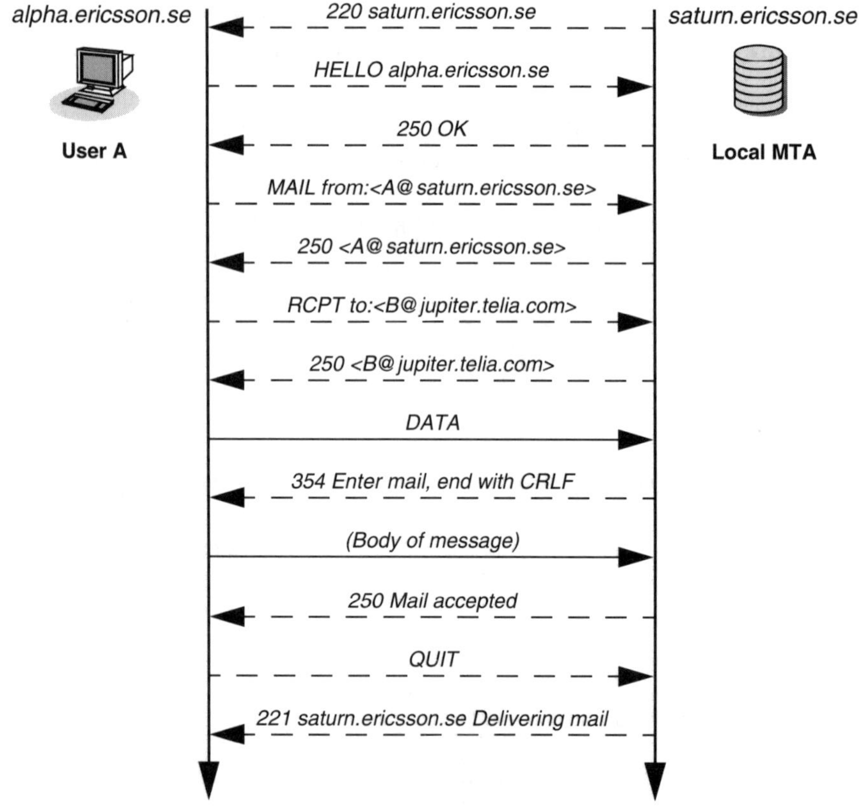

Figure H.7.14 Simple mail transfer protocol connection

The client gets the OK to sending the letter (*DATA*) and is also instructed how to end it (*354 Enter mail, end with <CRLF>.<CRLF>*), which means that the message is to be ended with a full stop (.) on a separate line (CRLF = carriage return line feed). Then the letter is sent and the server acknowledges receipt of it (*250 Mail accepted*). The client clears the connection (*QUIT*) and the server acknowledges the delivery of the letter (*221 saturn.ericsson.se Delivering mail*).

Delivering the letter

The same procedure is repeated when *saturn.ericsson.se* sends the letter to the final destination, except that in this case *saturn.ericsson.se* is the client and *mailc.ericsson.se* is the server. This connection can be set up to another mail server within the company or to an external mail server. The procedure is repeated until the letter is sent to the addressee's local mail server.

Receiving the letter

The addressee's local mail server receives the letter and puts it in B's mailbox. This is the first time the local part of the e-mail address is used, which means that the user name can be used by all mail servers (but only once by each server).

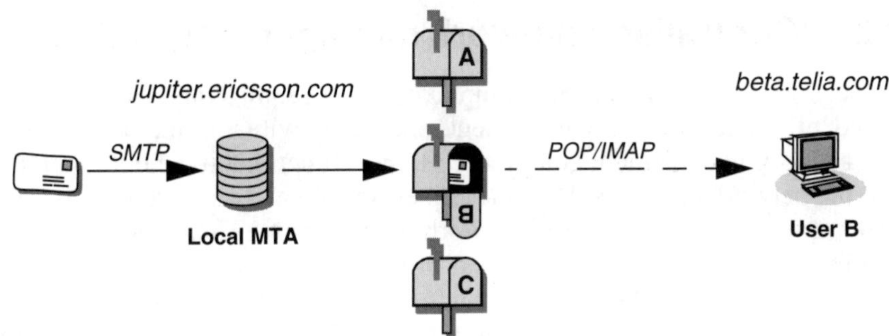

Figure H.7.15 Receiving the letter and putting it in user B's mailbox

Reading the letter

B takes the letter out of her mailbox using POP or IMAP, which is a more recent protocol and with additional functionality. POP is used to deliver letters to the user's terminal, and all subsequent processing is performed locally. IMAP performs the same operation but also allows the letters to be stored and processed on the server. This is an obvious advantage if users change terminals between logons. (See *Figure H.7.15*.) POP is specified in RFC 1939 (STD 53); IMAP is specified in RFC 2060.

8 Network management

8.1 Introduction

The Internet is becoming increasingly important in many users' daily work. Users expect the network to be dimensioned for the load it is exposed to through their (often lengthy) sessions, while at the same time they count on immediate fault-corrective action in the event of a malfunction. Smooth management and control of the network is thus essential. This includes configuration, performance, fault handling and, not least, security.

A number of competing protocols are provided for network management. The OSI world's common management and information protocol (CMIP) is comprehensive and used primarily in public telecom networks. SNMP, which forms part of the TCP/IP protocol suite, is commonly used in the Internet. Supplier-specific network management protocols are also available.

In this chapter we will only discuss SNMP. (See also Volume 1, Chapter 8, for a general description of network management.)

8.2 Centralised network management systems

As networks grow in size and complexity, they require increasingly automated, efficient network management, preferably with a minimum of separate network management equipment. Rather, functionality should be built into the network elements. Demands on efficiency and surveyability necessitate some form of centralised network management. There should be one or a few points that control all or part of the operator's (sub)network. Individual network elements should be addressable, and data on their characteristics should be stored at those central points. Agents for supporting such a strategy should be incorporated in the network elements.

A centralised network management system consists of management stations, agents, management information bases (MIBs) and network management protocols. Together, these components form the framework for network management.

Management station

A management station is a separate workstation or PC used exclusively for network management and containing all the relevant software. The following basic functions (to which special functions may be added) can be implemented in a management station:

- A user interface that makes it easy for users to survey the network. This interface also facilitates the network operator's control and supervisory activities.
- A set of tools for gathering and analysing data, configuring, handling faults and so forth.
- Functions that translate the network operator's wants into orders addressed to the appropriate network element.
- A database containing information collected from the network elements. Examples of such information are the current configuration, the contents of routing tables and traffic and fault statistics.

Agents

The network elements that the operator wants to control or supervise are equipped with agents, which may be said to serve as extensions of the network management system. (Agents are actually software units installed in the network elements concerned.)

An agent collects information about its node and ensures that orders and requests received from a management station are executed and answered. In certain cases, it is bound to report events to the management station without being requested to do so.

Management information base

The network information that SNMP can fetch and process is defined in an MIB with different, specified object types. The present standard specifies some 170 object types, such as system, interface and protocol.

An object is defined by:

- the attributes associated with it;
- the operations that can be performed on it;
- its response to the operations performed; and
- the messages it is capable of generating.

Network management protocols

A network management protocol defines the rules that govern the communication between the manager in the management station and the agent; that is, which commands, requests and replies are allowed. A common standard is important to users. A manufacturer whose products do not support standardised protocols runs the risk of being sorted out at an early stage when tenders have been requested in an investment programme.

The manager and agents use the network management protocol to exchange the information contained in the MIB. The following basic functions exist:

- *GET:* The manager requests information from an agent's MIB.
- *SET:* The manager wants to change parameters in an agent's MIB.
- *NOTIFY:* The agent notifies the manager of an event.

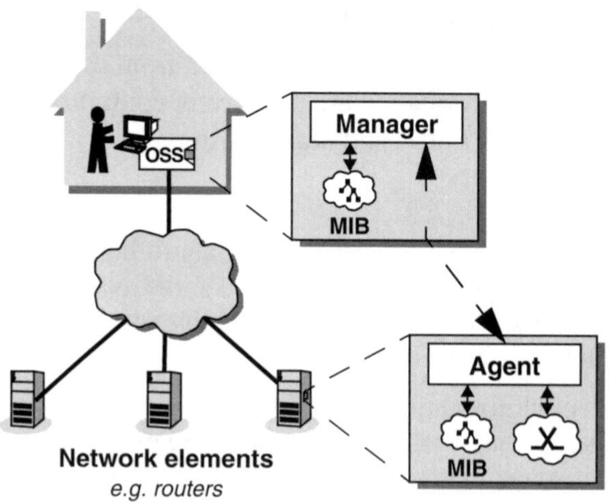

Figure H.8.1 Centralised network management system

8.3 SNMP and SNMPv2

SNMP was designed as a temporary tool for supervising and maintaining rapidly growing local and interconnected data networks. It was completed in 1988 and, despite its provisional character, soon came to play an important role. Most manufacturers of workstations, personal computers, gateways and routers can offer SNMP agent products that permit control by SNMP. SNMP messages are transported via UDP, which is a quicker procedure than transport via TCP.

As the name ("simple network management protocol") implies, one purpose of introducing SNMP was to design a simple protocol. SNMP defines a limited and easy-to-implement MIB with different variables that can be monitored and changed. The increased use of SNMP also revealed some weaknesses in the protocol. The most serious objection had to do with the lack of security functions. Hence, a new specification was drafted in 1993: SNMPv2 (version 2). The security problems solved by the introduction of SNMPv2 concern:

- *privacy*: messages are scrambled and/or encrypted so that only the addressee can interpret them;
- *authentication*: check to ensure that the network management message comes from the correct, authorised user; and
- *access control:* only authorised users will have access to specific network management functions.

SNMPv2 also allows network operators to organise their network management in a hierarchical pattern. Management stations can be installed at different levels, which is useful in large networks where network management will be too great a burden for a single management station. Some functions are therefore delegated to stations at lower levels.

8.4 Management of a "network of networks"

As we mentioned in the introduction, the Internet is not a single network but a large number of interconnected networks of various sizes. Obviously, this may give rise to management problems, especially as far as security and charging are concerned.

8.4.1 Configuration

No special rules govern the configuration of the operator's own network as long as it operates in accordance with applicable standards and RFC specifications. In other words, the subnetworks that constitute the Internet may be regarded as "black boxes" which meet the requirements stipulated in open standards.

9 Interworking between networks

9.1 Introduction

Cooperation between networks is the fundamental principle of Internet traffic management. The term "Internet" comes from *internetworking*, which primarily refers to "horizontal" cooperation between two or more constituent data networks (subnetworks). Another relevant feature is that the Internet often uses other networks as bearer networks ("vertical" cooperation). The Internet interacts with both connection-oriented and connectionless networks, and such interworking is facilitated by the fact that the Internet in itself is connectionless. IP's (future) capability to carry "everything over anything" (see Chapter 1, Subsection 1.1.2) makes it a powerful interworking tool. For the Internet, interworking between networks is a vast topic. Some aspects are discussed in Volume 1, Chapter 2, Sections 2.11 and 2.12, while different forms of interworking are dealt with in Chapters 3, 5 and 10 of this Part.

9.2 Addressing

One of the reasons for the Internet's success is the global address structure which identifies computers in networks of different technical design (Ethernet, token ring, ATM, PSTN, ISDN) by means of fixed or temporary numbers. The future of the Internet also includes telephony and multimedia services, so interworking between the PSTN/ISDN and PLMN on the one side and the Internet on the other will become an important issue. Since the terminals of the circuit-switched networks do not have IP addresses, network interworking requires that at least two numbering plans be handled. That problem has already been faced by N-ISDN, which has to cope with ITU-T's numbering plans E.163 (PSTN), E.164 (PSTN/ISDN) and X.121 (X.25). (See also *Part C – N-ISDN*, Chapter 9.)

9.3 Tunnelling

A common arrangement is to allow traffic between two subscribers to be carried by another network over a part of the distance. (See Volume 1, Chapter 9, Section 9.1 and Subsection 9.3.3.) This type of network interworking – called tunnelling – is used when IP is carried over ATM or frame relay. See also Chapter 3, Subsection 3.7.1, which gives a brief description of the tag switching method.

9.4 Interworking between networks in the Internet

In the introductory section of Chapter 5 we described the hierarchy that evolved in the US in the 1980s: local, regional and core networks. A transition point between a regional network and a core network can also be a gateway between different operators. This kind of connection is known as a network access point (NAP). Using a telephony term, the NAP might be called a *transit exchange*.

Other concepts are commercial Internet exchange (CIX) and global interexchange point (GIX). A GIX can be compared to an international exchange. Sweden's first GIX was the Royal Institute of Technology in Stockholm. Two of the most important GIX points in the US are MAE-West on the West Coast and MAE-East on the East Coast.

As commercialisation of Internet traffic increased, CIX came to denote a commercial gateway or a connection point between public, commercial Internet operators. CIX is also the name of an association of ISPs for public Internet services.

9.5 Interworking between the PSTN and the Internet

9.5.1 Telephone calls to Internet surfers

To overcome the blocking of incoming telephone calls to Internet "surfers", a local exchange can divert the calls to a voice gateway, where voice traffic is compressed and encapsulated in IP format. Calls are sent over the established Internet connection and displayed on the surfer's computer screen by means of special software. (See *Figure H.9.1.*) This method can also be used for sending outgoing telephone calls during "surfing".

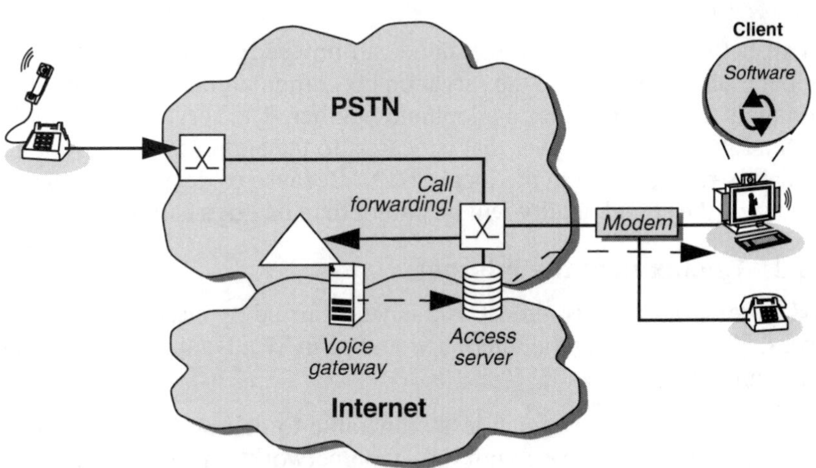

Figure H.9.1 Telephone call to an Internet surfer

9.5.2 Telephone calls over the Internet

One of the advantages of telephony over the Internet is the low cost of long-distance calls. The subject is vast and expanding. Here we will briefly discuss the aspects of interworking between the PSTN and the Internet.

An important network component is a telephony server: an Internet telephony gateway. See *Figure H.9.2*.

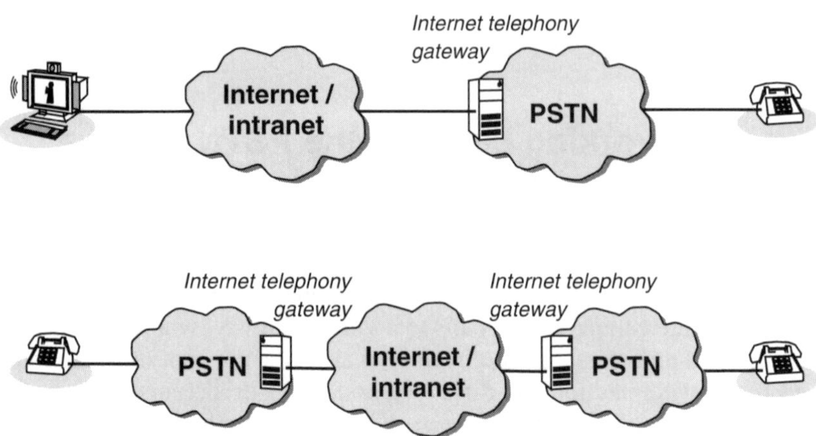

Figure H.9.2 Telephony over the Internet – An example

A call between a PC and a telephone can proceed as follows. The A-subscriber dials the number of the server on his computer, identifies himself and then dials the B-subscriber's telephone number. The server sets up the call via the Internet to the server that is nearest to the addressee, and from there the call is routed through the local PSTN. Because of delays and other disturbances, the sound quality will be poorer than that of a call over the PSTN.

9.5.3 Telefax over the Internet

Today, telefax traffic is almost exclusively carried by circuit-switched networks. However, using the Internet would be more advantageous, especially over long distances.

Since the fax service is much less vulnerable to delays than the telephony service, it fits in very well with data-type networks. After it "migrates" to the Internet, there will be a greater need for interworking between the PSTN and the Internet. See *Figure H.9.3*.

Figure H.9.3 Telefax over the Internet – An example

10 Network planning

10.1 Introduction

Because the Internet surfs on other networks to a large extent, it requires very special planning. There are basically four types of network: networks for dial-up access, networks for fixed access, regional networks and core networks, as shown in *Figure H.10.1*.

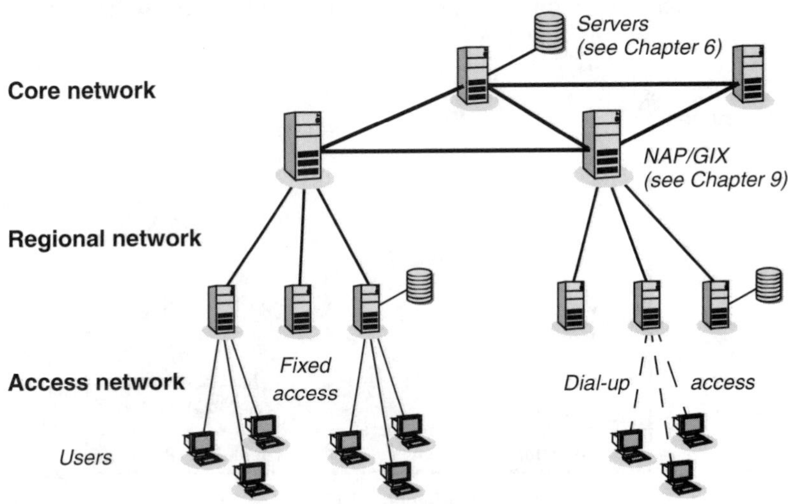

Figure H.10.1 Network architecture

Network planning is also influenced by the extraordinary growth of the Internet. Many experts predict that by the year 2000 the Internet will transport more bits per second than the entire telephone network.

The Internet has traditionally been regarded as a data network, but voice transmission has entered the spotlight in recent years. Also, operators' and users' interest in video and multimedia traffic continues to grow. Other factors that make the Internet special are its widespread ownership structure and the fact that it is a network of networks focusing on the exchange of information. Value-added services constitute a large portion of the range of Internet services. And because value-added services are server-based, the number of "service providers" is much greater in the Internet than in other networks. (See Subsection 10.5.1.)

This chapter deals mainly with the network and service planning done by operators and ISPs. Instead of focusing on individual ISPs, we have chosen to discuss network planning differently: to view the entire Internet from a user's perspective.

10.2 Internet services – Product plan

Today's Internet does not possess the capabilities needed to cope with isochronous services while maintaining high transfer quality. Delays and packet losses are too great and too widely varying. The Internet that is seen as a solution for all services in the long term is quite different from the present one.

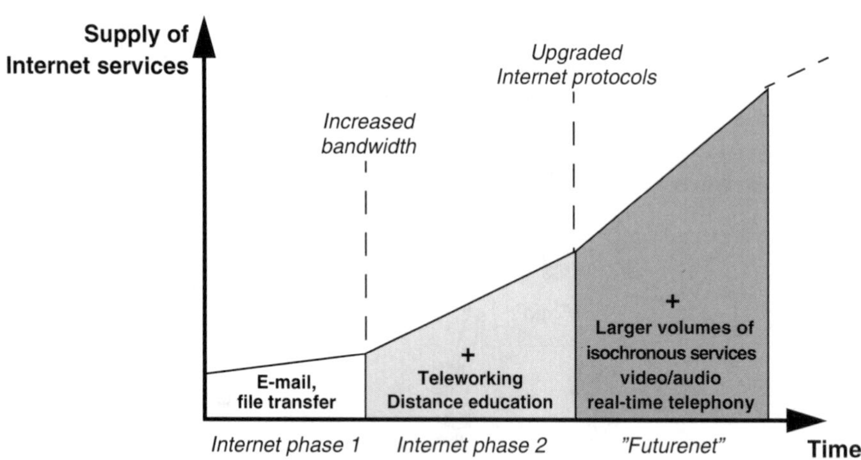

Figure H.10.2 Possible development of the Internet from a data transmission network to a multimedia network

Large volumes of interactive voice and video services are not foreseen in the short term, but planning for facilities to accommodate such services is well under way. The requirements can be categorised as follows:

- *Transparency*
  Large service bandwidth (Mbit/s; taking into account response times in client–server applications and video)
  Flexible bandwidth
  Acceptable real-time characteristics
  Acceptable quality (QoS) and extremely high availability
- *Accessibility*
  Mobility in access
  Support for information retrieval
  Network intelligence
- *Security*
  Support for safe payment routines
  Protection against unauthorised access
- *Charging*
  New forms of charging, such as time and distance-based fees for reserved network resources

10.3 Prerequisites

The planning of telephone networks differs greatly from the planning of networks with computers as terminals.

- "IP subscribers" are not as homogeneous a category as telephone subscribers, in terms of traffic characteristics. Examples of such characteristics are holding time, bandwidth, traffic interest and burstiness.
- In the long run, the continuous development of computer technology may create a demand for extremely broad bandwidths. This, in combination with the rapid increase in the number of computers connected to networks, will result in unparalleled growth of transported bit volumes.
- Internet communication is a new business concept in which revenue from advertising replaces much of the traditional revenue from traffic transport. This is because the computer offers facilities for presenting text, sound and video, suggesting a business concept similar to TV financed by advertising. Another reason for this development is the rapidly falling cost of optical transmission.

- The number of operators is much larger in the Internet than in the PSTN/ ISDN or PLMN.
- As we have pointed out, the Internet's ability to surf on other networks creates a special situation. On the "surfing sections", Internet traffic can be regarded as a service carried by the lower-level network, which must be dimensioned taking this and other traffic loads into account.

10.4 Technology plan

The purpose of the technology plan, the network development plan and the dimensioning of the network is to support the product plan according to the prerequisites stated in Section 10.3.

10.4.1 Transparency

The Internet (up to and including IPv4) employs best-effort methods without guaranteed QoS, which means that the Internet cannot identify packets that should be rejected instead of buffered in case of congestion. Work aimed at providing the resource reservation protocol with better real-time characteristics is in progress. As shown in *Figure H.10.3*, RSVP can be used to reserve capacity in the network in order to reach a certain QoS level.

RSVP is basically a one-way (simplex) protocol. To establish connections that are supported by secured resources, we need one sender and one or more receivers that establish a route through the network.

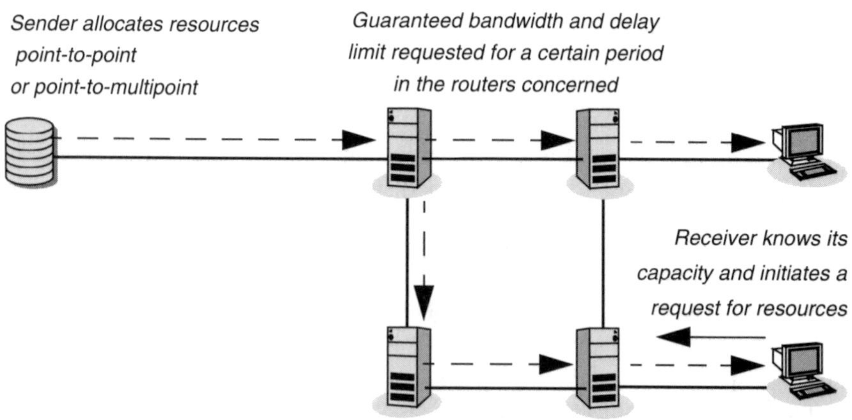

Figure H.10.3 Working mode for resource reservation protocol

RSVP compensates for delay variations occurring in the nodes. (See also Volume 1, Chapter 1, Subsection 1.5.3.)

Better transparency and real-time characteristics can be achieved by other methods, too:

- Development of wideband routers.
- Generous dimensioning of the network. This will favour multimedia connections. As we know, these connections contain several types of communication, all of which should have real-time characteristics in the multimedia case. This method is rather expensive. Who will pay?
  Possible bottlenecks are: The access network (faster access will gradually be provided in fixed and mobile networks); Access servers (this is where traffic is concentrated, thus increasing the risk of congestion); and Connection to information servers.
- Connection-oriented, interactive communication in real time, supported by ATM. See Chapter 3, Section 3.7, which describes bypassing router connections.

10.4.2 Accessibility

The following features can contribute to increased accessibility:

- radio access with larger capacity;
- Internet access using the ordinary TV network or power distribution networks;
- satellite systems with fixed or mobile access, especially in regions with undeveloped telephone networks;
- inexpensive network computers (see Chapter 1, Subsection 1.7.1);
- gateways to services of the same type in other networks; and
- further facilitating information retrieval – good availability of information servers gives ISPs an advantage over their competitors.

10.4.3 Security

See Chapter 6, Section 6.3.

10.5 Network development plan

Many paths of development are open to the Internet, but there is great uncertainty as to which path is best. Some possible scenarios are:

- The Internet is smoothly adapted to other technologies, mainly ATM Volume 1, Chapter 10, Section 10.8, describes a general network development plan for the switching and transport of traffic in either circuit mode or cell mode. A prerequisite is that large portions of packet-switched and frame-relay traffic are transported through the cell network. The same prerequisite may apply to IP traffic. Different methods are used for routing IP traffic in an ATM network. (See Chapter 3, Section 3.7.) The QoS characteristics of the ATM technology can be used in the ATM network sections.
- A merger between Internet technology and ATM technology (see Chapter 3, Section 3.7)
- The Internet forms autonomous router networks. A TCP/IP network evolves, relying exclusively on leased capacity in the SDH or PDH network. All routing and switching take place in routers.
- Distribution of the Internet into classes . We will have several Internet classes (comparable to 1st and 2nd class railway cars), differing mainly in terms of data transfer rate and QoS.

Another trend in the development of the Internet is towards some sort of remote-control network with IP addresses for different functional parts, for example, in a car. And why not turn your toaster on and off via the Internet?

10.5.1 Fundamental technical plans

Routing and addressing plans

These plans are dealt with in Chapters 3 and 9.

Charging plan

Stakeholders

In Sweden, Telia acts as both an ISP and access operator. A country usually has many more ISPs than access operators because many parties want to have their share of the "the Internet cake". Most of the financiers are advertisers, but this category also includes the original users, such as government authorities, universities and colleges. LANs are implemented and financed by the organisations that use them.

The Internet market is illustrated in *Figure H.10.4*.

Those who use dial-up access pay their ISP and access operators, unless these are the same organisation. If two different operators are involved, the distance between the user and the ISP's PoP will be of great importance. Large ISPs have a PoP in each local charging area. As an alternative, an access operator may develop into an intermediate access provider who builds data networks between ISPs' PoPs and local exchanges. This should result in lower costs, because transmission capacity can be used more efficiently. (See Chapter 5, Subsection 5.4.4.)

An Internet subscription usually includes the WWW, e-mail and chat services.

As yet, the Internet itself has not produced distance-based tariffs, while there are such tariffs for access to the Internet. This is one of the reasons why telephony over the Internet has attracted such great interest (for example, calling overseas at the local tariff).

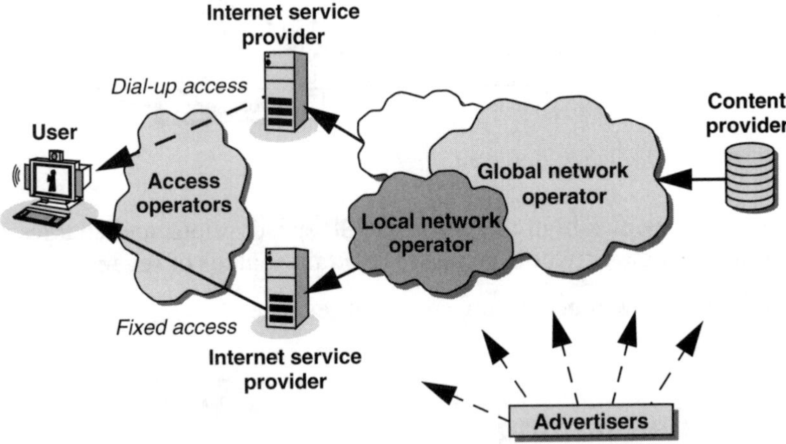

Figure H.10.4 The Internet market

Fixed connection to the Internet

A fixed connection to the Internet – via a router – is a solution that has been adopted by many companies. Strictly speaking, the connections are not always fixed but may use X.25 or frame relay.

The connection fee covers the allocation of an IP address and a domain name.

The transfer rate is 64 kbit/s or more. Swedish Telia offers a special tariff to companies located within 30 km of its nearest Internet connection PoP and a higher tariff for longer distances. The tariff is capacity-based.

The new business approach mentioned in Section 10.3 is illustrated in *Figure H.10.5*.

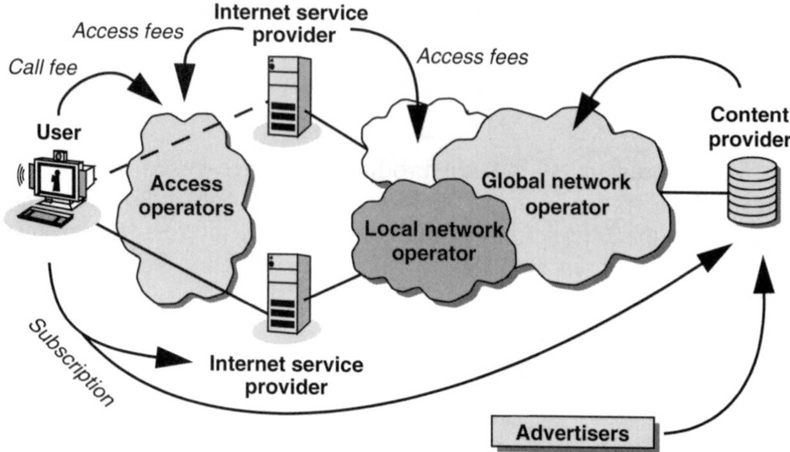

Figure H.10.5 Monetary flows on the Internet

Advertising generates high revenue, but ISP subscriptions and charges for "new traffic" in the networks are also important sources of revenue.

On-line shopping will be a future source of revenue.

10.6 Dimensioning

10.6.1 Introduction

Even the most enthusiastic Internet users (or perhaps these in particular) have at some time considered the Internet slow and underdimensioned. In many calls that are established, the server is situated in the US and the client on another continent, for example, Europe. Between the server and the client there are several possible bottlenecks – in addition to the access itself – that may affect accessibility:

- traffic capacity across the Atlantic, and
- availability in servers.

The capacity of transatlantic routes and the availability in servers can be increased. But one can also replicate servers and deploy *mirror servers* closer to the subscriber, for instance, somewhere in Europe. Information can also be stored temporarily in cache memories in clients and servers. This will reduce network load caused by the retrieval of information in great demand.

10.6.2 Dimensioning of dial-up access

Ordinary dial-up access to the Internet over the PSTN/ISDN forces the network to carry traffic volume for which it was not dimensioned. The mean holding time of a telephone call is 90–120 seconds, while calls to the Internet last on average 10 times longer. Besides, the spread is considerable, mainly because of the charging structure. Another difference is the peak traffic period. The distribution of Internet traffic over a 24-hour period has not stabilised yet, but the distribution for dial-up access shown in *Figure H.10.7* is possible. Taking into account the dimensioning of the PSTN/ISDN, the difference is quite advantageous. The relationship to charging is obvious; a low tariff during low-traffic periods will favour users and operators.

How, then, will large volumes of Internet traffic affect a PSTN/ISDN exchange? A common exchange configuration contains the three main parts shown in *Figure H.10.6.*

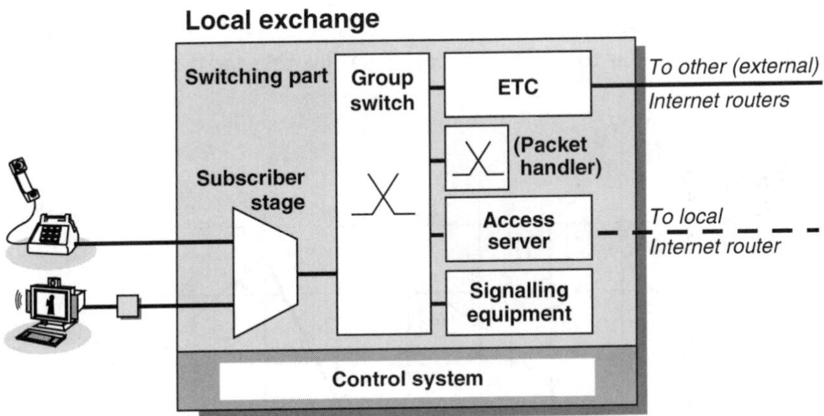

Figure H.10.6 Main parts of a PSTN/ISDN exchange

- subscriber stage;
- group switch; and
- central processor,e.g. control system.

A local exchange always has trunk circuits to other exchanges but it may also have ports facing the Internet.

If we assume that telephone traffic and Internet traffic do not replace each other, the total traffic on the subscriber lines will increase, of course, and we will have a higher Erlang value during the hour of overall peak traffic. If we also assume that a certain grade of service applies (see Volume 1, Chapter 10, Subsection 10.9.5), the Erlang table will be useful when making an approximate calculation of the dimensioning of the switching equipment. Calculations show that such dimensioning allows a certain margin, because a mix of telephony and Internet traffic requires somewhat less switching resources than pure telephone traffic at the same traffic intensity. Internet traffic should also be evenly distributed among different subscriber stages.

The situation is even more advantageous for processor dimensioning. At the same traffic intensity, and assuming that the holding time for an Internet call is 10 times longer than the holding time for a telephone call, Internet traffic will only require about one tenth of the processor power used for the corresponding volume of telephone traffic.

Nevertheless, a large proportion of Internet traffic poses a threat to a smoothly functioning telephone network. The Internet occupies resources in circuit-switched networks even if no traffic is being processed. If the network tends to become overloaded, this may trigger a snowball effect: surfers hold the lines longer to avoid having to repeat the logon procedure. This applies in particular to networks that use a flat-rate tariff for dial-up access.

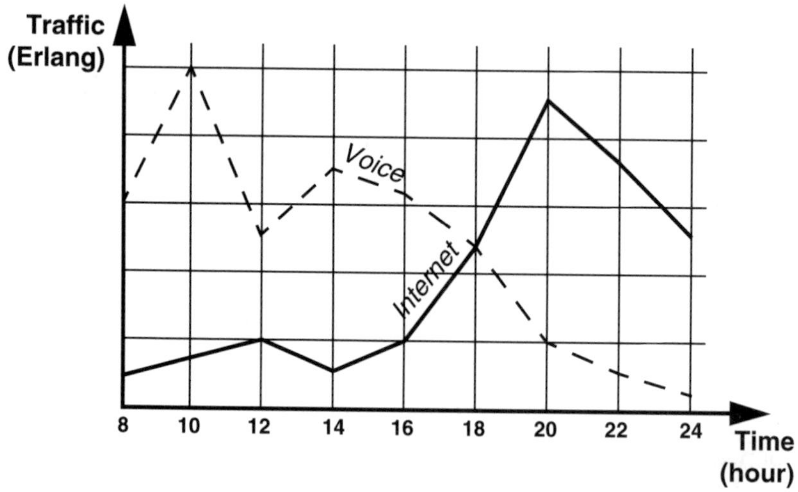

Figure H.10.7 Internet surfing generates new traffic patterns

Conclusion

As is evident from the chapters on network planning in our books, the complex world of telecommunications is and will continue to be full of challenges. We will very likely have a large number of different networks in operation for a long time to come – networks that are positioned to be able to provide a many-faceted range of user-friendly services, be it individually or in cooperation between networks.

The variety of possible network designs is illustrated in *Figure 0.1*, which succinctly summarises the present and the future we have described in our two-volume guide to telecommunications.

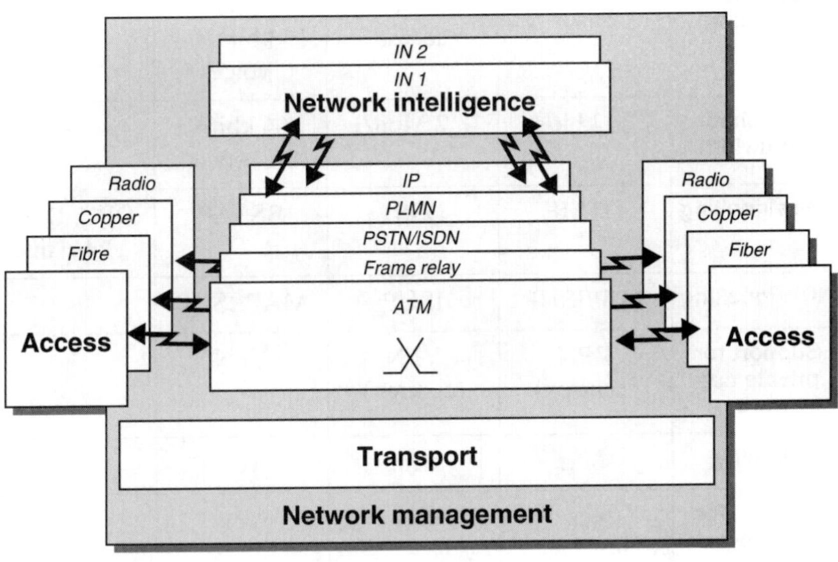

Figure 0.1 A complex telecommunications world – a multiplicity of networks

The table on the next two pages is a breif summary of the characteristics of the different networks in Part A – Part H.

	PSTN	ISDN	PLMN (GSM)	SS7
Transfer mode	circuit	circuit; packet (frame)	circuit; packet (GPRS)	packet (MSUs)
Type of service	voice; data	voice; data; video	voice; data	(data)
Type of circuit	switched (reserved)	normally switched (reserved)	normally switched (reserved)	connection-less transfer, SVC
Access bandwidth (if limiting)	300–3400 Hz	128 kbit/s for basic rate access	9.6 kbit/s for data 13 kbit/s for voice	-
Switched bandwidth	64 kbit/s	$\leq$2 Mbit/s	64 kbit/s (core network)	-
UNI signalling	DTMF	DSS1	BSSAP	OPC, DPC, global title
NNI signalling	TUP/ISUP	ISUP	MAP/ISUP	-
Support for private net-works	VPN (centrex)	VPN (centrex)	VPN	-
Mobility	some	some	yes	-
Support for the Internet	yes	yes	yes	-

	X.25	Frame relay	ATM	The Internet
Transfer mode	packet	frame	cell	packet (IP)
Type of service	data	data; (voice)	data; voice; video	data; (voice); (video)
Type of circuit	SVC PVC	PVC	PVC SVC	connection-less transfer
Access bandwidth (if limiting)	-	-	-	*Depends on underlying net-work, if any.*
Switched bandwidth (upper limit)	64 kbit/s– 2 Mbit/s	2–50 Mbit/s	>620 Mbit/s	*Depends on underlying net-work, if any. Routers up to Gbit/s range under develop-ment*
UNI signalling	X.25	(SVC sign.)	DSS2 (normally)	-
NNI signalling	X.75, internal	(SVC sign.)	B-ISUP B-ICI	-
Support for private net-works	CUG	CUG	VPN	Internet; extranets; VPN
Mobility	some	some	some	some
Support for the Internet	yes	yes	yes	-

Figure H.10.9 Characteristics of the networks

Index